PHYSICAL ANTHROPOLOGY AND ARCHAEOLOGY

Second

Canadian

Edition

PHYSICAL ANTHROPOLOGY AND ARCHAEOLOGY

Carol R. Ember
Human Relations Area Files

Melvin Ember
Human Relations Area Files

Peter N. Peregrine
Lawrence University

Robert D. Hoppa
University of Manitoba

PEARSON

Prentice
Hall

Toronto

Library and Archives Canada Cataloguing in Publication

Physical anthropology and archaeology / Carol R. Ember ... [et al.]. — 2nd Canadian ed.

First ed. by Carol R. Ember, Melvin Ember and Robert D. Hoppa.
Includes bibliographical references and index.

ISBN 0-13-127177-6

1. Physical anthropology—Textbooks. 2. Archaeology—Textbooks. 3. Human evolution—Textbooks. I. Ember, Carol R.

GN60.E42 2006   599.9   C2004-905758-8

ISBN 0-13-127177-6

Vice President, Editorial Director: Michael J. Young
Executive Acquisitions Editor: Christine Cozens
Sponsoring Editor: Carolin Sweig
Executive Marketing Manager: Judith Allen
Developmental Editor: Jennifer Murray
Production Editor: Söğüt Y. Güleç
Copy Editor: Susan Marshall
Proofreader: Barbara Czarnecki
Production Manager: Wendy Moran
Manufacturing Coordinator: Susan Johnson
Page Layout: Susan Thomas
Permissions Research: Amanda McCormick
Art Director: Julia Hall
Cover Design: Anthony Leung
Interior Design: Julia Hall
Cover Image: Brian Pieters/Masterfile (*Painting of Petroglyphs*)

For my students, who continue to inspire me . . .

—R.D.H.

Brief Contents

Contents

Boxes

HISTORICAL PERSPECTIVES

NEW PERSPECTIVES ON GENDER

Preface

Physical anthropology explores the intriguing questions that surround the emergence and evolution of humans, what they were like in the past and how they lived, and why they vary biologically. New discoveries, from work like the Human Genome Project on DNA, are providing evidence that the human past stretches back much further than scientists have predicted, and that humans share a genetic structure similar to other life forms. Archaeology deals with discovering and interpreting that past through remains of long-gone societies. Together, these two disciplines—physical anthropology and archaeology—attempt to reconstruct the past in a way that helps us to understand our roots, and to have greater insight into ourselves and some of the problems that concern contemporary societies.

This book is a Canadian adaptation of the physical anthropology and archaeological material in the eleventh edition of Carol R. Ember and Melvin Ember's *Anthropology*, a successful first-year university textbook. The Canadian edition of *Physical Anthropology and Archaeology* features new Chapters 2 and 3 that deal explicitly with archaeological methods and archaeological interpretation, so that readers will gain a firm understanding of how anthropologists reconstruct the past.

Many of the interest boxes feature work by Canadian anthropologists, and help to illustrate some of the fields in which anthropologists toil. As well, the text cites numerous examples of groundbreaking work that Canadian researchers are undertaking. The Canadian edition builds on a strong base, and highlights the contributions of Canadian anthropologists to the contiguous fields of physical anthropology and archaeology.

Highlights of the Chapters and What Is New in the Second Canadian Edition

Chapter 1: What Is Anthropology?

Chapter 1 introduces students to anthropology. We discuss what we think is special and distinctive about anthropology in general, and about each of its sub-fields in particular. We outline how each sub-field is related to other disciplines such as biology, psychology, and sociology. Boxes highlight the history of anthropology in Canada and the work of a medical anthropologist.

Chapter 2: Uncovering the Past: Tools and Techniques

This chapter introduces the basic concepts behind locating, excavating, and recovering skeletal remains and material culture from the palaeontological and archaeological record. The processes that affect how fossils are formed and where they are found, as well as how archaeological sites form and change over time, are discussed. We also discuss the methods of dating fossils. Chapter 2 explains methods of site surveying and recording, and highlights the importance of provenience, or association, between objects. Finally, we review dating techniques for determining the relative or absolute age of a site and its artifacts. Interest boxes explore the work of archaeologists and highlight the importance of archaeological recovery in reconstructing the past.

Chapter 3: Reconstructing the Past: Analysis and Interpretation

Chapter 3 builds on the methods of recovery and analysis outlined in Chapter 2, and discusses a variety of aspects of interpreting archaeological data. The first section of the chapter examines how we reconstruct the past from artifacts, features, and the biological remains of once living peoples. Individual sections show how anthropologists and archaeologists reconstruct past diets, environments, settlement patterns, and social systems. The chapter ends with a discussion of cultural change. Interest boxes discuss interpreting women's roles from artifacts, the evolution of disease, and reconstructing ancient Egyptian brewing techniques as a means for reconstructing past lifeways.

Chapter 4: Historical Development of Evolutionary Theory

This chapter discusses evolutionary theory as it applies to all forms of life, including humans. Following an extensive review of the historical development of the theory of evolution, this chapter ends with a discussion of natural selection and its importance to biological evolution, including how new species might develop. Chapter 4's Current Issues box illustrates the concept of natural selection by examining the current increase in drug-resistant strains of diseases.

Chapter 5: Modern Evolutionary Theory

Chapter 5 introduces the modern theory of evolution, incorporating natural selection and genetics as the processes and basis on which change occurs over time. We also discuss how natural selection may operate on behavioural traits and how cultural evolution differs from biological evolution. We consider the ethical issues posed by the possibility of genetic engineering. Interest boxes examine the evidence suggesting that evolution proceeds abruptly rather than slowly and steadily, and discuss whether Lamarck's theories of acquired inheritance have some validity. Another box discusses whether genetic engineering should be feared, and Historical Perspectives addresses the role of eugenics in North America.

Chapter 6: The Living Primates

This chapter describes the living non-human primates and their variable adaptations as background for understanding the evolution of primates in general and humans in particular. After describing the various species, we discuss some possible explanations of how the primates differ—in body and brain size, size of social group, and female sexuality. The chapter ends with a discussion of the distinctive features of humans in comparison with the other primates. The Research Frontiers box describes a primatologist and some of her work, while Current Issues examines how and why many primates are endangered and how they might be protected.

Chapter 7: Primate Evolution: From Early Primates to Hominoids

Chapter 7 begins with the emergence of the early primates and ends with what we know or suspect about the Miocene apes, and their relation to bipedal hominids. We describe the concept of the molecular clock for assessing timing of divergence between species, including hominids from other hominoids. To highlight how theory is generated and revised, Research Frontiers boxes deal with how a palaeoanthropologist has re-examined his own theory of primate origins, and focus on the work of a Canadian researcher who has studied the remains of a later Miocene ape. The Historical Perspectives box describes a giant ape that overlapped with *Homo erectus*, and why the ape became extinct.

Chapter 8: Early Hominids

Chapter 8 starts with the emergence of the first bipedal hominids. We first discuss trends in, and possible explanations of, the distinctive developments in the hominid line—bipedalism, the expansion of the brain, and the reduction of the face, teeth, and jaws. We then discuss the changing fossil evidence for understanding the evolution of early hominids. The Research Frontiers box discusses the puzzle posed by similarities between the robust australopithecines and *Homo*.

Chapter 9: *Homo erectus* and Archaic *Homo sapiens*

This chapter discusses the transition between *Homo erectus* and *Homo sapiens* and the emergence of early modern humans. In keeping with our global orientation, we discuss fossil and archaeological evidence from many areas of the world, not just Europe and the Near East, including evidence indicating that people were hunting big game at least 400 000 years ago. The first box discusses research evaluating the claim that *Homo erectus* should be divided into two species. We also explore how the earliest dating of *H. erectus* may affect ideas about when hominids first moved out of Africa. The Historical Perspectives box highlights the discoveries of Canadian anatomist Davidson Black, and their importance to the recognition of *H. erectus*, and another Research Frontiers box re-examines middle Palaeolithic hunting practices, and the hypotheses regarding subsistence strategies and Neandertals.

Chapter 10: Modern *Homo sapiens*

Chapter 10 discusses the origins of anatomically modern human populations, contrasting the two major competing models—the "single-origin" and multiregional hypotheses. The chapter also covers key changes in cultural practices during the Upper Palaeolithic, including the flourishing of art and new forms of tools. We finish with a discussion of the peopling of the New World and briefly introduce the student to early Arctic cultures. The first Research Frontiers box describes the evidence from mitochondrial DNA regarding the "out of Africa" hypothesis for modern human origins. Another describes the evidence from South America indicating that modern humans moved into the New World at least 12 500 years ago. The last introduces a Canadian Arctic archaeologist and his interpretations of early Arctic cultures.

Chapter 11: Human Variation

This chapter brings the discussion of human evolution into the present, dealing with biological variation in living human populations and how biological anthropologists study such variation. In a section on race and racism, we discuss why anthropologists think that the concept of race as applied to humans is not scientifically useful. According to this view, human variation is more usefully studied in terms of clinal variation in particular traits. For example, we show how differences between populations—in physical features such as body build, skin colour, height, and susceptibility to disease—can be explained as adaptations to differences in the physical and cultural environment. We discuss the myths of racism and demonstrate that race is largely a social category in humans. We also discuss population variation in susceptibility to diseases and the co-evolution of diseases and humans. A Research Frontiers box deals with obesity and hypertension in the context of long-term biocultural changes in populations. Finally, a Current Issues box explores the meaning of differences in average IQ scores in different races.

Chapter 12: Origins of Food Production and Settled Life

Chapter 12 deals with the emergence of broad-spectrum collecting and settled life, and the domestication of plants and animals in various parts of the world. Our discussion focuses mainly on the possible causes and consequences of these developments in southeast Asia, Africa, the Andes, and eastern North America, as well as the Near East and Europe. We discuss puzzles such as why much of Native North America switched to a dependence on corn, even though the earlier agricultural diet was apparently adequate. The first box is a historical perspective on the early model of gender division in hunting and gathering societies. A Research Frontiers box puts forward a theory about the domestication of dogs and cats, and a Current Issues box discusses the impact of food-getting on the environment.

Chapter 13: Origins of Cities and States

Chapter 13 deals with the rise of civilizations in various areas of the world and the theories that have been offered to explain the development of state-type political systems. The chapter concludes with a discussion of the decline and collapse of states. Environmental degradation may be due to events in the natural world, but the behaviour of humans may sometimes be responsible. Civilizations may also decline because human behaviour has increased the incidence of disease. One box discusses the links between imperialism, colonialism, and the state. The other box discusses the consequences for women's status in the context of ancient imperialism in the Andes.

Chapter 14: Applied Anthropology: Physical Anthropology and Archaeology

The first part of this chapter reviews the interaction between basic and applied research, a brief history of applied anthropology in Canada, the ethical issues involved in trying to improve people's lives, the difficulties in evaluating whether a program is beneficial, and ways of implementing planned changes. We point out how applied anthropologists are playing a role more as planners than as peripheral advisers to change programs already in place. The chapter examines several aspects of applied research in biomedical anthropology, environmental anthropology, forensic anthropology, nutritional anthropology and archaeology as culture history. The Current Issues box shows how anthropologists were able to explain why a health project in Guatemala did not work, and the Historical Perspectives box explores the effects of malnutrition on growth and health.

Features

Boxes in Each Chapter

Current Issues. These boxes deal with topics students may have heard about in the news (for example, the evolution of drug-resistant diseases, or endangered primates) or topics that are currently the subject of debate in the profession (the effect of food-getting on the environment).

Research Frontiers. These boxes look at researchers at work or take an in-depth look at new research or a research controversy (for example, the chemical analyses of bones and teeth; interpretation of findings of *Dryopithecus*; Middle Palaeolithic hunting).

Historical Perspectives. These boxes review historical aspects of research in physical anthropology and archaeology in Canada (for example, Canadian

anatomist Davidson Black's discovery of *Homo erectus*; the eugenics movement).

New Perspectives on Gender. These boxes involve issues pertaining to sex and gender, both in anthropology and everyday life (examples: depictions of women in art and changes in women's roles in prehistoric societies).

Readability

We get a lot of pleasure from describing research findings, especially complicated ones, in language that introductory students can understand. Thus, we try to minimize technical jargon, using only the terms students need to know to appreciate the achievements of anthropology and to encourage them to take advanced courses. Readability is important, not only because it enhances the reader's understanding of what we write but also because it makes learning about anthropology more enjoyable! When new terms are introduced, they are set off in boldface type and defined.

Glossary Terms

At the end of each chapter, we list the new terms that have been introduced (the terms that were identified by boldface type and defined in the text). We deliberately do not repeat the definitions at the end of the chapter to allow students to test themselves against the definitions provided in the end-of-the-book Glossary.

Internet Exercises

We have developed Internet Exercises for each chapter to provide students with web-based resources on the various topics covered. Students are encouraged to use the internet addresses (URLs) provided to discover more about the dynamic changes that are occurring in the field of anthropology.

Critical Questions

We also provide a series of questions at the end of each chapter to stimulate thinking about the implications of that chapter. The questions do not ask for repetition of what is in the text: We want students to imagine, to go beyond what we know or think we know.

Summaries and Suggested Reading

In addition to the outline provided at the beginning of each chapter, a summary appears at the end of each chapter that will help students review the major concepts and findings discussed. A Suggested Reading list provides general or more extensive references on the subject matter of the chapter.

A Complete Glossary at the End of the Book

As noted above, important glossary terms for each chapter are listed (without definitions) at the end of each chapter, so students can readily check their understanding after they have read the chapter. A complete Glossary is provided at the back of the book that serves as a review of all terms in the book and as a convenient reference for students.

Literature Cited at the End of the Book

The information and conclusions presented in this book are largely based on published research. These sources are cited in the text with full bibliographic references provided at the end of the book.

Interactive Anthropology CD-ROM

Available with every new copy of the text, this CD-ROM provides an exciting learning experience for students. Interactive simulations and exercises, a complete map atlas, and reference resources all help to illustrate the concepts described in the book. Throughout the text, a special **Interactive Anthropology CD-ROM** icon (see icon on left) appears to signal to students that they should consult the CD-ROM for further resources regarding the associated section in the text.

Supplements

The supplement package for this textbook has been carefully crafted to amplify and illuminate materials in the text itself.

Instructor's Resource CD-ROM. This instructor resource CD includes Instructor's Resource Manual, Pearson TestGen, and PowerPoint Presentations.

Instructor's Resource Manual. For each chapter of the text, this manual provides learning objectives, chapter outlines, teaching tips, suggestions for classroom activities, topics for class discussion, written assignments, and additional internet exercises.

Pearson TestGen. For each chapter of the text, this resource contains multiple-choice, true/false, and essay questions provided in TestGen format. TestGen is a testing software that enables instructors to view and edit the existing questions, add questions, generate tests, and distribute the tests in a variety of formats. Powerful search and sort functions make it easy to locate questions and arrange them in any order desired. TestGen also enables instructors to administer tests on a local area network, have the tests graded electronically, and have the results prepared in electronic or printed reports. TestGen is compatible with Windows and Macintosh operating systems, and can be downloaded from the TestGen website located at www.pearsoned.com/testgen. Contact your local sales representative for details and access.

PowerPoint Presentations. This instructor resource contains key points and figures to accompany each chapter in the text.

Contemporary Readings in Physical Anthropology. This special topics reader (ISBN 0-13-096269-4) includes articles from the *New York Times*, journals, and popular sources. It presents an intriguing introduction to currently debated issues in physical anthropology. The readings have been carefully selected and organized to challenge students with the basic inquiries about these controversial topics.

Companion Website. Students can now take full advantage of the World Wide Web to enrich their study of anthropology through the *Physical Anthropology and Archaeology*, Second Canadian Edition, Companion Website. This study resource will correlate the text with related material available on the internet. Features of the Companion Website include chapter objectives, study questions, news updates, as well as links to interesting material and information from other sites on the web that reinforce and enhance the content of each chapter. The address is **www.pearsoned.ca/ember**.

Acknowledgments

For the first Canadian adaptation, I would like to thank a number of people at Pearson Education Canada, including Duncan Mackinnon, Jessica Mosher, Lise Dupont, and Joe Zingrone. Special thanks must also go to copy editor Jenifer Ludbrook for using her keen eye on the manuscript.

For the second edition, Carolin Sweig, Jennifer Murray, and Söğüt Y. Güleç were very helpful and extremely patient with me. Thanks also to Susan Marshall and Barbara Czarnecki for their roles in copy editing and proofing the second edition.

To colleagues and friends who provided material and comments, I would like to thank Tina Moffat, Anne Keenleyside, Priscilla Renouf, Bob Park, Pascale Sicotte, Dongya Yang, Ariane Burke, Greg Monks, Haskel Greenfield, Shelley Saunders, David Begun, Sarah Gaunt, Luis Fondebrider (EAAF), Tracy Rogers, David Ebert, and Chris Meiklejohn. Brian Rahn and the Department of Anthropology, University of Manitoba, provided research assistance for the first edition, and Collin Moore and Travis Allard assisted with the second edition. Finally, many students provided important feedback on the textbook, including Maria Nunes.

The following individuals graciously gave up their time to provide constructive criticisms of the various drafts of the revisions. We are grateful to these people, and to a few who wish to remain anonymous, for their many useful comments and suggestions.

Ian Colquhoun, University of Western Ontario
Stan Freer, University of Manitoba
Scott Hamilton, Lakehead University
Anne Keenleyside, Trent University
Karen Lind, Capilano College
Moira H. M. McLaughlin, St. Thomas University
Lorraine McNeil, Fanshawe College
Pascale Sicotte, University of Calgary
Terry Webb, University of Western Ontario
Anne Zeller, University of Waterloo

—*Rob Hoppa*

About the Authors

Carol R. Ember started at Antioch College as a chemistry major. She began taking social science courses because some were required, but she soon found herself intrigued. There were lots of questions without answers, and she became excited about the possibility of a research career in social science. She spent a year in graduate school at Cornell studying sociology before continuing on to Harvard, where she studied anthropology primarily with John and Beatrice Whiting.

For her Ph.D. dissertation she worked among the Luo of Kenya. While there she noticed that many boys were assigned "girls' work," such as babysitting and household chores, because their mothers (who did most of the agriculture) did not have enough girls to help out. She decided to study the possible effects of task assignment on the social behaviour of boys. Using systematic behaviour observations, she compared girls, boys who did a great deal of girls' work, and boys who did little such work. She found that boys assigned girls' work were intermediate in many social behaviours, compared with the other boys and girls. Later, she did cross-cultural research on variation in marriage, family, descent groups, and war and peace, mainly in collaboration with Melvin Ember, whom she married in 1970. All of these cross-cultural studies tested theories on data for worldwide samples of societies.

From 1970 to 1996, she taught at Hunter College of the City University of New York. She has also served as president of the Society of Cross-Cultural Research and is one of the directors of the Summer Institutes in Comparative Anthropological Research, which are funded by the National Science Foundation. She is now executive director at the Human Relations Area Files, Inc., a non-profit research agency of Yale University.

After graduating from Columbia College, **Melvin Ember** went to Yale University for his Ph.D. His mentor at Yale was George Peter Murdock, an anthropologist who was instrumental in promoting cross-cultural research and building a full-text database on the cultures of the world to facilitate cross-cultural hypothesis testing. This database came to be known as the Human Relations Area Files (HRAF) because it was originally sponsored by the Institute of Human Relations at Yale. Growing in annual instalments and now distributed in electronic format, the HRAF database currently covers more than 355 cultures, past and present, all over the world.

Melvin Ember did fieldwork for his dissertation in American Samoa, where he conducted a comparison of three villages to study the effects of commercialization on political life. In addition, he did research on descent groups and how they changed with the increase of buying and selling. His cross-cultural studies focused originally on variation in marital residence and descent groups. He has also done cross-cultural research on the relationship between economic and political development, the origin and extension of the incest taboo, the causes of polygyny, and how archaeological correlates of social customs can help us draw inferences about the past.

After four years of research at the National Institute of Mental Health, he taught at Antioch College and then Hunter College of the City University of New York. He has served as president of the Society for Cross-Cultural Research and has been president since 1987 of the Human Relations Area Files, Inc.

Peter N. Peregrine came to anthropology after completing an undergraduate degree in English. He found anthropology's social scientific approach to understanding humans more appealing than the humanistic approach he had learned as an English major. He undertook an ethnohistorical study of the relationship between Jesuit missionaries and Native American peoples for his master's degree and realized that he needed to study archaeology to understand the cultural interactions experienced by Native Americans prior to contact with the Jesuits.

While working on his Ph.D. at Purdue University, Peter Peregrine did research on the prehistoric Mississippian cultures of the eastern United States. He found that interactions between groups were common and had been shaping Native American cultures for centuries. Native Americans approached contact with the Jesuits simply as another in a long string of intercultural exchanges. He also found that relatively little research had been done on Native American interactions and decided that comparative research was a good place to begin examining the topic. In 1990 he participated in the Summer Institute in Comparative Anthropological Research, where he met Carol R. Ember and Melvin Ember.

Peter Peregrine taught at Juniata College and is currently associate professor and chair of the anthropology department at Lawrence University in Appleton, Wisconsin. He serves as research associate for the HRAF Collection of Archaeology and is co-editor with Melvin Ember of the *Encyclopedia of Prehistory*. He continues to do archaeological research, and he recently celebrated his first decade of teaching anthropology and archaeology to undergraduate students.

Rob Hoppa received a B.Sc. in physical anthropology from the University of Toronto in 1990. Subsequently he pursued graduate work and received a joint M.Sc. in osteology, palaeopathology, and funerary archaeology from the Universities of Bradford and Sheffield (UK) in 1991 and a Ph.D. in physical anthropology from the Department of Anthropology, McMaster University in 1996. His doctoral research focused on issues of sampling for skeletal biology, particularly the impact of bias on palaeodemographic estimates under the supervision of Shelley Saunders. Following his doctoral research he undertook post-doctoral research in historical demography and epidemiology of a nineteenth-century subarctic Aboriginal community during the decline of the fur trade. In 1998, he joined the Laboratory of Survival and Longevity at the Max Planck Institute for Demographic Research in Rostock, Germany. In July 1999, he joined the Department of Anthropology at the University of Manitoba.

Dr. Hoppa's research has broadly focused on issues of health and well-being in past populations. His research seeks to answer questions regarding the relationship between health and mortality, and changing social, economic, and cultural conditions. His training is strongly anchored in the biocultural tradition that recognizes the complex interaction of biological and social factors related to health and disease in populations.

Dr. Hoppa is currently associate professor in the Department of Anthropology at the University of Manitoba and a Canada Research Chair in Skeletal Biology (**www.chairs.gc.ca**). His current program of research focuses on the biological anthropology of past populations. He is the recipient of the 2000 University of Manitoba Rh Award for Outstanding Contributions to Scholarship and Research, and two Canada Foundation for Innovation grants for the establishment of the Bioanthropology Digital Image Analysis Laboratory at the University of Manitoba. There, he and his students are exploring innovative approaches to examining and interpreting data from the past using two-dimensional and three-dimensional imaging techniques.

A Great Way to Learn and Instruct Online

The Pearson Education Canada Companion Website is easy to navigate and is organized to correspond to the chapters in this textbook. Whether you are a student in the classroom or a distance learner you will discover helpful resources for in-depth study and research that empower you in your quest for greater knowledge and maximize your potential for success in the course.

Companion Website

[www.pearsoned.ca/ember]

Enter

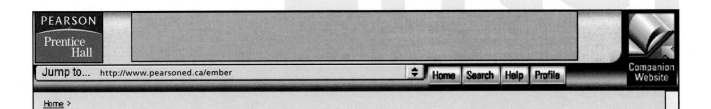

PEARSON
Prentice
Hall

Jump to...   http://www.pearsoned.ca/ember   Home Search Help Profile

Companion
Website

Home >

Companion Website

Physical Anthropology and Archaeology, Second Canadian Edition, by Ember, Ember, Peregrine, and Hoppa

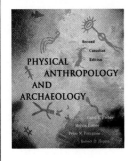

Student Resources

The modules in this section provide students with tools for learning course material. These modules include

- Chapter Objectives
- Destinations
- Multiple-Choice Quiz
- Key Terms Quiz
- True/False Quiz
- Review and Response Essay Questions
- Internet Exercises
- Net Search

In the quiz modules students can send answers to the grader and receive instant feedback on their progress through the Results Reporter. Coaching comments and references to the textbook may be available to ensure that students take advantage of all available resources to enhance their learning experience.

Instructor Resources

A link to this book on the Pearson Education Canada online catalogue (vig.pearsoned.ca) provides instructors with additional teaching tools. Downloadable PowerPoint Presentations and an Instructor's Manual are just some of the materials that may be available. The catalogue is password protected. To get a password, simply contact your Pearson Education Canada representative or call Faculty Sales and Services at 1-800-850-5813.

PHYSICAL ANTHROPOLOGY AND ARCHAEOLOGY

WHAT IS ANTHROPOLOGY?

1

Anthropology by definition is a discipline of infinite curiosity about human beings. The term comes from the Greek *anthropos* for "man, human" and *logos* for "study." Anthropologists seek answers to an enormous variety of questions about humans. They are interested in discovering when, where, and why humans appeared on the earth, how and why they have changed since then, and how and why modern human populations vary in certain physical features. Anthropologists are also interested in how and why societies in the past and present have varied in their customary ideas and practices. There is a practical side to anthropology too. Applied anthropologists solve practical problems using anthropological methods, information, and results.

Yet defining anthropology as the study of human beings is not complete, for such a definition would appear to incorporate a whole catalogue of disciplines: sociology, psychology, political science, economics, history, human biology, and perhaps even the humanistic disciplines of philosophy and literature. Needless to say, practitioners of the many other disciplines concerned with humans would not be happy if these disciplines were regarded as sub-branches of anthropology. After all, most of those disciplines have existed longer than anthropology, and each is somewhat distinctive. There must, then, be something unique about anthropology—a reason for its having developed as a separate discipline and for having retained a separate identity over the past 100 years.

The Scope of Anthropology

Anthropologists are generally thought of as individuals who travel to little-known corners of the world to study exotic peoples or who dig deep into

HISTORICAL PERSPECTIVES

A Short History of Anthropology in Canada

The fathers of Canadian ethnology were the missionaries who lived in French Canada in the 1600s. These men were deeply interested in knowing the lifeways and beliefs of the native people they lived among, and they provided the detailed descriptions that were used by modern anthropologists. Canadian anthropology grew from records written by Jesuits and other missionaries, or explorer-traders, or two centuries later from teachers in our early universities in the mid-1880s, such as Sir Daniel Wilson at the University of Toronto or John William Dawson at McGill University. Another important source of information came from government employees, in particular with the Geological Survey of Canada, who made records of their travels, including details about the native people they met and observed in the course of their work. The most important of these men is George Mercer Dawson, who at the end of

the nineteenth century, more than any other person, is responsible for the establishment of a professional Canadian anthropology.

In 1910 Prime Minister Wilfrid Laurier established a Division of Anthropology within the Geological Survey (now part of the Canadian Museum of Civilization), marking the beginning of professional anthropology in Canada. The Victoria Memorial Museum in Ottawa housed its offices, and professionally trained individuals were recruited from England and the United States. Edward Sapir, who studied under Professor Boas, had just completed his doctorate and was embarking on a brilliant career in anthropology. Charles Marius Barbeau, a Rhodes scholar born in rural Quebec, was the product of the tutelage of Oxford professors Tylor and Marett. Barbeau's work at the National Museum (as it became known) was only one part of his contribution to Canadian anthropology.

Les Archives de folklore at Université Laval originated in his great collections of French Canadian material culture, songs, stories and tales, and in his students', especially Luc Lacourcière's, work to establish the archives (1944). Barbeau also recruited to the museum a fellow student from Oxford, Diamond Jenness.

Sapir and Barbeau both made ethnographic studies and collections of the cultures of the natives of the Northwest Coast, following George Mercer Dawson and Boas in this area. Jenness is best known for his research in the Arctic among the Copper Inuit. But each of these scholars also worked in many other areas of Canada, recording traditions and songs, studying native languages, and collecting artifacts for the museum. In 1911, Sapir took an interest in Frederick Wilkerson Waugh, born in 1872 in Langford, Ontario, offering him a contract to study Iroquoian technology. In 1913,

the earth to uncover the fossil remains or the tools and habitations of people who lived long ago. These views, though clearly stereotyped, do indicate how anthropology differs from other disciplines concerned with humans. Anthropology is broader in scope, both geographically and historically. Anthropologists are concerned explicitly and directly with all varieties of people throughout the world, not just those close at hand or within a limited area, and they are also interested in people of all time periods. Beginning with the immediate ancestors of humans, who lived a few million years ago, anthropology traces the development of humans to the present. Every part of the world where a human population has lived is of interest to anthropologists.

Anthropologists have not always been as global and comprehensive in their concerns as they are today. Traditionally, they concentrated on non-Western cultures and left the study of Western civilization and similarly complex societies, with their recorded histories, to other disciplines. In recent years, however, this division of labour among the disciplines has begun to disappear. Now anthropologists work in a variety of societies, including their own.

What induces anthropologists to choose so broad a subject for study? In part, they are motivated by the belief that any generalization about human beings, any possible explanation of some characteristic of human culture or biology, should be shown to apply to many times and places of human existence. If a generalization or explanation does not prove to apply widely, we are entitled or even obliged to be skeptical about it. The skeptical attitude, in the absence of persuasive evidence, is our best protection against accepting invalid ideas about humans.

Waugh was formally hired to work in the Anthropology Division and he rose to Associate Ethnologist around 1923. William Wintemberg and Harlan Smith worked archaeological sites to build the collections of prehistoric artifacts. These men, with a very few others, had nearly sole responsibility for the development of the profession in Canada from 1910 until 1925, when Sapir left Canada and Thomas McIlwraith took the first academic position in anthropology in Canada at the University of Toronto. It would be over two decades before the next anthropologists would be hired in Canada, at the University of British Columbia and at McGill University in 1947.

In English Canada the development of anthropology was guided by the studies of small communities of native people, with research in other areas of Canada and the world gradually increasing during the 1960s and 1970s. Since the early studies by Boas, Jenness, and others of small, tradition-oriented communities in the Arctic, and the studies by Boas, Barbeau, Sapir, and others of Northwest Coast native communities, the empirical study of small and isolated communities has continued to occupy the interests of many Canadian anthropologists. In Quebec the studies of rural and small-town communities added to the cultural "mapping" of more isolated areas that continued through the 1960s, especially at Université de Montréal and at Université Laval. The most important figure was Leon Gerin, whose *L'Habitant de St-Justin* illustrated how, in rural Quebec, the old European patriarchal system continued to shape the community's lifeways. McGill University supported this research, but also developed a research program on social change among the James Bay Cree. Applied anthropology in Canada has grown partly in response to the needs of native people and organizations during the 1970s like the James Bay Project.

While anthropology remains a relatively young discipline, Canada has developed excellent resources for training professional anthropologists. As of 2003 there were graduate programs in anthropology at 17 universities across Canada and at least 14 professional organizations representing anthropologists in Canada. Despite being a young discipline, anthropology, fundamentally, remains one of humankind's oldest interests. In the past century, the study of human variety and of the universal human qualities that underlie the variety has developed successfully in Canada and in other areas of the world. As our knowledge increases in accuracy and completeness, our science of humankind provides reliable guidance for efforts to improve the condition of all people. Anthropologists study humanity and serve human interests and values.

Source: Adapted from Preston RJ, Tremblay MA. 1997. The Canadian Encyclopedia. Toronto: McClelland & Stewart. Copyright © 1997. Historica Foundation of Canada. **www.histori.ca.**

For example, when educators in the United States discovered in the 1960s that African American schoolchildren rarely drank milk, they assumed that lack of money or education was the cause. Evidence from anthropology suggested a different explanation. Anthropologists had known for years that in many parts of the world where milking animals are kept, people do not drink fresh milk; rather, they sour it before they drink it, or they make it into cheese. Why they do so is now clear. Many people lack an enzyme, lactase, which is necessary for breaking down lactose, the sugar in milk. When such people drink regular milk, it actually interferes with digestion. Not only is the lactose in milk not digested but other nutrients are less likely to be digested as well; in many cases, drinking milk will cause cramps, stomach gas, diarrhea, and nausea. Studies indicate that milk intolerance is found in many parts of the world (Harrison, 1975; Durham, 1991). The condition is common in adulthood among Asians, southern Europeans, Arabs and Jews, West Africans, Inuit, and North and South American Indians, as well as African Americans. As many as 75 percent of all Native Americans are lactose intolerant. It is because anthropologists are acquainted with human life in an enormous variety of geographic and historical settings that they are often able to correct mistaken beliefs about different groups of people.

The Holistic Approach

Another distinguishing feature of anthropology is its **holistic**, or multi-faceted, approach to the study of human beings. Anthropologists study not only all varieties of people but many aspects of human experience as well. For example, when describing a group of people, an anthropologist might discuss the history of the area in which the people live, the physical environment, the organization of family life, the general features of their language, the group's settlement patterns, political and economic systems, religion, and styles of art and dress.

In the past, individual anthropologists tried to be holistic and cover all aspects of a subject. Today,

as in many other disciplines, so much information has been accumulated that anthropologists tend to specialize in one topic or area. Thus, one anthropologist may investigate the physical characteristics of some of our prehistoric ancestors. Another may study the biological effect of the environment on a human population over time. Still another will concentrate on the customs of a particular group of people. Despite this specialization, however, the discipline of anthropology retains its holistic orientation in that its many different specialties, taken together, describe many aspects of human existence, both past and present.

The Anthropological Curiosity

Thus far we have described anthropology as being broader in scope, both historically and geographically, and more holistic in approach than other disciplines concerned with human beings. This statement again implies that anthropology is the all-inclusive human science. How, then, is anthropology really different from those other disciplines? We suggest that anthropology's distinctiveness lies principally in the kind of curiosity it arouses.

Anthropologists are concerned with many types of questions: Where, when, and why did people first begin living in cities? Why do some peoples have darker skin than others? Why do some languages contain more terms for colour than other languages? Why do women have more of a voice in politics in some societies than in others? Why do populations differ in their acceptance of birth control? Although these questions deal with very different aspects of human existence, they have at least one thing in common: they all deal with *typical characteristics* (traits, customs) of particular populations. The typical characteristic of a people might be relatively dark skin, a language with many colour terms, female participation in politics, or acceptance of birth control. This concern with typical characteristics of populations is perhaps the most distinguishing feature of anthropology. For example, whereas economists take a monetary system for granted and study how it operates, anthropologists ask why only some societies during the last few thousand years developed and used money. In short, anthropologists are curious about the typical characteristics of human populations—how and why such populations and their characteristics have varied throughout the ages.

Four Sub-fields of Anthropology

Different anthropologists concentrate on different typical characteristics of societies. Some are concerned primarily with physical or biological characteristics of human populations; others are interested principally in what we call cultural characteristics. As a result, anthropology can be divided into four major sub-fields:

- **Biological or physical anthropology**, which is concerned primarily with the biological diversity of humans, their ancestors and closely related primates;

- **Archaeology**, which is the study of past human cultures, primarily through their material remains;

- **Socio-cultural anthropology**, which is concerned with the study of recent or contemporary cultures; and

- **Anthropological linguistics**, which is the anthropological study of languages.

Within each sub-field, a variety of research specialities exist, some of which overlap sub-disciplines (see Figure 1–1).

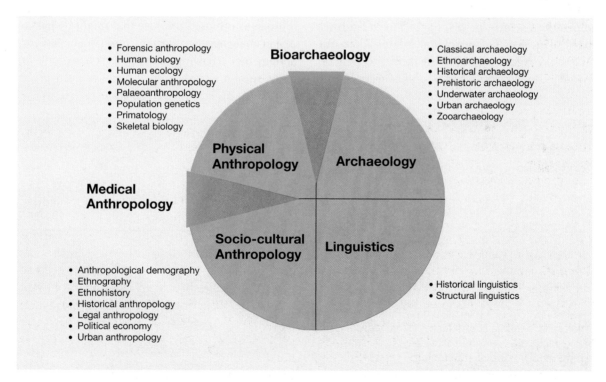

Figure 1–1 The Four Sub-fields of Anthropology

The four major subdisciplines of anthropology. There are applications of anthropology in all four, and examples of specialties for each subdiscipline are shown in the lists. Bioarchaeology, drawing from both physical or biological anthropology and archaeology, and medical anthropology, drawing from both physical anthropology and socio-cultural anthropology, are two examples of areas that overlap subdisciplines.

Physical Anthropology

Physical or biological anthropology seeks to answer a variety of questions about the human biological condition in both past and present populations. Some physical anthropologists are interested in the emergence of humans and their evolutionary relationship with other primates (this focus is called **human palaeontology** or **palaeoanthropology**). Others are interested in how and why contemporary human populations vary biologically, and in particular the interactions between biology, environment, and behaviour.

In order to reconstruct human evolution, palaeoanthropologists search for and study the buried, hardened remains or impressions, known as **fossils**, of humans, prehumans, and related animals. Palaeoanthropologists working in East Africa, for instance, have excavated the fossil remains of early human ancestors who lived more than 4 million years ago. These findings have suggested the approximate dates when our ancestors began to develop the facility to walk on two legs, very flexible hands, and a larger brain.

In attempting to clarify evolutionary relationships, palaeoanthropologists may use the fossil record and geological information about the succession of climates, environments, and plant and animal populations. Moreover, when reconstructing the past of humans, palaeoanthropologists are also interested in the behaviour and evolution of our closest relatives among the mammals—the prosimians, monkeys, and apes, which, like us, are members of the order of **Primates**. Anthropologists, psychologists, and biologists specializing in the study of primates are called **primatologists**. They observe the various species of primates in the wild and in the laboratory. One especially popular subject of study is the chimpanzee, which bears a close resemblance to humans in behaviour and physical appearance, has a similar blood chemistry, and is susceptible to many of the same diseases.

From primate studies, physical anthropologists try to discover characteristics that are distinctly human as opposed to those that might be part of the primate heritage. Further, observed behaviours among modern living primates serve as a model for how human ancestors may have behaved under

RESEARCH FRONTIERS

Researcher at Work: Owen Beattie

Owen Beattie was born in British Columbia. Now a professor of anthropology at the University of Alberta, Owen Beattie is a physical anthropologist who specializes in forensic anthropology. He has conducted forensic archaeological investigations in the Arctic, and worked on over 115 investigations into causes of human death for coroners, police agencies, and medical examiners in British Columbia, Alberta, the Northwest Territories, Saskatchewan, Ontario, Nova Scotia, and Prince Edward Island.

Owen Beattie is probably best known to the public for his involvement in the excavation and analysis of the frozen, mummified remains of members of the ill-fated Franklin expedition that were discovered in the permafrost of the Canadian Arctic. The demise of Franklin's expedition in the mid-nineteenth century has long been associated with rumours of cannibalism amongst the crew. The first direct evidence to substantiate these rumours surfaced in 1981 when Beattie observed cut marks on a femur recovered from a Franklin site

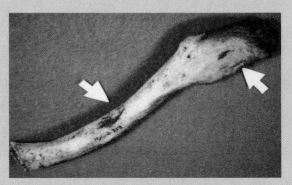

Cut marks on bones from the Franklin remains discovered in 1993 on King William Island.

on King William Island. This evidence, while rejected by many, was consistent with subsequent observations from remains discovered at a similar environmental conditions. With this information, these anthropologists may be able to infer what our distant ancestors were like. The inferences from primate studies are checked against the fossil record. The evidence from the earth, collected in bits and pieces, is correlated with scientific observations of our closest living relatives. In short, physical anthropologists piece together bits of information obtained from different sources. They construct theories that explain the changes observed in the fossil record and then attempt to evaluate their theories by checking one kind of evidence against another. Palaeoanthropology thus overlaps disciplines such as geology, general vertebrate (and particularly primate) palaeontology, comparative anatomy, and the study of comparative primate behaviour.

Another major focus of physical anthropology investigates how and why contemporary human populations differ in biological or physical characteristics. All living people belong to one species, **Homo sapiens**, for all can successfully interbreed. Yet there is much that varies among human populations. Investigators of **human variation** ask such questions as: Why are some peoples taller than others? How have human populations adapted physically to their environmental conditions? Are some peoples, such as Inuit, better equipped than other peoples to endure cold? Does darker skin pigmentation offer special protection against the tropical sun?

Physical anthropologists use the principles, concepts, and techniques of at least three other disciplines to further their understanding of human biological diversity: *human genetics* (the study of human traits that are inherited), *population biology* (the study of environmental effects on and interaction with population characteristics), and *epidemiology* (the study of how and why diseases affect different populations in different ways). Research on human variation, therefore, overlaps with research in other fields. Physical anthropologists, however, are concerned most with human populations and how they vary biologically.

Archaeology

The archaeologist seeks not only to reconstruct the daily life and customs of peoples who lived in the

new site in 1992 and investigated in 1993 by a team led by archaeologist Margaret Bertulli and physical anthropologist Anne Keenleyside. The analysis of the human remains showed cut marks on some 92 bones, representing about 25 percent of the total number of bones discovered.

The recovery of the remains of Kwaday Dän Sinchi on the glacier.

More recently, Owen Beattie has been involved in the examination of the recently discovered frozen remains of a prehistoric hunter. In co-operation with representatives from British Columbia and from Champagne and Aishihik First Nations, within whose tribal territory the hunter was found, he is heading the scientific team investigating the 550-year-old frozen remains of a hunter, discovered in 1999 in a remote area of northwestern British Columbia. The remains, named Kwaday Dän Sinchi, which means "Long Ago Person Found" in the Tutchone language, immediately invited comparison with Ötzi the Iceman, a hunter whose frozen body, dating to 5300 years ago, was discovered in the Italian Alps in 1991. However, radiocarbon tests on the hat and cloak Kwaday Dän Sinchi was wearing place his time of death sometime between A.D. 1415 and A.D. 1445. These dates suggest the individual died more than 50 years before Columbus reached the Caribbean and more than 300 years before the first known European contact on the Northwest Coast.

Sources: Beattie O, Geiger J. 1987. Frozen in Time. New York: E.P Dutton.

Who's Buried in the Ice? 15 September 1999. Archaeology. Online News.

Keenleyside A, Bertulli M, Fricke HC. 1997. The Final Days of the Franklin Expedition: New Skeletal Evidence. Arctic 50(1):36–46.

past but also to trace cultural changes and offer possible explanations for those changes. This goal is similar to that of the historian, but the archaeologist reaches much farther back in time. The historian deals only with societies that left written records and is therefore limited to the last 5000 years of human history. Human societies, however, have existed for more than a million years, and only a small proportion in the last 5000 years recorded their past in writing. For all those past societies lacking a written record, or where the written record is indecipherable or has disappeared, the archaeologist serves as historian. Lacking written records for study, archaeologists must try to reconstruct history from the remains of human cultures. Some of these remains are as grand as the Mayan temples at Chichén Itzá in Yucatán, Mexico. More often they are as ordinary as bits of broken pottery, stone tools, and garbage heaps.

Most archaeologists deal with the distant past—the time before written records. But there is a specialty within archaeology, called **historical archaeology**, that studies the remains of recent peoples who left written records. This specialty, as its name implies, employs the methods of both archaeologists and historians to study recent societies for which there is both archaeological and historical information.

In trying to understand how and why ways of life have changed through time in different parts of the world, archaeologists collect materials from sites of human occupation. Usually, these sites must be unearthed. On the basis of materials they excavate and otherwise collect, they then ask various questions such as: Where, when, and why did the distinctive human characteristic of toolmaking first emerge? Where, when, and why did agriculture first develop? Where, when, and why did people first begin to live in cities?

To collect the data they need to find answers to these and other questions, archaeologists rely on techniques and findings borrowed from other disciplines as well as what they can infer from anthropological studies of recent and contemporary cultures. For example, to guess where to dig for evidence of early toolmaking, archaeologists rely

on geology and physical geography to tell them where sites of early human occupation are likely to be found near the surface of the earth. To infer when agriculture first developed, archaeologists date relevant excavated materials by a process originally developed by chemists. To understand why cities first emerged, archaeologists may study information from historians, geographers, and others about how recent and contemporary cities are related economically and politically to their hinterlands. If we can discover what recent and contemporary cities have in common, we can speculate on why cities developed originally. Thus, archaeologists gather information from the present and recent past in trying to understand the distant past.

Socio-Cultural Anthropology

Cultural anthropologists are interested in how populations or societies vary in their cultural features. But what is culture? To an anthropologist, the term **culture** refers to the customary ways of thinking and behaving of a particular population or society. The culture of a social group includes many things—its language, religious beliefs, food preferences, music, work habits, gender roles, how children are reared, how houses are constructed, and many other learned behaviours and ideas that have come to be widely shared or customary among the group.

Ethnologists seek to understand how and why peoples today and in the recent past differ in their customary ways of thinking and acting. **Ethnology**, then, is concerned with cultural patterns of behaviour, such as marriage customs, kinship organization, political and economic systems, religion, folk art, and music, and with the ways in which these patterns differ in contemporary societies. Ethnologists also study the dynamics of culture, that is, how various cultures develop and change. As well, they are interested in the relationship between beliefs and practices within a culture. Thus, the aim of ethnologists is largely the same as that of archaeologists. Ethnologists, however, generally use data collected through observation and interviews with people. Archaeologists, on the other hand, must work with

Nadine Peacock, a biological anthropologist, studying reproduction and health among the Efe-Ituri Pygmies of the former Zaire.

fragmentary remains of past cultures on the basis of which they can only make inferences about the customs of **prehistoric** peoples.

One type of ethnologist, the **ethnographer**, usually spends a year or so living with, talking to, and observing the people whose customs he or she is studying. This fieldwork provides the data for a detailed description (an **ethnography**) of many aspects of the cultural behaviours and customs of the group. The ethnographer not only tries to describe the general patterns of their life but also may suggest answers to such questions as: How are economic and political behaviour related? How may a people adapt their customs to environmental conditions? Is there any relationship between beliefs about the supernatural and beliefs or practices about the natural world? In other words, the ethnographer depicts the way of life of a particular group of people and explains some of the customs observed.

Because so many cultures have undergone extensive change in the recent past, another type of ethnologist, the **ethnohistorian**, studies how the way of life of a particular group of people has changed over time. Unlike ethnographers, who rely mostly on their own observations,

ethnohistorians rely on the reports of others. Ethnohistorians investigate historical documents, such as missionary accounts, reports by traders and explorers, and government records, to try to establish the cultural changes that have occurred. Often, they must attempt to piece together and make sense of widely scattered, and even apparently contradictory, information. Thus, the ethnohistorian's research is very much like that of the historian except that the ethnohistorian is usually concerned with the history of a people who did not themselves leave written records. The ethnohistorian tries to reconstruct the recent history of a people and may also suggest why certain changes in their way of life took place.

With the data collected and analyzed by the ethnographer and ethnohistorian, the work of a third type of ethnologist, the **cross-cultural researcher**, can be done. The cross-cultural researcher is interested in discovering why certain cultural characteristics may be found in some societies but not in others. Why, for example, do some societies have plural marriages (one spouse of one sex and two or more spouses of the other sex), circumcision of adolescent boys, or belief in a supreme being? To answer such questions, cross-cultural researchers rely on the data from samples of different cultures to explain cultural variation.

Because ethnologists may be interested in many aspects of cultural behaviour, from economic behaviour to political behaviour to styles of art, music, and religion, ethnology overlaps with disciplines that concentrate on some particular aspect of human existence, such as sociology, psychology, economics, political science, art, music, and comparative religion. The distinctive feature of **cultural anthropology** is its interest in how all these aspects of human existence vary from society to society in all historical periods and in all parts of the world.

Anthropological Linguistics

Linguistics, or the study of languages, is a somewhat older discipline than anthropology. The early linguists concentrated on the study of languages that had a written form for a long time—for example, the English language has had a written form for nearly a thousand years. Then anthropological linguists began to do fieldwork in places where the language did not have a written form. To learn the language, anthropologists had to first construct a dictionary and grammar. Then they could study the structure and history of the language.

Like physical anthropologists, linguists study changes that have taken place over time, as well as contemporary variation. Some anthropological linguists are concerned with the emergence of language and also with the divergence of languages over thousands of years. The study of how languages change over time and how they may be related is known as **historical linguistics**. Anthropological linguists are also interested in how contemporary languages differ, especially in their construction. This focus of linguistics is generally called **structural** or **descriptive linguistics**. The study of how language is used in social contexts is called **sociolinguistics**.

In contrast with the palaeoanthropologist and archaeologist, who work with physical remains to help them reconstruct change over time, the historical linguist deals only with languages, and usually languages do not have a written form. (Remember that writing is only about 5000 years old, and most languages were not written.) Because an unwritten language must be heard in order to be studied, it does not leave any traces once its speakers have died. Linguists interested in reconstructing the history of unwritten languages must begin in the present, with comparisons of contemporary languages. On the basis of these comparisons, they draw inferences about the kinds of change in language that may have occurred in the past and that may account for similarities and differences observed in the present. The historical linguist typically asks such questions as these: Did two or more contemporary languages diverge from a common ancestral language? If they are related, how far back in time did they begin to differ?

Unlike the historical linguist, the structural (or descriptive) linguist is typically concerned with discovering and recording the principles that determine how sounds and words are put together in speech. For example, a structural description of a particular language might tell us that the sounds *t* and *k* are interchangeable in a word without causing a difference in meaning. In American Samoa, one could say *Tutuila* or *Kukuila* as the name of the largest island, and everyone, except perhaps the newly arrived anthropologist, would understand that the same island was being mentioned.

The sociolinguist is interested in the social aspects of language, including what people speak about and how they interact conversationally, their attitudes toward speakers of other dialects or languages, and how people speak differently in different social contexts. In English, for example, we do not address everyone we meet in the same way. "Hi, Sandy" may be the customary way a person greets a friend, but we would probably feel uncomfortable addressing a doctor in this manner. Instead, we would probably say, "Good morning, Dr. Brown." Such variations in language use, which are determined by the social status of the persons being addressed, are significant for the sociolinguist.

Specialization

As disciplines grow, they tend to develop more and more specialties. This trend is probably inevitable because, as knowledge accumulates and methods become more advanced, there is a limit to the amount of information that any one person can reasonably keep track of. So, in addition to the general divisions we have outlined already, particular anthropologists tend to identify themselves with a variety of specializations. It is common for anthropologists to have a geographic specialty, which may be as broad as the Old World or the New World or as narrow as the West Coast of Canada. Those who study the past (archaeologists or palaeoanthropologists) may also specialize in different time periods. Socio-cultural anthropologists often specialize in more specific subject matters such as kinship, identity, symbolism, and complexity, often in addition to one or two cultural groups.

Some socio-cultural anthropologists identify themselves as *economic anthropologists*, *political anthropologists*, or *psychological anthropologists*. Others may identify themselves by theoretical orientations, such as **cultural ecologists** who are concerned with the relationship between culture and the physical and social environments. These specialties are not mutually exclusive, however. A cultural ecologist, for example, might be interested in the effects of the environment on economic behaviour, or political behaviour, or how people raise their children.

Does specialization isolate an anthropologist from other kinds of research? Not necessarily. Some specialties have to draw on information from several fields, inside and outside anthropology. For example, *medical anthropologists* study the cultural and biological contexts of human health and illness. Thus, they need to understand the economy, diet, and patterns of social interaction,

NEW PERSPECTIVES ON GENDER

Getting Development Programs to Notice Women's Contributions to Agriculture

When Anita Spring first worked in the field in Zambia in the 1970s, she was not particularly interested in agriculture. Rather, medical anthropology was her primary interest. Her work focused on customary healing practices, particularly involving women and children. She was surprised at the end of the year when a delegation of women came to tell her that she didn't understand what it meant to be a woman. "To be a woman is to be a farmer," they said. She admits that it took her a while to pay attention to women as farmers, but then she began to participate in efforts to provide technical assistance to them. Like many others interested in women in development, Spring realized that all too often development agencies downplay women's contributions to agriculture.

How does one bring about change in male-centred attitudes and practices? One way is to document how much women actually contribute to agriculture. Beginning with the influental writing of Ester Boserup in *Woman's Role in Economic Development* (1970), scholars began to report that in Africa south of the Sahara, in the Caribbean, and in parts of Southeast Asia, women were the principal farmers or agricultural labourers. Moreover, as agriculture became more complex, it required more work in the fields, so the women's contribution to agriculture increased. In addition, men increasingly went away to work, so women had to do much of what used to be men's work on the farms.

In the 1980s, Spring designed and directed the Women in Agricultural Development Project in Malawi, funded by the Office of Women in the U.S. Agency for International Development. Rather than focusing just on women, the project aimed to collect data on both women and men agriculturalists and how they were treated by development agents. The project did more than collect information; mini-projects were set up and evaluated so that successful training techniques could be passed on to development agents in other regions. Spring points out that the success of the program was due not just to the design of the project but more so to the interest and willingness of Malawi itself to change. And it didn't hurt that the United Nations and other donor organizations increasingly focused attention on women. It takes the efforts of many to bring about change. Increasingly, applied anthropologists like Anita Spring are involved in these efforts from beginning to end, from the design stage to implementation and evaluation.

Source: Spring A. 1995. Agricultural Development and Gender Issues in Malawi. Lanham, MD: University Press of America.

as well as attitudes and beliefs regarding illness and health. They may need to draw on research in human genetics, public health, and medicine.

The Biocultural Model

Increased specialization reinforces the division between the subdisciplines of anthropology. However, there is increased realization by anthropologists that many of the questions being asked cannot ignore the fundamental interactions between environment, behaviour, and biology for human populations. In the 1990s anthropology embraced the **biocultural model**—the idea that human biological diversity is interrelated to changes in environmental conditions, and that one of humankind's greatest adaptive strategies is the development of culture. Thus, the interactions of biology, behaviour, and environment are ultimately linked together, and changes in one can often be explained by changes in the others. Early incarnations of this concept are seen in the many arguments in the social and behavioural sciences that surround the debate of "nature versus nurture" or biology versus behaviour. However, anthropologists now recognize that both are interconnected, and to understand much of the evolutionary changes in the human species, we must understand the changing relationships between these associated factors.

The biocultural approach to reconstructing human evolution will become clearer in subsequent chapters that discuss the early **hominids**—early human ancestors—and the emergence of the genus *Homo*. For example, a current argument for the emergence of the first bipedal ape—that is, the earliest hominids—links changes in the environment in which these primates lived to changes in behaviour and biology related to new survival strategies to cope with these new conditions. Similarly, the genus *Homo* was originally classified and distinguished from other hominids by the presence of culture in the form of manufactured tools. This new adaptive strategy—the development of culture—represented the beginning of an integrated relationship between biology, behaviour, and culture. With a changing environment, important biological changes like increased brain size and complexity, and behavioural strategies, especially increased cultural complexity, improved survival and eventually resulted in modern human populations. As the development of culture provided greater advantages for survival among early hominids, any genetic traits associated with these new behaviours were favoured in the population. Ultimately this relationship between biology and culture resulted in the rapid acceleration of human evolution.

Applied Anthropology

All knowledge is useful. In the physical and biological sciences it is well understood that technological breakthroughs like DNA splicing, a mission to Mars, and the development of minuscule computer chips could not have taken place without an enormous amount of basic research to uncover the laws of nature in the physical and biological worlds. If we did not understand these fundamental principles, the technological achievements we are so proud of would not have been possible. Researchers are often simply driven by curiosity, with no thought of where the research might lead, which is why such research is sometimes called *basic research*. The same is true of the social sciences. If a researcher finds out that societies with combative sports tend to have more wars, it may lead to other inquiries about the relationships between one kind of aggression and another. The knowledge acquired may ultimately lead to the discovery of ways to lessen social problems such as family violence and war.

Applied research is more explicit than basic research in its practical goals. Today many professional anthropologists are *applied anthropologists*. **Applied anthropology** is explicit in its concern with making anthropological knowledge immediately useful in public policy for example (Chambers, 1989). Applied anthropologists may be trained in any or all of the sub-fields of anthropology. In contrast to basic researchers, who are generally employed in colleges, universities, and museums, applied anthropologists are often employed in settings outside of traditional

RESEARCH FRONTIERS

Researcher at Work: Tina Moffat

Tina Moffat is a physical anthropologist who specializes in medical anthropology at McMaster University, Hamilton, Ontario. Her area of specialty is child health. In particular, her research focuses on the links between economic and environmental conditions and poor health status, specifically the ecological determinants of health in Nepal and Aboriginal communities in Canada.

Moffat's research for her master's degree documented high infant mortality rates among First Nations communities in Canada during the early twentieth century. Using archival sources, she reconstructed infant mortality rates for the beginning of the twentieth century in the Aboriginal First Nations community of Fisher River, Manitoba. Acute respiratory infections and high rates of post-neonatal (over 1 month of age) mortality suggested poverty and malnutrition as the major precipitating factors in infant mortality. Like other early-twentieth-century First Nations communities in Canada, Fisher River experienced socio-economic deprivation with the decline of the fur trade. Moffat's research incorporated economic and political marginalization in a model of disease processes to explain the high infant mortality rates.

For her doctoral research Tina Moffat studied the health and nutritional status of children living in a *peri-urban* (the transitional area between city and country) community in Kathmandu, Nepal, where she spent 12 months in 1994–95. She focused her research on urbanization in Nepal and the associated environmental conditions that lead to high rates of disease and impaired growth and development in children under 5 years of age. This study explored adaptation to city environments by following the growth of children, aged birth to 60 months, of rural-to-urban migrant women. She examined areas such as health-care utilization by different age groups, incidence of diarrhea, breastfeeding practices, and demographic and socio-economic characteristics. This research showed her that children of migrant mothers had reduced growth after 12 months of age. Confounding this observation though, children of long-term migrant mothers had better growth than those of recent migrant mothers, despite no differences in socio-economic and biobehavioural characteristics. Tina Moffat concluded that adaptation to an urban environment could not be explained by standard biobehavioural indicators of modernization, and that other venues should be explored. She continues to examine this issue, and her current research focuses on the

Physical anthropologist Tina Moffat working with mothers and children in peri-urban Nepal.

environment in which children are living and perceptions of child illness in peri-urban Nepal.

Sources: Moffat T. 1998. Urbanization and Child Health in Nepal. American Journal of Human Biology 10(3):307–316.

Moffat T, Herring DA. 1999. The Historical Roots of High Rates of Infant Death in Aboriginal Communities in Canada in the Early Twentieth Century: The Case of Fisher River, Manitoba. Social Science and Medicine 48:1821–1832.

academia, including government agencies, international development agencies, private consulting firms, businesses, public health organizations, medical schools, law offices, community development agencies, and charitable foundations.

Physical anthropologists may be called upon to give forensic evidence in court, work in public health, or design clothes and equipment to fit human anatomy. Archaeologists may be involved in preserving and exhibiting artifacts for museums and in finding and preserving cultural sites that might be damaged by construction or excavation. Linguists may work in bilingual educational training programs or may work on ways to improve

Tourism, shown here in Asmat county of western New Guinea, is one way to learn about other cultures. But anthropology is a better way. It not only tells us how cultures are different, but helps us to understand why.

communication. Ethnologists may work in a wide variety of applied projects ranging from community development, urban planning, health care, agricultural improvement to personnel and organizational management, and assessment of the impact that changes in programs have on people's lives (Kushner, 1991; Miracle, 1998). We discuss applied anthropology more fully in Chapter 14.

The Relevance of Anthropology

Anthropology is a comparatively young discipline. It was only in the late 1800s that anthropologists began to live with people in faraway communities. Compared with our knowledge of the physical laws of nature, we know little about people, about how and why they behave as they do. The fact that anthropology and other sciences dealing with humans began to develop only relatively recently is not in itself a sufficient reason for this discrepancy. Why, in our quest for knowledge of all kinds, did we wait so long to study ourselves? Leslie White suggests that those phenomena most remote from

us and least significant as determinants of human behaviour were the first to be studied. The reason, he surmises, is that humans like to think of themselves as citadels of free will, subject to no laws of nature. Hence, there is no need to see ourselves as objects to be explained (White, 1968).

The idea that it is impossible to account for human behaviour scientifically, either because our actions and beliefs are too individualistic and complex or because human beings are understandable only in otherworldly terms, is a self-fulfilling notion. We cannot discover principles explaining human behaviour if we neither believe such principles exist nor bother to look for them. The result is assured from the beginning. People who do not believe in principles of human behaviour will have their disbelief reinforced by their finding none. If we are to increase our understanding of human beings, we first have to believe it is possible to do so.

If we aim to understand humans, it is essential that we study humans in all times and places. How else can we understand what is true of humans generally or how they are capable of varying? If we study just our own society, we may give explanations

Simplicity of technology should not be taken to imply backwardness. The Inuit developed very ingenious ways of dealing with their extremely difficult environment. Constructing an igloo out of specially shaped blocks of ice, as shown here in the Canadian Arctic, is not easy.

that are culture-bound (**ethnocentric**), that is, not general or applicable to most or all humans. Anthropology is useful, then, to the degree that it contributes to our understanding of human beings everywhere.

As well, anthropology is a relevant field of study because it helps us avoid misunderstandings between peoples. If we can understand why other groups are different from ourselves, we might have less reason to react to them in a negative way for behaviour that appears strange to us. We may then come to realize that many differences between peoples are products of physical and cultural adaptations to different environments. For example, someone who first finds out about the !Kung as they lived in the Kalahari Desert of southern Africa in the 1950s might think that the !Kung were "primitive." The !Kung wore little clothing, had few possessions, lived in meagre shelters, and enjoyed none of our technological benefits. But let us reflect on how a typical North American community might react if it woke to find itself in an environment similar to that in which the !Kung lived. People would find that the arid land made both agriculture and animal husbandry impossible, and they might have to think about adopting a nomadic

existence. They might then discard many of their material possessions so that they could travel easily, in order to take advantage of changing water and food supplies. Because of the extreme heat and the lack of water for washing clothes, they might find it more practical to be almost naked. They would undoubtedly find it impossible to build elaborate homes. For social security, they might start to share the food brought into the group. Thus, if they survived at all, they might have ended up looking and behaving far more like the !Kung than like typical North Americans.

Physical differences, too, may be seen as results of adaptations to the environment. For example, in our society we admire people who are tall and slim. If these same individuals were forced to live above the Arctic Circle, however, they might wish they could trade their tall, slim bodies for short, compact ones, because stocky physiques conserve body heat more effectively and may therefore be more adaptive in cold climates.

Exposure to anthropology might help to alleviate some of the misunderstandings that arise between people of different cultural groups from subtle causes operating below the level of consciousness. For example, different cultures have different conceptions of the gestures and interpersonal

Even before the emergence of high-tech medical science, people all over the world had discovered how plants could provide effective medicine. Here are some medicinal plants used by Native Americans in Arizona.

distances that are appropriate under various circumstances. Arabs consider it proper to stand close enough to other people to smell them (Hall, 1966). On the basis of the popularity of deodorants in our culture, we can deduce that North Americans prefer to keep the olfactory dimension out of interpersonal relations. We may feel that a person who comes too close is being too intimate. We should remember, however, that this person may only be acting according to a culturally conditioned conception of what is proper in a given situation. If our intolerance for others results in part from a lack of understanding of why peoples vary, then the knowledge accumulated by anthropologists may help lessen that intolerance.

Knowledge of our past may also bring both a feeling of humility and a sense of accomplishment. If we are to attempt to deal with the problems of our world, we must be aware of our vulnerability so that we do not think that our problems will solve themselves. But we also have to think enough of our accomplishments to believe that we can find solutions to our problems. Knowing something about our evolutionary past may help us to understand and accept our place in the biological world. Just as for any other form of life, there is no guarantee that any particular human population, or even the entire human species, will perpetuate itself indefinitely. The earth changes, the environment changes, and humanity itself changes. What survives and flourishes in the present might not do so in the future.

Yet our vulnerability should not make us feel powerless. There are many reasons to feel confident about the future. Consider what humans have accomplished. By means of tools and weapons fashioned from sticks and stones, we were able to hunt animals larger and more powerful than ourselves. We discovered how to make fire, and we learned to use it to keep ourselves warm and to cook our food. As we domesticated plants and animals, we gained greater control over our food supply and were able to establish more permanent settlements. We mined and smelted ores to fashion more complex and durable tools. We built cities and irrigation systems, monuments, and ships. We made it possible to travel from one continent to another in a single day. Illnesses that once cut life short are being controlled, and human life prolonged.

In short, human beings and their cultures have changed considerably over the course of history. Human populations have often adapted to changing circumstances. Let us hope that we continue to adapt to the challenges of the present and future.

Summary

1. Anthropology is literally the study of human beings. It differs from other disciplines concerned with people in that it is broader in scope. It is concerned with humans in all places of the world (not simply those places close to us), and it traces human evolution and cultural development from millions of years ago to the present day.

2. Anthropology is distinguished by its holistic approach to the study of human beings. Anthropologists study not only all varieties of people but also all aspects of those peoples' experiences.

3. Anthropologists are concerned with identifying and explaining typical characteristics (traits, customs) of particular human populations.

4. There are four major sub-fields of anthropology: physical or biological anthropology, archaeology, socio-cultural anthropology, and anthropological linguistics.

5. Physical or biological anthropology is one of the major fields of the discipline. Physical anthropology studies the emergence of humans and their evolutionary relationship to other primates (palaeoanthropology). It also studies how and why contemporary human populations vary biologically.

6. Archaeologists seek to reconstruct the daily life and customs of prehistoric peoples and trace cultural changes and offer possible explanations of those changes. Archaeologists try to reconstruct history from the remains of human cultures.

7. Socio-cultural anthropologists seek to understand how and why peoples of today and the recent past differ in their customary ways of thinking and acting. One type of ethnologist, the ethnographer, usually spends a year or so living with and talking to a particular population and observing their customs. Later, she or he may prepare a detailed report of the group's behaviour, which is called an ethnography. Another type of ethnologist, the ethnohistorian, investigates written documents to determine how the ways of life of a particular group of people have changed over time. A third type of ethnologist, the cross-cultural researcher, studies data collected by ethnographers and ethnohistorians for a sample of cultures and attempts to discover which explanations of particular customs may be generally applicable.

8. Anthropological linguists are concerned with the emergence of language and with the divergence of languages over time (historical linguistics). They also study how contemporary languages differ, both in construction (structural or descriptive linguistics) and in actual speech (sociolinguistics).

9. In all four major subdisciplines of anthropology, there are applied anthropologists, people who apply anthropological knowledge to achieve more practical goals, usually in the service of an agency outside the traditional academic setting.

10. Anthropology may help people to be more tolerant. Anthropological studies can show us why other people are the way they are, both culturally and physically. Customs or actions that appear improper or offensive to us may be other people's adaptations to particular environmental and social conditions.

11. Anthropology is also valuable in that knowledge of our past may bring us both a feeling of humility and a sense of accomplishment. Like any other form of life, we have no guarantee that any particular human population will perpetuate itself indefinitely. Yet knowledge of our achievements in the past may give us confidence in our ability to solve the problems of the future.

Glossary Terms

anthropological linguistics (p. 5)

anthropology (p. 2)

applied anthropology (p. 12)

archaeology (p. 5)

biocultural model (p. 12)

biological (physical) anthropology (p. 5)

cross-cultural researcher (p. 9)

cultural anthropology (p. 10)

cultural ecologists (p. 11)

culture (p. 8)

ethnocentric (p. 15)

ethnographer (p. 9)

ethnography (p. 9)

ethnohistorian (p. 9)

ethnology (p. 8)

fossils (p. 6)

historical archaeology (p. 8)

historical linguistics (p. 10)

holistic (p. 4)

hominids (p. 12)

Homo sapiens (p. 7)

human palaeontology (p. 6)

human variation (p. 7)

linguistics (p. 10)

palaeoanthropology (p. 6)

prehistoric (p. 9)

primates (p. 6)

primatologists (p. 6)

Critical Questions

1. Why study anthropology?

2. How does anthropology differ from other fields of study you have encountered?

3. What do you think about the suggestion that anthropology is the fundamental discipline concerned with humans?

Internet Exercises

1. Learn more about Canadian anthropology's past by reading "The History of Anthropology at University of Toronto" at **www.chass .utoronto.ca/anthropology/history.htm.**

2. Read some breaking anthropology news at **www.tamu.edu/anthropology/news.html.** Make a case for or against the legitimacy of popular media representations of anthropology.

3. Look through the site "Anthropology on the Internet: A Review and Evaluation of Networked Resources" at **www.journals .uchicago.edu/CA/articles/intro.html.** Do you think the internet will advance the discipline of anthropology? Address the issues of "information overload," "popularization," and "peer review" in your answer.

Suggested Reading

Boaz NT, Almquist AJ. 1997. Biological Anthropology: A Synthetic Approach to Human Evolution. Upper Saddle River, NJ: Prentice Hall. After briefly reviewing the principles and sequences of biological evolution, the authors review human evolution from earliest times to the present. The book also includes chapters on human variation, human growth and adaptability, and applied biological anthropology.

Fagan BM. 2000. People of the Earth: An Introduction to World Prehistory. 10th edition. Upper Saddle River, NJ: Prentice Hall. A survey of world prehistory, describing what we know from archaeology about hunters and gatherers, farmers, and cities and civilizations in all areas of the world.

Foley WA. 1997. Anthropological Linguistics: An Introduction. Malden, MA: Blackwell. An overview of anthropological linguistics, including the evolution of language, linguistic universals, linguistic relativism, and the ethnography of speaking.

Hedican EJ. 1995. Applied Anthropology in Canada: Understanding Aboriginal Issues. Toronto: University of Toronto Press. An overview of applied anthropology particularly in the context of Canadian Aboriginal peoples.

Herring DA, Chan L, editors. 1994. Strength in Diversity. A Reader in Physical Anthropology. Toronto: Canadian Scholars' Press, Inc.. A collection of papers to provide students with an understanding of the breadth and relevance of research in physical anthropology by leading scholars in Canada.

Howells W. 1993. Getting Here: The Story of Human Evolution. Washington, DC: Compass Press. An accessible introduction to the study of human evolution.

Konner M. 1987. The Tangled Wing: Biological Constraints on the Human Spirit. New York: Harper & Row. A biological anthropologist discusses the biological and cultural roots of human behaviour and emotions.

Trigger BG. 1989. A History of Archaeological Thought. New York: Cambridge University Press. A comprehensive review of the history of archaeology from medieval to modern times, examining the changing trends in the way that archaeologists view their data and its impact for understanding the human condition.

UNCOVERING THE PAST: TOOLS AND TECHNIQUES

2

Reconstructing the past using archaeological and palaeoanthropological evidence requires a firm understanding of the methods for acquiring data. This chapter deals specifically with the associated methods of site identification and recovery. The methods discussed are broadly applicable to both palaeoanthropological and archaeological research; in some instances issues are more relevant to one field than the other. The material covered in this chapter forms part of the foundation for subsequent chapters, which go on to introduce the biological and cultural evolution of human populations, through the archaeological and palaeontological record.

Understanding past life from the archaeological and palaeontological record requires expertise in a variety of areas. First, specialized methods, mostly borrowed from geological sciences and physics, have been developed to augment the traditional anthropological methods to locate *archaeological sites*—areas of human habitation or where fossil remains are found. Second, archaeological techniques are used for the excavation of remains—whether fossil remains of a hominid (a human, or the direct ancestor of a human), a prehistoric cemetery, or an entire settlement—so as to maximize and preserve the information that can be derived from the excavation of a site.

An important fact to remember is that archaeological remains are the most valuable source of data when the information about where they were buried in relation to all other remains is preserved—something called **provenience**. This is why it is so important that illegal or amateur excavation of sites must be prevented. Archaeology, by its very nature, is destructive—once material has been removed, all information regarding its burial environment is lost. As a result, archaeologists have developed extremely rigorous methods for recording this information before and while remains are excavated from a site.

Reconstruction of the past is not an easy task. It requires the careful analysis of the environment in which the materials are found in order to say something about the circumstances by which that material came to be there. **Material culture**—the objects that people have and make—is a direct reflection of human culture and behaviour. Archaeologists and their colleagues in related disciplines attempt to understand a complex process as it is reflected in the remains of the everyday belongings of past peoples. For example, if we want to understand how a community changed over the course of its history, we need to recognize that those changes would have been influenced by a variety of factors. These would include changes in the environment, in the population numbers, in religion, and in culture, to name just a few. However, unravelling these factors is sometimes difficult, which is why the researcher has to pay careful attention to the context in which material culture is found. Further, while material culture is a direct reflection of past culture, the archaeological record is not always a direct reflection of material culture. A number of factors can affect where the remains of material culture are found and the patterns of deposition. The archaeologists must be able to recognize these influences.

Site Formation Processes

The archaeological record is not simply a sterile snapshot of society as it once was. Material culture is subjected to a host of **site formation processes**, including environmental and cultural, that affect how and where materials are deposited. Cultural factors can be as simple as past populations dumping waste in the same area for a long duration of time. This creates a garbage heap or **midden** as it is called in the archaeological record. The materials contained within a midden are waste products of the human population that produced them. However, examining the kinds of materials that were being produced and how they were being produced and contemplating their possible functions are fundamental aspects of archaeological reconstruction. Imagine what archaeologists 1000 years in the future might be able to say about life today by excavating a modern landfill site. Think about what a stranger could infer about your own life by what you throw out each week.

Modern landfill sites provide a cross-section of human material culture today.

Similarly, how a community constructed its dwellings might have an impact on the formation of an archaeological site, such as whether its people were nomadic, moved around in an annual pattern, or lived a more sedentary life, building permanent or semi-permanent dwellings. Locations where a community lived continuously over long periods tend to have layers of accumulated materials left by successive occupations, and these layers are superimposed on one another—people tend to build or rebuild on the rubble left from the dwellings of the previous occupants of a site. A community constantly on the move affects the quantity and distribution of the materials left in any one area. If a site is a product of seasonal habitation, the kind of material culture left behind will not be random, but will reflect the activities occurring at one time of the year but not another. Further, the composition and position of materials within the archaeological record can affect preservation of those remains. For example, in the contact period in Canada—when Europeans were first meeting with and interacting with Aboriginal populations—burials that contain copper artifacts tend to show increased preservation of organic materials that are in direct association with the copper. Coffins provide a different burial environment for bodies than does burial directly in the soil.

People also reuse materials and trade materials over distances. Old timbers may be used in the construction of a new house. Material from another region may be imported and valued for its rarity. For example, we see in the archaeological record the movement of native copper from northern Wisconsin and northwestern Canada into the interior regions of western Canada, where it was used by people who otherwise would not have had access to it.

Material culture can have functional, social, and aesthetic purposes. Consider the number of items that were once utilitarian in your own home that serve no functional purpose today. Pottery is a good example. Old glass and earthenware containers such as glass milk jugs or hand-thrown pottery that were used as everyday items in homes

Finding fossil hominids requires patience and endurance.

in the past might be used as decorative items within modern households. Fine ceramics may not be routinely used for food processing, storage, or service, but they do serve important social functions. These functions may be embedded in the meaning imparted to the vessels. Fine ceramics might be family heirlooms, or expensive icons of social prestige. Such items might "function" to impart social messages about affluence and social position. So it can be difficult to untangle the many cultural processes that contribute to the formation of an archaeological site.

Natural physical processes can affect the survival of artifacts. Deposits from wind erosion and water can cover or submerge whole communities, depending on the environmental conditions at the time that they were occupied. Those same natural processes can cause erosion, exposure, and destruction of archaeological sites. Soil chemistry, temperature, water level, and bacterial action can all affect the rate of decay of organic and inorganic material. As a result, the archaeological record tends to favour the presence of inorganic materials, such as stone, metals, and baked clay, but under good preservation

conditions organic materials such as bone, shell, hair, paper, and even soft muscle tissue can survive for extended time periods.

Locating Sites

The first and most important aspect of archaeology is actually finding the remains of the past. Archaeologists have developed specialized techniques, some borrowed from other disciplines, to accurately identify, map, and excavate sites. However, identification of **archaeological sites**, that is, locations of human occupation, and *fossil locales* where fossilized remains of once living organisms are found, requires somewhat different prospection strategies.

Fossil Locales

Fossil locales are those places where the fossilized remains of animals are found. For the most part, a locale has no bearing on the life of the animal but is a product of a series of processes that affect the remains following death. Candidate locations for fossil sites are identified based on the environment that would have existed tens of thousands or even millions of years ago. Once identified, it is a long and tedious process of field survey on foot, carefully looking for tell-tale signs in the hopes of finding that rare fossilized specimen. Oftentimes a whole field season can pass by without any new discoveries. Sometimes though, the combination of skill and luck prevails, and the remains of a fossilized specimen are discovered.

What Are Fossils?

A fossil may be an impression of an insect or leaf on a muddy or other surface that now is stone. Or it may consist of the actual hardened remains of an animal's skeletal structure. It is this second type of fossil—bone turned to stone—that has given palaeoanthropologists the most information about the evolution of primates.

Fossilization. When an animal dies, the organic matter in its body quickly begins to deteriorate.

The fossil of a trilobite from the Cambrian period, 500 million years ago.

The teeth and skeletal structure are composed largely of inorganic mineral salts, and soon they are all that remains. Under most conditions, these parts eventually deteriorate too. But once in a great while conditions are favourable for preservation—for instance, when volcanic ash, limestone, or highly mineralized groundwater is present to form a high-mineral environment. If the remains are buried under such circumstances, the minerals in the ground may become bound into the structure of the teeth or bone, harden, and thus make them less likely to deteriorate. This process of **fossilization** leaves a combination of inorganic bone and mineral, while retaining microscopic detail of the original material. Fossilization requires very specific environmental conditions—organisms need to be at the right place at the right time before there is even a chance of their remains becoming fossilized. Further, the process takes considerable time—more than 10 000 years, depending on soil chemistry and other factors. In fact, given the relative rarity of fossilization, palaeontologists have collected an exceptional amount of information about hundreds of past species from various periods.

Unfortunately, we have fossil remains only of some species and sometimes only fragments from one or a few individuals. So the fossil record is very incomplete. Robert Martin estimates that the earth has probably seen 6000 primate species; and remains of only 3 percent of those species have been found. While this seems small, given the relative rarity of fossilization we should not expect to have as much information from the fossil record as we do. Nevertheless primate palaeontologists continue to explore the evolutionary connections between early and later fossil forms. The task is particularly difficult with small mammals, such as the early primates, which are less likely to be preserved in the fossil record than are large animals (Bilsborough, 1992).

Palaeoanthropologists have a more narrow interest in terms of the kinds of species they look at—primates at the broadest level, and more often hominids alone. Given these factors, it is amazing how much information we have actually accumulated regarding human evolution.

What Can We Learn from Fossils?

Palaeontologists can tell a great deal about an extinct animal from its fossilized bones or teeth, but that knowledge is based on much more than just the fossil record itself. Palaeontologists rely on comparative anatomy to help reconstruct missing skeletal pieces as well as the soft tissues attached to bone. New techniques, such as electron microscopy, CT scans, and computer-assisted biomechanical modelling, provide much information about how the organism may have moved, the microstructure of bone and teeth, and how the organism developed. Chemical analysis of bone can suggest what the animal typically ate. Palaeontologists are also interested in the surroundings of the fossil finds. With methods developed in geology, chemistry, and physics, palaeontologists use the surrounding rocks to identify the period in which the organism died. In addition, the study of associated fauna and flora can suggest what the ancient climate and habitat were like (Klein, 1989).

Since most of human evolution predates human material culture, palaeoanthropologists have only the biological remains of human ancestors from which to infer hominid behaviour. Because the environment in which these hominids lived and died was very different from that of today, palaeoanthropologists have turned to the expertise of geologists to interpret geological phenomena that reflect the environments that existed millions of years ago. Many fossils result from organic remains being deposited in lakes or rivers where they were quickly covered with sediment. Over time, lakes may have dried up, rivers may have changed course, and the land may have been uplifted. The old lake floors or riverbeds could now be represented by eroding sediments on hilltops. Consequently, the majority of fossil hominid remains found by palaeoanthropologists have been subject to long-term environmental processes before being found.

Taphonomy. The processes that affect an animal's remains following its death are important for understanding the context in which fossil remains are found. The study of the processes that affect the body of an animal following its death, known as **taphonomy**, is literally the science of burial. Taphonomic processes are certainly an important consideration in archaeological contexts, and palaeoanthropology requires an extensive understanding of them. For example, the distribution of bones observed in an area may reflect predation by a carnivore and subsequent disturbance by scavengers. This is relevant to the study of early hominids in particular, many of whom were often the prey for large carnivores rather than predators themselves. A carnivore may have brought a skull to a cave, for example, and it may be preserved because of the cave environment, yet the rest of the skeleton is missing from the cave. Of particular concern to palaeoanthropologists are any physical distortions to the fossil hominid remains. Skulls, for example, can be slowly crushed over the course of the fossilization process, leading to a distorted morphology, or form. Palaeoanthropologists need to try to determine the original morphology of the specimen in such instances.

Finding Archaeological Sites

Archaeological sites are generally viewed as geographic areas that contain evidence of past human behaviour and activity. An archaeological site can range from a small campsite to a large city, a place for growing food or killing game, a place for mining or processing raw materials, or a place of worship or a place of burial. All of these activities can leave varying degrees of evidence in the archaeological record. Further, some sites may be clearly identifiable, such as the Great Pyramids of Egypt, or go relatively unnoticed for long periods.

Although many archaeological sites are discovered accidentally, the process of finding a site still remains an important aspect of archaeology. Most development plans in Canada require an archaeological assessment to ensure that cultural heritage is not being destroyed by modern development. By building archaeological research into the environmental assessment, the protection and investigation of these fragile non-renewable resources can be more carefully managed. Even with this level of planning, many archaeological sites are discovered by accident. Whether a site is discovered accidentally or as a consequence of a deliberate search, one of the first phases of archaeological investigation involves documenting the boundaries of a site. This enables the most efficient use of time and resources for site investigation. In most cases, only a portion of a site can be excavated, and proper survey techniques can help identify the areas of greatest interest to the archaeologist.

Site Prospection

Detection of human modification of the landscape will depend on the scale of human activities. In the case of subtle landscape modifications, such as a single house or a burial, even a trained archaeologist may have difficulty recognizing the changes associated with these features. Often intuition, experience, and subsurface inspections will aid in the initial discovery of archaeological sites. The identification of a site is based on methods that can be broadly divided between *surface* and *subsurface surveying techniques* that can involve remote sensing or be intrusive, such as digging.

Surface Techniques. **Surface techniques** include *field walking* and *field surveying*. Much like the palaeoanthropologist, an archaeologist will patiently walk and survey the surface of a location for signs of artifacts or surface irregularities that may indicate structures. Surface inspection is appropriate in situations where disturbances have exposed archaeological materials. These disturbances could be natural processes like erosion. Human activities like cultivation, construction, or clearing of forests are examples of modern practices that might reveal the presence of material culture from the past. Artifacts collected as part of field walking provide important clues about the potential distribution and boundaries of the disturbed archaeological materials, and can aid in identifying areas that remain undisturbed.

Field surveying can be as simple as the archaeologist walking through an area and carefully watching for sometimes subtle clues that indicate the presence of material culture, or as complex as the systematic survey of a region aided by local histories of land use and occupation by local residents. Once the archaeologist identifies an area of increased density of recovered surface artifacts or specific structures, he or she will use subsurface techniques to define where more comprehensive excavations will proceed.

Past changes to the landscape on a larger scale, such as irrigation systems for fields or whole cities, may still be sufficiently distinct to be identified through field inspection or the examination of air photographs or satellite images. *Aerial photography* and *satellite imaging* can even provide clues to the remains of structures buried under thick accumulations of sediment, particularly if the underlying cultural deposits alter the soil chemistry or soil moisture to the point that can change the pattern of vegetation. Areas disturbed by past human occupation may produce differences in the kinds of vegetation that cover the area, and these may be detectable only from the air. Even when large-scale alterations to the landscape have been reduced through natural processes such as erosion or artificial processes such as plowing, they can leave distinct topographical patterns on the surface that are distinguishable from the air. Satellite imagery provides a similar tool although the cost of using it and the observable level of precision

Archaeological test pits and trenching (shown here) help define the boundaries of a site.

make it currently impractical for archaeologists except for the documentation of large-scale disturbances such as roads, canals, irrigated fields, or large communities with monumental architecture.

Subsurface Techniques. In most cases, surface surveying is not the most efficient means for locating archaeological sites. Those sites that have not yet been exposed, or whose distribution or pattern is not clearly recognizable on the surface, require other kinds of surveying techniques.

Subsurface techniques can be mechanical or electronic. Mechanical techniques tend to be invasive and include *shovel shining*, *test pitting*, or *trenching*. Electronic techniques tend to be non-invasive and allow the archaeologist to survey or map below the surface without actually disturbing the site.

Shovel shining is a simple method where the edge of a shovel is used to scrape off thin layers of the immediate and usually disturbed surface layer

A grid system is used at archaeological sites to accurately record the position of artifacts and features during excavation.

to reveal undisturbed soil. This method is suitable for unearthing features like post moulds, hearths, house foundations, or refuse that can be identified through their different soil colour and composition. Shovel shining is also used to systematically explore a site that has been disturbed, perhaps through cultivation, for intact deposits that remain below the disturbed zone. The site is then further assessed by systematically removing layers of the surface from a small, contained area. This approach is most effective where the approximate extent and cultural identity of a disturbed site has been defined through a field-walking survey and surface collection.

Where a newly discovered site is relatively undisturbed, the excavation of test pits at intervals across the site might offer a better and less destructive understanding of the site's extent and its artifacts. Such test pits are usually excavated with a shovel, are generally quite small (about 50 cm in diameter), and spaced at regular intervals across the site. The size, depth, and spacing of the test pits vary with the nature of the site deposits, the research objectives, and the resources available to the archaeologist. Each test pit should provide a sample of artifacts that can aid in dating the site's

age and function. The density and position of what is recovered, that is, the recoveries, may aid in determining the size and shape of the site. As each test pit is associated with a specific location within the site, the archaeologist can use the shovel test pit data to examine the changing pattern and density of recoveries across the site. This serves as a useful preliminary assessment tool in planning a full-scale excavation.

In instances where material is suspected to be at great depths beneath the surface, boring and core samples can be taken to retrieve a column that reflects the overall layering of a small but deep area. This technique is being employed by archaeologist Aubrey Cannon of McMaster University in his analysis of middens from prehistoric Northwest Coast sites (Cannon, 2000a; Cannon, 2000b). The method has the advantage of providing a snapshot of all the layers within a site without the need for a complete excavation. The primary assumption of this method is that the distribution of artifacts within the core will be representative of the distribution within the immediate surrounding area. The same technique may be used to sample sediments that aid in reconstructing past environments. For example, how and when deposits were laid down may be inferred from sediment particle size, or pollen recovery can indicate past climatic conditions and vegetation cover.

Non-invasive site inspection techniques have been borrowed from a variety of disciplines and applied to archaeological survey. These includes *ground-penetrating radar*, or methods based on *magnetic* or *electrical resistance* of subsurface features. Since archaeology is itself destructive, archaeologists would ideally like to obtain as much information as possible about the composition of a site without the need for excavation. Ground-penetrating radar involves radar waves that map subsurface sedimentary layers and buried archaeological features. Radar waves will "reflect" off subsurface features and produce pulses that can be detected on the surface. The speed at which the radar waves penetrate the surface varies due to soil

composition, but when the velocity is known and the time between pulses recorded, the depth of features below the surface can be calculated. The radar can provide a subsurface map of the relative locations and depths of features over a large area.

Electrical resistivity meters measure differences in the ability of sediments and other materials beneath the surface to conduct electricity. For example, features like stone or brick walls are less conductive than the surrounding deposits. Alternatively, a concentration of metallic objects or a pit that has filled over time and has different soil moisture levels may be more conductive than the surrounding deposits. When soil resistivity is measured along controlled grids, patterns of variation in electrical conductivity can be detected and mapped to aid in site interpretation. Similarly, a *magnetometer* can measure the relative magnetism of items below the surface. Clay when fired acquires

HISTORICAL PERSPECTIVES

Head-Smashed-In Buffalo Jump

One of the most ingenious methods of killing herd animals was the intentional driving of a whole herd toward and over the edge of a cliff. Head-Smashed-In Buffalo Jump is one of the oldest, largest, and best-preserved buffalo jumps in North America. Located near Fort Macleod in Alberta, at a place where the foothills of the Rocky Mountains meet the plains, Head-Smashed-In Buffalo Jump was designated as a UNESCO World Heritage Site in 1981. The name refers to the legend of the young Peigan brave who watched the kill from below and was found under a pile of dead buffalo with his skull crushed.

This particular site was unusually popular. Aboriginal peoples hunted here for more than 5000 years, claiming the lives of more than 10 000 buffalo. Ethnohistorical data about buffalo hunting have provided a great deal of information about

past techniques for killing and processing buffalo. Archaeological research at the site provided information about the nature of the cultural remains at the buffalo kill site.

Up to 11 metres of buffalo skeletons lie at the base of the cliff. Next to this is the butchering site, over a kilometre in width and strewn with the remnants of meat caches and cooking pits, and a metre of butchered bison bones. At the top of the cliff is a prime grazing range for buffalo herds. Some 10 kilometres west of the cliff begins a stretch of more than 500 stone cairns, where people built fires or waved blankets, to direct the bison into drive lanes approaching the edge of the cliff.

George Dawson of the Archaeological Survey of Canada first recorded the site in the 1880s. Nearly 60 years later, the first archaeological excavation of the site was undertaken by Junius Bird of

the American Museum of Natural History. In 1949, Boyd Wettlaufer, a pioneer of archaeology in Canada, spent a brief time excavating the kill site and butchering area. Following this, the site was subject to considerable looting by arrowhead collectors. Although a few more recent investigations have been undertaken, most of what we know about this site is the result of excavations in 1965 to 1966 conducted by Richard Forbis and Brian Reeves of the University of Calgary and Jack Brinks of the Archaeological Survey of Alberta. This research established the age of the site and identified the cultural and technological sequence represented in the 11 metres of stratified deposits.

Sources: www.ucalgary.ca/UofC/faculties/SS/ARKY/hsi/History.html; www.head-smashed-in.com/. Used by permission of Brian Kooyman and Head-Smashed-In Buffalo Jump Alberta Community Development.

a small magnetic field that can be detected with this instrument. Rocks with trace amounts of iron in them or iron metal objects can also be detected. By examining the patterns in variation in sediment magnetism, the archaeologist can identify zones of particular interest that can be investigated through subsurface excavation.

Excavation

Once a site has been identified, excavation can begin. Before, during, and after excavation, the archaeologist follows a series of methods to maintain maximum control over the relationships between items in the three-dimensional space of the site. To begin with, *site evaluation* involves an assessment of the size of the site, depth of the deposits, site formation processes (including taphonomic processes that may bias site integrity such as scavenger activity, water, etc.), and function. While horizontal control is important, vertical control of the excavation process can be critical when there are dramatic differences in the time that various layers of sediment took to accumulate (see discussion of *stratigraphy for relative dating* below). A preliminary assessment of the information from the site evaluation is critical for planning an appropriate research design that includes budgeting for the costs of excavation and analysis, and implementing detailed excavation. Detailed excavation is generally conventional. However, because excavation is destructive, permanent (once an artifact is out of the ground, its context is lost), and expensive in terms of both time and money, archaeologists try to obtain a sample of deposits that they hope is representative of the whole site.

How a sample is chosen is based on a careful analysis of preliminary survey information regarding the distribution and function of the site. For example, determining the sampling strategy at a buffalo jump site like Head-Smashed-In Buffalo Jump in southern Alberta depends on the kinds of research questions that people have. If the researcher is interested in the antiquity, seasonality, and cultural association of a stratified sequence of bison kill events, then a deep excavation focused at the base of the jump would be appropriate. In contrast, if you are interested in the full sequence of events involved in the communal bison drive of past populations, then a broader perspective and more diverse sampling strategy would be warranted (see Historical Perspectives, *Head-Smashed-In Buffalo Jump*).

The first step of a controlled excavation is choosing a datum point. The **datum** represents a fixed, permanent reference point within or near the site. This fixed reference point defines the location of all information and specimens collected from the site. As the datum is a permanent fixture, future investigations (perhaps using new, innovative techniques) can be spatially related to all previous work at the site. This enables an ongoing synthesis of information. Once a datum has been decided, a *grid system* is laid out, usually dividing the site into 1- or 2-metre squares. Under special circumstances, like cave archaeology or underwater archaeology, extra control over depth is necessary. Each square is defined by its location within the grid, and more detailed mapping and documentation of recoveries within the square is relative to the grid location of the control square. The careful recording of all information within the grid allows for all data to be incorporated into a single system at the end of the excavation, even though different people may have excavated certain grid squares at different times.

Depending on the scale of the excavation, archaeologists apply different techniques and equipment. For example, a backhoe or bulldozer might be used to remove disturbed or culturally sterile topsoil or sod from a location. Once this top disturbed layer has been removed, much finer excavation techniques using small hand tools are needed. In some circumstances, shovels are used to remove sediment. When beginning to excavate an area of interest most archaeologists use small mason's trowels, whisk brooms and paintbrushes, root cutters, teaspoons, and dental picks to carefully remove the sediment and expose and recover the artifacts. This care is necessary to preserve and record the spatial context of recovery, prevent damage to the specimens, and enable discovery and documentation of features that might be represented by subtle shifts in sediment colour, texture, and degree of compaction.

Depending on the context and research objectives, sediment removed from the excavation unit is examined for minute objects that might have been missed during excavation. This involves removing the backdirt—or pile of soil left from excavating an area—in buckets, and sifting it through fine screens to identify small artifacts. The mesh size of the screen depends on the objectives of the researchers and the time and fiscal resources

for the project. At most modern excavation projects, sediment is screened at least through 5-mm (¼-inch) hardware cloth, and a 2- to 3-mm (⅛-inch) screen size is routinely used at many projects. While the smaller screen size dramatically increases the rate of recovery of minute artifacts, there is a significant increase in associated time and costs of excavation and analysis. If the coarser 5-mm screen is used, then the archaeologist will often monitor artifact loss rates by regularly screening subsamples with the finer mesh.

RESEARCH FRONTIERS

Researcher at Work: Priscilla Renouf

Archaeologist Priscilla Renouf in the field.

In 1984 Priscilla Renouf, now a professor and Canada Research Chair in North Atlantic Archaeology at Memorial University, Newfoundland, investigated two sites on the west coast of the Island of Newfoundland—Port au Choix and Point Riche—for Parks Canada. For her this investigation began what would become a career of excavating Palaeo-Eskimo sites, significantly expanding on previous research in this area. The term Palaeo-Eskimo refers to groups of native peoples who inhabited the eastern Arctic from approximately 900 to 4000 years ago. They were distinct from the modern Inuit, who are not their direct descendants. Remains of Palaeo-Eskimo settlements have been

found from Greenland and Ellesmere Island to the shores of Hudson Bay and Labrador, and as far south as the Island of Newfoundland.

Port au Choix, which is now a National Historic Site, is located on limestone bedrock. This has allowed for the preservation of organic materials, providing archaeologists with a glimpse at the burial customs, subsistence practices, and skeletal biology of Palaeo-Eskimo and more recent native groups.

Late Palaeo-Eskimo (also known as *Dorset*) sites like Port au Choix are quite large and show evidence of a long-term occupation. Priscilla Renouf has excavated large quantities of harp seal bones at Port au Choix, suggesting that this was a prime location for the hunting of these animals. The peoples' sophisticated hunting technology may be the reason why Dorset sites are so numerous on the Island of Newfoundland—they were perhaps even the most numerous Aboriginal people ever to occupy the island. Nevertheless, Dorset culture seems to have disappeared from the island by about 1200 years ago, and from

Greenland and the Canadian Arctic shortly thereafter. Perhaps the people were displaced by the ancestors of modern Inuit—the Thule people.

In 1990 Priscilla Renouf continued with her investigations at Port au Choix. While a large Maritime Archaic Indian cemetery had been discovered in the 1960s at Port au Choix, no associated habitation site had been identified. In 1996 Priscilla Renouf and colleagues developed a model that utilized aspects of relative sea level, palaeogeography, and cultural history to predict a site location for occupation. The next year they found the site exactly where the model had predicted. Radiocarbon dating confirmed its contemporaneity with the Maritime Archaic Indian cemetery. Her ongoing research at Port au Choix continues to document 4500 years of occupation at the site.

Sources: Renouf MAP, Bell T. Searching for the Maritime Archaic Indian Habitation Site at Port au Choix, Newfoundland: An Integrated Approach Using Archaeology, Geomorphology and Sea Level History. Reports on file with the Government of Newfoundland and Labrador, Provincial Archaeology Office Culture and Heritage Division, Department of Tourism, Culture and Recreation.

Renouf, MAP. 1991. The Newfoundland Museum Notes #5, 1991.

Soil samples may also be bagged and labelled for future analysis. This might involve documenting sediment particle size, soil pH, charcoal and other organic materials, or the concentrations of chemicals such as phosphorus and nitrogen. The presence of *patterned variation*—systematic trends in the way in which material is distributed—of such materials may reflect the nature and intensity of past human activity, and is also very useful for reconstructing the past environmental context of the site. Such soil samples can also be useful for the recovery of minute organic materials. These could be charcoal and preserved wood fragments, carbonized seeds and other preserved plant parts, microscopic pollen, and **phytoliths** (microscopic granules of silicon dioxide that enter a plant's cells and take their shape), as well as land snails and other minute indicators of past climatic and vegetation conditions.

Throughout a site, the remains of human culture are represented by **artifacts**—items manufactured by people, **ecofacts**—natural objects that have been used or affected by humans, and **features**—the non-portable portions of a site, some of which can include artifacts. Artifacts are tools like projectile points or bone tools, and items like clay pots or stone figurines. Ecofacts include bone from animals, seeds, and pollen. Features include things like hearths or fireplaces, burials, houses, fences, or middens. For the archaeologist, the most important aspect of an excavation is the proper mapping and recording of the provenience or location of all features and artifacts. This is critical as the **association** of artifacts or features with one another is important for understanding past life at the site. Association is extremely important, for example, in the study of early hominids and the first appearance of manufactured stone tools. Unless the artifacts and fossils can be shown archaeologically to have been associated in the same *depositional context*, that is, from the same time period, one cannot assert that the tools were produced and used by that particular hominid species.

Artifacts

Anything made or modified by humans is an **artifact**. The book you are reading now, the chair you are sitting in, the pen you are taking notes with are all artifacts. In fact, we are surrounded by artifacts, most of which we will lose or throw away. And that is exactly how things enter the archaeological record. Think about it: How much garbage do you produce in a day? What kinds of things do you throw away? Mostly paper, probably, but also wood (from the ice-cream bar you had at lunch), plastic (like the pen that ran out of ink last night), and even metal (the dull blade on your razor). Into the garbage they go and out to the dump or landfill. Under the right conditions many of those items will survive for future archaeologists to find. Most of the artifacts that make up the archaeological record are just this kind of mundane waste—the accumulated garbage of daily life that archaeologists may recover and examine to reconstruct daily life long ago.

By far the most common artifacts from the past are stone tools, which archaeologists call **lithics**. Indeed, lithics are the only artifact available for 99 percent of human history. Humans started

A ceramic pot from China, dating to the period when agriculture first developed there—some 6000 years ago.

using stone tools more than 2.5 million years ago, and some stone tools (grinding and polishing stones, for example) are still used today. Stone has been used for making almost any object you can think of, from cutting tools to oil lamps, but hunting, butchering, and hide-processing tools were commonly made from stone. Another common kind of artifact is **ceramics** (pots and other items made from baked clay). Humans started making ceramics about 10 000 years ago, and ceramic objects such as storage and cooking vessels quickly became widespread. Because they are both fragile and relatively easy to make, ceramics show up frequently in the garbage that makes up the archaeological record. Wood and bone artifacts are common too, and tools for hide working, cooking, hunting, and even butchering were made of these materials. Humans have used wood and bone tools at least as long as stone tools, but unlike stone tools, these tend not to survive well in the archaeological record. In some places metals and glass are common artifacts. These survive well in the archaeological record, and hence they are often found where they were used.

Ecofacts

Ecofacts are natural objects that have been consumed or affected by humans. A good example are the bones of animals that people have eaten. These bones are somewhat like artifacts, but they haven't been made or modified by humans, just used and discarded by them. Another example is pollen found at archaeological sites. Because humans bring plants back to their homes for a number of reasons, pollens from many plants are commonly found. These pollens may not have come from the same location. The only reason they are together is that they have been brought together by human use. Yet another example are the remains of insect and animal pests that associate with humans, such as cockroaches and mice. Their remains are found in sites because they associate with humans and survive by taking advantage of the conditions that humans create. Their presence is in part caused by the human presence, and thus they are considered ecofacts too.

Features

Features are a kind of artifact, but archaeologists distinguish them from other artifacts because they cannot be easily removed from an archaeological site. Hearths are a good example. When humans build a fire on bare ground, the soil becomes heated and is changed—all the water is driven out of it and its crystalline structure is broken down and re-formed. It becomes hard, redder, and even slightly magnetic (as we discuss later). When an archaeologist finds a hearth, what exactly is found? An area of hard, reddish soil, often surrounded by charcoal and ash. Here, then, is an artifact—an object of human manufacture. But it would be very hard, if not impossible, for the archaeologist to pick the hearth up and take it back to the lab for study like a lithic or ceramic. A hearth is really an intrinsic feature of a site—hence the name *feature*.

Hearths are common features, but by far the most common features are called *pits*. Pits are simply holes dug by humans that are later filled with garbage or eroded soil. They are usually fairly easy to distinguish because the garbage or soil they are filled with is often different in colour and texture from the soil the pit was dug into. *Living floors* are another common type of feature. These are the places where humans lived and worked. The soils in these locations are often compacted through human activity and are full of minute pieces of garbage—seeds, small stone flakes, beads, and the like—that became embedded in the floor. A large or very deep area of such debris is called a *midden*. Middens are often the remains of garbage dumps or areas repeatedly used over long periods of time, such as caves. Finally, *buildings* are a common feature on archaeological sites. These can range from the remains of stone rings that once held down the sides of tents to palaces built of stones that had been shaped and fitted together. Even the remains of wooden houses (or parts of them) have been preserved under some conditions. Features are a diverse array of things that can provide lots of information about the past.

Dating Techniques

One must know the age of archaeological sites and fossils in order to reconstruct the evolutionary history of humans and their ancestors. For some time *relative dating methods*, that is, methods that could state that a fossil was older or younger than those from another area of the site, were the only methods available. These techniques generally addressed the sequence of layers by referring to the sedimentary context. The last 50 years have seen important advances in **absolute dating** or *chronometric dating*—methods that can estimate the age of a specimen or deposit in years—including techniques that allow the dating of the earliest phases of primate evolution (Bilsborough, 1992). **Relative dating** allows the age of a specimen or deposit relative to another specimen or deposit to be determined.

Relative Dating Methods

The earliest and still the most common method of relative dating is based on **stratigraphy**, the study of how different layers of sediments and soils, artifacts and fossils are laid down in successive deposits, or *strata*. The **law of superposition** states that older layers are generally deeper or lower than more recent layers (see Figure 2–1). On the basis of this law, researchers can make inferences about the relationship and relative date of cumulative layers of different strata.

Animals (*fauna*) and plants (*flora*) that spread widely over short periods, died out fairly rapidly, or evolved rapidly provide the most suitable indicator fossils for establishing a stratigraphic sequence for the relative dating of new finds. These life forms help in the relative dating of less well-known specimens found in association with them. Different animals and plants can serve as indicators of relative age in different areas of the world. In Africa, the fossils of elephants, pigs, and horses have been particularly important in establishing stratigraphic sequences. Once the stratigraphy of an area is established, the relative ages of two different fossils in the same or different sites are indicated by the associated flora and fauna (Klein,

1989). Major transitions in flora and fauna define the epochs and larger units of geologic time. The dates of the boundaries between such units are estimated by absolute dating, described below.

If a site has been disturbed, stratigraphy will not be a satisfactory way of determining relative age. A site may be disturbed in various ways: remains from different periods may be washed or blown together by water or wind, or a landslide may superimpose an earlier layer on top of a later layer. Still, it may be possible using chemical methods to estimate the relative age of the different fossils found together in a disturbed site.

Three of the chemical methods used in the relative dating of fossil bones are the fluorine, uranium, and nitrogen tests, sometimes known as the **F-U-N trio** (Oakley, 1963). All are based on the same general principle: bones and teeth undergo a slow transformation in chemical composition when they remain buried for long periods, and this transformation reflects the mineral content of the groundwater in the area in which they are buried. Fluorine is one mineral present in groundwater; therefore, the older a fossil is, the higher its fluorine content will be. Uranium, like fluorine, is also present in groundwater, so the longer the time that bones or teeth remain in the ground, the greater their uranium content. The relationships are reversed for nitrogen: the older the fossil, the smaller the amount of nitrogen present in it. Thus, older bones have relatively higher concentrations of fluorine and uranium and less nitrogen than do recent bones.

However, a problem can arise with the F-U-N tests because the mineral content of bones reflects the mineral content of the groundwater in the area. A 30-million-year-old fossil from a high-mineral area may have the same fluorine content as a 50-million-year-old fossil from a low-mineral site. So these chemical relative dating methods cannot be used to compare the relative ages of specimens from widely separated sites. The F-U-N tests are restricted, then, to specimens from the same site or from neighbouring sites.

Each of the chemical relative dating methods, used alone, can give only tentative evidence.

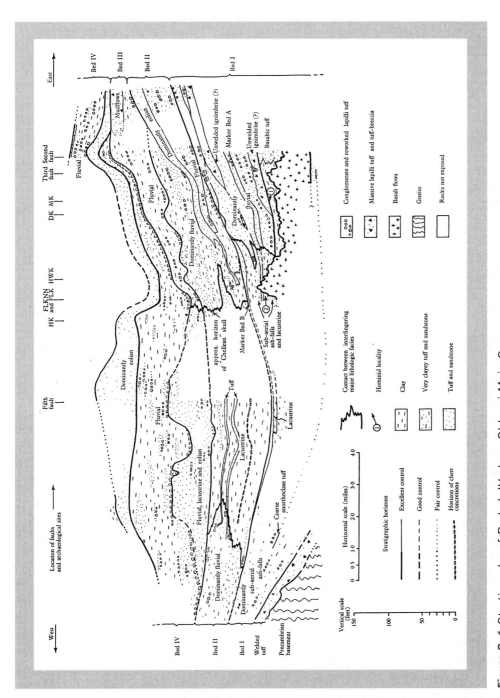

Figure 2–1 Stratigraphy of Beds I–IV along Olduvai Main Gorge

Notice how complex the four stratigraphic layers are—each has numerous layers of soil and rock within them. Index fossils, particularly those of pigs, along with a series of potassium-argon dates, allowed the researchers to identify the four major strata of the site, which correspond to four major periods of human occupation.

Source: Leakey LSB. 1965. Olduvai Gorge, 1951–61. Volume I. Cambridge: Cambridge University Press. Copyright © 1965. Reprinted with the permission of Cambridge University Press.

However, when the three methods are combined and confirm one another, they are very effective. Of the three methods we have discussed, the uranium test is by far the most reliable when used alone. It is not strictly a relative dating method. There seems to be some consistency in the increase in radioactivity with age, even in bones from different deposits. The uranium test has another distinct advantage over the other tests. Because uranium is radioactive, measuring the radioactivity does not require the destruction of any part of the sample in testing.

Absolute Dating Methods

Dendrochronology. Through **dendrochronology**, an archaeologist can estimate the age of wood samples by examining the annual growth rings. A.E. Douglass first used it in the 1920s to date a prehistoric settlement in New Mexico (Douglass, 1929). During each year of its life, a new layer of wood grows in a tree's trunk and branches, creating annual rings that can be seen when the trunk is examined in cross-section. The nature of each ring is a function of the growing conditions during that year, and the rings act as a kind of fingerprint of climatic conditions during the life of the tree. Dendrochronology becomes useful as an archaeological dating technique if a *master chronology* of tree ring patterns can be developed. A chronology is the result of linking overlapping sequences of tree rings from modern living trees with those in ancient trees found in palaeontological or archaeological contexts. With the establishment of a regional master chronology, analysts then examine the archaeologically recovered wood sample of unknown age and seek to match the ring pattern to one observed in the master sequence. Since the master sequence counts back from the modern period, the calendrical date of the archaeological wood sample can be calculated. Dendrochronology obviously is limited to the dating of wood and wood products, and has a limited temporal range. It generally is only useful at a regional level, reflecting local climatic conditions. The most useful dendrochronological sequences have been developed for arid areas. While most individual trees do not live for thousands of years, dendrochronological research has been considerably furthered by the study of very long-lived trees such as the bristle cone pine (see Figure 2–2). In this way, dendrochronology is useful for measuring the age of wood that may be several thousand years old or before present (B.P.).

Many of the absolute dating methods are based on the decay rate of a radioactive isotope. The age of the specimen can be determined by measuring the remaining quantity of the isotope in the sample since the rate of decay or **half-life** is known, and the original concentration of the isotope can be estimated, within a range of possible error. Radiocarbon, or carbon-14 (^{14}C), dating is perhaps the most popularly known method of determining the absolute age of an organic specimen.

Radiocarbon Dating. **Radiocarbon dating** is a reliable method for dating remains up to 50 000 years old (Brown, 1992). It is based on the principle that all living matter possesses a certain amount of a radioactive form of carbon (^{14}C). Radioactive carbon is produced when atmospheric nitrogen-14 is bombarded by cosmic rays. This material is absorbed from the air by plants and then ingested by animals that eat the plants. After an organism dies, it no longer takes in any of the radioactive carbon (see Figure 2–3 on page 36). Carbon-14 decays at a slow but steady pace and reverts to nitrogen-14. (By "decays," we mean that the ^{14}C releases a certain number of beta radiations per minute.) The rate at which the carbon decays is known: ^{14}C has a half-life of 5730 years. In other words, half of the original amount of ^{14}C in organic matter will have disintegrated 5730 years after the organism's death; half of the remaining ^{14}C will have disintegrated after another 5730 years; and so on.

To discover how long an organism has been dead—that is, to determine how much ^{14}C is left in the organism and therefore how old it is—we count the number of beta radiations given off per minute per gram of material. Modern ^{14}C emits about 15 beta radiations per minute per gram of material, but ^{14}C that is 5730 years old emits only half that amount (the half-life of ^{14}C) per minute per gram. So if a sample of some organism gives off 7.5 radiations a minute per gram, which is only half the amount given off by modern ^{14}C, the organism must be 5730 years old (Hole and Heizer, 1973). This is why radiocarbon dating usually is not accurate for anything more than 50 000 years old—the amount of ^{14}C remaining in the organic matter is too small to permit reliable dating.

Is it really that simple though? Unfortunately, the answer is no. One of the problems with radiocarbon dating is that it assumes the relative level of ^{14}C present in the atmosphere remains constant over all time. In fact we now know that this is not

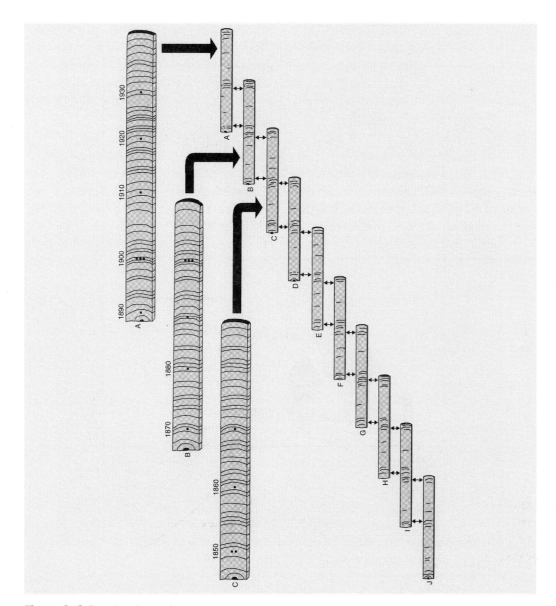

Figure 2–2 Dendrochronology

In order to establish a tree-ring chronology, core samples are removed from living trees, and the annual rings established. Wood specimens taken from other sources are matched up with specific years from the control cores in order to establish a date. In a similar manner, cores from trees of varying, overlapping ages can be compared in order to push back the dendrochronological record even farther into the past.

Source: Fagan BF. 2000. In the Beginning. Upper Saddle River, NJ: Prentice Hall. p 142. Reproduced with permission of Pearson Education Inc., Upper Saddle River, NJ.

true, and that there are fluctuations because of variation in the intensity of solar radiation. The question is then, how do we compensate for these unknown fluctuations when estimating age using

carbon-14 dating? The solution is to calibrate the expected values against observed values using dendrochronology. By taking samples of wood that can be dated accurately using dendrochronology

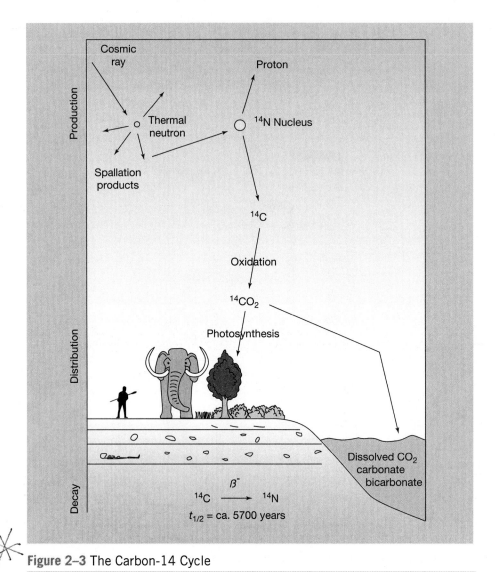

Figure 2–3 The Carbon-14 Cycle

Source: Taylor, RE. 1997. The Carbon-14 Cycle, Radiocarbon Dating. In: Taylor RE, Aitken, MJ, editors. Chronometric Dating in Archaeology. New York: Plenum. Copyright © 1997 by Plenum Publishers. Reprinted by permission of Plenum Publishers.

and radiocarbon dating, we can assess any deviation between the two dates. By plotting the distribution of these two dates for many different samples that span the last several thousand years, we can create a *calibration curve* (see Figure 2–4). Then, we can calculate the radiocarbon date of organic archaeological material, and the date can be calibrated against the curve. This method provides a calibration curve with a time range of about 9000 years ago for carbon-14 dating (Brown, 1992).

Accelerated mass spectrometry (AMS) radiocarbon dating provides a number of advantages over traditional radiocarbon dating, and has revolutionized the dating of archaeological specimens. First, this new method can date specimens that are up to 80 000 years old because it is more capable of accurately measuring minute quantities of ^{14}C (Brown, 1992). It also has the advantage of requiring considerably less raw material to generate a useful date. Since the material to be dated is destroyed in the testing process, the smaller the

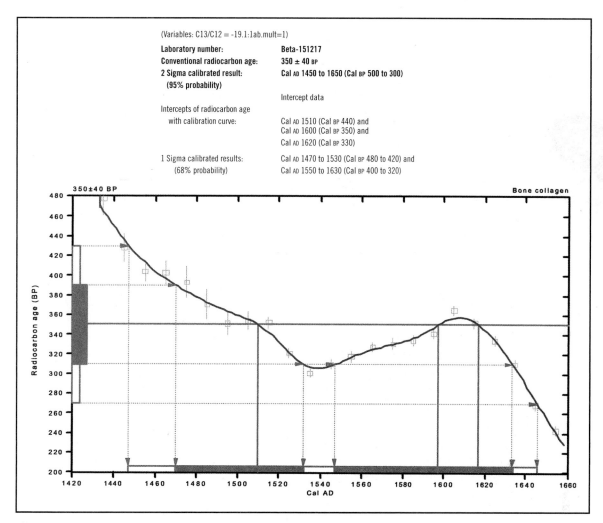

(Variables: C13/C12 = -19.1:1ab.mult=1)

Laboratory number:	**Beta-151217**
Conventional radiocarbon age:	**350 ± 40 BP**
2 Sigma calibrated result:	**Cal AD 1450 to 1650 (Cal BP 500 to 300)**
(95% probability)	

Intercept data

Intercepts of radiocarbon age with calibration curve:	Cal AD 1510 (Cal BP 440) and
	Cal AD 1600 (Cal BP 350) and
	Cal AD 1620 (Cal BP 330)
1 Sigma calibrated results:	Cal AD 1470 to 1530 (Cal BP 480 to 420) and
(68% probability)	Cal AD 1550 to 1630 (Cal BP 400 to 320)

Figure 2–4 An Example of a Calibration Curve for a Carbon-14 Date

This example is based on AMS dating of collagen extracted from bone. Here a conventional radiocarbon age of 350 ± 40 years ago is obtained. In order to calibrate this age, the estimate and its outer limits (40 years on either side for a 66-percent probability and 80 years on either side for a 95-percent probability of being correct) are plotted against the C-14 dates taken on wood dated by dendrochronology. The resultant fluctuations reflect variations in atmospheric carbon during this time period. By examining the points at which the C-14 date limits cross the calibration curve, we come up with a calibrated estimate of the age of the specimen. In this case, the C-14 date of 350 years B.P. crosses the calibration curve at three different points—the years 1510, 1600, and 1620. As a result, the calibration makes the estimate less well defined with the specimen being between 300 and 500 years old or from between A.D. 1450 and A.D. 1650.

Source: Courtesy of Beta Analytic Inc., Miami, Florida.

sample required, the smaller the portion of the archaeological specimen that needs to be sacrificed. Taking only a very small sample is crucial when dating extremely rare items like a unique Northwest Coast atlatl (spear-throwing tool) (Fladmark et al., 1987). The reduced sample size also enables the dating of carbon that clearly derives from the organic component of bone (*collagen*). This greatly reduces the risk of sampling and dating carbon that may have percolated into the bone from groundwater.

Potassium-Argon Dating and Argon-Argon Dating. Potassium-40 (^{40}K), a radioactive form of potassium, decays at an established rate and forms argon-40 (^{40}Ar). The half-life of ^{40}K is a known quantity, so the age of a material containing potassium can be measured by the amount of ^{40}K it contains compared with the amount of ^{40}Ar (Gentner and Lippolt, 1969) that it also contains. Radioactive potassium's (^{40}K's) half-life is very long—1330 million years. This means that **potassium-argon (K-Ar) dating** may date samples from 5000 years old up to 3 billion years old.

The K-Ar method is applied to date potassium-rich minerals in rock, not the fossils that may be found in the rock. While it is an absolute dating technique, it is nevertheless indirect in that it is used to date geological deposits or layers that temporally surround the fossils or artifacts of interest. Very high temperatures, which for example occur during a volcanic event, drive off any original argon in the rock. Such volcanic events might involve the deposition of lava, or the accumulation of volcanic dust over top of the fossil-bearing strata. Therefore, the amount of argon that accumulates afterward from the decay of radioactive potassium is directly related to the amount of time since the volcanic event has passed. This type of dating has been extremely useful in East Africa, where volcanic events have occurred frequently since about 24 million years ago (Klein, 1989). If the material to be dated is not rich in potassium, or the area did not experience any high-temperature events, other methods of absolute dating are required.

One problem with the K-Ar method is that the amounts of potassium and argon must be measured from different rock samples, so that researchers must assume that the potassium and argon are evenly distributed in all the rock samples from a particular stratum. Researchers got around this problem by developing the **^{40}Ar-^{39}Ar dating** method. After measuring the amount of ^{40}Ar, a researcher, by using a nuclear reactor, converts another kind of argon, ^{39}Ar, to potassium so that the potassium/argon ratio can be measured from the same sample (Brown, 1988; Bilsborough, 1992).

Fission-Track Dating. The **fission-track dating** method is another way to determine the absolute age of fossil deposits (Fleischer et al., 1965). Like the K-Ar method, it dates minerals contemporaneous with the deposit in which fossils are found and it also requires the prior occurrence of a high-temperature event, such as a volcanic eruption. The kinds of samples it can date—such as crystal, glass, and many uranium-rich minerals—include a much wider variety than those that can be dated by the K-Ar method. The age range of fission-track dating, like that of K-Ar dating, is extensive—20 years to 5 billion years (Fleischer and Hart Jr, 1972).

How does it work? This method is basically the simplest of all the methods discussed here. It entails counting the number of paths or tracks etched in the sample by the fission, or explosive division, of uranium atoms as they disintegrate. Scientists know that ^{238}U, the most common uranium isotope, decays at a slow, steady rate. This decay takes the form of spontaneous fission, and each separate fission leaves a scar or track on the sample, which can be seen through a microscope when chemically treated. To find the age of a sample, one counts the tracks, then measures their ratio to the uranium content of the sample.

The fission-track method was used to date Bed I at Olduvai Gorge in Tanzania, East Africa, where some early hominid remains were found (Fleischer et al., 1965). And the results corroborated earlier K-Ar estimates that the site dated back close to 2 million years. That the K-Ar and fission-track methods use different techniques and have different sources of error makes them effective as checks on each other. When the two methods support each other, they provide very reliable evidence.

Palaeomagnetic Dating. Most fossils of interest to anthropologists occur in sedimentary rocks, but the potassium-argon and argon-argon methods are suitable only for dating igneous rocks. When rock of any kind forms, it records the ancient magnetic field of the earth, which has reversed itself many times. **Palaeomagnetic dating** can identify the geomagnetic patterns in rocks and therefore date the fossils within those rocks. Strictly speaking, palaeomagnetic dating is not an absolute dating method, but geomagnetic time periods have been dated absolutely in conjunction with potassium-argon dating. Palaeomagnetic dating has been used to date primate finds from the Eocene and Miocene epochs (Kappelman, 1993).

Uranium-Series Dating. The decay rates of two kinds of uranium, ^{235}U and ^{238}U, into other isotopes (such as ^{230}Th, thorium) have also proved useful for dating *Homo sapiens* (modern human) sites, particularly in caves where there are stalagmites and other calcite formations. Because water that seeps into caves usually contains uranium but not thorium, the calcite formations trap uranium. The time that has elapsed since the formation of the materials can be estimated from the ratio of those isotopes—a process called **uranium-series dating**. The thorium-uranium ratio is useful for dating cave sites less than 300 000 years old where there are no volcanic rocks, which could be dated using the potassium-argon method. Early *Homo sapiens* from European cave sites in Germany, Hungary, and Wales were dated this way (Brown, 1992; Schwarcz, 1993).

Thermoluminescence Dating. Many minerals emit light when they are heated (*thermoluminescence*), even before they become red hot. This so-called "cold light" comes from the release under heat of "outside" electrons trapped in atoms within the crystal structure of the material. **Thermoluminescence dating** (Aitken, 1985) is based on the principle that if an object is heated to a high temperature during its production or use, it will release all its trapped electrons. This is the process that clay undergoes when it is fired to produce a pot. Subsequent to heating, the object continues to trap electrons from radioactive elements (potassium, thorium, uranium) found in the sediments around it. The greater the time interval subsequent to its last firing, the greater the accumulation of electrons.

The amount of thermoluminescence emitted when the object is heated during testing allows researchers to calculate the age of the object. Of course, the analyst must have a sample of sediment that was associated with the object (for example, the surrounding soil in which a clay pot is found). This will determine the kind and amount of radiation that the object has been exposed to subsequent to its last heating event. Thermoluminescence dating is well suited to samples of ancient pottery, brick, tile, or terracotta that were originally heated to a high temperature when they were made. This method can also be applied to burnt flint tools, hearth stones, lava or lava-covered objects, meteorites, and meteor craters (Aitken, 1985).

Electron Spin Resonance Dating. Electron spin resonance dating is a technique that, like thermoluminescence dating, measures trapped electrons from surrounding radioactive material. In this case, the method is different. The material to be dated is exposed to varying magnetic fields, and a spectrum of the microwaves absorbed by the tested material is obtained. Since no heating is required for this technique, electron spin resonance is especially useful for dating organic material such as bone and shell, which decompose if heated (Aitken, 1985).

Amino Acid Racemization. Amino acid racemization is a non-radiometric technique that can be applied to organic material such as bone, mollusc shells, and eggshells. It is useful for dating materials from a few centuries old to several hundred thousand years old. Most amino acids in protein occur in one of two forms termed *D-* and *L-isomers*. Both have the same molecular structure, but are mirror images of one another.

Only L-isomers are found in living organisms. When an organism dies, maintenance of the L-form ceases and there is a slow process toward equal distributions of the L- and D-isomers. This process of change in composition of the amino acids is called *racemization*, and can be applied to dating prehistoric shell and bone—the older a fossil shell or bone, the further along the process of racemization should be.

Obsidian Hydration. *Obsidian* is naturally formed volcanic glass, used by many prehistoric populations for the production of extremely sharp-edged tools. When a piece of obsidian is newly exposed to the atmosphere through natural forces or human activity, that surface begins to absorb water. This process is known as **obsidian hydration**. The layer that is being weathered is invisible, but its thickness can be measured. The thickness will depend on the time it has been exposed, as well as the amount of moisture available, and what kind of sediment surrounded the artifact (Fagan, 2000). Obsidian hydration can be used as both a relative and an absolute dating technique for tools fashioned from obsidian.

Each dating technique has its own benefits (see Figure 2–5). Which ones are used will be determined by the material available and the expected age of the remains to be tested. Overall, anthropologists, whether examining archaeological sites or palaeoanthropological locales, use the techniques we have described to gather information about remains that they find. In the next chapter we will look at ways in which they interpret this information to reconstruct the past.

Figure 2–5 Summary of Dating Techniques Available to Archaeologists

Name	Age Range	Materials Dated
Relative		
Stratigraphy		anything between two clearly defined sediment layers
F-U-N trio		bone and teeth
Absolute		
Amino Acid Racemization	2000 to 1 million years ago	bone, charcoal, other organic material
Dendrochronology	Up to 9000 years ago	wood
Electron Spin Resonance	Up to 1 million years ago	bone and shell
Fission-Track	20 to 5 billion years ago	crystal, glass, and many uranium-rich minerals
Obsidian Hydration	Up to 800 000 years ago	volcanic glass
Palaeomagnetic	Up to 10 000 years ago	geological deposits
Potassium-Argon (K-Ar)	5000 to 3 billion years ago	volcanic rock
Radiocarbon (C14)	Up to 50 000 years ago	bone, mollusc shells, eggshells
Thermoluminescence	Unlimited	baked clay, pottery, and burnt rocks
Uranium-Series	Less than 300 000 years ago	calcite formations

Summary

1. Understanding past human life from the archaeological record requires expertise in a variety of areas. Archaeological techniques for the excavation of remains are used so as to maximize the amount of information gained during the excavation of a site.

2. Archaeological context, or the association of artifacts and features with one another, is a crucial aspect of archaeological interpretation. Without controlled provenience, archaeological data are of little value.

3. The formation of sites is an important aspect for understanding what they represent. The study of taphonomy—post-depositional changes to remains—is critical for reconstructing the past.

4. The process of fossilization is a relatively rare process in which the organic components of an organism are replaced with minerals percolating through the surrounding environment over a period of thousands of years.

5. Site prospection includes a variety of techniques including surface and subsurface surveying, field walking, test pitting, and trenching.

6. Excavation requires control over spatial aspects of a site, which can be accomplished by establishing a grid system, with more detailed mapping and documentation of recoveries within subunits relative to the grid location of the control square. The careful recording of all information within the grid allows for all data to be incorporated into a single system at the end of the excavation.

7. Both relative and absolute dating techniques can be employed to assess the age of a site. Relative techniques like stratigraphy provide a basis on which to determine whether a feature or object is younger or older than other features in adjacent layers. Absolute dating techniques provide methods for assessing the age of an object or site in actual years.

Glossary Terms

absolute dating   (p. 32)

amino acid racemization   (p. 39)

^{40}Ar-^{39}Ar dating   (p. 38)

archaeological sites   (p. 22)

artifacts   (p. 30)

association   (p. 30)

ceramics   (p. 31)

datum   (p. 28)

dendrochronology   (p. 34)

ecofacts   (p. 30)

electron spin resonance dating   (p. 39)

features   (p. 30)

fission-track dating method   (p. 38)

fossil locales   (p. 22)

fossilization   (p. 23)

F-U-N trio   (p. 32)

half-life   (p. 34)

^{40}K (potassium-40)   (p. 38)

law of superposition   (p. 32)

lithics   (p. 30)

material culture   (p. 20)

midden   (p. 20)

obsidian hydration   (p. 40)

palaeomagnetic dating   (p. 38)

phytoliths   (p. 30)

potassium-argon (K-Ar) dating   (p. 38)

provenience   (p. 20)

radiocarbon dating   (p. 34)

relative dating   (p. 32)

site formation processes   (p. 20)

stratigraphy   (p. 32)

subsurface techniques   (p. 25)

surface techniques   (p. 24)

taphonomy   (p. 24)

thermoluminescence dating   (p. 39)

uranium-series dating   (p. 39)

Critical Questions

1. Why is careful mapping and recording of archaeological sites so crucial for interpreting the past?

2. How do relative dating methods differ from absolute dating methods? Are there circumstances when one technique is more appropriate than another? Explain your answer.

Internet Exercises

1. Go to the webpage for the Canadian Archaeological Association at **www.canadianarchaeology.com**. Explore the resources available there, and make some constructive criticisms about this public face of the CAA.

2. Compare events surrounding these two recent "politicized" North American archaeological finds: "Kennewick Man" (**www.mnh.si.edu/arctic/html/kennewick_man.html**) and the "Yukon Iceman" at **www.climateark.org/articles/1999/lostwome.htm.**

3. Find out much more about fossils and the geologic record at **www.ucmp.berkeley.edu/fosrec/.**

Suggested Reading

Bahn PG. 2001. Archaeology: Very Short Introduction. Oxford, UK: Oxford University Press. A survey of the technological developments in the field of archaeology, and how archaeology can be used. This popular book explores the main areas of archaeological research today, and the origin and development of the field.

Fagan B. 2001. In the Beginning. Upper Saddle River, NJ: Prentice Hall. Brief and highly engaging, this introduction to the fundamental principles of methods and theory in archaeology begins with the goals of archaeology, then goes on to consider the basic concepts of culture, time, and space, and the finding and excavation of archaeological sites.

Peregrine PN. 2001. Archaeological Research: A Brief Introduction. Upper Saddle River, NJ: Prentice Hall. This concise yet thorough introduction to archaeological research presents students with the basic methods of data collection, analysis, and interpretation. Focusing on the research process itself, the text explores why archaeologists choose particular methods over others, along with the varying circumstances of their research. It also provides a brief overview of archaeological literature and legal and ethical issues in the fields.

RECONSTRUCTING THE PAST: ANALYSIS AND INTERPRETATION

3

The relationship between humans and their environment has long been a focus of study, particularly among archaeologists and physical anthropologists. To reconstruct how past populations lived, researchers examine evidence from the archaeological record. They draw upon a variety of related disciplines to help reconstruct former ecological conditions, determine what people ate and how and where they obtained their food, and study the diseases of the past. Analysis of human remains is important for determining diet and disease, as well as revealing demographic information, such as lifespan and infant mortality. Settlement patterns are another focus of study, specifically, where people established permanent and seasonal dwellings, as well as the size of the settlements, how many people lived there, and how long the sites were occupied. The archaeological record can also give clues about the society itself—whether some people had a higher socio-economic status than others, for example, and what the patterns of resource distribution and allocation were. In this chapter, we explore some of the anthropological methods for reconstructing these aspects of lives of past populations.

Reconstructing the past is not an easy task. It is not enough to simply dig up material left behind by people who once lived in a place. Rather, it requires the careful analysis of the environment in which the materials are found in order to say something about the circumstances by which that material came to be there. Archaeologists and others attempt to understand a past society as it is reflected in the remains of the everyday belongings of past peoples. For example, if we want to understand how a community changed over the course of its history, we need to recognize that those changes would have been influenced by a variety of factors, including changes in the environment, in population numbers, and in culture, to name a few. However, unravelling these factors is sometimes difficult. The archaeologist has to pay careful attention to the context in which material culture is found. Further, while material culture is a direct reflection of past culture, the archaeological record is not always a direct reflection of material culture.

A number of factors can affect where the remains of material culture are found in the archaeological record and the patterns of deposition. The archaeologist must also be able to recognize the influence of these factors.

Analyzing Artifacts

Conservation is the process of treating artifacts, ecofacts, and in some cases even features to stop decay and, if possible, even reverse the deterioration process. Some conservation is very simple, involving only cleaning and drying the item. Some conservation is highly complex, involving long-term chemical treatments and, in some cases, long-term storage under controlled conditions. The so-called "Ice Man," for example, the frozen

A conservator applying preservative to a decaying Alaskan totem pole.

remains of a man who lived 5000 years ago found in 1993 in the Italian Alps, is kept in permanently glacial-like conditions after investigators found to their dismay that warming the remains for study induced the growth of mould. The archaeologists removed the mould, but decided that his remains would have to be kept under the same conditions that preserved them in the first place, and so a complex storage facility had to be built to recreate the glacial environment in which he was originally found (Nash, 2001; Makristathis et al., 2002; Dickson et al., 2003; Murphy, Jr. et al., 2003).

Reconstruction is like building a puzzle—but a three-dimensional puzzle where you're not sure which pieces belong and you know not all of the pieces are there. First, materials have to be sorted into similar types. For example, to reconstruct ceramics from a site, all the ceramics have to be sorted into types with similar colour, decoration, and shapes. Then the similar pieces are compared to see if any seem to come from the same vessel. Once all the pieces thought to be from the same vessel are located, they can be assembled. Reconstruction is clearly a long, difficult process—in some cases taking years.

What Can We Learn from Artifacts?

Once conservation and reconstruction are complete, the archaeologist or paleoanthropologist can begin to analyze the artifacts they've found. Archaeologists have developed specific and often unique ways to analyze the many different types of artifacts. Stone tools are examined in different ways from ceramics, and both are examined differently from bone. But there are some commonalities in the way artifacts are analyzed, regardless of what they are made of.

First, archaeologists typically examine the *form* of an artifact—how it is shaped. For most common artifacts, such as lithics and ceramics, forms are known well enough to be grouped into typologies. Placing artifacts into a **typology** is often the primary purpose of *formal analysis,* because typologies allow archaeologists to place a particular artifact into context with other artifacts found

at the site or even at other sites. Typologies often provide a lot of information about an artifact, including its age, the species or culture with which it is affiliated, and in some cases even how it was made, used, or exchanged in the past. Second, archaeologists often measure artifacts, recording their size in various, often strictly defined, dimensions. Such analysis is used to group artifacts into a typology. Figure 3–1 shows the standard measurements taken from projectile points.

Third, archaeologists often attempt to understand how an artifact was made. By examining the material the artifact is made from and how that material was manipulated, archaeologists can learn about the technology, economy, and exchange systems of the peoples who made the artifact. For example, if the material is not locally available, that means the people traded for it. Archaeologists can also study present-day peoples and how they make similar artifacts in order to understand how ancient artifacts were made.

Finally, archaeologists attempt to understand the function of an artifact. Knowing the function

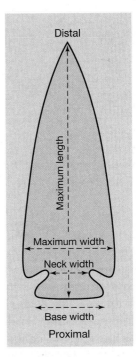

Figure 3–1 Standard Metrical Measurements of Chipped Stone Tools

of an artifact allows the archaeologist a direct window into ancient life. Since this information is so important, a number of sophisticated techniques have been developed to determine how artifacts were used. For stone, bone, and wood tools, a technique called *use-wear analysis* has been developed, which can determine how a tool was used through the careful examination of the wear on its edges. For ceramic vessels, techniques have been developed to extract residues trapped in the clay and determine what the vessel held.

But what can archaeologists really learn by placing artifacts in typologies through formal and metric analysis, or by learning how an artifact was manufactured and used? Knowing how an artifact was made allows the archaeologist to understand the technology and technical abilities of peoples in the past. Artifacts and their context with other features can help inform us about the social organization of a past people and may also reveal religious beliefs. Even gender roles can be explored archaeologically (see New Perspectives on Gender, *Women in the Shell Mound Archaic*).

Analyzing Human Remains

Osteology or skeletal biology is the specialized subdiscipline of physical anthropology that deals with the biological remains of humans from past populations. Osteological reconstruction contributes a significant amount of information to our understanding of the past. The analysis of demographic structure (palaeodemography), health and disease (palaeopathology), diet and nutrition (palaeonutrition) as well as population affinity are just a few of the areas that skeletal biology can contribute to.

The first step to any analysis is identifying skeletal remains as being human. While this is relatively straightforward for well-preserved samples, this can be a difficult task for small fragmentary skeletal remains. For early hominids the task of identification and classification becomes increasingly difficult. Estimation of the age and sex of individuals within a skeletal sample is the first step toward interpretation.

NEW PERSPECTIVES ON GENDER

Women in the Shell Mound Archaic

One of the main issues addressed by archaeologists interested in gender is how we can learn about and understand gender roles in prehistoric cultures. Gender roles might seem impossible to study in archaeological contexts. How is gender preserved in the archaeological record? How can knowledge about gender roles be recovered? Information about gender roles can be recovered if one maintains an awareness of how material culture that is associated ethnographically with particular gender roles changes over time. Archaeologists argue that such an awareness leads not only to a better understanding of gender in prehistory but can also lead to a fuller understanding of prehistoric cultures overall.

An example is Cheryl Claassen's work on the Shell Mound Archaic culture of the Tennessee River valley. The Shell Mound Archaic represents the remains of people who lived in Tennessee and Kentucky between about 5500 and 3000 years ago. They were hunters and gatherers who lived in small villages, and probably moved seasonally between summer and winter communities. The most distinctive feature of the Shell Mound Archaic is the large mounds of mollusc shells they constructed for burying their dead. Tens of thousands of shells were piled together to create these mounds. Yet, around 3000 years ago, shellfishing and thus the creation of shell burial mounds stopped abruptly. Claassen wondered why.

Suggested explanations include climate change, overexploitation of shellfish themselves, and emigration of shellfishing peoples from the area. None has proven wholly satisfactory. In contemporary cultures shellfishing is typically done by women and children, and Claassen wondered whether an approach that considered gender roles might be more productive. She decided to approach the problem through the perspective of women's workloads, since it would have been women who would have most likely been the ones shellfishing. The end of shellfishing would have meant that women would have had a lot of free time—free time that could have been put to use in some other way. What might have changed to lead women to stop shellfishing?

Estimation of Age

The age of an adult skeleton can be estimated using a variety of techniques. These methods are referred to as **skeletal age-indicator techniques**. These techniques depend on both *macroscopic*—visible by naked eye—observation and *microscopic* changes in the shape and structure of bone for estimating the age of an individual. Many macroscopic techniques focus on the pattern of age-related degeneration of bone. These include examination of the pubic symphysis and auricular surface on the hipbone, the closure of sutures between bones on the skull, and the ends of the fourth rib (see Figure 3–2). Other methods focus on **remodelling** to see how microscopic fractures may occur normally from everyday wear and tear. The physical anthropologist is trained to evaluate several criteria that indicate age, and then estimate an overall age range for the individuals within the sample.

The estimation of age from the skeletal remains of children is based on the development of dental and skeletal tissues—that is, the growing bones and developing teeth (see Figure 3–3 on page 49). Age estimation for a child is much easier and more accurate than age estimation for an adult. While there are fewer specific techniques that can be used, these methods have a smaller range of error than do most adult aging techniques. Overall, estimation of age of a juvenile is accurate to within a range of about half a year.

Sex Determination

It is widely recognized by physical anthropologists that the pelvis or hipbone is the most reliable part of the skeleton for determination of sex. Both metric (based on measurements) and non-metric or morphological (based on size and shape) techniques are better than 95 percent accurate for correctly determining sex (see Figure 3–4 on page 50). Accuracy rates based on other parts of the skeleton are usually lower than those using the hipbone.

Unfortunately, determination of sex from the skeleton is restricted to remains of sexually mature adults. A variety of studies have investigated traits

Would something else have perhaps become more important, so that women's labour was needed more for those other tasks?

Women's labour might have been redirected toward domesticated crops. There is archaeological evidence that about 3000 years ago several productive but highly labour-intensive crops became widely used. For example, *chenopodium,* one of the more plentiful and nutritious of these new crops, has tiny seeds that require considerable labour to harvest, clean, and process. Women were likely the ones burdened with such work. They not only would have harvested these crops but also would have been the ones to process and prepare meals from them. Thus, the emergence of agricultural economies would have required women to undertake new labour in food production

and processing that may well have forced them to stop other tasks, like shellfishing.

The development of agricultural activities might also have brought about changes in ritual and ceremonialism. The shell burial mounds were clearly central to Shell Mound Archaic death ceremonies. Considerable labour, mostly by women, would have been required to collect the shells and to build these mounds. Later societies in the region buried their dead in earthen mounds. Could this be a reflection of the new importance earth had in an emerging agricultural economy? If so, what role did women play in ceremonies of death and burial? If they were no longer the providers of the raw materials needed for burial, does that mean their status in society as a whole changed?

We may never know exactly why the Shell Mound Archaic disappeared, or how women's work and women's roles in society changed. But as Claassen points out, taking a gender perspective provides new avenues along which to pursue answers to these questions, and interesting new questions to pursue.

Sources: Claassen C. 1991. Gender, Shellfishing, and the Shell Mound Archaic. In: Gero J, Conkey M, editors. Engendering Archaeology: Women and Prehistory. Oxford: Blackwell. p 276–300.

Claassen C. 2002. Gender and Archaeology. In: Peregrine PN, Ember CR, Ember M, editors. Archaeology: Original Readings in Method and Practice. Upper Saddle River, NJ: Prentice Hall. p 210–224. Also in: Ember CR, Ember M, editors. New Directions in Anthropology. Upper Saddle River, NJ: Prentice Hall, CD-ROM, 2003.

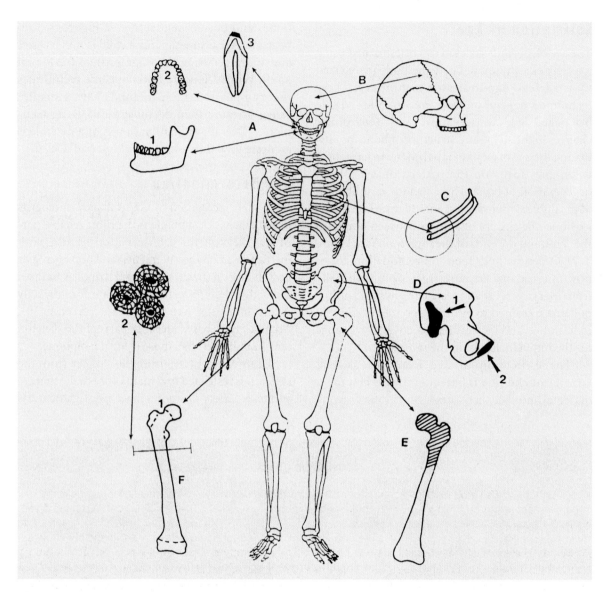

Figure 3–2 Commonly Used Skeletal Age-Indicator Techniques for Estimating the Age of Adult Remains

A: 1 dental development and eruption; 2 dental wear; 3 dental microstructure. **B**: cranial suture closure. **C**: sternal rib ends. **D**: 1 auricular surface; 2 pubic symphysis. **E**: radiographs of trabelucar bone from femur. **F**: 1 epiphyseal union; 2 cortical bone microstructure (osteon counting).

Source: Hunter J, Roberts C, Martin A. 1996. Studies in Crime: An Introduction to Forensic Archaeology. Chrysalis Books Ltd. Reprinted with permission.

that might be **sexually dimorphic**—showing size and shape differences between males and females—in infants and juveniles, but only a few studies of such traits have demonstrated sufficient levels of accuracy to warrant applying these traits in osteological analyses. More promising, but still restricted by costs, are methods of sex determination that are based on *ancient DNA* extracted from the bones or teeth of individuals.

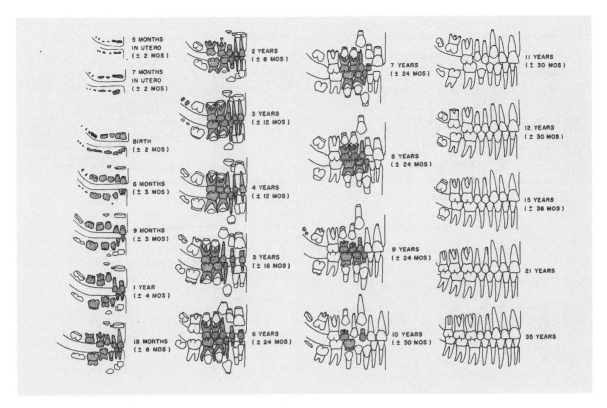

Figure 3–3 Pattern of Dental Development in Children

Age estimation in non-adult skeletons can be determined from dental development. Here a composite chart of development patterns is presented as a quick reference.

Source: Ubelaker D. 1989. Human Skeletal Remains: Excavations, Analysis and Interpretation. Third edition. Washington: Taraxacum Press. Figure 71, p 64. Reprinted with permission.

Ancient DNA

It appears in most living organisms that heredity is controlled by the same chemical substance, **DNA— deoxyribonucleic acid**. The possibility of extracting DNA from prehistoric bone or other tissues has, over the last decade, led to the development of intense research in the field of **ancient DNA (aDNA)**. It was first proposed in the 1980s that DNA could be successfully extracted from archaeologically recovered bone that was thousands of years old. Researchers around the world became excited by the possibilities of this new technology. However, like all new discoveries, several key methodological problems still had to be resolved. First, DNA is known to deteriorate over time. As a result, the actual quantity of DNA that might be present in a specimen could be very small and

might represent comparatively fragmentary sections of the DNA sequence. Further, any DNA present might be damaged or degraded beyond the point of providing any useful information.

A significant advance in the field came with the discovery of the **polymerase chain reaction (PCR)** technique for the accurate recovery of ancient DNA. The major benefit of the PCR method is that it allows for the amplification of DNA sequences from trace amounts of the original genetic material. However, because the PCR method requires only a few molecules of DNA, it brought with it the heightened threat of sample contamination from both the burial environment and the laboratory environment. As a result, rigorous protocols have been developed to ensure the integrity

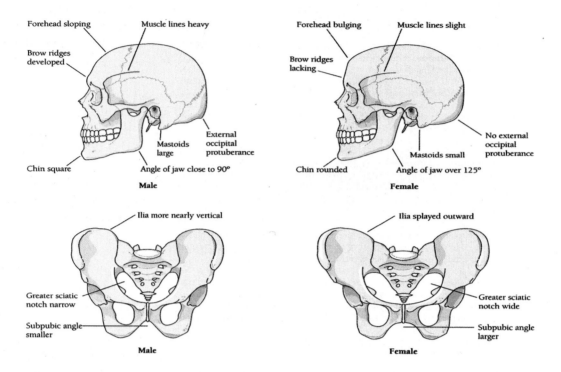

Figure 3–4 Common Traits of the Human Skeleton That Are Used to Assess Sex of Adults

Sex determination of the adult skeleton can be made from a variety of morphological techniques, as illustrated above. Determination of sex of children's skeletons cannot be done, as the growth process in children's skeletons is not yet complete.

Source: Feder KL, Park MA. 1989. Human Antiquity: An Introduction to Physical Anthropology and Archaeology. Third edition. Mountain View CA: Mayfield Publishing Company. Reprinted with permission.

of the original DNA sample, and minimize any possibilities of accidental contamination during the laboratory processing.

The ability to extract DNA from prehistoric remains has become an important aspect of anthropological research. Determination of sex was one of the first areas of study for the application of DNA techniques to human skeletal samples. The ability to accurately identify sex from DNA is relatively straightforward now, although the time and cost associated with this methodology is still prohibitive for large samples. Another area of focus has been on population affinity or identification of maternal biological lineages through the analysis of mitochondrial DNA, from analysis of DNA extracted from skeletal samples. And most recently, researchers have begun trying to identify the DNA of agents associated with diseases that can be identified in the skeletal remains of individuals from the past. All of these areas, and those that have yet to be explored, will greatly enrich our understanding of past populations and how they lived.

Palaeopathology

The study of **palaeopathology** seeks to answer questions concerning the origins, prevalence, and spread of diseases in past populations from human skeletal remains. The diagnosis and distribution of disease, within both individuals and the population, form the basis of interpretation for palaeopathological studies. Aided by macroscopic and microscopic examination, and some of the techniques already discussed, researchers attempt to

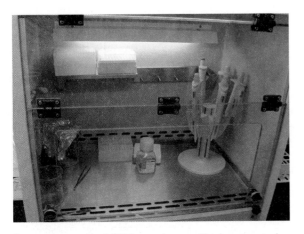

Processing ancient DNA requires meticulous control over the processing of samples. Seen here, an ultraviolet light is used to help prevent contamination.

and of those, only a small percentage will actually result in changes to the skeleton. For example, pulmonary tuberculosis will affect the skeleton in only 3 to 7 percent of those individuals infected (Steinbock, 1976).

Skeletal evidence of health in the past is not limited to the effect of infectious diseases. Other conditions can leave distinct marks or lesions on bones and teeth, including but not limited to joint, autoimmune, and metabolic diseases as well as other more specific maladies such as Paget's disease. The frequency of lesions caused by any of these conditions within archaeological samples is affected by factors such as differential preservation, incomplete or biased excavation, and the age and sex distributions within the sample. Anthropologists must attempt to deal with these issues before they can make interpretations of general population health from skeletal samples.

A primary question that palaeopathologists must ask themselves is, what does the presence of infectious lesions on the skeleton mean, for both the health of the individual and the population from which such an individual comes (Ortner, 1991)? The basic assumption of palaeopathology is that there is a consistent relationship between the presence of skeletal lesions produced by a specific disease process in the individual (infectious or otherwise), and the risks of sickness and death associated with that disease within the population as a whole (Ortner, 1991). Simply put, it is assumed that the more often you see evidence for a specific disease in the archaeological record, the greater the risk of illness or death from that disease for individuals in the living population who were exposed to it.

In the early 1990s, Jim Wood and colleagues cautioned palaeopathologists against drawing conclusions about past health based on this assumption (Wood et al., 1992). Palaeopathological interpretations of health assume that the individual immune response and environmental conditions do not influence the presence of skeletal lesions. Therefore, different levels of disease observed archaeologically must be related to cultural differences between populations (Cohen and Armelagos, 1984a; Goodman et al., 1984b; Cohen, 1989;

identify and assess the prevalence of diseases within an archaeological sample. Then they may be able to draw conclusions about the prevalence of a disease within the population as a whole.

Like clinical medicine that deals with the whole person in his or her environment, palaeopathology must attempt to interpret the appearance, spread, and distribution of diseases in a biocultural context (Manchester, 1987). Increasingly, palaeopathologists have become aware that human behaviour and its social and cultural determinants play a prominent role in the distribution and spread of infectious diseases. As a result, temporal and spatial differences in most disease patterns are largely the result of cultural differences in behavioural and not biological variation (Dunn and Janes, 1986; Inhorn and Brown, 1990; Sattenspiel, 1990).

A crucial aspect of palaeopathological studies has been to give precise descriptions and differential diagnoses from individual remains. **Differential diagnosis** is the process of listing each disease or condition that is consistent with the evidence observed, and then assessing which diagnosis is the most probable. The last few decades have seen a shift in emphasis to analysis of health and disease in populations. Interpretations of general population health from palaeopathological analyses have their limitations, however. First, only diseases that affect the hard tissues will generally be available for study,

CURRENT ISSUES

Evolution of Disease

One of the areas where palaeopathology can contribute useful knowledge is in the co-evolution of diseases, or how some diseases influence how others change over time. Evidence from the archaeological record in some cases can clearly provide a much-needed perspective on the relationship between diseases and human cultural conditions.

Without an understanding of the interaction of various diseases with each other (there is no reason to assume that a population will suffer from only one kind of disease), interpretations of health within a population can become too simplistic and unrealistic. This is particularly relevant to the concept of understanding why some people are susceptible to a particular disease and understanding how new diseases emerge. To illustrate this point, we can discuss the palaeopathological evidence for two major diseases—tuberculosis and leprosy.

The concept of differential susceptibility to specific diseases is well recognized in the clinical literature. For example, the clinical response (observable changes in the body) to infection by *Mycobacterium tuberculosis*, which causes tuberculosis, is not dependent upon immunity. There is a range of response by the immune system to the *Mycobacterium leprae*, which causes leprosy, with the clinical response to infection ranging from severe and highly infective to mild, depending on the level of immunity that an individual was born with.

The *Mycobacterium* virus causes both leprosy and tuberculosis. Both diseases can produce skeletal lesions at the later stages of development. In the early 1950s researchers proposed *cross immunity* between the two diseases, that is, the idea that inoculation with one disease may prevent establishment of the other. The con-

cept of this interaction has since been applied to the history of the two diseases in human populations. The question is, what can palaeoepidemiology tell us about this concept?

Tuberculosis may have been present in small bands of hunter-gatherers although it was not likely to have posed a substantial health threat at the population level at the time. The move toward a more settled style of life and the subsequent social changes likely altered the occurrence of diseases like tuberculosis that were once transmitted by eating infected meat or drinking milk from infected cattle. The resulting pulmonary infection is easily transmittable from human to human when they are in close contact.

A decline in the prevalence of leprosy associated with a rise in tuberculosis until the seventeenth century has been observed in Britain. Keith Manchester, a physician and palaeopathologist who specializes in leprosy, has argued that during the later Roman and Anglo-Saxon periods in Britain, tuberculosis existed primarily as a gastrointestinal disease. With the development of towns and markets, the disease developed into the airborne form that affects humans. Tuberculosis is a chronic infectious disease: it is transmitted when airborne droplets carrying the bacilli enter the upper respiratory tract. Primary tuberculosis usually occurs in children under 5 years of age, with an initial inflammatory focus followed by recovery or secondary infection that is usually fatal. Individuals who recover from the initial infection acquire a degree of immunity to subsequent infection, although health or nutritional stress later in life can result in post-secondary tuberculosis occurring in the second or third decade.

In leprosy, transmission between infected and non-infected hosts is respiratory via water droplets in the breath, or through the skin. The bacilli can also be found on occasion in the placenta or in the breast milk of a mother who has leprosy. Infection, however, is uncommon in infants. This may be due to passively transferred immunity through breast milk or the long incubation period of the disease.

While the exact age of maximum risk to leprosy is not known, some modern evidence suggests that exposure occurs at a much later age than for tuberculosis. As a result, the *Mycobacterium leprae* may occur in a population that has developed a certain level of immunity to tuberculosis from earlier exposure to primary infections with *M. tuberculosis*. The cross immunity that exists between the two diseases may have resulted in limited immunity to leprosy, which prevented the establishment of the clinical disease. Clinical studies have noted that in simultaneous exposure to both viruses in populations sensitized to the *Mycobacterium tuberculosis*, the development of both diseases may be inhibited. From this, Manchester argues that the observed decline in leprosy from the end of the medieval period was facilitated by the rise of tuberculosis in Britain. In turn, this relationship between the diseases was associated with the development of large urban centres in the Middle Ages.

Sources: Bryceson A, Pfaltzgraff RE. 1990. Leprosy. Edinburgh: Churchill Livingstone.

Roberts C, Manchester K. 1997. The Archaeology of Disease. Ithaca, NY: Cornell University Press.

Manchester K. 1984. Tuberculosis and Leprosy in Antiquity: An Interpretation. Medical History (55):162–173.

Manchester K. 1991. Tuberculosis and Leprosy: Evidence for Interaction of Disease. In: Ortner DJ, Aufderheide AC, editors. Human Palaeopathology: Current Syntheses and Future Options. Washington, DC: Smithsonian Institution Press. p 23–35.

Goodman et al., 1989). Wood and co-workers, however, have strongly urged palaeopathologists to reconsider this supposition and critically examine the concepts of differential risk and susceptibility to disease and death within population samples. That is, each individual may or may not have the same chance of being exposed to a particular disease. Further, even when an individual is exposed, biological factors specific to the individual's immune response will result in some contracting the disease while others do not.

Many researchers have expressed concern over the fact that skeletal samples are intrinsically biased because they are the products of selective mortality (Buikstra, 1979; Cook, 1981; Cook, 1984; Cook and Rathbun, 1984; Saunders, 1992; Wood et al., 1992; Saunders and Hoppa, 1993). *Selective mortality* refers to the notion that skeletal samples represent not all the people who were susceptible (susceptibles) for a given age group, but only those individuals who died at that age. For example, 5-year-old individuals in a skeletal sample represent only those 5-year-olds who died and not all of the 5-year-olds who were alive in the population at risk; other surviving susceptibles continued to live, in effect contributing to, or being members of, older mortality groups (Wood et al., 1992). The obvious problem, then, is whether the evidence of disease in a skeletal sample accurately represents the real prevalence of infectious agents in the living population during the past.

A promising future direction is palaeopathological studies that seek to examine the epidemiology or the course taken by specific diseases. The application of computer simulations of disease processes allow such studies. Researchers can then examine a variety of biocultural factors that might have influenced the population's response to the disease. This approach to past health has become an important focus of anthropological research.

Palaeodemography

Demography focuses on the age and sex structure of the population, and patterns of mortality, fertility, and population growth. **Palaeodemography** is the study of demographic structure in the past.

Palaeodemographic studies have focused primarily on the interpretation of human skeletal samples recovered archaeologically. The basic assumption is that mortality statistics derived from the skeletal sample are sufficient to make inferences about the past population. As well, archaeological evidence for settlement size and distribution of settlements has been used to estimate population growth or to address broader questions of population structure in the past.

Anthropological demography of contemporary or recent historic hunter-gatherer and foraging populations can also provide us with models for prehistoric populations. This is known as **ethnographic analogy**. However, ethnographic analogy based on patterns of subsistence or mobility is extremely problematic. More recently, evidence from genetic studies has begun to be used to make inferences about long-term evolutionary changes in demographic structure in modern human populations that have lived over the past 250 000 years or so. In particular, genetic studies that examine variation within living human populations provide information on human demography since patterns of gene differences contain information about the demographic history of a species (Harpending et al., 1998).

Traditionally, palaeodemographers have used the abridged **life table** to place individuals into a series of age groups. They start by assuming that the past population numbers were **stationary**—in other words, that there was no in-migration or out-migration and the number of deaths equalled the number of births. They can then use the mean or average age-at-death in the skeletal sample to estimate life expectancy at birth. However, this assumption is not likely to apply in past populations, particularly over short periods and in small populations. In growing populations, age-at-death distributions are extremely sensitive to changes in birth rates but not to changes in death rates. Thus, if population numbers are not stationary—and changing populations never are—small variations in fertility have large effects on age-at-death distribution, while even quite large changes in mortality have virtually none (Wood et al., 1992). Recognizing this, many researchers have concluded that the age distribution of skeletal samples provides less information about mortality than it does about fertility. In fact, the same fertility and mortality patterns can produce different birth and death rates in populations with different age structures.

Two key factors that affect stationarity in populations are *growth* and *migration*. The immediate effects of migrations into or out of a population are obvious. People who move to a new location are not always representative of all age groups and therefore can affect birth and death rates unequally at the new location. Similarly, potential changes in the gene pool or genetic background of migrants can change the overall susceptibility to different kinds of diseases. The impact of such changes depends on the source of migration and the cultural forces that are propelling the migration. War or invasion, persecution, plague, and social, political, or economic factors can alter the demographic structure of a population in both the short and the long term. Failure to recognize the possible effects of migration on the age structure of past populations can distort conclusions (Johansson and Horowitz, 1986). If rates of population growth can be assessed independently of the skeletal evidence—that is, from other archaeological evidence—palaeodemographic analyses are less uncertain. However, such assessments are difficult to obtain (Moore et al., 1975; Milner et al., 1989).

In the 1970s demographers expressed concern over the scant evidence on which to base palaeodemographic analyses. As a result, model life tables from modern demographic studies, linking death rates, birth rates, and age structure within a population, formed the basis upon which anthropological demographers began to assess life tables for past populations. Information from skeletal samples could then be compared with that in a model life table, and the fit between the model data and observed mortality distributions could then be assessed. Model life tables in anthropological demography have two functions. First, they provide a means of assessing or compensating for biased and incomplete data, and second, they allow for the estimation of fertility rates and construction of an initial population at risk—that is, all individuals alive at the time, not just those who died. In the early 1970s, Weiss developed a set of model fertility and mortality schedules derived from ethnographic samples of contemporary hunter-gatherer societies and prehistoric skeletal samples (Weiss, 1973). Many investigators agreed that demographic statistics derived from contemporary non-Western societies represented an accurate comparison to past populations. However, given the variety of conditions under which many contemporary populations live, it is difficult to be certain that ethnographic analogy will always be appropriate. Further, the application of ethnographic data to archaeological samples with sparse socio-cultural information further compounds the problem.

Ultimately, physical anthropologists have tried to improve methods for estimating age from the skeleton in order to combine individual estimates to create a demographic profile of the age structure. More recently, researchers have begun to estimate the age structure of a sample directly from the distribution of skeletal age indicator methods before assigning an age to each single individual. While the difference is subtle, it is important. This approach attempts to avoid the broad range of error associated with estimates at the individual level. If you are interested in the pattern of distribution of mortality within a population (that is, who died at what age), then you must begin by estimating the overall age structure in the sample, and then estimate individual ages (Konigsberg and Frankenberg, 1994; Hoppa and Vaupel, 2002).

Reconstructing Past Diets

The only direct evidence for what people ate in the past is the preserved remains of the food itself. Such remains can be found in rare cases where mummified human remains may still have preserved stomach contents. Another form of direct evidence occurs in the form of *coprolites*—the fossilized remains of human feces. Other evidence for how people obtained their food and nutrition comes from a variety of sources. The study of the faunal or animal remains (*zooarchaeology*) and flora or plant remains (*palaeoethnobotany*) associated with settlement sites plays a major role in revealing the kinds of food people acquired and consumed. Evidence can also come from the analysis of human skeletons, that is, from biochemical analysis of bone.

Zooarchaeology

Zooarchaeology or *archaeozoology* is the study of animal remains from the archaeological record. The analysis of animal remains includes determining the number of different species represented, the minimum number of individuals of each species, and the age structure of those species. This information can provide clues about seasonal hunting strategies, specialized hunting practices, and the process of *domestication*—the modification of plants and animals for human use. However, it is critical to properly interpret the zooarchaeological data. For example, it is important to be able to distinguish between human-made butchering marks and marks from carnivore gnawing. Animals associated with human populations may reflect the kinds of foods that were consumed (including whether they were wild or domesticated, as we will see in Chapter 12). They may also reflect the strategies, such as big-game hunting techniques, used to acquire these food resources (see also the discussion of middle Palaeolithic hunting practices in Chapter 9).

An example of the interpretation of animal remains is Aubrey Cannon's research on the Northwest Coast. Using zooarchaeological data from the site of Namu, downstream from Bella Coola on British Columbia's coast, Cannon has argued that the increased focus on catching fish on the Northwest Coast was not the result of population pressure or lack of food from land-based sources. Rather, **sedentism**—living in one place for a prolonged period—and intensive salmon fishing seemed to be independent of increased salmon productivity and human population

Interpreting butchering marks on animal bones helps us to reconstruct what people ate and how they procured and processed their food.

growth. He suggests that evidence of increased storage capacity associated with the development of wood plank housing, and social feasting could explain the apparent intensification of fishing economies on the Northwest Coast (Cannon, 1998). By examining when and how this behaviour developed in a region, we can better understand its importance in a complex society where social and political power are based on resource control by the elite.

However, faunal remains are not associated only with food consumption. Jim Savelle of McGill University has examined zooarchaeological assemblages of bowhead whalebone, which was a major component of house construction in Thule occupation sites throughout the Canadian Arctic around 1000 years ago. He has suggested that the use of whalebone in house construction is the primary reason that we find whalebone at all Thule sites (Savelle, 1997). This is of interest because most people would consider life, now as in the past, in the Arctic as involving small, widely dispersed populations of hunter-gatherers who are highly mobile, and follow an intensive seasonal economy and settlement pattern. However, Thule people lived in winter villages in pit houses composed of whalebone rafters and covered with skins and turf. The question is, why did these people invest in semi-permanent housing given what we might expect regarding their seasonal subsistence and mobility patterns? Part of the answer is that there was an increase in whale hunting associated with warmer climatic conditions during this period. With the intensification of this kind of subsistence strategy, people became more sedentary because they did not have the technology, population size, or need to move all that material around.

Experimental Archaeology

Experimental archaeology explores a variety of historical questions, especially those related to diet and subsistence. The goal of experimental archaeology is to reproduce or replicate technological traits and patterns observed in the archaeological record. For example, many modern flint knappers attempt to reconstruct the process that would lead to the production of the kinds of chipped stone tools found in the archaeological record. Reconstruction may give the analyst insight into human behaviour and site formation processes. For example, animal carcasses were left to be scavenged to help palaeoanthropologists better understand the patterns in the distribution of bones found in sites associated with early hominids. The resultant tooth marks and distribution of bones were then analyzed and compared with that observed in the archaeological record (Hudson, 1993; Schick and Toth, 1994).

Similarly, Haskel Greenfield of the University of Manitoba is interested in food production and the origins of metallurgy. He has conducted experiments in which meat was butchered using replicas of stone tools and early metal tools, fabricated in a manner consistent with early metallurgy, so as to better understand how the transition from stone tools to early metal tools could be observed in the archaeological record. The results of this experiment will provide information for better understanding this technological evolution associated with food production.

The analysis of polishes or wear patterns and organic residues left on the tools used in food-related tasks by past populations is another relatively new area of research. Because of experimental archaeology, scientists now know that butchering an animal carcass and processing vegetable matter with stone tools lead to different microscopic wear patterns or polishes on the edge of the tools. Archaeologists can now look at the stone tools used by prehistoric peoples and examine them microscopically for patterns that are consistent with ones produced by experiment.

Even more exciting is the potential of **molecular anthropology**, which examines anthropological questions using genetic evidence. Researchers in molecular anthropology analyze and identify microscopic traces of organic material left on prehistoric tools (Loy et al., 1990; Loy et al., 1992; Loy and Hardy, 1992; Loy, 1998). New technology now allows stone tool edges to be examined for microscopic traces of blood from killed or butchered animals that might be preserved on such tools.

Examples of success include blood retrieved from Australian stone tools, dated to 9000 years ago (Loy and Hardy, 1992), and mastodon blood on a tool found in Chile, dated to 13 000 years ago (Tuross and Dillehay, 1995). Blood residues of a variety of large mammal species, including mammoth, have also been detected on projectile points from Beringia, providing for the first time a direct association between the use of these tools and big-game hunting of Pleistocene mammals in Arctic and sub-arctic North America (Loy and Dixon, 1998). Residue analysis on the interior of clay vessels has formed an important part of reconstructing aspects of ancient diet (see Research Frontiers, *Archaeology Helps Brew Ancient Beer*).

Palaeoethnobotany

Palaeoethnobotany or archaeobotany is the study of the relationships between plants and people in prehistory. Palaeoethnobotanists are especially trained in the identification of seeds found, often burnt or carbonized, in ancient garbage heaps (middens), cooking vessels, and hearths at archaeological sites. Soil removed from a site must be processed to recover the seeds from the archaeological record. The soil is placed in a flotation

RESEARCH FRONTIERS

Archaeology Helps Brew Ancient Beer

Archaeological evidence from ancient civilizations in Mesopotamia and Egypt has shown some of the earliest evidence for the brewing of beer. At Godin Tepe, a site in the Zagros Mountains in Iran, excavators from the Royal Ontario Museum have found some of the earliest chemical evidence for beer. Clay pots have been identified; these were used for the storage and fermentation of beer. Grooves on the interior of these vessels below the shoulder are consistent with early Sumerian examples for beer storage. Further, residue analysis from the grooves of some of these vessels found the chemical remnants of calcium oxalate—a primary component of barley beer that settles on the surface of storage tanks during fermentation. These findings represent some of the earliest evidence of beer production in the fourth century B.C.

In the second century B.C., evidence for beer production from the New Kingdom period in Egypt can also be observed from the archaeological record. During this period, which covers the reign of the Pharaoh Tutankhamen, evidence

includes residue from fermentation in vessels, and botanical remains. In 1990, the Egyptian Exploration Society approached Scottish and Newcastle Breweries in the United Kingdom to assist them in an investigation into beer making in ancient Egypt. Ancient Egyptian inscriptions and documents show that beer with bread was a daily food, giving nourishment to both the wealthy and poor. The established view of ancient Egyptian brewing, drawn from tomb scenes, was that beer loaves were made from a rich yeast dough, possibly with malt added. The dough was lightly baked and the resulting bread was then crumbled and strained through a sieve with water. Ingredients like dates or extra yeast might have been added at this stage. Fermentation occurred in large vats, and when complete, the liquid was poured into vessels and sealed for transportation.

Using a scanning electron microscope (SEM), researchers were able to examine residues on the interiors of fermentation pots, and have found evidence for yeast colonies and possibly lactic acid bacteria. In ancient Egypt, emmer and barley were the

two major cereals for producing beer. Additional clues from SEM research on residues provide insight into the actual brewing process. For example, changes in the structure of starch granules, associated with starch being heated in water, can be observed in some residues. Comparisons between samples are difficult though, given that contamination of the residues over the last 3000 years can obscure analyses. However, there now seems to be enough evidence from microscopic analysis of pot residues to suggest the ancient Egyptians used a variety of techniques for brewing, and that bread probably did not play a role in the production of beer in the ancient world.

Sources: Armelagos G. 2000. Take Two Beers and Call Me in 1,600 Years. Natural History 109(4):50–53.

Samuel D. 1996. Archaeology of Ancient Egyptian Beer. Journal of the American Society of Brewing Chemists 54:3–12.

Samuel D. 1996. Investigation of Ancient Egyptian Baking and Brewing Methods by Correlative Microscopy. Science 273: 488–490.

Samuel D, Bolt P. 1995. Rediscovering Ancient Egyptian Beer. Brewers' Guardian 124(12):26–31.

In ancient Egypt, figures were made depicting household activities such as bread and beer preparation. Above is a Middle Kingdom model.

device in which the light seeds and charcoal float to the surface of the water, where they are skimmed off for analysis. The heavier sediments such as clay, rock, and pebbles sink. Phytoliths, which are microscopic particles of silica from plants, can also be collected from archaeological remains, including artifacts, teeth, and feces, to provide clues as to the kinds of plants that were being processed and consumed. Gary Crawford and David Smith of the University of Toronto are examining sites at the western end of Lake Ontario and in the lower Grand River Valley in south-central Ontario that were occupied during the period from about A.D. 500 to A.D. 1100. They hope to gain an understanding of the transition from earlier seed crops to maize (corn) agriculture in southern Ontario prehistory (Crawford and Smith, 1996; Crawford et al., 1997). As we shall see in Chapter 12, the analysis of carbonized seeds from the archaeological record provides us with clues as to the increasing dependence on seed crops at the beginning of the Neolithic era.

Coprolites

Coprolites, or fossilized feces, provide evidence for diet because humans do not digest all food that they consume. Some of what an individual consumed can be identified in coprolites. Of course, this kind of evidence represents a snapshot of dietary intake. Coprolites occur most frequently in cave sites, where the dry air naturally desiccates, or removes the moisture from, organic material. Only foods consumed by a specific individual within a very narrow time frame will be present in preserved coprolites. However, if cave sites are frequently used by certain groups of people, there may be a sufficient sample of coprolites to provide a broader cross-section of the kinds of foods being consumed by the group.

Stable Isotopes and Trace Elements

Researchers are often interested in changes in nutrition for past populations. These changes may provide a link to broad biocultural adaptations, such as changes in the environment or in how people obtained their food. Researchers make inferences regarding the general levels of nutrition from skeletal samples through biochemical techniques, including the analysis of **stable isotopes**—isotopes of the same elements with different atomic masses—and **trace elements**—elements found in extremely small amounts within the body (Klepinger, 1984; Price, 1984; Boutton et al., 1991; Katzenberg, 1992; Sandford, 1992; Sandford, 1993; Schoeninger, 1995; Katzenberg, 2000) (see Research Frontiers, *You Are What You Eat: Chemical Analyses of Bones and Teeth*).

With respect to dietary reconstruction, the past consumption of two broadly different types of plants—tropical grasses and temperate climate plants—is commonly explored though stable isotope analysis. There are two types of photosynthetic pathways that plants can follow. The photosynthetic pathway for temperate-climate plants is different than the pathway for the tropical plants. Maize, like other tropical grasses, is a C4 pathway plant. Temperate climate plants are called C3 plants. C3 plants tend to absorb proportionately more carbon-12 (^{12}C) because they discriminate more strongly against the carbon-13 (^{13}C) isotope. In contrast, C4 plants produce more complex sugar molecules, and tend to more readily accept the ^{13}C isotope. This means that organisms that regularly consume C4 plants will display a different ratio of ^{13}C to ^{12}C than animals that routinely consume C3 plants. As a result, stable carbon isotope analysis on skeletal remains can be used extensively to assess the importance of maize in North American populations. Stable isotope analyses have shown the absence of maize in the diet of prehistoric Ontario populations prior to about A.D. 700 (Schwarcz et al., 1985; Katzenberg, 1993; Katzenberg et al., 1995). However, carbon isotope ratios increase after A.D. 1000 and peak around three to four centuries later, reflecting the adoption of maize agriculture in the region (Katzenberg et al., 1995). This is consistent with studies of other areas in eastern North America, although regional variations likely reflect a shorter growing season farther north.

Carbon isotopic analyses can also be used to study the diets of people who lived at coastal sites, particularly in determining the relative importance of marine versus terrestrial foods. Carbon absorbed by marine animals derives from dissolved carbonate, while terrestrial animals rely upon atmospheric carbon. As the relative abundance of ^{13}C is higher in marine environments than in the atmosphere, the entire marine food web reflects a high proportion of ^{13}C. This means the isotopic profile of human bones should show if past populations relied more heavily on marine foods than on terrestrial foods. For example, David Lubell and his colleagues have used this analysis to show an abrupt shift from marine to terrestrial food resources between Mesolithic and later Neolithic populations in Portugal (Lubell et al., 1994).

In the late 1980s researchers demonstrated that the ratio of stable isotopes of nitrogen could be used to detect the consumption of breast milk in an infant's diet (Fogel et al., 1989). The higher an organism is on the food chain, the more its tissues are enriched with the ^{15}N isotope. For example, carnivores that consume herbivores (plant-eating animals) have tissues enriched with ^{15}N. So we would expect that the tissues of breast-fed babies should be more enriched in ^{15}N than the tissues of their mothers. Many studies have explored whether high ^{15}N levels in infant skeletons, in contrast to decreased levels in older children, may reflect the weaning process (Katzenberg, 1991; Tuross and Fogel, 1994; White and Schwarcz, 1994; Katzenberg and Pfeiffer, 1995).

Annie Katzenberg, a physical anthropologist at the University of Calgary, and her colleagues have examined the issue of infant weaning, sickness, and mortality from a variety of skeletal samples. In a small protohistoric (around the time of contact with Europeans) sample from southern Ontario, Katzenberg and colleagues found that both carbon and nitrogen isotope ratios varied with age. This variation reflected a change in dietary intake associated with breastfeeding and weaning (Katzenberg et al., 1993). However, we must remember that infants and children in skeletal samples may reflect health and nutritional

RESEARCH FRONTIERS

You Are What You Eat: Chemical Analyses of Bones and Teeth

Archaeologists study ancient diets in several ways, which are mostly indirect. They can infer indirectly some of what ancient people ate from recovered food wastes. For example, if you find a lot of corncobs, chances are that the people ate a lot of corn. Plant and animal foods can be identified in the charred remains of cooking fires and (when preserved) in the ancient people's feces. Such inferences are usually biased in favour of hard food sources such as seeds, nuts, and grains (which are likely to be preserved); rarely are the remains of soft plants such as bananas or tubers found. Archaeologists can also indirectly infer diet from the artifacts they find, particularly of course ones we can be pretty sure were used in obtaining or processing food. So, for example, if you find a stone with a flat or concave surface that looks similar to stones that some people use now in some places to grind corn, it is very likely that the ancient people also ground grain (or other hard things such as seeds) for food. However, plant remains or implements do not tell us *how much* people relied on particular sources of food.

There is a more direct way to study ancient diets. Anthropologists have discovered that in many ways "you are what you eat." In particular, chemical analyses of bones and teeth, the most common remains found in excavations, can reveal distinctive traces of the foods that metabolically went into the bones and teeth. One kind of informative chemical analysis involves the ratio of strontium to calcium in bone.

This analysis can indicate the relative amounts of plant and animal food in the diet. So, for example, we know from strontium analysis of bones that just before the beginnings of cereal agriculture in the Near East, people were eating a lot of plant food, probably wild cereals that were intensively collected. Then there was a temporary decline in such collecting, suggesting overexploitation of the wild resources, or at least their decreasing availability. The cultivation and domestication (modification) of cereals presumably solved this problem.

Carbon isotope ratios also can tell us what types of plants people were eating. Trees, shrubs, and temperate-zone grasses (for example, rice) have carbon isotope ratios that are different from those of tropical and subtropical grasses (such as millet and corn). People in China were relying heavily on cereals about 7000 to 8000 years ago, but the cereals were not the same in the north and south. Contrary to what we might expect, the carbon isotope ratios tell us that an originally temperate-zone cereal (rice) was the staple in subtropical southern China; in the more temperate north, an originally tropical or subtropical grass (millet) was most important. The dependence on millet in the north was enormous. It is estimated that 50 to 80 percent of the diet between 5000 and 500 B.C. came from millet.

In the Americas, seed crops such as sunflower, sumpweed, and goosefoot were domesticated in eastern North America long before corn, introduced from Mexico, became the staple. We know this partly from the archaeology; the remains of the early seed crops are older than the remains of corn. Corn, an originally subtropical plant, has a carbon isotope ratio that is different from the ratio for the earlier, temperate-zone seed crops. Thus, the shift in carbon isotope ratios after A.D. 800 to A.D. 900 tells us that corn had become the staple.

Traditionally, non-chemical analyses of human bones and teeth were used by physical anthropologists and archaeologists to study similarities and differences between peoples in different geographic regions, between living humans and possible fossil ancestors, and between living humans and other surviving primates. Much of the research involved surface measurements, particularly of the skull (outside and inside). In recent years, physical anthropologists and archaeologists have begun to study the "insides" of bones and teeth. The new kinds of chemical analysis mentioned here are part of that trend. In N. J. van der Merwe's pithy words: "The emphasis in studies of human evolution has shifted from a preoccupation with the brain to an equal interest in the stomach."

Sources: Larsen, CS. 1998. Bare Bones Anthropology: The Bioarchaeology of Human Remains. In: Ember CR, Ember M, Peregrine PN, editors. Research Frontiers in Anthropology. Upper Saddle River, NJ: Prentice Hall. Prentice Hall/Simon & Schuster Custom Publishing.

Van der Merwe NJ. 1992. Reconstructing Prehistoric Diet. In: Jones S, Martin R, Pilbeam D, editors. The Cambridge Encyclopedia of Human Evolution. New York: Cambridge University Press. p 369–372.

problems that prevented survival. As such, very young newborns might not have had the opportunity to nurse if very ill. Katzenberg analyzed skeletal samples of European descent from historic cemeteries. She found no difference in stable nitrogen ratios between newborns and adults, in contrast to very high levels among the infants and young children (Katzenberg, 1991).

In their analysis of the skeletal remains of 64 individuals from a historic Methodist cemetery in Newmarket, Ontario, Katzenberg and Pfeiffer observed that nitrogen isotope ratios rose rapidly from birth to about 1 year of age, after which they declined to adult levels by about 2 years of age (Katzenberg and Pfeiffer, 1995). In their study of infant mortality in a nineteenth-century pioneer cemetery in Belleville, Ontario, Ann Herring and colleagues suggested that the introduction of other food sources in relatively poor living conditions resulted in increased infant mortality by 5 months of age, even though breast milk remained a major component of infant nutrition until just over a year of age (Herring et al., 1998). It may be that the introduction of other foods in environments that were relatively unsanitary may have impacted on infant mortality and morbidity patterns, not nutritional decline associated with the weaning process itself (Katzenberg et al., 1996; Schurr, 1997; Herring et al., 1998).

Trace element analyses have also been used in reconstructing the diet of past populations. These studies have focused on identifying levels of calcium, strontium, and barium in bones. The pattern of absorption of strontium into the skeleton is opposite to the absorption pattern for nitrogen isotope ratios—instead of increasing from plant to herbivore to carnivore, it decreases. This means that amounts of calcium and strontium in skeletal remains can be analyzed for reconstructing prehistoric diets in animals and hominids (Katzenberg, 1984). Herbivores have the highest levels of strontium in their skeletons, while carnivores have the lowest; and omnivores fall somewhere in between (Sandford and Weaver, 2000). Calculating the ratio of strontium and calcium (Sr/Ca) in infant skeletons has also been a method for detecting the beginning of the weaning process. This approach was based on the assumption that supplemental foods in the early weaning stage in past populations were cereals that were enriched in strontium. Because the infant digestive system is less able to discriminate against strontium, infant bones absorb more than you would expect, and researchers need to take this into consideration. In addition, issues of **diagenesis**—the artificial uptake of trace elements from the burial environment—produce additional methodological problems to this approach. As a result, current studies now rely on the analysis of stable isotopes for understanding infant feeding practices.

Reconstructing Past Environments

Archaeological reconstructions of past environmental conditions are derived from the analysis of soils, sediments, and remains of former life forms. These life forms include pollen, plant macrofossil remains of all kinds, invertebrates (including parasitic nematodes, insects and other arthropods, and molluscs), and vertebrates (Reitz et al., 1996; Evans and O'Connor, 1999; Dincauze, 2000). Researchers can make inferences about environmental conditions through time and in different locations based on changes in the relative abundance of these life forms. Once researchers reconstruct the past environmental conditions, they can then address whether there are observable changes in the human populations living in the region that might be a function of the shifting environmental conditions.

Environmental Archaeology

Environmental archaeology is distinct from *palaeoecology*. Palaeoecology identifies and explains past ecological phenomena like changes in forest growth or the numbers of types of organisms living in a given location. Environmental archaeology is interested specifically in ecological and climatic conditions of the past as a means for better understanding how various peoples lived—what conditions they lived in and how those conditions affected their lives. While the ultimate goals of these two disciplines are somewhat different, their research tools are similar.

Environmental archaeology employs a number of methods to assess both general and specific ecological conditions in the past. This evidence can be divided into two broad classes: *biotic evidence*, which represents the remains of biological organisms from the past, and *abiotic evidence* or the remains of chemical components of sediments and their associated landforms. Biotic evidence includes the fossilized remains of bones, shells, seeds, and pollen. Abiotic evidence includes geological structures and the associated processes, soil sediments, and their chemical makeup.

Another source of evidence is **palynology**— the study of pollen from different periods. Pollen can be preserved within sediments and in water-saturated conditions. The relative abundance of different plant species can be inferred from the relative abundance of pollen grains. This will give some indication of vegetative conditions within a given region. If the materials are recovered in a dated stratigraphic context, the analyst can document regional vegetation change over time. Since certain kinds of plants thrive under specific climatic conditions, palynology can offer indirect evidence of the general environmental conditions that existed in the past. Like pollen, phytoliths can also be collected from the soil, artifacts, and human teeth, and analyzed to identify plant species.

Another source of evidence for reconstructing past climatic conditions at a global scale is measuring the ratio of oxygen isotopes. Sea water naturally contains both ^{18}O and the lighter ^{16}O. The lighter ^{16}O evaporates first, and when this water vapour falls as snow, some remains "locked up" as glacial ice in northern latitudes. Thus, the relative abundance of ^{18}O goes up. During warmer periods less precipitation falls as snow and glacial meltwater returns to the oceans, thereby reducing the relative abundance of ^{18}O. Past isotopic concentrations in sea water cannot be measured directly. Scientists use the fossilized remains of a small marine organism called *foraminifera* to measure these concentrations.

Foraminifera absorb oxygen into its skeletal system, and its fossilized remains can be used as a proxy for broad changes in global temperatures.

At McMaster University, Henry Schwarcz is supervising research on beaver teeth to test seasonal changes in the ratio of ^{18}O to ^{16}O precipitation. Fricke and co-workers traced changes over time in oxygen isotope ratios in the tooth enamel of Inuit and European populations in western Greenland and Denmark (Fricke et al., 1995). The results were consistent with an increasing cool trend in the North Atlantic region from A.D. 1400 to A.D. 1700. This may corroborate the theory that the abandonment of the Viking Greenland settlement was due to environmental stress (Scott et al., 1991; Buckland et al., 1996).

Reconstructing Settlement Patterns

Settlement archaeology is concerned with two aspects of human occupation: the distribution of sites across a landscape and the relationship of structures within a community.

We can learn a great deal about a past society from the distribution of archaeological sites, and the relationship of these sites to their surrounding physical environments. The size, organization, and location of buildings and other structures within a community reflect the social and political structure of the community. Recognizing this, archaeologists undertake the analysis of settlement patterns to make inferences about past cultures.

Settlement data can tell us about such things as family organization and who performs certain tasks within a household. They can help us to understand the economy of a social group, what resources are important to them, and whether or not people moved during different seasons. They may also reveal clues regarding the different levels of social status, and perhaps even political or religious views within a community. By examining changes over time in the relationship between communities, and structures within communities, a researcher can gain considerable insight about the socio-cultural evolution of a society. For example, Brian Hayden analyzed a series of winter houses at Keatley Creek (about 20 kilometres north of Lillooet on terraces of the Fraser River) in British Columbia. The earliest occupation of the site was around 4800 B.P. (before present era) Hayden's analysis revealed that there was socio-economic variation in wealth between houses between 2400 and 1200 B.P. As well, he found possible evidence for long-term regional resource control by key families (Hayden, 1997). In this instance there was one village that contained some huge pit houses that stand out in sharp contrast from other villages in the region. The question is, why do we see these pit houses developing here at this particular time? Hayden argues that powerful families emerged because they were in a position to strategically control important resources. This in turn led to complex social alliances involving many families. As a result, the Keatley Creek sites provide a model for understanding the transition from small kin-based political systems based on family relationships—as we see in hunter-gatherer groups—to larger, more complex political units under the leadership of powerful chiefs.

Settlement archaeology is also interested in the distribution of sites and communities across the landscape as well as human changes to the landscape (for a discussion of landscape archaeology, see Chapter 14). Cultural ecology has become a central concept in settlement archaeology, and it is based on the notion that settlement distribution patterns are strongly related to local and regional changes in economic, environmental, social, subsistence, and technological factors (Fagan, 2000). As an example, annual flooding of river systems might influence the distribution of dwellings or dwelling types within a community situated along a river shore.

A tool that has recently emerged is **Geographic Information Systems (GIS)** analysis (Allen et al., 1990; Wheatley and Gillings, 2002). Stewart and colleagues have recently combined archaeological evidence of seasonal site occupation and oral histories regarding caribou crossings, camps, and other places of cultural significance to interpret recent Inuit land use along the lower Kazan River, Nunavut. These researchers employed Geographic Positioning System (GPS) technology to record individual archaeological features (for example, tent rings, caches) at sites throughout the area. The

Understanding the relationship within and between dwellings is a major component of settlement archaeology.

resulting GIS database showed considerable variation in regional land use including the types of sites observed and season of occupation (Stewart et al., 2000). GIS techniques can also help us to integrate complex data from a variety of sources. Using a GIS analysis of multiple surface and subsurface surveying techniques, Haskel Greenfield demonstrated distinct but complementary patterns of subsurface conditions at the stratigraphically complex Neolithic site of Blagotin in Serbia (Greenfield, 2000).

Archaeological evidence can also shed light on issues of population size and composition (the number of men and women of different ages) in the distant past. Researchers can estimate population size and rates of growth—how fast a population is increasing in size—from settlement data. The size and area of the living site, and how many dwellings are present can help the archaeologist to assess how many people were living in an area. As well, the distribution of artifacts and food remains can also help the archaeologist to refine estimates. For example, the archaeologist can tell the difference between a large dwelling of a single family versus a dwelling housing many families. Finally, ethnohistoric data of population size from recent populations living under similar conditions can serve as models for our estimates from the archaeological record.

However, even when data are available, estimates of population size must often be made through ethnographic analogy. This is a method where the relationship between population size and material remains seen in modern or historic groups is imposed on the archaeological site. One of the major questions that archaeologists have been interested in for many New World (North, South, and Central America) populations is demographic collapse—the drastic decline in population size. What factors led to the demise of entire populations? Can archaeology help us to understand the series of events associated with population collapse, such as that which affected the Maya?

Population collapse has been explored through analyses of *carrying capacity* and *site catchment area*. **Carrying capacity** is the estimated population number and density that a given area of land can support, given the technology used by the people at the time. However, because prehistoric resource patterns are difficult to determine, most studies have focused their efforts on the types and availability of raw resources, and the impact on population structure of changes in resources (Fagan, 2000). **Site catchment analysis** is based on the simple assumption that the more dispersed resources are from habitation sites, the less likely they are to be exploited by a population (Bailey, 1981). Of course, the technology, workforce size, and political organization of a population will have an impact on determining the relative "costs" associated with resource exploitation. For example, the benefits of acquiring labour-intensive resources for a large population may outweigh the costs, relative to a small population that would have to invest a greater proportion of their group's labour to acquire a smaller amount of material.

Alternative approaches to examining the relationship between resource availability and population structure have also been explored. Based on dietary trends from palaeopathological and stable isotope analysis, Lori Wright and Christine White have argued that there is no evidence to link reduced food resources with the demographic collapse of the Maya civilization (Wright and White, 1996). In addition, Katherine Emery and colleagues used stable isotopes to analyze the diet of deer, a common agricultural pest in ancient Mesoamerica, to suggest that ecological decline was not a factor associated with the collapse of the Mayan empire (Emery et al., 2000).

Reconstructing Social Systems

Reconstructing aspects of social systems from the archaeological record is possible by understanding the social context in which material culture accumulates. In addition, the items produced by past peoples can provide information about their social systems. For example, the manufacture of clay pots might include stylistic variations associated with the producer or the producer's family.

Jewellery and other items of personal adornment can reflect aspects of self-identity and views of the world. The kinds of foods being consumed may also reflect broad class differences between groups within a society.

One of the major areas of archaeology concerning social status is burials. Human burials and burial practices are an important source of both biological and cultural information for the anthropologist. At the most extravagant, high-status burials like the tombs of Pharaohs from ancient Egypt or a Chinese emperor buried with an army of life-sized ceramic soldiers capture the imagination of the public. Burials can reveal information about social status, as well as trade, religion, and economics. As well, burials and mortuary practices reflect the attitudes, values, symbolism, status, and other beliefs held by prehistoric peoples (Noble, 1968). **Funerary archaeology**—the study of burials—can reveal information regarding social status, trade networks, population structure, and social organization within the society. Lewis Binford proposed that increased social complexity resulted in increased variation in burial practices, and that social organization (not necessarily ritual practices or religion) was the primary cause of such variation (Binford, 1972). Based on this notion, the more differences in the manner in which individuals were buried (including the type or number of any goods in the grave), the more socially complex and stratified a society was. By following the changing trends in mortuary customs, archaeologists may better understand the changing relationships between various peoples, as well as the changes associated with the influence of native and foreign cultures through time.

Christine White is a physical anthropologist at the University of Western Ontario who specializes in stable isotope analysis. Much of her research has focused on Mayan sites in Mesoamerica, and includes dietary reconstruction, migration, and social status. Using carbon isotope analyses of human skeletal remains, White has observed differences in the consumption of maize between high-status and low-status individuals. However, these differences are not always consistent. In Belize at the site of Pacbitun the presence of maize in the diet was associated with high-status individuals, while at the site of Lamanai maize was associated more with the diet of low-status individuals. White has argued that this difference suggests that high-status individuals from Lamanai may have better diets and greater access to protein than their counterparts at Pacbitun (White and Schwarcz, 1989; White et al., 1993). At other Mayan sites like Copan in present-day Honduras, no differences in stable isotope ratios in bones have been detected between different classes (Reed, 1994).

Trading Patterns

Most prehistoric populations also engaged in some sort of long-distance trade. This can be inferred by the location of raw materials relative to the location of the produced artifact. Trade can also be inferred by observing the physical composition of the material and whether it was made locally or not. Other times more precise chemical techniques are required to determine the precise composition of an item. Regardless, trade is an important part of *cultural diffusion*. Lowie believed that any given cultural trait is derived either from a *cultural antecedent* within the culture or through importing ideas from other foreign populations (Lowie, 1988). The latter process, cultural diffusion (see below), has been and continues to be a major area of investigation in the attempt to explain cultural change.

Cultural Change

The sources of all culture change are discoveries and inventions, which may originate inside or outside a society. However, they do not necessarily lead to social change. If an invention or discovery is ignored, no change in culture results. It is only when society accepts an invention or discovery and uses it regularly that we can begin to speak of culture change.

Discovery and Invention

The new thing discovered or invented, the *innovation*, may be an object—the wheel, the plow, the computer—or it may involve behaviour and ideas—buying and selling, democracy, monogamy.

One type of invention can be the consequence of a society's setting itself a specific goal, such as eliminating a specific disease or finding a way to preserve a food. Another type emerges less intentionally. This second process of invention is often referred to as *accidental juxtaposition* or *unconscious invention*. Ralph Linton suggested that some inventions, especially those of prehistoric days, were probably the consequences of literally dozens of tiny initiatives by "unconscious" inventors. These inventors made their small contributions, perhaps over many hundreds of years, without being aware of the part they were playing in bringing one invention, such as the wheel or a better form of hand axe, to completion (Linton, 1936). Consider the example of children playing on a fallen log, which rolls as they walk and balance on it, coupled with the need at a given moment to move a slab of granite from a cave face. The children's play may have suggested the use of logs as rollers and thereby set in motion a series of developments that culminated in the wheel.

Some discoveries and inventions arise out of deliberate attempts to produce a new idea or object. It may seem that such innovations are obvious responses to perceived needs. Nevertheless, perceived needs and the economic rewards that may be given to the innovator do not explain why only some people innovate. We know relatively little about why some people are more innovative than others. The ability to innovate may depend in part on individual characteristics such as high intelligence and creativity. And creativity may be influenced by social conditions.

Types of Cultural Diffusion

The source of new cultural elements in a society may be another society. The process by which cultural elements are borrowed from another society and incorporated into the culture of the recipient group is called **diffusion**. Borrowing sometimes enables a group to bypass stages or mistakes in the development of a process or institution. There are three basic patterns of diffusion:

direct contact, intermediate contact, and *stimulus diffusion.*

Direct contact occurs when elements of a society's culture are first taken up by neighbouring societies and then gradually spread farther and farther afield. The spread of the use of paper (a sheet of interlaced fibres) is a good example of extensive diffusion by direct contact. The invention of paper is attributed to the Chinese Ts'ai Lun in A.D. 105. Within 50 years, paper was being made in many places in central China. While the art of papermaking was kept secret for about 500 years, paper was distributed as a commodity to much of the Arab world through the markets at Samarkand. But when Samarkand was attacked by the Chinese in A.D. 751, a Chinese prisoner was forced to set up a paper mill. Paper manufacture then spread to the rest of the Arab world; it was first manufactured in Baghdad in A.D. 793, Egypt about A.D. 900, and Morocco about A.D. 1100. Papermaking was introduced as a commodity in Europe by Arab trade through Italian ports in the twelfth century. The Moors built the first European paper mill in Spain about 1150. The technical knowledge then spread throughout Europe with paper mills being built in Italy in 1276, France in 1348, Germany in 1390, and England in 1494 (Anonymous, 1980; Anonymous, 1998). In general, the pattern of accepting the borrowed invention was the same in all cases. Paper was first imported as a luxury, then in ever-expanding quantities as a staple product. Finally, and usually within one to three centuries, local manufacture was begun.

Diffusion by *intermediate contact* occurs through the agency of third parties. Frequently, traders carry a cultural trait from the society, where it originated, to another group. As an example of diffusion through intermediaries, Phoenician traders spread the idea of our alphabet, which may have been invented by another Semitic group, to Greece. At times, soldiers serve as intermediaries in spreading a cultural trait. European crusaders, such as the Knights Templar and the Knights of St. John, acted as intermediaries in two ways: they carried Christian culture to Muslim societies of North Africa and brought Arab culture back to Europe. In the nineteenth century, Western missionaries in all parts of the world encouraged indigenous peoples to wear Western clothing. The result is that in Africa, the Pacific Islands, and elsewhere, all peoples can be found wearing shorts, suit jackets, shirts, ties, and other typically Western articles of clothing.

In *stimulus diffusion*, knowledge of a trait belonging to another culture stimulates the invention or development of a local equivalent. A classic example of stimulus diffusion is the Cherokee syllabic writing system created by Sequoya, a Cherokee, so that his people could write down their language. Sequoya got the idea from his contact with Europeans. Yet he did not adopt the English writing system; indeed, he did not even learn to write English. What he did was use some English alphabetic symbols, alter others, and invent new ones. All the symbols he used represented Cherokee syllables and in no way echoed English alphabetic usage. In other words, Sequoya took English alphabetic ideas and gave them a new, Cherokee form. The stimulus originated with Europeans; the result was peculiarly Cherokee.

The Selective Nature of Diffusion

Although there is a temptation to view the dynamics of diffusion as similar to a stone sending concentric ripples over still water, this view would be an oversimplification of the way diffusion actually occurs. Not all cultural traits are borrowed as readily as the ones we have mentioned, nor do they usually expand in neat, ever-widening circles. Rather, diffusion is a selective process.

We would expect societies to reject items from other societies that are repugnant to them and we would also expect them to reject ideas and technology that do not satisfy some psychological, social, or cultural need. Diffusion is also selective because cultural traits differ in the extent to which they can be communicated. Elements of material culture, such as mechanical processes and techniques, and other traits, such as physical sports and the like, are not especially difficult to demonstrate. Consequently, they are accepted or rejected on their merits. But the moment we move out of the material context into the realm of ideas, we encounter real difficulties. For

instance, how do you communicate the complex idea of democracy?

Finally, diffusion is selective because the overt form of a particular trait, rather than its function or meaning, frequently seems to determine how the trait will be received. For example, the enthusiasm for bobbed hair (short haircuts) that swept through much of North America in the 1920s never caught on among the First Nations women of northwestern California. To many women of European ancestry, short hair was a symbolic statement of their freedom. To these First Nations women, who traditionally cut their hair short when in mourning, it was a reminder of death (Foster, 1962).

In the process of diffusion, then, we can identify a number of different patterns. Cultural borrowing is selective rather than automatic, and we can describe how a particular borrowed trait has been modified by the recipient culture. However, current knowledge does not allow us to specify when one or another of these outcomes will occur, under what conditions diffusion will occur, and why it occurs the way it does.

Acculturation

On the surface, the process of change called *acculturation* seems to include much of what we have discussed under the label of diffusion, since acculturation refers to the changes that occur when different cultural groups come into intensive contact. As in diffusion, the source of new cultural items is the other society. More often than not though, the term **acculturation** describes a situation in which one of the societies in contact is much more powerful than the other. Thus, acculturation can be seen as a process of extensive cultural borrowing in the context of an unequal power relationship between societies (Bodley, 1990).

External pressure for cultural change can take various forms. In its most direct form—conquest or colonialization—the dominant group uses force or the threat of force to bring about cultural change in the other group. For example, in the Spanish conquest of Mexico, the conquerors forced many of the native groups to accept Roman Catholicism. Although such direct force is not always exerted in conquest situations, dominated peoples often have little choice but to change. Examples of such indirectly forced change abound in the history of Aboriginal peoples in Canada. A strong European missionary movement led to many Aboriginal communities being forced to adopt non-religious aspects of Euro-Canadian culture. After Confederation, the federal government displaced many native populations from their lands, and obliged them to give up many aspects of their traditional ways of life, language, and cultures. Aboriginal children were required to go to residential schools, which taught the dominant society's values. In most cases these attempts at assimilation and acculturation were a misplaced attempt at "improving" the lives of Aboriginal people. In order to survive, they had no choice but to adopt many of the dominant society's traits.

A subordinate society may acculturate to a dominant society even in the absence of direct or indirect force. The dominated people may elect to adopt cultural elements from the dominant society in order to survive in their changed world. Or, perceiving that members of the dominant society enjoy more secure living conditions, the dominated people may identify with the dominant culture in the hope that by doing so they will be able to share some of its benefits. For example, in Arctic areas many Inuit and Lapp groups seemed eager to replace dogsleds with snowmobiles without any coercion (Pelto and Miller-Wille, 1987).

In the following chapters, we will see how the interpretation and reconstruction techniques outlined in this chapter have been applied to tracing the evolution of humans.

Summary

1. Interpretation of the archaeological record is based on a variety of related disciplines that provide data to help reconstruct ecological conditions (environmental archaeology), diet (palaeonutrition), disease load (palaeopathology), settlement patterns, socio-economic status, resource distribution, and allocation (political ecology).

2. Osteology or skeletal biology is the specialized subdiscipline of physical anthropology that deals with the biological remains of humans from past populations.

3. The study of palaeopathology seeks to answer questions about the appearance, prevalence, and spread of diseases in past populations from human skeletal remains.

4. Palaeodemography is the study of demographic structure and population processes in the past.

5. What people ate can be explored from a variety of sources including zooarchaeology (the study of animal remains), experimental archaeology, palaeoethnobotany (the study of plant remains), coprolites, stable isotopes, and trace elements.

6. Environmental archaeology reconstructs ecological and climatic conditions of the past as a means for better understanding people in the past and how environmental conditions affected their lives.

7. Settlement archaeology is concerned with the distribution of sites across a landscape and relationship of structures within a community.

8. Reconstructing the culture of past peoples from the archaeological record is possible by understanding the social context in which material culture accumulates.

9. Culture is always changing. Discoveries and inventions are a major source of cultural change. The process by which cultural elements are borrowed from one society and incorporated into another is called diffusion. However, diffusion is a selective process, and does not occur automatically.

Glossary Terms

acculturation   (p. 67)

ancient DNA (aDNA)   (p. 49)

carrying capacity   (p. 64)

conservation   (p. 44)

coprolites   (p. 58)

diagenesis   (p. 61)

differential diagnosis   (p. 51)

diffusion   (p. 66)

DNA (deoxyribonucleic acid)   (p. 49)

environmental archaeology   (p. 61)

ethnographic analogy   (p. 53)

experimental archaeology   (p. 56)

funerary archaeology   (p. 65)

Geographic Information Systems (GIS)   (p. 63)

life table   (p. 53)

molecular anthropology   (p. 56)

osteology   (p. 46)

palaeodemography   (p. 53)

palaeoethnobotany   (p. 57)

palaeopathology   (p. 50)

palynology   (p. 62)

polymerase chain reaction (PCR)   (p. 49)

remodelling   (p. 47)

sedentism   (p. 55)

settlement archaeology   (p. 62)

sexually dimorphic   (p. 48)

site catchment analysis   (p. 64)

skeletal age-indicator techniques   (p. 47)

stable isotopes   (p. 59)

stationary   (p. 53)

trace elements   (p. 59)

typology   (p. 45).

zooarchaeology   (p. 55)

Critical Questions

1. How do you think that cultural views of the past affect archaeological research in different societies?

2. Anthropology is a holistic science, yet research is becoming increasingly specialized. How do you think this affects the way in which anthropologists are trained to do research?

3. For various levels of interpretation, different assumptions are made by anthropologists. What are these assumptions, and why do you think they are valid or not valid?

Internet Exercises

1. Take a virtual tour of the Smithsonian exhibit "Osteology: Hall of Bones" at **www.mnh.si .edu/museum/VirtualTour/Tour/Second/ Bones** and prepare a short report on your visit.

2. Learn about the early days of genetics research at the now-famous Cold Spring Harbor Laboratory (**www.cshl.org/History/100years- prologue.html**). Compare the Cold Spring Harbor educational model with that at your institution.

3. "DNA from the Beginning," an excellent site containing a wealth of information on DNA, can be found at **http://vector.cshl.org/dnaftb/**. Prepare a list of what are in your view the major milestones in DNA research.

Suggested Reading

Chamberlain AC. 1994. Human Remains: Interpreting the Past. University of California Press. A very brief introduction to the analysis and interpretation of skeletal remains.

Fagan B. 2004. In the Beginning. Upper Saddle River, NJ: Prentice Hall. A very thorough introduction to archaeological methods and interpretation.

Katzenberg MA, SR Saunders, editors. 2000. Biological Anthropology of the Human Skeleton. New York, NY: John Wiley & Sons, Inc. A detailed overview of a variety of specialized areas of skeletal biology, including palaedemography, stable isotopes, trace elements, ancient DNA, and ethics in osteological studies.

Larsen CS. 1999. Bioarchaeology: Interpreting Behavior from the Human Skeleton. Cambridge University Press. A thorough synthesis of the many facets of reconstructing the past from the study of human skeletal remains from archaeological samples.

Roberts C, Manchester K. 1997. Archaeology of Disease. Cornell University Press. An overview of the field of palaeopathology and how it can contribute to our understanding of health and disease in the past.

HISTORICAL DEVELOPMENT OF EVOLUTIONARY THEORY

4

Astronomers estimate that the universe has been in existence for some 15 billion years, plus or minus a few billion. To make this awesome period of time more understandable, Carl Sagan devised a calendar that condenses this span into a single year (Sagan, 1975). Sagan used as a scale 24 days for every 1 billion years and 1 second for every 475 years. This meant that if the "Big Bang" or beginning of the universe occurred on January 1, for example, the Milky Way was formed on May 1.

Galaxies began to form as the universe cooled. By 4.5 billion years ago, our sun was formed, and the earth took shape shortly after that. Around 4 billion years ago, organic molecules existed on earth in the form of amino acids. Shortly thereafter, around 3.6 billion years ago, evidence for the first signs of life—bacteria-like organisms—is observable in the fossil record (Lopuchin, 1975; Mojzsis et al., 1996; Schopf, 2000). In Sagan's scheme, September 9 marks the beginning of our solar system, and September 25 the origin of life on earth.

It was originally assumed that life had evolved in situ on earth—the idea that life emerged from a primordial soup. However, the appearance of bacteria nearly 4 billion years ago creates a problem for this theory. It does not allow enough time between the formation of the earth and the first signs of life for the evolution of these first organisms. As a result, alternative theories have begun to emerge. One of these is that space provided the crucial chemical ingredients for life, and that bacteria from interstellar dust or even Mars was delivered to earth by way of asteroids and meteorites. This theory received heightened attention in 1996 with the announcement by NASA scientists that they had found possible evidence for fossil bacteria on Mars (see Figure 4–1).

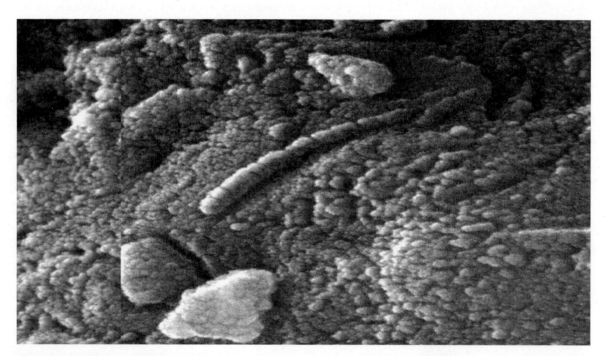

Figure 4–1 Life from Mars

This high-resolution scanning electron microscope image shows an unusual tube-like form that in size is less than 1/100th the width of a human hair. It was found in a 4.5-billion-year-old rock believed to have once been a part of Mars. This structure is suggested to be fossil evidence that primitive life may have existed on Mars more than 3.6 billion years ago. The rock is a portion of a meteorite that was dislodged from Mars by a huge impact about 16 million years ago and that fell to earth in Antarctica 13 000 years ago. The meteorite was found in Allan Hills icefield, Antarctica, by an annual expedition of the National Science Foundation's Antarctic Meteorite Program in 1984.

Source: SETI League photograph—used by permission, **www.setileague.org**.

Regardless of the origin of bacteria on earth, these early single-celled organisms photosynthesized, that is, they were able to make nutrients from water, sunlight, and carbon dioxide, a process from which oxygen is a by-product. As a result, by about 1.8 billion years ago an oxygen-rich atmosphere existed on earth, and soon afterward oxygen-using organisms evolved (Fortey, 1999; Fry, 2000). Around 1.7 billion years ago the first multicellular organisms appeared. At 1 billion years ago, organisms appeared that employed sexual reproduction strategies, that is, combining the genetic material from two parents. This is a key facet for the evolution of life, since for the first time natural selection had greater variation on which to act.

By 570 million years ago at the beginning of the Cambrian period, a variety of complex organisms existed on the earth, starting with worms and jellyfish and later hard-shelled organisms. Sixty million years later the first organisms with internal skeletal structure evolved (*vertebrates*) and around 425 million years ago, plants and insects evolved on land and fish in the sea (Fortey, 1999; Fry, 2000). By 350 million years ago the first reptiles had emerged. By about 150 million years ago there was a proliferation of three major vertebrate groups: fish, amphibians, and reptiles. Reptiles showed evolutionary changes when compared with their amphibian ancestors, including the development of amniotic eggs for reproduction. This reflects a major **adaptation** (traits that increase the chances of survival to leave offspring that will survive) to terrestrial life (Fortey, 1999; Fry, 2000). Soon mammal-like reptiles appeared and eventually we see the rise of mammals around 65 million years ago.

Mammals have a number of advantages over reptiles. They are warm-blooded, allowing them to live in a wider range of environments, have increased intelligence compared with reptiles, and have placental reproduction and an extended postpartum developmental period, both of which allow for increased brain development (Fortey, 1999; Fry, 2000). With the extinction of many reptiles around 65 million years ago, mammals had a variety of new evolutionary niches in which

to adapt. The result was the rapid diversification, expansion, and proliferation of mammals into new and relatively unoccupied habitats.

Some 55 million to 65 million years ago, the first primates appeared. They were ancestral to all living primates, such as lemurs, monkeys, apes, and humans. The earliest primates may or may not have lived in trees, but they had flexible digits and could grasp things. Later, about 35 million years ago, the first monkeys and apes appeared. About 15 million years ago, some 20 million years after the appearance of monkeys and apes, the immediate apelike ancestors of humans probably emerged. About 4 million years ago the first human-like beings appeared. Modern-looking humans evolved only about 100 000 years ago.

Using Sagan's scheme it was 10:30 in the evening of December 31 when the first human-like primates appear. Human-like beings have been around for only about 90 minutes out of Sagan's 12-month period! In this book we are concerned with what happened in those last few hours of that year.

How do we account for the biological and cultural evolution of humans? The details of the emergence of primates and the evolution of humans and their cultures are covered in subsequent chapters of this book. In this chapter we discuss the general evolution of life, and the historical development of ideas for understanding these changes, especially as relevant to humans. In Chapter 5 we will discuss more specifically the modern theory of evolution.

The Evolution of Evolution

Views from Biology

In the nineteenth century, Western ideas about forms of life on earth were very different from **Charles Darwin**'s *theory of evolution*, which suggested that different species developed one from another over long periods of time. In the fourth century B.C., the Greek philosophers Plato and Aristotle stated that animals and plants formed a single, graded continuum moving increasingly toward perfection. For Plato, who was a student and follower of Socrates, variation in animals had no meaning—only the essence of an organism mattered. Aristotle was trained first in medicine before he was sent to Athens in 367 B.C. to study philosophy with Plato. Aristotle's classification of animals grouped those with similar characters into *genera* and then distinguished subgroups of *species* within the genera. Humans, of course, were the species at the top of this scale.

Later Greek philosophers added the idea that the creator gave life or "radiance" first to humans, but at each subsequent creation some of that essence was lost (Lovejoy, 1964). Macrobius, summarizing the thinking of Plotinus, used an image that was to persist for centuries, the image of what came to be called the "chain of being":

> The attentive observer will discover a connection of parts, from the Supreme God down to the last dregs of things, mutually linked together and without a break. This is Homer's golden chain, which God, he says, bade hand down from heaven to earth (Lovejoy, 1964).

Belief in the chain of being was accompanied by the conviction that an animal or plant species could not become extinct. In fact, all things were linked to each other in a chain, and all links were necessary. Moreover, the notion of extinction threatened people's trust in a supreme being; it was unthinkable that a whole group of these creations could simply disappear.

The idea of the chain of being persisted through the years, but it was not discussed extensively by philosophers, scientists, poets, and theologians until the eighteenth century (Lovejoy, 1964). Those discussions prepared the way for *evolutionary theory*. It is ironic that, although the chain of being did not allow for evolution, its idea that there was an order of things in nature encouraged studies of natural history and comparative anatomical studies, which stimulated the development of the idea of evolution. People were also now motivated to look for previously unknown creatures. Moreover, humans were not shocked when naturalists suggested that humans were close to apes. This notion was perfectly consistent with the idea of a chain of being; apes were simply thought to have been created with less perfection.

Early in the eighteenth century, an influential scientist, **Carolus Linnaeus** (1707–78), looked at the similarities and differences among organisms and created a system that is still in use today for naming, ranking, and classifying organisms. This system defined the fundamentals of biology in terms of nomenclature and classification, from *kingdom* to *class*, *order*, **genus**, and *species*. Part of Linnaeus's innovation was the grouping of genera into higher groups or *taxa* that were also based on shared similarities. Thus, the kingdom Animalia contained the class Vertebrata, which in turn contained the order Primates. This order was further divided into genus and species, so that Primates contained the genus *Homo* with the species *sapiens*—or modern humans. The Linnaean classification scheme is hierarchical and categories are based on inclusive traits—those at the top (kingdom) being the most inclusive, and those at the bottom (species) the least inclusive. Each category contains groups of related organisms that share common traits. Linnaeus's classification or *systema naturae* placed humans in the same order (Primates) as apes and monkeys. Linnaeus did not suggest an evolutionary relationship between humans and apes; he seems to have accepted the notion that all species were created by God and fixed in their form. Not surprisingly, then, Linnaeus is often viewed as an anti-evolutionist. However, Linnaeus's hierarchical classification scheme provided a framework for the idea that humans, apes, and monkeys had a common ancestor (Eiseley, 1970; Mayr, 1982). (See Figure 4–2.)

Others did not believe that species were fixed in their form. According to the French naturalist **Jean Baptiste Lamarck** (1744–1829), acquired characteristics could be inherited and therefore species could evolve; individuals who in their lifetime developed characteristics helpful to survival would pass those characteristics on to future generations, thereby changing the physical makeup of the species, a process that became known as the theory of **acquired inheritance**. He argued that the lower

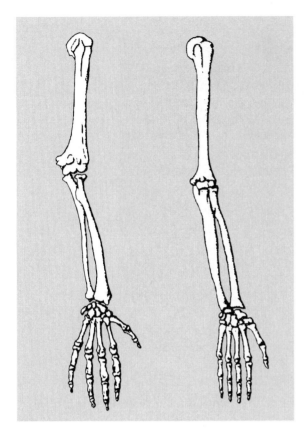

Figure 4–2

The idea that chimpanzees and humans descend from a common ancestor is suggested by anatomical similarities, such as in their forelimbs. Chimpanzee forelimb skeleton (left); human forelimb skeleton (right).

Lamarck was the first uncompromising advocate of a theory of evolution, and one of the first to try to provide a mechanism to explain this process. Lamarck also argued that evolution was progressive. Because Lamarck and later biologists failed to produce evidence to support the hypothesis that acquired characteristics can be inherited, this explanation of evolution is now generally dismissed (Mayr, 1982). One should note, however, that while the mechanism proposed by Lamarck is different from Charles Darwin's theory of evolution (see below), the predictions are the same.

Views from Geology

One of the major components in the development of the whole idea of evolution was an understanding of how old the earth actually was. For most people in Western societies this understanding came from direct interpretation of the Bible, which made the earth relatively young. One of the earliest Western attempts at quantifying the earth's age was undertaken by Archbishop James Ussher, an Irish cleric who in 1650, referring to biblical events, calculated that the world was created in 4004 B.C. His result was based on simple mathematics and a thorough historical analysis of the events as detailed in the Bible.

The study of natural sciences emerged in the period of the seventeenth through to the nineteenth centuries. Most natural scientists then believed that natural catastrophes such as floods, volcanic eruptions, and earthquakes accounted for the variety of layers of rock that they observed. **Catastrophism**, as the theory became known, argued that the world changed over time by a series of divine catastrophic events like Noah's flood.

By the nineteenth century, some thinkers were beginning to accept the theory of evolution, while others sought to refute it (Mayr, 1972). For example, Georges Cuvier (1769–1832) was a leading opponent of evolution. Cuvier, an anatomist who is considered one of the founders of the field of palaeontology, observed that different strata of sedimentary rock contained different kinds of fossils. He supported the notion that changes in the animal world could be attributed to catastrophes that had

forms of life arise continually from inanimate matter by spontaneous creation, and progress inevitably toward greater complexity and perfection by "powers conferred by the supreme author of all things"—that is, by an inherent tendency toward complexity (Jordanova, 1984; Bowler, 1989). This evolutionary progress was guided by changing environments that altered the needs of organisms. For example, Lamarck explained that the long neck of the giraffe was the result of successive generations of giraffes stretching their necks to reach the high leaves of trees. The stretched muscles and bones of the necks were somehow transmitted to the offspring of the neck-stretching giraffes, and eventually all giraffes came to have long necks.

The history of the earth and the plant and animal forms that evolved on it is often revealed to us by rock formations that become visible because of uplifting and erosion. The emergence of geology—the study of the earth's structure and history—stimulated evolutionary thinking.

destroyed whole populations of living things. Cuvier's theory of catastrophism proposed that a quick series of catastrophes accounted for changes in the earth and the fossil record. Cataclysms and upheavals such as Noah's flood had killed off previous sets of living creatures, which after each period of devastation were replaced by new creations.

Opponents to the catastrophist view slowly emerged, as geologists observed more slow-acting processes such as erosion by wind or water. They believed that these gradual processes, rather than natural catastrophes, accounted for changes over time. In the late seventeenth century, the Reverend Thomas Burnet believed the condition of the earth could be explained by the slow-acting processes of erosion by ice, wind, and water. Burnet still concluded that the earth was very young, arguing that if the earth were ancient, the process of erosion would have already worn away the greatest of mountains.

At the same time, a contemporary of Burnet, Robert Hooke, an English natural scientist, became interested in fossils. Up until this time, most natural scientists believed fossils were "tricks of nature." However, Hooke interpreted fossils as the remains of plants and animals that no longer existed, believing that these organisms became extinct as the earth changed. He thought that these changes included both catastrophes and slow-acting processes, but like Burnet, Hooke also thought the earth was very young because there was no historical record of fossilization in the ancient documents of China and Egypt. He did not realize, of course, how long the process of fossilization took.

In 1774, George Buffon (1707–88), a French natural scientist, published *A Natural History* in which he proposed the notion of **uniformitarianism**. This was the idea that repeated uniform processes, such as rivers cutting channels, wind, and rain eroding mountains, operated throughout time. Shortly after, James Hutton (1726–97), a Scottish geologist, published *The History of the Earth* in which he advanced the notion of studying the uniform, slow-acting processes of erosion to estimate the age of earth, and argued that using this measurement the earth was at least a few hundred thousand years old.

Major changes in geological thinking occurred in the nineteenth century. In contrast to Hutton's work, which was largely ignored, English geologist Sir Charles Lyell's (1797–1875) volumes of the *Principles of Geology,* published from 1830 to 1833, built on Hutton's earlier work and received immediate acclaim. The concept of uniformitarianism suggested that the earth is constantly being shaped and reshaped by natural forces that have operated over vast periods of time. By examining specific geological data, Lyell estimated the age of specific features of the earth, such as the Mississippi delta. Since the rate of silt deposition and the total size of the existing deposit at the delta could be measured or estimated, Lyell argued that the amount of time required for the delta to form could be calculated. Using this method of calculation, Lyell estimated the age of the delta to be 100 000 years (Lyell, 1863). Ultimately, Lyell was proven incorrect, but his thinking represented the first step toward an understanding of the real antiquity of the earth. Lyell also discussed the formation of geological strata and palaeontology. He used fossilized fauna to define different geological epochs. Lyell's works were read avidly by Charles Darwin before Darwin's now-famous voyage on the *Beagle.* The two corresponded and subsequently became friends.

Many people in Western society were shocked by the implications of the works of Hutton and Lyell. However, when a nineteenth-century Scottish theologian and mathematician, Thomas Chalmers (1780–1847), the first Moderator of the Free Church of Scotland, accepted the principle of uniformitarianism, other scientists soon followed suit. After studying changes in plants, fossilized remains of animals, and varieties of domestic and wild pigeons, Charles Darwin (1809–82) rejected the notion that each species was created in a fixed form all at one time in the history of earth. The results of his investigations pointed clearly, he thought, to the evolution of species through the mechanism of *natural selection.* While Darwin was completing his book on the subject, Lyell sent him a manuscript by Alfred Russel Wallace (1823–1913), a naturalist who had independently reached conclu-

sions about the evolution of species that matched Darwin's own (Wallace, 1858). In 1858, the two men presented the astonishing theory of natural selection to their colleagues at a meeting of the Linnaean Society of London (Mayr, 1982).

Both Darwin and Wallace observed that there was individual variation in appearance within a species. Lamarck's theory of acquired inheritance did not support such variation within a species since it predicted that eventually all organisms would adapt to the same form in the same environment. Expanding on Linnaeus's inference that similarities and differences among organisms represented biological relationships, they suggested that these relationships were the result of descent from previous similar organisms. Both Darwin and Wallace concluded that all species descended from other species.

In 1859, when Darwin published *The Origin of Species by Means of Natural Selection*, he wrote, "I am fully convinced that species are not immutable; but that those belonging to what are called the same genera are lineal descendants of some other and generally extinct species, in the same manner as the acknowledged varieties of any one species." His conclusions outraged those who believed in the biblical account of creation, and the result was years of bitter controversy.

The major contributions of Darwin's work were that evolution has no direction and that selection acts on existing variation. Populations of species in different environments may have different selective pressures. Therefore, if such pressures select certain traits over very long periods, the populations may become so distinct as to become separate species. The idea of **natural selection** was that nature selects from existing variation those species best adapted to their environment and which will therefore have the greatest chance of surviving and reproducing successfully.

In 1871 Darwin published *The Descent of Man and Selection in Relation to Sex,* in which he proposed that humanity was derived from an animal related to the progenitors of the orangutan, chimpanzee, and gorilla. In this work he also developed his important supplementary theory of

A nineteenth-century cartoon shows Charles Darwin with the body of a monkey while revealing the physical similarities between monkeys and humans.

of creation, saw an opportunity to attack the Darwinists. Concluding his speech, he faced Thomas Huxley, one of the Darwinists' chief advocates, and inquired, "Was it through his grandfather or his grandmother that he claimed descent from a monkey?" Huxley responded,

> If . . . the question is put to me would I rather have a miserable ape for a grandfather than a man highly endowed by nature and possessing great means and influence and yet who employs those faculties and that influence for the mere purpose of introducing ridicule into a grave scientific discussion—I unhesitatingly affirm my preference for the ape.

At the same time as a theory of evolution began to develop, scientists began to explore cultural theories to explain the evolution of "civilization." During the mid-nineteenth century, the discovery of stone tools prompted investigations into the origins of these items. In 1847 Jacques Boucher de Perthes published some of the earliest archaeological evidence for the association of human artifacts (chipped stone tools) and extinct animals that had been found together in a quarry (Bahn, 1999). Forty years earlier, C. J. Thomsen (1788–1865), a Danish archaeologist and scholar, had published his idea that the development of civilization should be divided into three ages—the Stone Age, the Bronze Age, and the Iron Age (Bahn, 1999). The validity of this model was later demonstrated in 1843. His colleague and successor at the Museum of Denmark, Jens Jacob Asmussen Worsaae (1821–85), whose excavations uncovered stone tools in archaeological layers below bronze and iron tools, led to the widespread acceptance of Thomsen's system throughout Europe in the mid-nineteenth century.

Herbert Spencer (1820–1903) borrowed the biological model of an organism for explaining changes in society. He believed that society was like a biological organism, being a system of structures and functions. Spencer believed that the level of evolution of a society was based on its structural differences from other societies (Bohannan and Glazer, 1988).

One of the first cultural evolutionists, Edward Burnett Tyler (1832–1917), published *Primitive*

sexual selection. Until then, Darwin avoided stating categorically that humans were descended from non-human forms, but the implications of his theory were clear. Controversy immediately ensued, with passionate advocates for each side. In June 1860, at the annual meeting of the British Association for the Advancement of Science, Bishop Wilberforce, representing the biblical view

Culture in 1871 in which he argued that the presence of what Western thinkers at the time considered "primitive societies" could be explained in one of two ways: either all cultures were created at an equal level and primitive societies represented degeneration, or modern societies developed over a very long period from an initial state of barbarism in which, for some reason, primitive societies remained. Tyler rejected the former explanation (Bohannan and Glazer, 1988).

Lewis Henry Morgan (1818–81) was an American anthropologist who followed Tyler's explanation of cultural evolution. In 1877 he published *Ancient Society*, arguing that cultures passed through three stages from savagery to barbarism, and then to civilization. Morgan suggested that cultures could remain in certain stages if key inventions or innovations such as the bow and arrow, domestication, or iron smelting were not made (Bohannan and Glazer, 1988). Both Tyler and Morgan, like their biological counterparts Linnaeus and Lamarck, believed that cultural evolution was unilinear—that all cultures passed through the same stages of technological innovation and cultural complexity.

By the early nineteenth century, a number of scholars began to challenge these notions of cultural evolution. Franz Boas (1858–1942) introduced the notion of **cultural relativism**—the idea that all societies are equal and comparable (Bohannan and Glazer, 1988). There are no superior or inferior societies, and as a result, it is not possible to order cultures in an evolutionary scheme. Robert H. Lowie (1883–1957) also rejected Morgan's scheme for the evolution of society. He argued that diffusion or cultural contact was important for cultural development—borrowing ideas was always easier than originating ideas—and that both simple and complex societies participated in the exchange of ideas (Bohannan and Glazer, 1988). Marshall D. Sahlins suggested that both biological and cultural evolution move in two directions at the same time, producing diversity and progress. He defined *diversity* as meaning adaptive changes that resulted in new forms from old forms, and *progress* as referring to the fact that

evolution creates more complex forms (Bohannan and Glazer, 1988).

The Principles of Natural Selection

Darwin was not the first person to view the creation of new species in evolutionary terms, but he was the first to provide a comprehensive, well-documented explanation—natural selection—for the way evolution had occurred. Natural selection is the main process that increases the frequency of **adaptive traits** through time. The operation of natural selection involves three conditions or principles (Brandon, 1990). The first is **variation**: every species is composed of a great variety of individuals, some of which are better adapted to their environment than others. The existence of variety is important. Without it, natural selection has nothing on which to operate; without variation, one kind of characteristic could not be favoured over another. The second principle of natural selection is **heritability**: offspring inherit traits from their parents, at least to some degree and in some way. The third principle of natural selection is **differential reproductive success**: since better-adapted individuals generally produce more offspring over the generations than the less well-adapted, the frequency of adaptive traits gradually increases in subsequent generations. A new species emerges when changes in traits or geographic barriers result in the reproductive isolation of the population.

When we say that certain traits are adaptive or advantageous, we mean that they result in greater reproductive success in a particular environment. The term *particular environment* is very important. Even though a species may become more adapted to a particular environment over time, we cannot say that one species adapted to its environment is "better" than another species adapted to a different environment. For example, we may like to think of ourselves as "better" than other animals, but humans are clearly less adapted than fish for living under water, bats for catching flying insects, or raccoons for living on suburban garbage. Because Darwinian evolution is not premeditated, the product of evolution is about being in the right place at the right time.

If certain kinds of variation are not selected for in one environment, then a species might follow a different evolutionary path than it would have if it had been in a different environment at that time. Similarly, if there is no adaptive variation within a species, it may have difficulty surviving a specific environment, and may run the risk of becoming extinct. To illustrate this point, consider that if there had not been a global catastrophic event in the form of a meteor impact that led to the extinction of the dinosaurs 65 million years ago, primates including humans might never have evolved. The presence of a group of dinosaurs that had some of the key morphological features we claim were important to human evolution—opposable digits, stereoscopic vision, and a large brain—led palaeontologist Dale

The changes that occurred in the moth population in different areas of England show natural selection in action. Before industrialization, tree trunks were lighter, and light-coloured moths predominated. With industrial pollution and the darkening of tree trunks, light-coloured moths became more visible to predators. Darker-coloured moths quickly increased in number in the new industrial environment. Rural areas today, with little or no industrial air pollution, show that natural selection in unpolluted areas still favours light-coloured moths.

The giraffe's long neck is adaptive for eating tree leaves high off the ground. When food is scarce, longer-necked giraffes would get more food and reproduce more successfully than shorter-necked giraffes; in this environment, natural selection would favour giraffes with longer necks.

Russell to propose in 1982 how dinosaurs may have evolved had they not become extinct (Russel and Sequin, 1982). The earth would have been a very different place were it not for small mammals being in the right place at the right time.

Although the theory of natural selection suggests that disadvantageous or maladaptive traits will generally decline in frequency or even disappear eventually, it does not necessarily follow that all such traits will do so. After all, species derive from prior forms that have certain structures. This means that not all changes are possible; it also means that some traits are linked to others that might have advantages that outweigh disadvantages. Choking may be very maladaptive for any animal, yet all vertebrates are capable of choking because their digestive and respiratory systems converge in the throat. This trait is a genetic legacy, probably from the time when the respiratory system developed from tissue in the digestive system of some ancestral organism. Apparently, the propensity to choke has not been evolutionarily correctable (Williams, 1992).

Changes in a species can be expected to occur as the environment changes or as some members of the species move into a new environment. With environmental change, different traits become adaptive. The members of the species that possess the more adaptive traits will become more numerous, whereas those members whose characteristics make continued existence more difficult or impossible in the modified environment will eventually become extinct.

Consider how the theory of natural selection would explain why giraffes became long-necked. Originally, the necks of giraffes varied in length, as happens with virtually any physical characteristic in a population. During a period when food was scarce, those giraffes with longer necks that could reach higher tree leaves might be better able to survive and suckle their offspring, and thus they would leave more offspring than shorter-necked giraffes. Because of heredity, the offspring of long-necked giraffes are more likely to have long necks. Eventually, the shorter-necked giraffes would diminish in number and the longer-necked giraffes would increase. The resulting population of giraffes would still have variation in neck length but on the average would be longer-necked than earlier forms.

Natural selection does not account for all variation in the frequencies of traits. In particular, it does not account for variation in the frequencies of neutral traits—that is, those traits that do not seem to confer any advantages or disadvantages on their carriers. Changes in the frequencies of neutral traits may result rather from random processes that affect *gene frequencies* in isolated populations (*genetic drift*) or from matings between populations (*gene flow*). We discuss these other processes in Chapter 11 on human variation.

The Origin of Species

One of the most controversial aspects of Darwin's theory was the suggestion that one species could, over time, evolve into another. A **species** is a population that consists of organisms able to interbreed and produce fertile and viable offspring. In general, individuals from one species cannot successfully mate with members of a different species because of genetic and behavioural differences. If members of different species did mate, it is unlikely that eggs would be fertilized, or, if they were, that the embryos would survive. If offspring were born, they would soon die or be infertile. So how could one species evolve into another? What is the explanation for the differentiation? How does one group of organisms become so unlike another group with the same ancestry that it forms a totally new species?

Speciation, or the development of a new species, may occur if one subgroup of a species finds itself in a radically different environment. In adapting to their separate environments, the two populations may undergo enough genetic changes to prevent them from interbreeding should they renew contact. Numerous factors can prevent the exchange of genes. Two species living in the same area may breed at different times of the year, or their behaviour during breeding—their courtship rituals—may be distinct. The difference in body structure of closely related forms may in itself bar interbreeding. Geographic barriers may be the most common barriers to interbreeding.

Once species differentiation does occur, the evolutionary process cannot be reversed; the new species can no longer mate with other species related to its parent population. Humans and gorillas, for example, have the same distant ancestors but their evolutionary paths have diverged irreversibly.

Observed Examples of Evolution

Since the process of evolution may involve nearly imperceptible gradations over generations, it is usually difficult to observe directly. Nevertheless, because some life forms reproduce rapidly, some examples of natural selection have been observed over relatively short periods in changing environments. For example, scientists think they have observed natural selection in action in British moths. In 1850, a moth that was mostly black was spotted for the first time in Manchester. That was quite unusual, for most of that species of moth were speckled grey. A century later, 95 percent of

Former Quebec Premier Lucien Bouchard was forced to battle necrotizing fasciitis ("flesh-eating disease").

the moths in industrial parts of Britain were black; only in the rural areas were the moths mostly grey. How is this to be explained? It seems that in the rural areas, the grey-speckled moth is hard to spot by bird predators against the lichen growing on the bark of trees. In industrial areas though, lichen is killed by pollution. The grey-speckled moths, formerly well-adapted to blend into their environment, became clearly visible against the darker background of the lichen-free trees and were easier prey for birds. In contrast, the black moths, which previously would have had a disadvantage against the lighter bark, were now better adapted for survival. Their dark colour was an advantage, and subsequently the darker moths became the predominant variety in industrial regions.

How can we be sure that natural selection was the mechanism accounting for the change? Consistent evidence comes from a series of experiments performed by H. B. D. Kettlewell. He deliberately released specially marked moths, black and grey, into two areas of England—one urban industrial and one rural—and then set light traps to recapture them. The proportions of the two kinds of moths recovered tell us about differential survival. Kettlewell found that proportionately more black moths compared with grey moths were recovered in the urban industrial area. The reverse happened in the rural area; proportionately more grey-speckled moths were recovered (Smith, 1989). The same transformation—the switch to darker colour occurred in 70 other species of moth, as well as in a beetle and a millipede. It did not occur only in Britain; it also happened in other highly polluted areas—the Ruhr area of Germany and the Pittsburgh area of the United States. Moreover, in the Pittsburgh area, anti-pollution measures in the last 30 years have apparently caused the black moth to dwindle in number once again (Devillers and Chaline, 1993).

Another well-known example of observed natural selection is the acquired resistance of houseflies to the insecticide DDT. Beginning in the 1940s when DDT was first used to kill insects, several new DDT-resistant strains of housefly evolved. Many houseflies were killed but the few that survived were the ones that reproduced, and their resistant characteristics became common to the housefly populations. To the chagrin of medical practitioners, similar resistances develop in bacteria. A particular antibiotic may lose its effectiveness after it comes into wide use because new, resistant bacterial strains emerge.

A good example of the increased prevalence of highly virulent forms of old diseases that affect humans is *Streptococcus A*. Medical experts including Florence Nightingale recorded streptococcal toxic-shock syndrome (TSS) by names such as malignant ulcer, hospital gangrene, Fournier's gangrene, or phagedena. Streptococcal infections in the past, such as the scarlet fever epidemics that killed thousands of children during the nineteenth and early twentieth centuries, also reached epidemic

CURRENT ISSUES

Selection Favours the Evolution of Drug-Resistant Diseases

Over the last decade or so, the threat of old diseases returning with renewed resistance to previously effective drug therapies has become a serious concern to public health officials. This unease has slowly gained the attention of the general public through media attention regarding the breakout of virulent diseases in tropical "hot zones." An example of an old disease that is emerging as a renewed threat is tuberculosis (TB)—the "consumption" or "white plague" of the nineteenth and early twentieth centuries.

Tuberculosis was once one of the most dreaded diseases in the world. In 1926, one in 13 North Americans died of the disease. Prior to the mid-1980s, the prevalence of tuberculosis cases was decreasing. Streptomycin and other antibiotics in use since the 1960s had been highly effective in steadily reducing new cases of tuberculosis. However, between 1985 and 1995, TB rates in industrialized countries stabilized, and in some cases increased slightly. This change in pattern was due in part to the rise of drug-resistant strains of *Mycobacterium tuberculosis*, the micro-organism that causes the disease. The World Health Organization (WHO) estimates that approximately one-third of the world's population is now infected with multi-drug-resistant forms of *M. tuberculosis* (MDR-TB) and that 30 million people will eventually die from tuberculosis.

Recently, the WHO identified "hot zones" where the incidences of TB and MDR-TB are on the rise, or are at levels to warrant concern. These currently include the Baltic states of Estonia and Latvia, Iran, the Russian regions of Ivanovo and Tomsk, and the Hunan province of China. In Canada, tuberculosis rates have followed the pattern of most Western industrialized nations. Over the last decade the overall rate of tuberculosis in Canada has dropped from roughly 7.4 cases per 100 000 in 1992 to 5.9 cases per 100 000 in 1998.* The highest rates were in Manitoba, with a reported 9.2 cases per 100 000 inhabitants. However, these figures do not tell the whole story. There is a substantial disparity in infection rates between Aboriginal and non-Aboriginal populations, with Aboriginal patients making up nearly 50 percent of cases in Manitoba, while representing only 9 percent of the general population.

While "standard" TB is treatable with a 95- to 100-percent survival rate, multi-drug-resistant-tuberculosis can have survival rates below 50 percent. In 1998, of 1423 TB cases reported in Canada, 168 or 11.8 percent were resistant to one or more drugs and 1.2 percent were MDR-TB. As with many diseases, an important tool in the fight against MDR-TB is the sequencing of the *M. tuberculosis* genome. Researchers have begun to identify which mutations to the *M. tuberculosis* genome correspond to various drug resistances.

*Tuberculosis in Canada, 1998. 2001. Health Canada.

Sources: Stokstad E. 31 March 2000. Infectious Disease: Drug-Resistant TB on the Rise. Science 287(5462): 2391.

Tuberculosis: Drug Resistance in Canada 2000. 2001. Reported susceptibility results of the Canadian Tuberculosis Laboratory Network Surveillance System, Minister of Public Works and Government Services Canada, available at **www.hcsc.gc.ca/hpb/lcdc.**

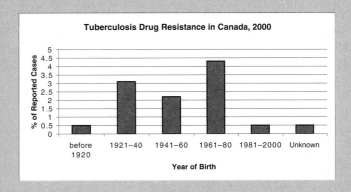

Rates of drug-resistant tuberculosis in Canada by age group in 2000. Data from: Tuberculosis: Drug Resistance in Canada 2000. 2001. Reported susceptibility results of the Canadian Tuberculosis Laboratory Network Surveillance System, Minister of Public Works and Government Services Canada, Table 4.

proportions. In recent years, catastrophic *Streptococcus A.* infections have been observed in patients who are not normally affected by these diseases, that is, in young adults with no prior illnesses. Most disturbing, the progress of the disease in these new cases is much more rapid, earning some of the TSS effects the popular term "flesh-eating disease." Some high-profile cases, such as the 1990 death of Muppet creator Jim Henson, the media hype following a rash of TSS deaths in Britain in the mid-1990s, and the very public battle of former Quebec Premier Lucien Bouchard with necrotizing fasciitis in 1993, spurred public awareness and fears over the last decade.

These new strains of common diseases will become more frequent than the original ones because of natural selection. In Canada now, an increasing number of disease strains are resistant to antibiotics currently on the market, a fact that worries medical practitioners (see Current Issues, *Selection Favours the Evolution of Drug-Resistant Diseases*, on page 83). One possible way to deal with the problem is to stop using certain antibiotics for a few years so that resistance to those antibiotics might not develop or will develop only slowly.

The theory of natural selection answered many questions but it also raised at least one whose answer eluded Darwin and others. The appearance of a beneficial trait may assist the survival of an organism, but what happens when the organism reproduces by mating with members that do not possess this new variation? Will not the new adaptive trait eventually disappear if subsequent generations mate with individuals that lack this trait? Darwin knew variations were transmitted through heredity, but he did not have a clear model of the mode of inheritance. As we will see in Chapter 5, Gregor Mendel's pioneering studies in the science of genetics provided the foundation for such a model, but his discoveries did not become widely known until 1900.

Summary

1. If we think of the history of the universe as represented by 12 months, the history of human-like primates would take up only about 90 minutes. The universe is some 15 billion years old; modern-looking humans have existed for about 100 000 years.

2. Ideas about evolution took a long time to be accepted in Western society because they contradicted the biblical view of events; species were viewed as fixed in their form by the creator. But in the eighteenth and early nineteenth centuries, scientists increasingly interpreted evidence so as to suggest that evolution was a viable theory. In geology, the concept of *uniformitarianism* suggested that the earth is constantly subject to shaping and reshaping by natural forces working over vast stretches of time. A number of thinkers during this period began to discuss evolution and how it might occur.

3. Charles Darwin and Alfred Wallace proposed the mechanism of natural selection to account for the evolution of species. Basic principles of the theory of natural selection are that (1) every species is composed of a great variety of individuals, some of which are better adapted to their environment than others; (2) at least to some degree and in some way offspring inherit traits from their parents; and (3) since better-adapted individuals generally produce more offspring over the generations than those that are more poorly adapted, the frequency of adaptive traits increases in subsequent generations. In this way, natural selection results in increasing proportions of individuals with advantageous traits.

4. Natural selection depends on variation within a population.

5. Speciation, the development of a new species, may occur if one subgroup becomes separated from other subgroups. In adapting to different environments, these subpopulations may undergo enough genetic changes to prevent interbreeding, even if they re-establish contact. Once species differentiation occurs, it is believed that the evolutionary process cannot be reversed.

Glossary Terms

acquired inheritance   (p. 74)

adaptation   (p. 73)

adaptive traits   (p. 79)

catastrophism   (p. 75)

cultural relativism   (p. 79)

Darwin, Charles   (p. 73)

differential reproductive success   (p. 79)

genus   (p. 74)

heritability   (p. 79)

Lamarck, Jean-Baptiste   (p. 74)

Linnaeus, Carolus   (p. 74)

natural selection   (p. 77)

speciation   (p. 81)

species   (p. 81)

uniformitarianism   (p. 76)

variation   (p. 79)

Critical Questions

1. Do you think the theory of natural selection is compatible with religious beliefs? Explain your reasoning.

2. How are humans influencing the evolution of other species? Of our own species?

3. How do you think human biology might be different 1000 years from now? Ten thousand years from now?

Internet Exercises

1. Visit **www.nap.edu/readingroom/books/evolution98/** and read about the teaching of evolution. In reference to the American education system, the authors write, "The teaching of science in the nation's public schools often is marred by a serious omission ... biological evolution." Has this been your experience in the Canadian educational system?

2. Darwin's seminal *Origin of Species* can be found online at **www.tbi.univie.ac.at/Origin/origin_toc.html**. Read Chapter VI, "Difficulties of the Theory," and summarize each of Darwin's main points and counter-points.

3. Read through some of the "creation vs. evolution" debate at **www.pbs.org/wgbh/nova/odyssey/debate/index.html**. Suggest why or why not science and religion must remain at odds.

Suggested Reading

Boyd R, Richerson PJ. 1985. Culture and the Evolutionary Process. Chicago: University of Chicago Press. The authors develop mathematical models to analyze how biology and culture interact under the influence of evolutionary processes.

Brandon RN. 1990. Adaptation and Environment. Princeton, NJ: Princeton University Press. After defining basic concepts regarding adaptation and the theory of natural selection, the author emphasizes that the process of adaptation and its outcomes cannot be understood without analysis of the environment.

Devillers C, Chaline J. 1993. Evolution: An Evolving Theory. New York: Springer-Verlag. Aimed at the general audience, this book addresses the questions: What is the place of humans in the living world? What is evolution? How can the observed data be explained? Appendices give more detailed information.

Dobzhansky T. 1962. Mankind Evolving: The Evolution of the Human Species. New Haven, CT: Yale University Press. A classic demonstration that the mechanisms of evolution, primarily natural selection, are still active.

Durham WH. 1991. Coevolution: Genes, Culture, and Human Diversity. Stanford, CA: Stanford University Press. A discussion of the evolution of culture that considers how theory and research point to the interaction of genes and culture in human populations.

Mayr E. 1982. The Growth of Biological Thought: Diversity, Evolution, and Inheritance. Cambridge, MA: Belknap Press of Harvard University Press. A history of ideas that discusses the successful and unsuccessful attempts to understand problems in the study of evolution.

5 MODERN EVOLUTIONARY THEORY

In the last chapter we learned that, according to Darwin's theory of evolution, natural selection is the process by which evolution occurred. Both Darwin and Wallace emphasized that natural selection operated on variation that already existed between individuals, but they did not know why or how that variation was created. Darwin thought that traits in offspring were somehow a blend of the parents' traits. At the same time he was developing his theory of evolution by natural selection, an Augustinian monk from the Czech Republic was experimenting with how heredity worked. In this chapter we will discuss how the discovery of the gene influenced theories of evolution, and outline the modern theory of evolution. Biological evolution is not simply a process of change, but rather of changes in gene frequencies within a population.

In this chapter we begin by examining the roles of genes as the units of heredity—how they are inherited and how those genes are manifest in the individual. This section reviews the basis of cell biology and the structure and role of DNA in organisms. Next, we discuss sources of variation, that is, how similar genetic material is recombined in a variety of different expressions to produce variation, as well as how mutations occur within a species to also produce variation. These concepts form the fundamental basis for the modern theory of evolution. At the end of this chapter, we discuss the influence of genetics and environment on individual behaviour and the role of selection for behavioural traits.

Heredity

Mendel's Experiments

Gregor Mendel (1822–84), an amateur botanist, bred several varieties of pea plants and made detailed observations of their offspring. He chose as breeding partners plants that differed by only one observable trait. He crossed tall plants with short ones, and yellow ones with green, for example.

When Mendel transferred the pollen from a yellow pea plant to a green pea plant, he observed a curious phenomenon: all of the first-generation

Gregor Mendel.

offspring bore yellow peas. It seemed that the green trait had disappeared. But when he crossed seeds from this first generation, they produced both yellow and green pea plants in a ratio of three yellow pea plants to one green pea plant (see Figure 5–1). Apparently, Mendel reasoned, the green trait had not been lost or altered; the yellow trait was simply **dominant** and the green trait was **recessive**. Mendel observed similar results with other traits. Tallness dominated shortness, and the factor for smooth-skinned peas dominated the factor for wrinkled ones. In each cross, the 3-to-1 ratio appeared in the second generation. Self-fertilization, however, produced different results. Green pea plants always yielded green pea plants, and short plants always produced short plants.

From his numerical results, Mendel concluded that some yellow pea plants were pure for that trait, whereas others also possessed a green factor. That is, although two plants might both have yellow peas, one of them might produce green peas. In such cases, the genetic makeup, the **genotype**, differed from the observable appearance, or **phenotype**.

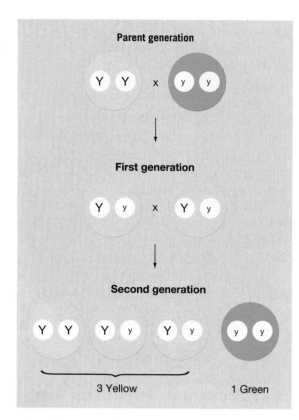

Parent generation

Y Y x y y

First generation

Y y x Y y

Second generation

Y Y   Y y   Y y   y y

3 Yellow   1 Green

Figure 5–1

When Mendel crossed a plant having two genes for yellow peas (YY) with a plant having two genes for green peas (yy), each offspring pea was yellow but carried one gene for yellow and one gene for green (Yy). The peas were yellow because the gene for yellow is dominant over the recessive gene for green. Crossing the first generation yielded three yellow pea plants for each green pea plant.

Genes: The Conveyors of Inherited Traits

Mendel's units of heredity were what we now call **genes**. He concluded that these units occurred in pairs for each trait and that offspring inherited one unit of the pair from each parent. Each member of a gene pair or group is called an **allele**. If the two genes, or alleles, for a trait are the same, the organism is **homozygous** for that trait; if the two genes for a characteristic differ, the organism is **heterozygous** for that trait. A pea plant that contains a pair of genes for yellow is homozygous for the trait. A yellow pea plant with a dominant gene for yellow and a recessive gene for green, although phenotypically yellow,

has a heterozygous genotype. As Mendel demonstrated, the recessive green gene can reappear in subsequent generations. However, Mendel knew nothing of the composition of genes or the processes that transmit them from parent to offspring. Many years of scientific research have yielded much of the missing information.

The genes of higher organisms (not including bacteria and primitive plants such as green-blue algae) are located on ropelike bodies called **chromosomes** within the nucleus of every one of the organism's cells. Chromosomes, like genes, usually occur in pairs. Each allele for a given trait is carried in the identical position on corresponding chromosomes. The two genes that determined the colour of Mendel's peas, for example, were opposite each other on a pair of chromosomes.

 Mitosis and Meiosis. Each body cell of every plant or animal carries a number of chromosome pairs, and this number is specific to each species. A human body cell has 23 pairs, or a total of 46 chromosomes, each chromosome carrying many times that number of genes. Each new body cell receives this number of chromosomes during cellular reproduction, or **mitosis**, as each pair of chromosomes duplicates itself.

What happens, though, when a sperm cell and an egg cell unite to form a new organism? What prevents the human baby from receiving twice the number of chromosomes characteristic of its species—23 pairs from the sperm and 23 pairs from the egg? The process by which the reproductive cells are formed, **meiosis**, ensures that this will not happen (see Figure 5–2 on page 90). Each reproductive cell contains *half* the number of chromosomes appropriate for the species. Only one member of each chromosome pair is carried in every egg or sperm. At fertilization, the human embryo normally receives 23 *separate* chromosomes from its mother and the same number from its father, which add up to the 23 pairs.

 DNA. As we have said, genes are located on chromosomes. Each gene carries a set of instructions encoded in its chemical structure. It is from this coded information carried

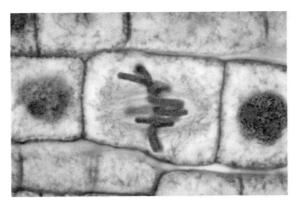
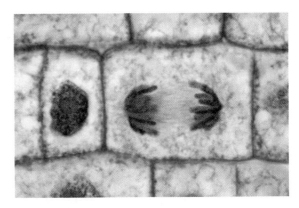

Mitosis in a plant cell. The left image shows the metaphase stage. Note how the chromosomes (stained red) lie against and even on top of one another. The right image shows the anaphase stage, when the chromosomes separate and the cell is ready to divide.

in genes that a cell makes all the rest of its structural parts and chemical machinery. It appears that in most living organisms, heredity is controlled by the same chemical substance, DNA—deoxyribonucleic acid. An enormous amount of research has been directed toward understanding DNA—what its structure is, how it duplicates itself in reproduction, and how it conveys or instructs the formation of a complete organism.

One of the most important keys to understanding human development and genetics is the structure and function of DNA. In 1953, the American biologist James Watson, with the British molecular biologist Francis Crick, proposed that DNA is a long, two-stranded molecule shaped like a double helix (Alberts et al., 1983) (see Figure 5–3). Genetic information is stored in the linear sequences of the bases; different species have different sequences, and every individual is slightly different from every other individual. Notice that in the DNA molecule each base always has the same opposite base; adenine and thymine are paired, as are cytosine and guanine. The importance of this pattern is that the two strands carry the same information, so that when the double helix unwinds, each strand can form a template for a new strand of complementary bases (Alberts et al., 1983). Since DNA stores the information required to make up the cells of an organism, it has been called the language of life. As George and Muriel Beadle put it, the deciphering of the DNA

code has revealed our possession of a language much older than hieroglyphics, a language as old as life itself, a language that is the most living language of all—even if its letters are invisible and its words are buried deep in the cells of our bodies (Beadle and Beadle, 1966).

Once it was understood that genes are made of DNA, concerted efforts were begun to map DNA sequences and their locations on the chromosomes of different organisms. A project known as the Human Genome Project set out to assemble a complete genetic map for humans. Much progress has already been made, but it may take many years and an enormous amount of research to finish this task (Stephens et al., 1992; Friedlaender, 1993).

 Messenger RNA. DNA stores the information to make cells, but it does not directly affect the formation of cells. One type of ribonucleic acid (RNA), **messenger RNA (mRNA)**, is copied from a portion of DNA and moves outside the cell nucleus to direct the formation of proteins (Alberts et al., 1983). Proteins have so many functions that they are considered to be responsible for most of the characteristics of an organism. They act as catalysts for synthesizing DNA and RNA and for the activities of cells; they also contribute many of the structural elements that determine the shape and movement of cells (Berg and Singer, 1992). Messenger RNA is like DNA in that it has a linear sequence of bases

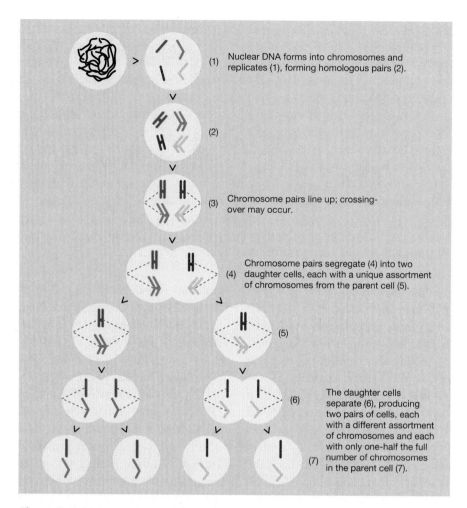

Figure 5–2 Meiosis (Sex Cells)

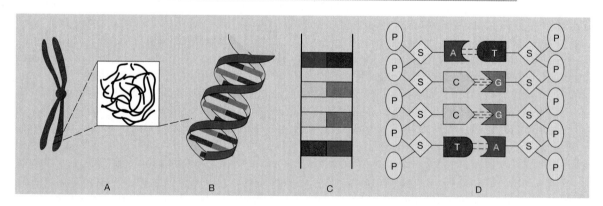

Figure 5–3 DNA

Chromosomes are built of DNA (A), which consists of two spiral sugar-phosphate strands (B) linked by the nitrogenous bases adenine, guanine, thymine, and cytosine (C). When the DNA molecule reproduces, the bases separate and the spiral strands unwind (D). Because adenine can bond only to thymine, and cytosine can bond only to guanine, each original strand serves as a mould along which a new complementary chain is formed.

attached to a sugar-phosphate backbone, but it is slightly different chemically. One difference is that messenger RNA has the base *uracil* instead of the base thymine. Messenger RNA also has a different sugar-phosphate backbone and is single- rather than double-stranded. Messenger RNA is formed when a double-stranded DNA molecule unwinds and forms a template for the mRNA. After a section of DNA is copied, the RNA releases from the DNA and leaves the nucleus, and the double helix of the DNA is re-formed (Alberts et al., 1983).

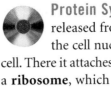 **Protein Synthesis.** Once the mRNA is released from the DNA, it travels out of the cell nucleus and into the body of the cell. There it attaches to a structure in the cell called a **ribosome**, which uses the information on the mRNA to make proteins. The ribosome essentially "reads" the chemical bases on the mRNA in commands that tell the ribosome the specific amino acids to join together to form a protein (see Figure 5–4 on page 94). For example, the mRNA sequence adenine, adenine, guanine (AAG) tells the

RESEARCH FRONTIERS

Was Lamarck Right after All?

In our discussion of the mechanisms for evolution in Chapter 3, we noted that Lamarck's theory of acquired inheritance was not correct. Now we know that Lamarck may have been partly right.

Lamarck's theory of acquired inheritance re-emerged in the 1970s when Ted Steele, an Australian immunologist, proposed a modern version of Lamarckian evolution that could be tested through experiment. His idea was that mutations in the immune system of an individual would be selected for on the basis of exposure to specific *antigens* (foreign substances that cause the body to produce an immune reaction and antibodies) during the lifetime of the individual. However, the genetic blueprints for an organism are protected from change because only germ cells contain inheritable material. While all cells contain DNA for the production of the organism, the DNA in the nucleus of a cell is separated from the proteins within the cell. As such, changes in DNA can produce new proteins, but changes in proteins cannot affect the DNA. Therefore, a mechanism is required that would allow for the passing on of genetic modification acquired during life.

Steele proposed that cells with these mutations could be picked up by RNA viruses and could then be incorporated into the DNA of the sex cells through infection of the ova or sperm. Steele's theory met with some debate, partly because of inconsistent results of experiments on mice.

However, in the late 1980s researchers suggested that organisms may in fact be able to purposefully "evolve" in response to differing environmental stresses through the existence of non-random mutations within the genome. In studies of mutations in both bacteria and yeast, there seems to be some evidence for the occurrence of certain mutations only under selective pressure that would favour those mutations, but researchers have argued that if mutations are random, then they should occur randomly prior to selection.

What does this mean? In Lamarckian terms it means that cells are somehow able to anticipate the impact of genetic changes on the organism's fitness and therefore choose or *direct mutations* toward those most advantageous. This idea is referred to as directed mutation. However, if this theory is correct,

the mechanism by which individual-level directed evolution occurs is not understood.

The next question, of course, is whether a theory that may be supported by data about simple organisms can be extrapolated to complex multi-celled organisms like humans. Humans are perhaps unique in that culture has become a major adaptive strategy for survival. Anthropologists recognize the importance of cultural responses to environmental stimuli for the evolution of our species, and the impact that the interaction of behaviour and biology have under different environmental circumstances.

As a result, culture can be viewed as a form of Lamarckian evolution, whereby innovative and directed responses to environmental stresses can be acquired during the lifetime of an individual and subsequently passed on to the next generation.

Source: Saunders SR. 1994. The Enduring Tension: Darwinian and Lamarckian Models of Inheritance. In: Herring, DA, Chan L, editors. Strength in Diversity: A Reader in Physical Anthropology. Toronto: Canadian Scholars' Press. p 1–20.

CURRENT ISSUES

Is Evolution Slow and Steady or Fast and Abrupt?

Darwin's evolutionary theory suggested that new species emerge gradually over time. Through the process of natural selection, frequencies of traits would slowly change, and eventually a new species would appear. However, Darwin's theory did not allow for speciation (the development and divergence of different species). If trait frequencies change only gradually over time, wouldn't descendant populations retain their ability to interbreed and wouldn't they, therefore, continue to belong to the same species?

In the 1930s and 1940s, Theodosius Dobzhansky, Julian Huxley, Ernst Mayr, George Simpson, and others advanced what came to be called the "modern synthesis" in evolutionary theory, adding what was known from genetics about heredity. Mutation and the recombination of genes now provided for genetic variety. The driving force of change was still adaptation to environments through natural selection; gene frequencies of a population presumably changed slowly as adaptive traits

(because of existing genes or mutations) increased in prevalence and maladaptive traits decreased. As for speciation, the modern synthesis postulated that it would occur when subpopulations became isolated by geographic barriers or when different subpopulations encountered different climatic conditions or moved into new ecological niches; those environmental isolating processes would eventually result in the development of reproductive isolation and therefore new species.

This gradualist view of evolution was challenged in 1972 by Niles Eldredge and Stephen Jay Gould. Their alternative model of evolution is referred to as "punctuated equilibrium." They still assume that natural selection is the primary mechanism of evolutionary change, but they see the pace of evolution quite differently. In their view, new species evolve quickly; but once a successful species emerges, its characteristics are likely to change very little over long periods. Thus, in contrast to the modern synthesis, Eldredge and Gould do not think it is common

for the world's species to change gradually into descendant species. Rather, individuals of a species are born more or less abruptly, they have lifetimes during which they do not change much, and they become extinct. As examples, Eldredge and Gould cite the history of North American trilobites and Bermudan land snails. In both groups of animals, the different species did not seem to change for a long time—millions of years for some species—but then certain species seem to have been quickly replaced by related species from nearby areas. In short, Eldredge and Gould believe that the succession of one species after another involves replacement more often than gradual change over time.

Evolution may or may not occur according to the model of punctuated equilibrium, but most evolutionists today agree that change could occur relatively quickly. Recent research suggests that some relatively quick climate changes in the earth's history helped bring about massive extinctions of species and families of species and exponential increases in

---

ribosome to place the amino acid lysine in that location, whereas the sequence adenine, adenine, cytosine (AAC) calls for the amino acid histidine. There are also mRNA commands that tell the ribosome when to begin and when to stop constructing a protein. Thus, the DNA code copied onto mRNA provides all the information necessary for ribosomes to build the proteins that make up the structures of organisms and drive the processes of life.

Sources of Variability

Natural selection proceeds only when individuals within a population vary. There are two genetic

sources of variation: genetic recombination and mutation.

Genetic Recombination

The distribution of traits from parents to children varies from one offspring to another. Brothers and sisters, after all, do not look exactly alike, nor does each child resemble 50 percent of the mother and 50 percent of the father. This variation occurs because when a sperm cell or an egg is formed from 23 chromosomes, each chromosome is randomly received. Each reproductive cell, then, carries a *random assortment* of chromosomes and their respective genes. At fertilization, the egg and sperm that unite are

the subsequent number of new families. For example, there is considerable evidence that a large meteorite collided with the earth at the end of the Cretaceous geological period, about 65 million years ago. Louis Alvarez and his colleagues proposed that so much dust was sent into the atmosphere by the collision that the earth was shrouded in darkness for months, if not longer. Some investigators now think that the meteorite impact may also have triggered a great deal of volcanic activity, even on the opposite side of the world, which would also have reduced solar radiation to the earth's surface. Not only the dinosaurs disappeared about 65 million years ago, so also did many sea animals and plants. Afterward, the earth saw the proliferation of many other kinds of animals, such as fish, lizards, birds, and mammals, as well as flowering trees. As we shall see in Chapter 7 on primate evolution, our own biological order, the Primates, is believed to have emerged around that time.

Peter Grant has recently studied the same finches on the Galápagos Islands that partially inspired Darwin's theory. Unlike Darwin

though, Grant had the chance to see natural selection in action—and it was surprisingly quick. Central to Grant's study was the attachment of coloured bands to each individual bird, which allowed each bird to be identified at a distance. In the midst of the project, in 1977, when half the birds had been banded, there was a serious drought. Of the two main species of finch on one island, the cactus finch and the medium finch, only the cactus finches were able to breed, but they had no surviving offspring. During the next 18 months, 85 percent of the adult medium finches disappeared. Those finches that survived tended to be larger and to have larger beaks than the ones that died. Why larger beaks? Both species of finch eat seeds, but small seeds produced by grasses and herbs are scarce in a drought; bigger seeds are more available. So it seems that natural selection under conditions of drought favoured finches with bigger beaks, which are better at cracking the husks of large seeds.

If it were not for the fact that wet years, which favour smaller finches, occur between years of drought, we

might see the rapid evolution of new finch species. It is estimated that 20 drought episodes would be sufficient to produce a new species of finch. Darwin's (and Grant's) finches do not really provide an example of punctuated equilibrium (no replacement from outside occurred), but they do suggest that evolutionary change could be a lot quicker than Darwin imagined.

Controversy continues over whether evolution is slow and steady or fast and abrupt. Many scholars though, including Gould, point out that there is no need to pit one model against the other. Both may be correct in different instances. In any case much more investigation of evolutionary sequences is needed to help us evaluate the competing theoretical models.

Sources: Devillers C, Chaline J. 1993. Evolution: An Evolving Theory. New York: Springer-Verlag.

Grant PR. October 1991. Natural Selection and Darwin's Finches. Scientific American 82–87.

Tattersall I. 1998. Paleoanthropology and Evolutionary Theory. In: Ember CR, Ember M, Peregrine PN, editors. Research Frontiers in Anthropology. Upper Saddle River, NJ: Prentice Hall. Prentice Hall/Simon & Schuster Custom Publishing.

different from every other egg carried by the mother and every other sperm carried by the father. **Genetic recombination** then results in a *unique* offspring being produced through a random shuffling of the parents' genes. One cause of this shuffling is the random **segregation**, or sorting, of chromosomes in meiosis. Conceivably, an individual could get any of the possible assortments of the paternal and maternal chromosomes. Another cause of the shuffling of parental genes is **crossing-over**, the exchange of sections of chromosomes between one chromosome and another (Alberts et al., 1983). Thus, after meiosis, the egg and sperm do not receive just a random mixture of complete paternal and maternal

chromosomes; because of crossing-over they also receive chromosomes in which some of the sections may have been replaced (see Figure 5–5 on page 95).

The traits displayed by each organism are not simply the result of combinations of dominant and recessive genes, as Mendel had hypothesized. In humans, most traits are influenced by the activity of many genes. Skin colour, for example, is the result of several inherited characteristics. A brownish shade results from the presence of a pigment known as *melanin*; the degree of darkness in the hue depends largely on the amount and distribution of melanin in the skin. Another factor contributing to the colour of all

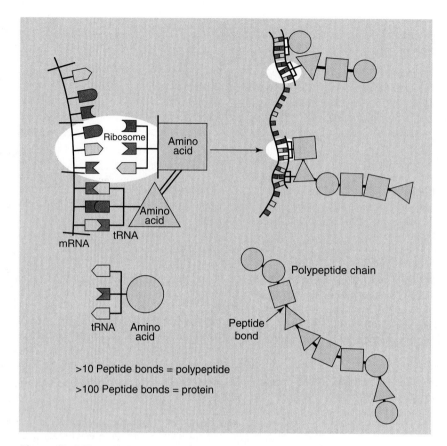

Figure 5–4 Translation and Protein Synthesis

The mRNA copy of the cellular DNA is "read" by a ribosome that attaches
the amino acid with the corresponding transfer RNA (tRNA) to a growing
chain of amino acids (called a polypeptide chain because the amino acids
are linked together by peptide bonds). A chain more than 100 amino acids
long is called a protein.

human skin is the blood that flows in blood vessels located in the outer layers of the skin. Humans carry at least five different genes for the manufacture of melanin and many other genes for the other components of skin hue. In fact, almost all physical characteristics in humans are the result of the concerted action of many genes. Some traits are sex-linked. The X chromosome, which together with the presence or absence of a Y chromosome determines sex, may also carry the gene for hemophilia or the gene for colour blindness. The expression of these two characteristics depends on the sex of the organism.

Genetic recombination produces variety, which is essential for the operation of natural selection. Ultimately, however, the major source of new variation is mutation. This is because mutation replenishes the supply of variability, which is constantly being reduced by the selective elimination of less fit variants. Mutation also produces variety in organisms that reproduce asexually.

Mutation

A **mutation** is a change in the DNA sequence. Such a change produces an altered gene. The majority of mutations are thought to occur because of occasional errors in the chemical bases that make up DNA. Just as a typist will make errors in copying a manuscript, so will DNA, in duplicating itself,

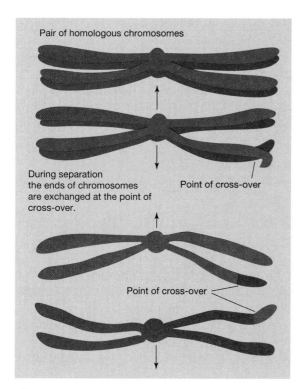

Pair of homologous chromosomes

During separation the ends of chromosomes are exchanged at the point of cross-over.

Point of cross-over

Point of cross-over

Figure 5–5 Crossing-Over

Source: Boaz and Almquist. 1997. Biological Anthropology. Upper Saddle River, NJ: Prentice Hall. Copyright © 1997. Reprinted by permission of Pearson Education, Inc., Upper Saddle River, NJ 07458.

occasionally change its code (Beadle and Beadle, 1966). A mutation will result from such an error. Some mutations have more drastic consequences than others. Suppose the error is in one base on a DNA strand. The effect depends on what that portion of the DNA controls. The effect may be minimal if the product hardly affects the organism. On the other hand, if the change occurs at a place where the DNA regulates the production of many proteins, the effect on the organism can be serious (Alberts et al., 1983).

Although it is very difficult to estimate the proportions of mutations that are harmful, neutral, or beneficial, there is no doubt that some mutations have lethal consequences. We can discuss the relative merits or disadvantages of a mutant gene only in terms of the physical, cultural, and genetic environment of that gene (Dobzhansky, 1962). Galactosemia, for example, is caused by a recessive

mutant gene and usually results in mental retardation and blindness. However, it can be prevented by dietary restrictions begun at an early age. In this instance, the intervention of human culture counteracts the mutant gene and allows the afflicted individual to lead a normal life. Thus, some cultural factors can modify the effects of natural selection by helping to perpetuate a harmful mutant gene. People with the galactosemia trait who are enabled to function normally can reproduce and pass on one of the recessive genes to their children. Without cultural interference, natural selection would prevent such reproduction. Usually, natural selection acts to retain only those mutations that aid survival.

Even though most mutations may not be adaptive, those that are will multiply in a population relatively quickly, by natural selection. As Theodosius Dobzhansky has suggested:

> Consistently useful mutants are like needles in a haystack of harmful ones. A needle in a haystack is hard to find, even though one may be sure it is there. But if the needle is valuable, the task of finding it is facilitated by setting the haystack on fire and looking for the needle among the ashes. The role of the fire in this parable is played in biological evolution by natural selection (Dobzhansky, 1962:139).

The black moth that was spotted in Manchester in 1850 probably resulted from a mutation. If the tree trunks had been light coloured, that moth or its offspring probably would have died out. However, as industrialization increased and the tree trunks became darker, a trait that was once maladaptive became adaptive.

Darwin and Wallace proposed a mechanism for evolution—natural selection acting on existing variation. Mendel's work provided the foundation for genetics, which we now know are the source of existing variation and how it becomes established. As discussed above, new variation within a species can occur only through mutation—changes in the existing genetic structure of an organism. However, the distribution of individual variation within a species is based on two fundamental concepts—*gene flow* and *genetic drift*. You will learn later in Chapter 11 how these two fundamental concepts—gene flow and genetic drift—affect the distribution of variation within a species.

The Theory of Evolution

Opponents of the idea of evolution often note that it is a theory, not a fact. However, it is important to recognize the process of the modern scientific method in establishing what we call a theory. The *Canadian Oxford Dictionary* defines the **scientific method** as "a method of procedure that has characterized natural science since the seventeenth century, consisting of systematic observation, measurement, and experiment, and the formulation, testing, and modification of hypotheses."

So, using the scientific method, researchers can collect data through observation. These observations in turn result in generalizations about the way things work (the process of induction), which are called hypotheses. If new observations contradict the predictions of an existing hypothesis, that hypothesis must be rejected and a new, more plausible explanation proposed. An hypothesis that is well supported by evidence and experimental testing is called a theory.

The theory of evolution therefore is a generalized theory of the development of life. Scientists continue to explore specific hypotheses that try to explain how evolution operates. Therefore, as a theory, evolution is supported by evidence—a feature that most people would accept as factual.

Natural Selection of Behavioural Traits

Until now we have discussed how natural selection might operate to change a population's physical traits, such as the colour of moths or the neck length of giraffes. But natural selection can also operate on the behavioural characteristics of populations. Although this idea is not new, it is now receiving

Prides of lions living in open country are more successful in catching large animals than are solitary lions. This social behaviour may have evolved because it provided selective advantages in the lion's open-country environment.

Mountain lions live in wooded environments and hunt individually. Here we see one that has killed a mule deer in western Montana.

more attention. The approaches called **sociobiology** (Barash, 1977) and **behavioural ecology** (Krebs and Davies, 1984, 1987) apply evolutionary principles to the behaviour of animals. Behavioural ecology is interested in how all kinds of behaviour are related to the environment; sociobiology is particularly interested in social organization and social behaviour. The typical behaviours of a species are assumed to be adaptive and to have evolved by natural selection. For example, why do related species exhibit different social behaviours even though they derive from a common ancestral species?

Consider the lion, as compared with other cats. Although members of the cat family are normally solitary creatures, lions live in social groups called *prides*. Why? George Schaller has suggested that lion social groups may have evolved primarily because group hunting is a more successful way to catch large mammals in open terrain. He has observed that not only are several lions more successful in catching prey than are solitary lions, but several lions are more likely to catch and kill large and dangerous prey such as giraffes. Then, too, cubs are generally safer from predators when in a social group than when alone with their mothers. Thus, the social behaviour of lions may have evolved primarily because it provided selective advantages in the lions' open-country environment (Schaller, 1972).

It is important to remember that natural selection operates on expressed characteristics, or the phenotype, of an individual. In the moth example, the colour of the moth is part of its phenotype, subject to natural selection. Behaviour is also an expressed characteristic. If hunting in groups, which is a behavioural trait, gets the individuals in that group more food than if each individual were to hunt on his or her own, then individuals who hunt in groups will do better. We must also remember though, that natural selection requires traits to be heritable. Can the concept of heritability be applied to learned behaviour, not just genetically transmitted behaviour? And, even more controversially, if the concept of heritability can include learning, can it also include cultural learning?

Early theorizing in sociobiology and behavioural ecology appeared to emphasize the genetic component of behaviour. However, Bobbi Low points out that, although the term *biology* may have been interpreted to mean "genetic," most biologists understand that expressed or observable characteristics are the results of genes and environment and life history, all interacting. Behaviour is a product of all three. If we say that some behaviour is heritable, we mean that the child's behaviour is more likely to resemble the parents' behaviour than the behaviour of others (Wilson, 1975; Wilson, 1998). Learning from a parent could be an important part of why the offspring is like the parent. If the child is more like the parent than like others, then the likeness is heritable, even if it is entirely learned from the parent.

Nature or Nurture?

Many researchers have tried to discover if variation in child-rearing customs can account for observed psychological differences. Anthropologists and psychologists use the term **socialization** to describe the development in children of patterns of behaviour, attitudes, and values that conform to cultural expectations. Socialization occurs through the influence of parents, their peer group, and others. People often try to socialize children directly by rewarding certain behaviours and ignoring or punishing other behaviours. Socialization can be indirect or subtle as well as direct. By assigning tasks to children, parents can encourage the development of specific skills needed for adult life, and at the same time subtly communicate what kind of person they want their children to become. Whether children go to school may affect their psychological, particularly cognitive, development.

Finally, parents may affect the psychological development of their children by the way they communicate how they generally feel about them.

Some researchers have suggested that genetic or physiological differences between populations predispose them to have different personality characteristics. Daniel Freedman found differences in "temperament" in newborn babies of different ethnic groups; because he observed newborns, the differences between them were presumed to be genetic. Freedman compared Chinese and European American newborns in families that were matched in such factors as income, number of previous children, and so on. He found that European American babies cried more easily, were harder to console, and fought experimental procedures more. Chinese babies, on the other hand, seemed calmer and more adaptable. Navaho babies were similar to the Chinese, showing even more calmness (Low, 1998). Freedman also suggested that an infant's behaviour can influence how the parents respond. A calm baby may encourage a calm parental response; a more active baby may encourage a more active response (Scarr and McCartney, 1983; Low, 1998). So, in

One major difference in child rearing between Western societies and other places is the degree to which an infant is held by a caretaker during the day. In North America and other Western countries, an infant spends much of the day in a crib, playpen, or stroller. This Bai baby from Yunnan province in China (right) spends a good deal of time in physical contact with the mother.

Freedman's view, babies' genetically determined behaviour can lead to ethnic differences in adult personality and caretaking styles.

Nevertheless, we cannot rule out non-genetic explanations of babies' behaviour. For example, the mother's diet or her blood pressure could affect the baby's behaviour, and it may be that the baby can learn even in the womb. After all, babies in the womb apparently can hear and respond to sounds and to other stimuli. Therefore, it is possible that in societies in which pregnant women are calm, their babies may have learned calmness even before they were born. Last, we still do not know if the initial differences observed in newborn babies persist to become personality differences in adulthood.

Just as the diet of the mother, including the intake of alcohol and drugs, may affect the developing fetus, the diet of infants and children may also affect their intellectual development and their behaviour. Studies have shown that malnutrition is associated with lower levels of activity, less attentiveness, lack of initiative, and low tolerance of frustration. Behaviour of children can change with short-term nutrition supplements. For example, Guatemalan children who were given nutritional supplements were observed to have less anxiety, more curiosity, and greater involvement in games than children who were not given supplements (Barrett, 1984; Dasen et al., 1988). The problem of malnutrition is not just a matter of nutrition, but also a matter of care and interaction with adults. For example, caretakers of malnourished children may interact with them less than do caretakers of healthy children. As a malnourished child shows reduced activity, caretakers tend to respond to the child with less frequency and enthusiasm. Then the malnourished child withdraws from interaction, creating a potentially serious vicious cycle (Dasen et al., 1988).

Physiological (not necessarily genetic) differences between populations may also be responsible for some personality differences in adulthood. Research by Ralph Bolton suggests that a physiological condition known as hypoglycemia may be responsible for the high levels of aggression recorded among the Qolla of Peru (Bolton, 1973).

(People with hypoglycemia experience a big drop in their blood sugar level after they ingest food.) Bolton found that about 55 percent of the males he tested in a Qolla village had hypoglycemia. Moreover, those men with the most aggressive life histories tended to be hypoglycemic. Whether hypoglycemia is induced by genetic or environmental factors or both, the condition can be alleviated by a change in diet.

The sociobiological approach has aroused considerable controversy in cultural anthropology, probably because of its apparent emphasis on genes, rather than experience and learning, as determinants of human behaviour. Cultural ecologists have argued that the customs of a society may be more or less adaptive because cultural behaviours also have reproductive consequences. It is not just an individual's behaviour that may have reproductive consequences. So does natural selection also operate in the evolution of culture? Most biologists think not. They say there are substantial differences between biological and cultural evolution. How do cultural evolution and biological evolution compare? To answer this question, we must remember that the operation of natural selection requires three conditions, as we have already noted: *variation*, *heritability* or mechanisms that duplicate traits in offspring, and *differential reproductive success*. Do these three requirements apply to cultural behaviour?

In biological evolution, variability comes from genetic recombination and mutation. In cultural evolution, it comes from the recombination of learned behaviours and from invention (Campbell, 1995). Cultures are not closed or reproductively isolated, as species are. A species cannot borrow genetic traits from another species, but a culture can borrow new things and behaviours from other cultures. The custom of growing corn, which has spread from the Americas to many other parts of the world, is an example of this phenomenon. As for the requirement of heritability, although learned traits obviously are not passed to offspring through purely genetic inheritance, parents who exhibit adaptive behavioural traits are more likely to "reproduce" those traits in their children, who may learn them by imitation or by parental instruction. Children and adults may also copy adaptive traits they see in people outside the family. Finally, as for the requirement of differential reproductive success, it does not matter whether the trait in question is genetic or learned or both. As Henry Nissen emphasized, "behavioural incompetence leads to extinction as surely as does morphological disproportion or deficiency in any vital organ. Behaviour is subject to selection as much as bodily size or resistance to disease" (Nissen, 1958).

Many theorists are comfortable with the idea of applying the theory of natural selection to cultural evolution, but others prefer to use other terminology when dealing with traits that do not depend on purely genetic transmission from one generation to the next. For example, Robert Boyd and Peter Richerson discuss human behaviour as involving "dual inheritance." They distinguish cultural transmission, by learning and imitation, from genetic transmission, but they emphasize the importance of understanding both and the interaction between them (Boyd and Richerson, 1985). William Durham also deals separately with cultural transmission, using the term *meme* (analogous to the term gene) for the unit of cultural transmission. He directs our attention to the interaction between genes and culture, calling that interaction "co-evolution," and provides examples of how genetic evolution and cultural evolution may lead to changes in each other, how they may enhance each other, and how they may even oppose each other (Durham, 1991).

So biological and cultural evolution in humans

HISTORICAL PERSPECTIVES

Blaming Nurture on Nature: The Rise and Demise of Eugenics

The term "eugenics" was coined in the early 1870s by Francis Galton, a cousin of Charles Darwin. *Eugenics* was deemed to be the scientific study of "racial" improvement, or the science of increasing human happiness through the improvement of inherited characteristics. During the early twentieth century, Charles B. Davenport was one of the most influential geneticists in the United States. In 1911 he published *Heredity in Relation to Eugenics* in which he stated:

> The general program of the eugenicist is clear—it is to improve the race by inducing young people to make a more reasonable selection of marriage mates; to fall in love intelligently. It also includes the control by the state of the propagation of the mentally incompetent. It does not imply the destruction of the unfit either before or after birth.

Davenport's friend Madison Grant built on Davenport's work to produce a master plan for ending crime and poverty. In 1916 Davenport published *The Passing of the Great Race*, which became a bestselling book. The central thesis of Davenport's book was the instigation of a rigorous process of selection through the elimination of those who are weak or unfit—in other words, of those society considered social failures. While such concepts are shocking to read today, the eugenics movement was a part of mainstream science during this time, with most of its support coming from the medical profession.

Of course, there is inherent danger in applying Darwin's theory of natural selection to moral and social issues within a population. But this is exactly what the eugenics movement was proposing. The morally and socially inferior, in the eyes of dominant society, were considered the product of "bad breeding." This is the classic argument of nature versus nurture or genes versus behaviour. Of course there is often a complex interaction between the two, but clearly the eugenics movement was an attempt to attribute social problems to genetic inheritance. This resulted in the rise of the theory of social Darwinism, which came to serve as a "scientific" justification for racism, although at the time eugenicists did not perceive themselves as racists. In particular, in North America eugenics became a vehicle for social discrimination against immigration.

The eugenics movement was not limited to the United States. Both Britain and Canada developed eugenics programs. The main support for eugenics in Canada and elsewhere came from the medical profession, who believed that understanding heredity could improve public health. With this support the movement gained ground in the early part of the twentieth century. The major effort in Canada was the development of large-scale programs of reproductive sterilization of the

MODERN EVOLUTIONARY THEORY 101

may not be completely separate processes. As we will discuss, some of the most important biological features of humans—such as two-legged walking and relatively large brains—may have been favoured by natural selection because our ancestors made tools, a cultural trait. Conversely, the cultural trait of informal and formal education may have been favoured by natural selection because humans have a long period of immaturity, a biological trait.

As long as the human species continues to exist and the social and physical environment continues to change, there is reason to think that natural selection of biological and cultural traits will also continue. However, as humans learn more and more about genetic structure, they will become more and more capable of curing genetically

caused disorders and even altering the way evolution proceeds. Today, genetic researchers are capable of diagnosing genetic defects in developing fetuses, and parents can and do decide often whether to terminate a pregnancy. Soon genetic engineering will probably allow humans to fix what society sees as defects and even try to "improve" the genetic code of a growing fetus. Whether and to what extent humans should alter genes will undoubtedly be the subject of continuing debate. Whatever the decisions we eventually make about genetic engineering, they will affect the course of human biological and cultural evolution.

"unfit" or "feeble-minded" and the screening of non-Western- European immigrants who were considered lower on the social scale. In the late 1920s and early 1930s the Eugenics Board was established in some provinces, and legislation for the sterilization of the mentally unfit instigated in some provinces. While there were ongoing critics of eugenics during this period, it was not until World War II, and the Nazi shift in the application of the theory of eugenics from mass sterilization to mass genocide, that support of eugenics began to diminish in Canada.

While the eugenics movement in Canada is now just an echo, we must be careful not to forget the lessons of the past as we cross the threshold toward unlocking the human genome. Because of information from the Human Genome Project, family history and genetic screening may be the most powerful diagnostic tools available to physicians in the near future. While the mapping of the human genome will revolutionize the areas of disease prevention

and treatment, one must also consider the possibility and implications of genetic discrimination. Consider recurring popular expressions of this theme in Aldous Huxley's *Brave New World* and recently with the film *Gattica*. Genetic screening may also lead to an increase in selective termination of pregnancies.

How can we discriminate between proper and improper use of genetic information? Should genetic information be revealed to third parties such as insurance companies and employers? Critics of genetic testing have cited various kinds of harm that might result from dissemination of its results. If it is widely known that someone will die young, or is vulnerable to a particular disease, others may treat that person differently. They may regard marriage and even friendship with such a person as less attractive. In some cases, people might be unemployable or uninsurable as a consequence of what others know about their genes.

Can humans use such technology for eugenic purposes, such as

creating superhumans or for biological warfare? Possibly, but recombinant DNA techniques are not the problem. After all, the lack of such technology has not prevented genocide, ethnic cleansing, sterilization, and rape. The absence of recombinant technology did not prevent the use of natural biological weapons (such as smallpox-infected blankets given to Native Americans in the United States in the nineteenth century) or the manufacture and use of poison gas in World War I and since. It is not technology or the absence of it that explains evil; it is other things. All technology has advantages and disadvantages, and we have a responsibility to curb the disadvantages as much as we can, which is why an ethics assessment is needed in the application of these advances in scientific knowledge.

Source: McLaren A. 1990. Our Own Master Race: Eugenics in Canada 1885–1945. Toronto: McClelland and Stewart Inc.

CURRENT ISSUES

Do We Need to Fear Genetic Engineering?

So much is known about molecular genetics that it is now possible to alter individual genes and even whole organisms in very precise ways. The genetic revolution occurred very quickly after the structure of DNA was first identified in 1953 by James Watson and Francis Crick. Particular genetic traits could then be linked to particular sequences of DNA messages. In the 1970s, the development of *recombinant DNA* (rDNA) techniques allowed researchers to splice pieces of DNA from one organism into the DNA of another, in precise locations. Researchers learned how to make copies by putting these "recombined" strands into host organisms such as bacteria, which reproduce by *cloning*. The applications of these techniques are potentially enormous. *Biotechnology* companies are already applying genetic engineering to manufacture medicines (such as insulin and a vaccine against hepatitis B) and to produce more desirable plant and animal products (for example, a strain of tomato that can be shipped when it's ripe without spoiling). They are also working on how to reintroduce altered cells into organisms to fix genetic defects. As of now about 4000 human disorders are known to be caused by defects in a few genes; theoretically it should be possible to "fix" these disorders some day through genetic engineering. As more becomes known about the precise location of genes and the DNA sequences that convey particular information, much more engineering will be possible. Already some imagine that genetic therapy will eventually cure various cancers and heart disease.

Might there be risks associated with such interventions? Some fear that recombinant DNA engineering may have disastrous consequences. Could a dangerous runaway strain of bacteria or virus be produced in the lab? Might a kind of Frankenstein be produced? Could unscrupulous governments mandate certain kinds of alterations? Do we have reason to entertain such fears?

It is important to remind ourselves that although DNA alteration by recombinant techniques is new, genetic engineering is not new. Humans have genetically altered plants and animals for thousands of years. We usually do not call it genetic engineering—we call it domestication or breeding. To be sure, the mechanism of traditional genetic engineering—selective breeding—is different from DNA splicing, but the effect is genetic alteration nonetheless.

By breeding animals and plants for preferred traits, humans are able to produce breeds of horses, dogs, cattle, varieties of corn and beans, and all of the other animals and plants we depend on for food, fibre, and other materials and chemicals. All of them are different, often very different, from their wild progenitors. Humans have also domesticated micro-organisms. An example that goes back thousands of years is the yeast used for brewing beer and baking bread; a more recent example is a particular mould used to produce penicillin. And live vaccines that are deliberately weakened viruses, as, for example, in the vaccine against polio, have already been widely used to prevent illness.

So what does our past engineering tell us about the risks of future engi-

Summary

1. Mendel's and subsequent research in genetics and our understanding of the structure and function of DNA and mRNA help us to understand the biological mechanisms by which traits may be passed from one generation to the next.

2. The two sources of biological variation are genetic recombination and mutation.

3. Natural selection can also operate on the behavioural characteristics of populations. The approaches called sociobiology and behavioural ecology involve the application of evolutionary principles to the behaviour of animals. Much controversy surrounds the degree to which the theory of natural selection can be applied to human behaviour, particularly cultural behaviour. There is more agreement that biological and cultural evolution in humans may influence each other.

4. The sociobiological approach has aroused considerable controversy in cultural anthro-

neering? In general, the past suggests that no serious harm is attributable to domestication. In fact, domesticated animals and plants are less likely to do well if reintroduced into the wild than their wild cousins. They usually need human help to eat, to get shelter from the elements, and to care for their offspring. So why should genetic engineering be any different? It has basically the same purpose as selective breeding—humans want organisms, large or small or microscopic, to be useful to humans. However, a major difference is that modern genetic engineering is introducing new genetic material into many of these organisms. Unlike forced selection, where domesticated plants and animals are bred for certain forms of pre-existing variation, genetic engineering introduces genetic material across species boundaries. For example, a new type of genetically engineered corn reduces the need for powerful weed killers through the incorporation of a bacterial gene that acts as a natural pesticide. One argument against this development has been the potential for these crops to be more vulnerable to devastation if insects develop immunity to this genetically

engineered "pesticide." There is no reason not to expect this development—we have seen the emergence of drug-resistant strains of bacteria as a result of selection. Another concern is the potential for genetically engineered organisms to replicate, spread, and mutate beyond our control, although it is reassuring that DNA in nature can cross over from one organism to another and that such natural genetic alteration is not generally harmful to us.

Health concerns over genetically altered organisms include the possibility that transgenic plants and animals could stimulate allergic reactions in some people, and that biological contamination can occur in the recombinant DNA process that might cause illness and even death. For example, in the 1980s, a genetically altered food supplement, L-tryptophan, was associated with over 30 deaths and sickness in at least 5000 people. There is the public fear that a dangerous microbe could be accidentally released from a laboratory and multiply uncontrollably. But, as already noted, any microbe or new genetic form is unlikely to be as hardy as its

wild cousins. If a bacterium were to be mistakenly released, it would not enter an artificially empty environment like a sterile petri dish. The natural environment is already filled with bacteria (most of them beneficial to humans), as well as other organisms that attack bacteria. In short, it is not so easy to produce a harmful microbe.

The improbability of making destructive organisms does not mean that humans should not guard against the possibility. That is why we have government agencies to certify new products, along with guidelines for testing procedures and oversight panels. A new product of recombinant DNA research has to be approved before it can be widely used.

Sources: Berg P, Singer M. 1992. Dealing with Genes: The Language of Heredity. Mill Valley, CA: University Science Books. p 221–244.

Campbell AM, Microbes: The Laboratory and the Field; Davis BD, The Issues: Prospects versus Perceptions, and Summary and Comments: The Scientific Chapters; Miller HI, Regulation. All in: Davis BD, editor. 1991. The Genetic Revolution: Scientific Prospects and Public Perceptions. Baltimore: Johns Hopkins University Press. p 28–44, 1–8, 239–265, 196–211.

pology because of its emphasis on genes, rather than experience and learning, as determinants of human behaviour. The biocultural approach taken by anthropology recognizes the interplay between genetic (nature) and environmental (nurture) factors.

5. Genetic engineering is becoming an important aspect of modern society with improved crops that help feed our populations, medical breakthroughs, and improvements to quality of life. However, like any technology, it has advantages and disadvantages and we must be careful to

minimize the negative impact that such technologies will have for all living things.

Glossary Terms

allele   (p. 88)

behavioural ecology   (p. 97)

chromosomes   (p. 88)

crossing-over   (p. 93)

dominant   (p. 87)

genes   (p. 88)

Critical Questions

1. What are the moral and ethical implications of genetic engineering? How far should such processes be allowed to go?

2. How might the discovery of genetic cures and the use of genetic engineering affect the future of evolution?

3. Why do you think humans have remained one species?

4. There is a strong interrelationship between environmental and genetic influences on behaviour. How do these affect the way in which we view and try and solve current social problems in Canada? in the world?

Internet Exercises

1. Explore the Human Behavior and Evolution Society at **www.hbes.com/**. Select the Articles/Journal section and summarize at least two recent articles related to human evolution.

2. Visit the home page of *Evolution (International Journal of Organic Evolution)* at **http://lsvl.la.asu.edu/evolution/**. By looking at the table of contents, provide a bibliography of at least 15 articles related to human evolution.

3. Read the article on speciation as it relates to Darwinian evolution at **www.santarosa.edu/lifesciences/ensatina.htm**. Summarize your findings.

Suggested Reading

Boyd R, Richerson PJ. 1985. Culture and the Evolutionary Process. Chicago: University of Chicago Press. The authors develop mathematical models to analyze how biology and culture interact under the influence of evolutionary processes.

Brandon RN. 1990. Adaptation and Environment. Princeton, NJ: Princeton University Press. After defining basic concepts regarding adaptation and the theory of natural selection, the author emphasizes that the process of adaptation and its outcomes cannot be understood without analysis of the environment.

Chan L. 1994. Changing Conceptions of Evolutionary Theory. In: Herring DA, Chan L, editors. Strength in Diversity: A Reader in Physical Anthropology. Toronto: Canadian Scholars' Press. p 21–46. This paper outlines the conceptual development of alternative approaches to evolutionary theory including the role of behaviour.

Chiras DD. 1995. Human Biology: Health, Homeostasis, and the Environment. Second edition. St. Paul, MN: West. An Introductory Textbook in Human Biology. See Chapters 3 to 5 for a detailed discussion of chromosomes, DNA, RNA, principles of heredity, and genetic engineering.

Devillers C, Chaline J. 1993. Evolution: An Evolving Theory. New York: Springer-Verlag. Aimed at the general audience, this book addresses the questions: What is the place of humans in the living world? What is evolution? How can the observed data be explained? Appendices give more detailed information.

Dobzhansky T. 1962. Mankind Evolving: The Evolution of the Human Species. New Haven, CT: Yale University Press. A classic demonstration that the mechanisms of evolution, primarily natural selection, are still active.

Durham WH. 1991. Coevolution: Genes, Culture, and Human Diversity. Stanford, CA: Stanford University Press. A discussion of the evolution of culture that considers how theory and research point to the interaction of genes and culture in human populations.

May E. 2002. The Growth of Biological Thought: Diversity, Evolution, and Inheritance. Cambridge, MA: Belknap Press of Harvard University Press. A history of ideas that discusses the successful and unsuccessful attempts to understand problems in the study of evolution.

Shanahan T. 2004. The Evolution of Darwinism: Selection, Adaptation and Progress in Evolutionary Biology. Cambridge: Cambridge University Press. A historical critique of the key concepts in Darwin's theory of evolution.

6 THE LIVING PRIMATES

The goal of *primatology*, the study of primates, is to understand how different primates have adapted anatomically and behaviourally to their environments. The results of such studies may help us to understand the behaviour and evolution of the human primate.

But how can living primates such as chimpanzees tell us anything about humans or the primates that were our ancestors? After all, each living primate species has its own history of evolutionary divergence from the earliest primate forms. All living primates, including humans, evolved from earlier primates that are now extinct. Nonetheless, by observing how humans and other primates differ from and resemble each other, we may be able to infer how and why humans diverged from the other primates.

Together with fossil evidence, anatomical and behavioural comparisons of living primates may help us reconstruct what early primates were like. For example, if we know that modern primates that swing through the trees have a particular kind of shoulder bone structure, we can infer that similar fossil bones probably belonged to an animal that also swung through the trees. Differing adaptations of living primates may also suggest why certain divergences occurred in primate evolution. If we know what traits belong to humans, and to humans alone, this knowledge may suggest why the line of primates that led to humans branched away from the line leading to chimpanzees and gorillas.

In this chapter we first examine the common features of the living primates. Next we introduce the different animals that belong to the order Primates, focusing on the distinctive characteristics of each major type. Following this, we discuss briefly how we can apply what we know about behaviour in living primate groups as models for hominid behaviour. Then we discuss possible explanations for some of the adaptations exhibited by different primate species. We close with a look at the traits that make humans different from all other primates. The purpose of this chapter is to help us understand more about humans. Therefore, we emphasize the features of primate anatomy and behaviour that perhaps have the greatest bearing on human evolution.

Common Primate Traits

All primates belong to the class Mammalia, and they share all the common features of mammals. Except for humans, the bodies of primates are covered with dense hair or fur, which provides insulation. Even humans have hair in various places, though perhaps not always for insulation. Mammals are *warm-blooded*; that is, their body temperature is more or less constantly warm and usually higher than that of the air around them. Almost all mammals give birth to live young that, while still in the mother's womb, develop to a considerable size, and all are nourished once they are born by suckling from the mother's mammary glands. The young have a relatively long period of dependence on adults after birth. This period is also a time of learning, for a great deal of adult mammal behaviour is learned rather than instinctive. Play is a learning technique common to mammal young and is especially important to primates, as we shall see later in this chapter.

In addition to their mammalian features, the primates have a number of physical and social traits that set them apart from other mammals.

Physical Features

No single physical feature of the primates is unique to them; animals from other orders share one or more of the characteristics described below. However, the complex of all these physical traits is unique to primates (Napier and Napier, 1967; Smuts et al., 1987).

Many skeletal features of the primates reflect an **arboreal** (tree-living) existence. All primate hind limbs are structured principally to provide support, but the feet in most primates can also grasp things. Some primates—orangutans, for instance—can suspend themselves from their hind limbs. The forelimbs are especially flexible, built to withstand both pushing and pulling forces. Each of the hind limbs and forelimbs has one bone in the upper portion and two bones in the lower portion (with the exception of the tarsier). This feature has changed little since the time of the earliest primate ancestors. It has remained in modern primates (although many other mammals have lost it) because the double bones give great mobility for rotating arms and legs. Another characteristic structure of primates is the clavicle, or collarbone. The clavicle also gives primates great freedom of movement, allowing them to move the arms at the shoulders both up and down and back and forth. Although humans obviously do not use this flexibility for arboreal activity, they do use it for other activities. Without a clavicle we could not throw a spear or a ball; no fine tools could be made and no doorknobs turned if we did not have rotatable forearms.

Primates generally are **omnivorous**; that is, they eat all kinds of food, including insects and small animals, tree gums, flowers and nectar as well as fruits, seeds, leaves, and roots. The teeth of primates reflect this omnivorous diet. The chewing teeth—the **molars** and **premolars**—are very unspecialized, particularly in comparison with those of other groups of animals, such as the grazers. The front teeth—the **incisors** and **canines**—are often very specialized, principally in the lower

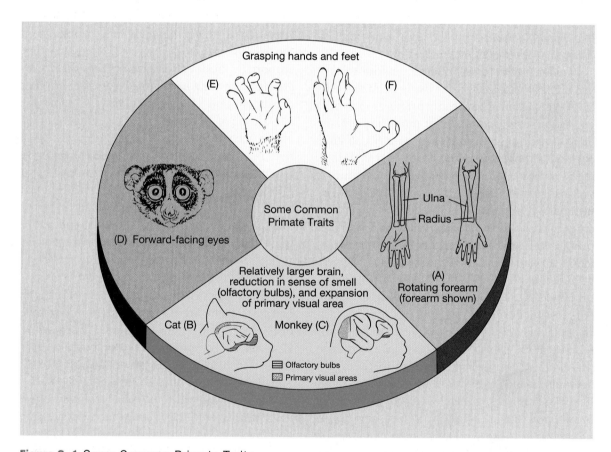

Figure 6–1 Some Common Primate Traits

Sources: (A): Wolff RG. 1991. Functional Chordate Anatomy. Lexington, MA: D. C. Heath and Company. p 255.

(B, C): Deacon T. 1992. Primate Brains and Senses. In: Jones S, Martin R, Pilbeam D, editors. The Cambridge Encyclopedia of Human Evolution. New York: Cambridge University Press. p 110. Reprinted with permission of Cambridge University Press.

(D): Cartmill M. Non-Human Primates. In: Jones S, Martin R, Pilbeam D, editors. The Cambridge Encyclopedia of Human Evolution. New York: Cambridge University Press. p 25. Reprinted with permission of Cambridge University Press.

(E, F): Ibid., p 25. Reprinted with permission of Cambridge University Press.

primates. For example, in many species of the suborder prosimians the slender, tightly packed lower incisors and canines form a "dental comb" the animals use in grooming or for scraping hardened gum (which is a food for them) from tree trunks (Bearder, 1987). Primate hands are extremely flexible. As Figure 6–1 indicates, all primates have **prehensile**—grasping—hands, which they can wrap around an object. Primates have five digits on on each hand and foot (in some cases, one digit may be reduced to a stub), and their nails, with few exceptions, are broad and flat, not clawlike. This structure allows them to grip objects; the hairless, sensitive pads on their fingers, toes, heels, and palms also help them to grip. Most primates have **opposable thumbs**, a feature that allows an even more precise and powerful grip.

Vision is extremely important to primate life. Compared with other mammals, a relatively larger portion of the primate brain is devoted to vision rather than smell. Primates are characterized by *stereoscopic vision*. Their eyes are directed forward rather than sideways, as in other animals—a trait that allows them to focus on an object (insects or other food or a distant branch) with both eyes at once. Most primates also have colour vision, perhaps to recognize when plant foods are ready to eat, although the extent of this vision varies by region and species. By and large, these characteristics are more developed in anthropoids (monkeys, apes, and humans) than in prosimians.

Another important primate feature is a large brain relative to body size. That is, primates generally have larger brains than do animals of similar size, perhaps because their survival depends on an enormous amount of learning, as we discuss later. In general, animals with relatively large brains seem to mature more slowly and to live longer than animals with relatively small brains (Richard, 1985). The more slowly an animal grows up and the longer it lives, the more it can learn.

Finally, the primate reproductive system sets this order of animals apart from other mammals. Males of most primate species have a pendulous penis that is not attached to the abdomen by skin, a trait shared by a few other animals, including bats and bears. Females of most primate species have two nipples on the chest (a few prosimians have more than two nipples). The uterus is usually constructed to hold a single fetus (although some prosimians give birth to twins or triplets), not a litter, as with most other animals. This reproductive system can be seen as emphasizing quality over quantity—an adaptation possibly related to the dangers of life in the trees (Martin, 1975). Primate infants tend to be relatively well developed at birth, although humans, apes, and some monkeys have helpless infants. Most infant primates, except for humans, can cling to their mothers from birth. Primates typically take a long time to mature. For example, the rhesus monkey is not sexually mature until about 3 years of age, the chimpanzee not until about age 9.

Social Features

For the most part, primates are social animals. Just as physical traits such as grasping hands and stereoscopic vision may have developed as adaptations to the environment, so may have many patterns of social behaviour. For most primates, particularly those that are **diurnal**—that is, active during the day—group life may be crucial to survival, as we will see later in this chapter.

Dependency and Development in a Social Context. Social relationships begin with the mother and other adults during the fairly long dependency period of primates. (For the dependency period of primates, the infancy and juvenile phases, see Figure 6–2.) The prolonged dependency of infant monkeys and apes probably offers an evolutionary advantage in that it allows infants more time to observe and learn the complex behaviours essential to survival while enjoying the care and protection of mature adults.

Primates without a warm, social relationship with a mother or another individual do not appear to develop appropriate patterns of social interaction. In many primate groups the mother is not the only individual providing care to the dependent young. Among grey langur monkeys, the birth and subsequent rearing of a baby absorb the

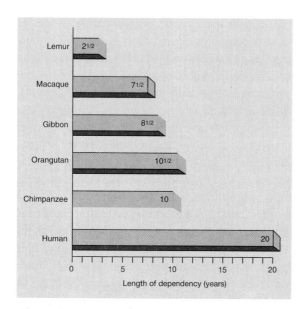

Figure 6–2 A Comparison of the Dependency Periods of Primate Offspring

Source: Data from Jolly A. 1985. The Evolution of Primate Behavior. Second edition. New York: Macmillan. p 292.

attention of most female members of the troop (Nicolson, 1966). In some primate species, the father may expend as much time caring for infants as the mother (Gray, 1985).

Primates at Play. We know, from early investigations of social learning in young primates, the importance of maternal care to baby rhesus monkeys. Play is another crucial ingredient of normal development during the dependency period. Just as monkeys raised without mothers showed abnormal behaviour as adults, so did monkeys raised with mothers but lacking peers to play with. In fact, when some of the monkeys raised without mothers were allowed a regular playtime with peers, many of them behaved more normally (Russon, 1990).

Play is important for learning (Dohlinow and Bishop, 1972). It provides practice for the physical skills necessary or useful in adulthood. For example, young monkeys racing through the trees at top speed are gaining coordination that may save their lives if they are chased by predators later on. Play is also a way of learning social skills, particularly in interacting and communicating with

other members of the group. Some dominance relationships seem to be established partly through the rough-and-tumble games that older juveniles play, where winning depends on such factors as size, strength, and agility. These qualities, or the lack of them, may influence the individual's status throughout adult life. Other factors also help determine an individual's status. For instance, the mother's status has been shown to be very important in some primates (Sade, 1965; Hausfater et al, 1982).

Learning from Others. We know that primates, non-human and human alike, learn many things in social groups. Among humans, children often imitate others, and adults often deliberately teach the young. In English we say, "Isn't it cute how Tommy 'apes' his father." But do apes (and monkeys) imitate others, or do they just learn to do similar things whether or not a model is observed? There is controversy among researchers as to how much imitation versus independent learning occurs in non-human primates. Even more arguable is whether deliberate teaching occurs among non-human primates (Tomasello, 1990; Visaberghi and Munkenbeck Fragaszy, 1990).

Some fieldworkers have suggested that chimpanzees may learn by imitation to use tools. For example, Jane Goodall cited an occasion when a female with diarrhea picked up a handful of leaves to wipe her bottom. Her 2-year-old infant watched closely, and then twice picked up leaves to wipe its own clean behind (van Lawick-Goodall, 1971). Termite "fishing," using a grass stalk to withdraw termites from a termite mound, is probably the best known example of chimpanzee tool use. Immature chimpanzees in the wild have been observed to watch attentively and pick up stalks while others are "fishing." And mothers let their infants hold on to the stalks while the mothers "fish." But some observers do not think these reports provide clear evidence of imitation or teaching. Even though the mother lets the infant hold on to the "fishing" stalk, the infant is doing the activity with her, not watching it and then independently repeating it soon after (Visaberghi and Munkenbeck Fragaszy, 1990).

Primates can learn from direct teaching, but they learn mostly by imitation and trial and error.

Primate Communication. Systems of communication are not unique to human beings. Other animal species communicate in a variety of ways, including sound, odour, and body movement. For example, chemical signatures (detectable by odour) may communicate information about identity, age, or sex of an individual (Zeller, 1987). Facial expressions also are a means of communication in primates: Anne Zeller, a physical anthropologist at the University of Waterloo who specializes in primates, has identified 33 different components of facial expressions in macaques. Primates can learn to interpret messages communicated through facial

expressions. Infants are born only able to communicate and understand a few messages. The evidence is clear that social learning is the main source of this ability (Zeller, 1992; Zeller, 1994).

Although primates use all three methods of communication (sound, odour, and body movement), sound is the method that most concerns us because spoken language is human beings' major means of communication. Non-human primates also communicate vocally, but their range is limited in comparison with that of humans. Anne Zeller suggests that communication may have evolved to maintain social systems, although it also promotes survival and reproduction since it transmits ecological information as well (Zeller, 1992).

Recent research suggests that some monkey and ape calls in the wild are also *referential* (vocalizations that seem to refer to an object or event). However, when we say that a communication (call, word, sentence) is *symbolic*, we mean at least two things. First, the communication has meaning even when its referent (whatever is referred to) is not present. Second, the meaning is arbitrary; the receiver of the message could not guess its meaning just from the sound(s) and does not know the meaning instinctively. In other words, symbols have to be learned. There is no compelling or "natural" reason that the word *dog* in English should refer to a smallish four-legged omnivore.

Vervet monkeys in Africa are not as closely related to humans as are African apes, but provide an example of symbolic communication. Scientists who have observed vervet monkeys in their natural environment consider at least three of their alarm calls to be symbolic because each of them *means* (refers to) a different kind of predator—eagles, pythons, or leopards—and monkeys react differently to each call. For example, they look up when they hear the "eagle" call. Experimentally, in the absence of the referent, investigators have been able to evoke the normal reaction to a call by playing it back electronically. Another indication that the vervet alarm calls are symbolic is that infant vervets appear to need some time to learn the referent for each. Very young infants apply a particular call to more animals than adult vervets do. So, for example, infant vervets will often make the eagle warning call when they see any flying bird. The infants learn the appropriate referent apparently through adult vervets' repetition of infants' "correct" calls; in any case, the infants gradually learn to restrict the call to eagles. This process is probably not too different from the way some North American infants in English-speaking families first apply the "word" *dada* to all adult males and gradually learn to restrict it to one person (Seyfarth and Cheney, 1982).

All of the non-human vocalizations we have described so far enable individual animals to convey messages. The sender gives a signal that is received and "decoded" by the receiver, who usually responds with a specific action or reply. How is human vocalization different? Since monkeys and apes appear to use symbols at least some of the time, it is not appropriate to emphasize symbolism as the distinctive feature of human language. However, there is a significant quantitative difference between human language and other primates' systems of vocal communication. All human languages employ a much larger set of symbols. Another and perhaps more important difference is that the other primates' vocal systems tend to be *closed*; different calls are not often combined to produce new, meaningful utterances. In contrast, human languages are *open* systems, governed by complex rules about how sounds and sequences of sounds can be combined to produce an infinite variety of new meanings (Hockett and Ascher, 1964).

The idea that humans can transmit many more complex messages than any other animal does not begin to convey how different human language is from other communication systems. No chimpanzee could say the equivalent of "I'm going to the ball game next Wednesday with my friend Jim if it's not raining." Humans not only can talk (and think) with language about things completely out of context but they also can be deliberately or unconsciously ambiguous in their messages. If a person asks you for help, you could say, "Sure, I'll do it when I have time," leaving the other person uncertain about whether your help is ever going to materialize.

Primates in the wild do not exhibit anything close to human language. However, recent successful attempts to teach apes to communicate with humans and with each other using human-created signs have led some scholars to question the traditional assumption that the gap between human and other animal communication is enormous. Chimpanzees Washoe and Nim and the gorilla Koko were taught hand signs based on American Sign Language (ASL, which is used by the hearing impaired in the United States). The chimpanzee Sarah was trained with plastic symbols, but Lana, Sherman, Austin, and a Bonobo, Kanzi, were trained on symbol keyboards connected to computers. Sherman and Austin began to communicate with each other about actions they were intending to do, such as the types of tools they needed to solve a problem, and they were able to classify items into categories, such as "food" and "tools." In contrast to other apes, Kanzi learned symbols just by seeing people point to them when they spoke to him. He did not need rewards or to have his hands put in the right position and he understood a great deal of what was spoken to him. For example, when he was 5 years old, Kanzi heard someone talk about throwing a ball in the river, and he turned around and did so. Kanzi has come closest of all the "students" to having a primitive English grammar when he strings symbols together (Savage-Rumbaugh, 1992). If chimpanzees and other primates have the capacity to *use* non-spoken language and even to understand spoken language, then the difference between humans and non-humans may not be as great as people used to think.

Are these apes really using language? There is a lot of agreement among investigators that non-human primates have the ability to "symbol"—to refer to something (or a class of things) with an arbitrary "label"—that is, a gesture or a sequence of sounds (Hill, 1978). For example, the gorilla Koko (with a repertoire of about 375 signs) extended the sign for drinking straw to plastic tubing, hoses, cigarettes, and radio antennae. Washoe originally learned the sign *dirty* to refer to feces and other soil and then began to use it insultingly, as in "dirty Roger" when her trainer Roger

Fouts refused to give her things she wanted. Even the mistakes made by the apes suggest that they are using signs symbolically, just as words are used in spoken language. For example, the sign *cat* may be used for dog if the animal learned *cat* first.

In spite of the new evidence, Jane Hill believes that the answer about whether apes use language is still controversial because language is not one unitary thing. Every human language has certain ways of combining sounds and ways of *not* combining those sounds. Although apes do not use sounds, the combination of symbols can be thought of as analogous to the combining of sound elements. Yet there does not appear to be anything comparable to linguistic rules that dictate how sound elements can be combined. Another major difference is that humans have many kinds of discourse. Humans may make lists and speeches, tell stories, argue, and recite poetry. Apes do none of those things, but as these experiments suggest, they do have some of the capacities for some of the elements of human language. Therefore, understanding their capacities may help us better understand the evolution of human language (Hill, 1998).

Classification of Primates

Classification provides a useful way to refer to groups of species that are similar in biologically important ways. Sometimes classification schemes vary because the classifiers emphasize somewhat different aspects of similarity and difference. For instance, one type of classification stresses the evolutionary branching that led to the primates of today; another the quantity of shared features. A third approach considers the evolutionary lines as well as similarity and difference of features, but not all features are equally weighted. More "advanced" and specialized features that develop in an evolutionary line are emphasized in this approach (Conroy, 1990; Martin, 1992). Figure 6–3 gives a classification scheme that follows this last approach, but this is not the only way to classify the primates (adapted from Martin, 1992).

Despite the different ways to classify, there is generally little disagreement about how the various primates should be classified. Most of the disagreement, as we shall see when we discuss the various primates, revolves around the classification of tarsiers and humans.

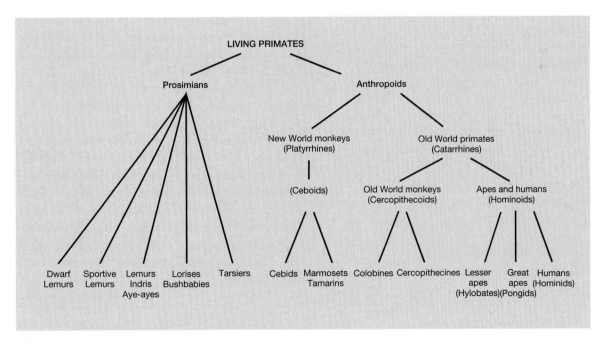

Figure 6–3 A Simplified Classification of the Living Primates

The order Primates is often divided into two suborders: the **prosimians** (literally, premonkeys) and the **anthropoids**. The prosimians include lemurs, lorises, and tarsiers. The anthropoid suborder includes New World monkeys, Old World monkeys, the lesser apes (gibbons, siamangs), the great apes (orangutans, gorillas, chimpanzees), and humans.

The Various Primates

Now that we have discussed their common features, let us focus on some of the ways in which the primates living in the world today vary.

Prosimians

The prosimians resemble other mammals more than the anthropoid primates do. For example, the prosimians depend much more on smell for information than do anthropoids. Compared with anthropoids, they typically have more mobile ears and whiskers, longer snouts, and little facial expression. The prosimians also exhibit many traits shared by all primates, including grasping hands, stereoscopic vision, and enlarged visual centres in the brain.

Lemur-like Forms. Lemurs and their relatives, the indris and the aye-aye, are found only on two island areas off the southeastern coast of Africa: Madagascar and the Comoro Islands. In fact, it is thought that these populations of lemurs were introduced to the Comoros Islands within the last 2000 years by humans since the time they first arrived on Madagascar. These primates range in size from the mouse lemur to the 1.2-metre-long indri. Members of the lemur group usually produce single offspring, although twins and even triplets are common in some species. Many of the species in this group are **quadrupeds**—animals that move on all fours, in the trees as well as on the ground. Some species, such as the indris, use their hind limbs alone to push off from one vertical position to another in a mode of locomotion called **vertical clinging and leaping.** Lemurs are mostly vegetarians, eating fruit, leaves, bark, and

flowers. Lemur species vary greatly in their group size. Many lemur species, particularly those that are **nocturnal** (active during the night), are solitary during their active hours. Others are much more social, living in groups ranging in size from a small family to as many as 60 members (Doyle and Martin, 1979; Tattersall, 1982). An unusual feature of the lemur-like primates is that females often dominate males, particularly over access to food. In most primates, and in most other mammals, female dominance over males is rarely observed (Richard, 1987).

Loris-like Forms. Representatives of the loris group, found in both Southeast Asia and sub-Saharan Africa, are all nocturnal and arboreal. They eat fruit, tree gum, and insects, and usually give birth to single infants (Bearder, 1987). There are two major subfamilies, the lorises and the bushbabies (galagos), and they come from distinct geographic regions and show wide behavioural differences. Bushbabies, found only in sub-Saharan Africa, are quick, active animals that hop between branches and tree trunks in the vertical-clinging-and-leaping pattern. On the ground they often resort to a kangaroo-like hop. Lorises, which are found in sub-Saharan Africa as well as in southern India, Sri Lanka, and Southeast Asia, are much slower, walking sedately along branches, hand over hand in the quadrupedal fashion. Using searchlights and technical aids such as radio tracking, field researchers have learned a good deal about these nocturnal primates. For example, we now know that among bushbabies, females, particularly mothers and young adult daughters, stay together in small groups, whereas the males disperse. Newborns are born in nests or hollows of trees (which related females may share), and mothers return to nurse them regularly. A few days after birth, a mother may carry her infant in her mouth to nearby trees, "parking" it while she eats (Charles-Dominique, 1977; Martin and Bearder, 1979; Bearder, 1987).

Tarsiers. The nocturnal, tree-living tarsiers, found now only on the islands of the Philippines and Indonesia, are the only primates that depend completely on animal foods. They are usually

Prosimians such as these ring-tailed lemurs depend much more on smell than do anthropoids. Prosimians also have more mobile ears, whiskers, longer snouts, and relatively fixed facial expressions.

Nocturnal tree-living tarsiers, like this one in the Philippines, are the only primates that depend completely on animal foods. Their enormous eyes equip them to find insects and other prey in the night. Their elongated ankle bones (tarsals) make them very good at vertical clinging and leaping.

insect-eaters, but they sometimes capture and eat other small animals. They are well equipped for night vision, possessing enormous eyes, extraordinary eyesight, and enlarged visual centres in the brain. The tarsiers get their name from their elongated tarsal bones (the bones of the ankle), which give them tremendous leverage for their long jumps. Tarsiers are very skilled at vertical clinging and leaping. They live in family groups composed of a mated pair and their offspring. Like some higher primates, male and female tarsiers sing together each evening, presumably to advertise their territories (MacKinnon and MacKinnon, 1980).

The classification of tarsiers is somewhat controversial. Instead of placing them with the suborder prosimians, as we have done here, some classifiers group tarsiers with anthropoids. In this other classification scheme the suborders of primates are labelled **strepsirhines** (which means *wet noses* and includes lemurs and lorises) and **haplorhines** (which means *single noses*, and includes tarsiers and anthropoids). Tarsiers have chromosomes similar to those of other prosimians; they also have claws on some of their toes that they use for grooming, more than two nipples, and a uterus shaped like the uterus of other prosimians (two-horned). Like bushbabies, tarsiers move about through vertical clinging and leaping. In other respects tarsiers are more like the anthropoids. They have a reduced dependence on smell; not only are their noses smaller, but they lack the wet, doglike snout of lemurs. In common with the anthropoids, their eyes are closer together and are protected by bony orbits. Reproductively, the tarsier, like anthropoids, has a placenta that allows contact between the mother's blood and that of the fetus (Fleagle, 1988; Cartmill, 1992b).

Anthropoids

The anthropoid suborder includes humans, apes, and monkeys. Most anthropoids share several traits in varying degree. They have rounded braincases; reduced, non-mobile outer ears; and relatively small, flat faces instead of muzzles. They have highly efficient reproductive systems, including a placenta that is formed more fully than in any prosimian. They also have highly dextrous hands

(Napier and Napier, 1967). The anthropoid suborder is divided into two main groups: **platyrrhines** and **catarrhines**. These groups take their names from the nose shape of the different anthropoids, but as we shall see they differ in other features as well. Platyrrhines have broad, flat-bridged noses, with nostrils facing outward; these monkeys are found only in the New World, that is, in Central and South America. Catarrhines have narrow noses with nostrils facing downward, and include monkeys of the Old World (Africa, Asia, and Europe), as well as apes and humans.

New World Monkeys. Besides the shape of the nose and position of the nostrils, other anatomical features distinguish the New World monkeys (platyrrhines) from the catarrhine anthropoids. The New World species have three premolars, whereas the Old World species have two. Some New World monkeys have a prehensile (grasping) tail; no Old World monkeys do. All the New World monkeys are completely arboreal; they vary a lot

This howler monkey, like all platyrrhines, has a broad, flat-bridged nose. Platyrrhines live in the wild only in Central and South America and are arboreal.

in the size of their groups; and their food ranges from insects to nectar and sap to seeds, fruits, and leaves (Richard, 1985).

There are two main families of New World monkeys; one family contains marmosets and tamarins, the other cebid monkeys. The marmosets and tamarins are very small, have claws instead of fingernails, and give birth to twins who mature in about 2 years. Perhaps because twins are so common and the infants have to be carried, marmoset and tamarin mothers cannot take care of them alone. Fathers and older siblings have often been observed carrying infants. Indeed, males may do more carrying than females. Marmoset and tamarin groups may contain a mated pair (monogamy) or a female mated to more than one male (polyandry). The marmosets and tamarins eat fruit and tree sap, but like other very small primates, they obtain a large portion of their protein requirements from insects (Eisenberg, 1977; Sussman and Kinzey, 1984; Goldizen, 1987; Cartmill, 1992b).

Cebids are generally larger than marmosets, take about twice as long to mature, and tend to bear only one offspring at a time (Eisenberg, 1977). The cebids vary widely in size, group composition, and diet. For example, squirrel monkeys weigh about 1 kilogram, whereas woolly spider monkeys weigh more than 7 kilograms, making them the largest New World Monkey. Some cebids have small groups with one male-female pair; others have groups of up to 50 individuals. Some of the smallest cebids have a diet of leaves, insects, flowers, and fruits, whereas others are mostly fruit-eaters with lesser dependence on seeds, leaves, or insects (Crockett and Eisenberg, 1987; Robinson et al., 1987; Robinson and Janson, 1987).

Old World Monkeys. The Old World monkeys, or **cercopithecoids**, are related more closely to humans than to New World monkeys. They have the same dental formula as apes and humans. The Old World monkey species are not as diverse as their New World cousins, but they live in a greater variety of habitats. Some live both in trees and on the ground; others, such as the gelada baboon, are completely **terrestrial**, or ground-living. Macaques are found both in tropical jungles and on

A troop of baboons in Kenya spends most of its time on the ground.

snow-covered mountains, and they range from the Rock of Gibraltar to Africa to northern India, Pakistan, and Japan. There are two major subfamilies of Old World monkeys.

Colobine Monkeys. The colobine group includes Asian langurs, the African colobus monkeys, and several other species from Asia. These monkeys live mostly in trees, and their diet consists principally of leaves and seeds. Their digestive tracts are equipped to obtain maximum nutrition from a high-cellulose diet; they have pouched stomachs, which provide a large surface area for breaking down plant food, and very large intestinal tracts.

One of the most noticeable features of colobines is the flamboyant colour typical of newborns in several species. For example, in one species dusky grey mothers give birth to brilliant orange babies (Blaffer Hrdy, 1977). Observational studies suggest that the colobines are also unusual among the primates (except for humans) in that mothers let other group members handle their infants shortly after birth. However, males who are not members

of the group are dangerous for infants; males trying to enter and take over a group have been observed to kill infants. Infanticide is not typical of colobines and while documented first in colobines, it is found in several species outside of colobines. Although this description may suggest that a one-male group is the typical group structure, there does not appear to be a typical pattern for a given species. When more than one site of a species has been studied, both one-male and multiple-male groups have been found (Blaffer Hrdy, 1977).

Cercopithecine Monkeys. The cercopithecine subfamily of monkeys is found primarily in Africa (in Asia the cercopithecines are represented only by the genus Macaca), and includes more terrestrial species than any other subfamily of Old World monkeys. Many of these species are characterized by a great deal of *sexual dimorphism* (the sexes look very different); the males are larger, have longer canines, and are more aggressive than the females. Cercopithecines depend more on fruit than do colobines. They are also more capable of surviving in arid and seasonal environments (Napier, 1970). Pouches inside the cheeks allow cercopithecines to store food for later eating and digestion. An unusual physical feature of these monkeys is the *ischial callosities*, or calluses, on their bottoms—an adaptation that enables them to sit comfortably in trees or on the ground for long periods (Fedigan, 1982).

Studies of baboons and macaques suggest that closely related females form the core of a local group, or *troop*. In large groups, which are common among rhesus monkeys, many social behaviours seem to be determined by degree of biological relatedness. For example, an individual is most likely to sit next to, groom, or help an individual who is closely related maternally (Fedigan, 1982). Moreover, a closely related subgroup is likely to stay together when a large troop divides (Lee, 1983).

The Hominoids: Apes and Humans. The **hominoid** group includes three separate families: the lesser apes, or **hylobates** (gibbons and siamangs); the great apes, or **pongids** (orangutans, gorillas, and chimpanzees); and humans, or *hominids*. Several characteristics distinguish the hominoids from the other primates. Their brains are relatively large, especially the areas of the cerebral cortex associated with the ability to integrate data. The hominoids have several skeletal and muscular traits that point toward their common ancestry. All have fairly long arms, short, broad trunks, and no tails. The wrist, elbow, and shoulder joints of hominoids allow a greater range of movement than in other primates. Hominoid hands are longer and stronger than those of other primates. These skeletal features probably evolved along with the hominoids' unique abilities in suspensory locomotion. Unlike other anthropoids, who move quadrupedally along the ground or along tops of tree branches, hominoids often suspend themselves from below the branches and swing or climb hand over hand from branch to branch (Fleagle, 1988). This suspensory posture also translates to locomotion on the ground (see a more detailed discussion of bipedalism in the chapter on the first hominids).

The dentition of hominoids demonstrates some unique features as well (see Figure 6–4). Hominoid molars are flat and rounded compared with those of other anthropoids, and have what is called a **"Y-5" pattern** on the lower molars—that is, the lower molars have five cusps with a Y-shaped groove opening toward the cheek running between them. Other anthropoids have what is called a **bilophodont** pattern—their molars have two long ridges or "loafs" running parallel to the cheeks. All hominoids except for humans also have long canine teeth that project beyond the tops of the other teeth, and a corresponding space on the opposite jaw, called a **diastema**, where the canine sits when the jaws are closed. The contact of the upper canine and the lower third premolar creates a sharp cutting edge, in part due to the premolar being elongated to accommodate the canine (LeGros Clark, 1964). These dental features are related to the hominoids' diets, which often include both fibrous plant materials, which can be efficiently cut with sharp canines against elongated premolars, and soft fruits, which can be efficiently chewed with wide, flat molars.

The skeletal and dental features shared by the hominoids point toward their common ancestry. Their blood proteins show many similarities, too. This blood likeness is particularly strong among

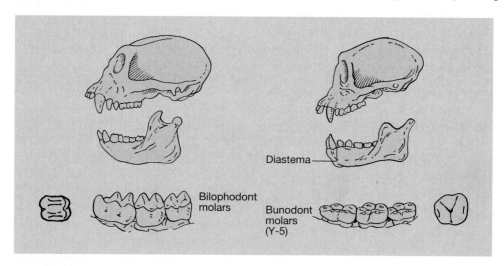

Figure 6–4

Difference in dentition between an Old World monkey (left) and an ape (right). In Old World monkeys, the cusps of the lower molars form two parallel ridges; in apes, the five cusps form a Y-shaped pattern. Apes also have a space between the lower canine and first premolar, called a diastema.

Source: Adapted from Boaz NT, Almquist AJ. 1999. Essentials of Biological Anthropology. Upper Saddle River, NJ: Prentice Hall. p 164.

RESEARCH FRONTIERS

Why Are Primates So Smart?

The fact that you are capable of reading this sentence is one of the most unique aspects of who you are as a modern human. No other animal is capable of reading, much less of complex language. And researchers are not entirely sure that other animals are even capable of thinking in the self-reflexive way that allows you to consider how unique your ability to read is. We humans have unique intellectual abilities. One way of understanding which of our abilities are unique is to look at our closest relatives—the non-human primates—and compare their intellectual abilities with ours. Joan Silk and Robert Boyd do precisely this, and through their comparative look at primate intellectual abilities, attempt to answer the question "Why are primates so smart?"

Primates are unusual, if not unique, in the relatively large size of their brains and the complexity of their social behavior. Monkeys and apes have larger brains in relation to their body size than members of any other taxonomic group, except the toothed whales and dolphins. Humans, of course, carry these evolutionary trends to even greater extremes.

One of the central questions of human evolution is, why has evolution made humans so smart? Understanding the nature and causes of the cognitive abilities of our closest living relatives, the non-human primates, will help us to answer this question . . . There is now considerable debate about the primary factors that favoured the evolution of relatively large brains and enhanced cognitive capabilities among non-human primates. Some researchers argue that ecological factors associated with locating and processing inaccessible food items are principally responsible for the elaboration of cognitive skills and the increase in brain size within the primates. Others have suggested that social demands associated with life in large and stable groups provided the primary selective force favoring cognitive complexity and intelligence among non-human primates.

Source: Silk JB, Boyd R. 2002. Why Are Primates So Smart? In: Peregrine PN, Ember CR, Ember M, editors. Physical Anthropology: Original Readings in Method and Practice. Upper Saddle River, NJ: Prentice Hall. p 53–67. Also in: Ember CR, Ember M, editors. 2003. New Directions in Anthropology. Upper Saddle River, NJ: Prentice Hall. CD-ROM.

---

chimpanzees, gorillas, and humans. For this reason, primatologists think chimpanzees and gorillas are evolutionarily closer to humans than are the lesser apes and orangutans, which probably branched off at some earlier point.

Gibbons and Siamangs. The acrobatic gibbons and their close relatives the siamangs are found in the jungles of Southeast Asia. The gibbons are small, weighing only about 5 to 7 kilograms. The siamangs are somewhat larger, no more than 11 kilograms. Both are mostly fruit-eaters, although they also eat leaves and insects. They are spectacular **brachiators**, with long arms and fingers that let them swing hand over hand through the trees (Preuschoft et al., 1984). A gibbon can move more than 9 metres in a single forward swing.

Gibbons and siamangs live in small family groups, with each group consisting of an adult pair, who appear to mate for life, and one or two immature offspring. When the young reach adulthood,

A white-handed gibbon demonstrates its ability as a brachiator.

they are driven from home by the adults. There is little sexual dimorphism—males and females do not differ in size or appearance—nor is there any clear pattern of dominance by either sex (although some species have sex-specific colouring). These lesser apes are also highly territorial; an adult pair advertises its territory by singing and defends it by chasing others away (Carpenter, 1940; Chivers, 1974; Chivers, 1980).

Orangutans. Orangutans survive only on the islands of Borneo and Sumatra. Unlike gibbons and siamangs, they are clearly recognizable as males or females. Males not only weigh almost twice as much as females (up to 90 kilograms), but they also have large cheek pads, throat pouches, beards, and long hair (Rijksen, 1978). Like gibbons and siamangs, orangutans are primarily fruit-eaters and arboreal. They are the heaviest of the arboreal primates, and perhaps for this reason they move slowly and laboriously through the trees. Orangutans are unusual among the higher primates in living basically solitary lives, except for mothers and their young; however, a recent field

Orangutans are unusual among the higher primates in living basically solitary lives, except for mothers with their young.

study of orangutans on Sumatra found that groups of as many as ten adults fed together in the same tree (Normile, 1998).

Different ideas have been proposed about the solitary habit of the orangutans that live in the mountainous areas of Borneo. One is that there may be insufficient food in any one tree or home range to support more than a single adult orangutan, a pretty large animal, as animals go. Orangutans may therefore live alone rather than in groups to obtain sufficient food each day without having to travel over a huge area (Galdikas, 1979). Another idea is that animals live in groups when they are subject to heavy predation; the large size of orangutans may make them immune to attacks from most animals, so living alone may be a viable option (Cheney and Wrangham, 1987). In fact, the clouded leopard has been suggested as the primary predator of orangutans (Seidensticker, 1985). A third idea, which on the face of it seems opposite to the second, is that living alone may be an adaptation to heavy predation by humans. The orangutan's best defence against humans with guns may be to hide alone in the trees (Rijksen, 1978).

Gorillas. Gorillas are found in the lowland areas of western equatorial Africa and in the mountain areas of the Democratic Republic of Congo, Uganda, and Rwanda (Fossey, 1983). Unlike the other apes, who are mostly fruit-eaters, gorillas mostly eat other parts of plants—stems, shoots (for example, bamboo), pith, leaves, roots, and flowers. The amount of fruit eaten by gorillas varies greatly. In many populations fruit eating is rare (for example, mountain gorillas); in some, such as the western gorillas and even some eastern populations, however, fruit is a common part of the diet (Tuttle, 1986). Gorillas are by far the largest of the surviving apes. In their natural habitats, adult males weigh up to 205 kilograms and females up to 113 kilograms. To support the weight of massive chests, gorillas travel mostly on the ground on all fours in a form of locomotion known as **knuckle walking**: they walk on the thickly padded middle joints of their fingers. Gorillas' arms and legs, especially those of the young, are well suited for climbing. As adults, their heavier bodies make climbing

Pascale Sicotte taking notes on a group of mountain gorillas.

more precarious (Schaller, 1963; Schaller, 1964) although Melissa Remis's work on lowland gorillas has shown that adult males stay close to the trunk while foraging for fruit in tree crowns, while the smaller and lighter females will venture into the crowns of trees by using major boughs as pathways (Remis, 1995). They sleep on the ground or in tub-shaped nests they make from non-food plants each time they bed down (Fossey, 1983).

Gorillas tend to live in groups and each group consists of a dominant male, called a *silverback*, other adult males, adult females, and immature offspring. Both males and females, when mature, seem to leave the groups into which they were born to join other groups. The dominant male is very much the centre of attention; he acts as the main protector of the group and the leader in deciding where the group will go next (Harcourt, 1979). In her study of mountain gorillas in Rwanda, Pascale Sicotte, a biological anthropologist at the University of Calgary, observed that female and juvenile gorillas can and do take an active and intentional role in defusing conflicts between males in the same group. It may be that availability of females for reproduction may partially explain the presence of multimale gorilla groups—more available females reduce the competition pressure on the dominant male, leading to the tolerance of young maturing silverbacks in the group. Some of these young males may end up staying in their natal group for many years past sexual maturity. Interestingly, once a group includes more than one adult male, the males can co-operate in trying to prevent their females from leaving during encounters with other groups. Indeed, Sicotte showed that herding of females during inter-group encounters occurred more often in groups that included more than one male (Sicotte, 1993; Sicotte, 1995; Czekala and Sicotte, 2000; Sicotte, 2002).

Chimpanzees. Perhaps because they form larger social communities and are easier to find, chimpanzees have been studied far more than gorillas. Chimpanzees live in the forested areas in Africa, from Sierra Leone in the west to Tanzania in the east.

Although they are primarily fruit-eaters, chimpanzees show many similarities to their close relatives the gorillas. Both are arboreal and terrestrial. Like gorillas, chimpanzees are good climbers, especially when young, and they spend many hours in the trees. Chimpanzees move best on the ground though, and when they want to cover long distances, they come down from the trees and move by knuckle walking. Occasionally, they stand and walk upright, usually when they are travelling

Chimpanzees in the wild, as shown here in Ivory Coast, use tools—in this case, a stone to crack nuts. But as far as we know, they don't use tools to make other tools, as humans do.

through tall grass or trying to see long distances. Chimpanzees sleep in tree nests that they carefully prepare anew, complete with a bunch of leaves as a pillow, each time they bed down (Goodall, 1963; van Lawick-Goodall, 1971).

Chimpanzees are only slightly sexually dimorphic. Males weigh a little more than 45 kilograms on the average, females somewhat less. Males do have longer canines though. For some time it was thought that chimpanzees ate only plant food. Although most of their diet is vegetarian, a small proportion comes from meat (Stanford, 1998). After three decades of studies at Gombe National Park in Tanzania and elsewhere, researchers have found that chimpanzees not only eat insects, small lizards, and birds, but they actively hunt and kill larger animals (Teleki, 1973). They have been observed hunting and eating monkeys, young baboons, and bushbucks in addition to smaller prey. At Gombe, the red colobus monkey is by far the most often hunted animal. So it is not only humans who endanger other primates (see Current Issues, *Endangered Primates*); the red colobus monkey population is quite small in areas of intense chimpanzee hunting. Hunting appears to be undertaken more often during the dry season when food is scarce—a time when the forest canopy is more open and the red colobus monkey is more visible (Stanford, 1998). Prey is caught mostly by the males, which hunt either alone or, most successfully, in small groups. It is then shared with—or perhaps more accurately begged by—as many as 15 other chimpanzees in friendly social gatherings that may last up to nine hours (Stanford, 1998).

Despite considerable observation, the organization of chimpanzee social groups is still not clear. Groups usually are multimale and multifemale, but the size may range considerably from a few to 100 or so members. In Gombe, males typically remain in their natal group throughout life, and females often move to a neighbouring group; but males in Guinea do not tend to stay in their natal groups (Normile, 1998). It appears that chimpanzees come together and drift apart depending upon circumstances, such as the availability of food and the risk of predation (Tuttle, 1986).

Hominids. According to the classification we use here, the hominoids we call hominids include only one living species—modern humans. Humans have many distinctive characteristics that set them apart from other anthropoids and other hominoids, which lead many to place humans in a category separate from the pongids. These traits will be discussed later in this chapter and also throughout much of the rest of the book. However, others believe that the differences are not so great as to justify a separate hominid category for humans. For example, humans, chimpanzees, and gorillas are very similar in their proteins and DNA and it is widely agreed that the lines leading to humans, chimpanzees, and gorillas diverged from a common ancestor, perhaps 5 million to 6 million years ago (Goodman, 1992). Whether we stress the similarities or differences between humans and apes does not matter that much; what does matter is that we try to understand the reasons for those similarities and differences.

Models for Hominid Behaviour

The idea that natural selection can operate on the behavioural or social characteristics of populations and not just on their physical traits is shared by cultural ecology and another, more recent, theoretical orientation called *behavioural ecology* (or, earlier, known as *sociobiology*). Developed mainly by biologists, particularly those who concentrated on the social insects (such as ants), the behavioural ecology or sociobiological orientation applies biological evolutionary principles to the social behaviour of animals, including humans. Some cultural anthropologists have employed behavioural ecology theory to explain some aspects of cultural variation (Irons, 1979; Boyd and Richerson, 1985).

How is behavioural ecology different from cultural ecology? Although both orientations assume the importance of natural selection in cultural evolution, they differ in important ways. Cultural ecology focuses mostly on what biologists

CURRENT ISSUES

Endangered Primates

In contrast to many human populations that are too numerous for their resources, many populations of non-human primates face extinction because they are not numerous enough. The two trends—human population growth and non-human primate extinctions—are related. Were it not for human expansion in many parts of the world, the non-human primates living in those habitats would not be endangered. Various lemur and other prosimian species of Madagascar, the mountain gorilla and red colubus monkeys of Africa, and the lion tamarin monkeys of Brazil are among the species most at risk.

Many factors are responsible for the difficulties faced by non-human primates, but most of them are directly or indirectly the result of human activity. Undoubtedly the biggest problem is the destruction of tropical rain forest, the habitat of most non-human primates, because of encroaching agriculture and cattle ranching and the felling of trees for wood products. The people who live in these areas are partly responsible for the threats to non-human primates—population pressure in the human populations increases the likelihood that more forest will be cleared and burned for agriculture, and in some areas non-human primates are an important source of hunted food. For example, in West Africa the local bush meat trade is having the most severe impact on primate and other mammal populations. However, in other areas world market forces are probably more important. The increasing need for "American" hamburger in fast-food restaurants has accelerated the search for places to raise beef inexpensively. There is also enormous demand for wood products from tropical forests; Japan imports half of all the timber from rain forests to use for plywood, cardboard, paper, and furniture.

Some would argue that it is important to preserve all species. Primatologists remind us that it is especially important to preserve primate diversity. One reason is scientific—we need these populations to study and understand how humans are similar and different and how they came to be that way. Another reason is the usefulness of non-human primates in biomedical research on human diseases; we share many of our diseases, and most of our genes, with many of our primate relatives. For example, chimpanzees can contract a slightly altered version of human immunodeficiency virus (HIV) called SIV. It is possible that HIV was transmitted to humans through the butchering of "bush meat" infected with SIV. However, chimpanzees do not get sick from SIV—their bodies seem to be able to cope with the virus. Thus, understanding the way in which this disease affects our closest primate relatives may help us in developing a cure for HIV in human populations.

So how can non-human primates be protected from us? There are only two major ways the non-human primates can be protected from extinction. Either human population growth into primate habitats has to be curtailed, or we have to find a way to preserve substantial populations of non-human primates in their native habitats.

Anthropologists have joined the initiative toward conservation of primate populations. Dian Fossey's study site, Karisoke, became an international centre for gorilla research when she established the Karisoke Research Center in 1967. Her murder in 1985 is considered by many as retaliation for her efforts to stop the poaching of gorillas and other animals in Africa. As a result of her efforts, mountain gorillas are now protected by the government of Rwanda. Jane Goodall's years of experience studying the chimpanzees in the forests of Gombe National Park revolutionized our understanding of their behaviour. She has now turned that knowledge toward conservation with the establishment of the Jane Goodall Institute for Wildlife Research, Education and Conservation. Biruté Galdikas, another student of the famous Louis Leakey, and a colleague of Dian Fossey and Jane Goodall, has also focused on primate conservation. She is a professor of anthropology at Simon Fraser University in British Columbia, and is one of the world's foremost authorities on the life and behaviour of orangutans. In 1986, in order to assist her research and work in Borneo and to help support orangutans around the world, Biruté Galdikas co-founded the Orangutan Foundation International, which is based in Los Angeles and has chapters in Australia, Canada, Indonesia, Taiwan, and the United Kingdom.

Sources: Mittermeier RA, Sterling EJ. Conservation of Primates. 1992. In: Jones S, Martin R, Pilbeam D, editors. The Cambridge Encyclopedia of Human Evolution. Cambridge: Cambridge University Press. p 33–36.

Nishida T. 1992. Introduction to the Conservation Symposium. In: Itoigawa N, Sugiyama Y, Sackett GP, Thompson RKR, editors. Topics in Primatology, volume 2. Tokyo: University of Tokyo Press. p 303–304.

The Jane Goodall Institute (**www.janegoodall .org/**).

would call **group selection**, or the natural selection of group characteristics. Cultural ecologists talk mostly about how a certain behavioural or social characteristic may be adaptive for a group or society in a given environment; a newly emergent behavioural or social trait that is adaptive is likely to be passed on to future generations by cultural transmission. In contrast, behavioural ecology focuses mostly on what biologists call **individual selection**—the natural selection of individual characteristics. Behavioural ecologists talk mostly about how a certain characteristic may be *adaptive* for an individual in a given environment (Irons, 1979). By **adaptive** is meant the ability of an individual to transmit her or his genes to future generations. Does this viewpoint imply that behaviour is transmitted only through genes? No, say behavioural ecologists. What matters is that behaviour is *heritable*—transmitted in some way, by genes or learning, to persons (usually offspring) who share one's genes (Low, 1998). If a certain behaviour is adaptive for individuals in a particular environment, it should become more widespread in future generations as the number of individuals with those traits increases.

The idea that behaviour is an adaptive mechanism to changing environmental pressures is the reason that anthropologists use living primates as models for understanding how early hominids may have behaved. Knowing something about their changing biology from the fossil record, and their changing environment from palaeoclimatic reconstructions, anthropologists can infer something about early hominid behaviour by observing modern primate behaviour under similar conditions. Culture of course is the ultimate extension of human behaviour and becomes an increasingly important aspect of evolutionary change, thus reinforcing the importance of the biocultural approach to anthropological research.

While studying a single primate species will not provide us with an ideal model for early hominids, understanding the variation in primate behaviour can help in understanding social organization in early hominids. There are two kinds of models for understanding the behaviour of human ancestors.

The first is living non-human primates, which are primarily models for hominid behaviour. The second is contemporary and recent (because there are few societies today that are unaffected by Western culture) non-Westernized populations of small, foraging societies that may have behavioural patterns similar to prehistoric human populations existing under similar conditions for the last several tens of thousands of years. This second model is known as *ethnographic analogy*.

Non-human primate models are based on either *experimental* or *natural* observations, and either *referential* or *conceptual* perspectives. The advantage of experimental observation is that specific variables can be strictly controlled, so the results of changing only one variable can often be explained. Of course, the disadvantage of experimental observation is imposing an artificial environment on the animals to be studied. The effect of this on the behaviour of the animals cannot be completely known. Field observation of primates in their natural environment tends to provide a truer picture of animal behaviour. The disadvantage of field studies, however, is that they are very expensive and extremely time consuming. Stanford's (1998) research on chimpanzee hunting behaviour is a classic example of referential modelling (for example, the chimpanzee hunting behaviour serves as a model for the hunting behaviour of early hominids). The conceptual approach—known as ecological, or strategic, modelling—doesn't focus on one particular species. Rather, researchers look for behavioural patterns among species, and those patterns become a model of early hominid behaviour (Dunbar, 1989).

Ethnographic analogy assumes that recent foraging or horticultural societies might have similar patterns of behaviour to prehistoric groups who lived under similar environmental conditions. However, two cautionary notes regarding ethnographic analogy are worth mentioning. First, modern or even recent historical groups are not completely isolated from the outside influences of the rest of the world, and therefore may exhibit behaviours that derive through cultural diffusion. Second, all such groups will have their own set of cultural qualities, which may not reflect any one universal behavioural pattern from prehistory. While there are no true completely foraging societies remaining, a number of cultures, including the Inuit, several groups of Australian aborigines, and !Kung San (Kalahari bushmen), have served as classic models for anthropology over the last century.

Explanations of Variable Primate Adaptations

Thus far we have discussed the common features of primates and introduced the different primates that survive in the world today. Now let us examine possible explanations, suggested by research, of some of the ways in which the surviving primates vary physically.

Body Size

Surviving primates vary enormously in body size, ranging from the 50 grams or so of the average grey mouse lemur to the 160 kilograms of the average male gorilla. What accounts for this significant variation? Three factors seem to predict body size—the time of day the species is active, where it is active (in the trees or on the ground), and the kinds of food eaten (Clutton-Brock and Harvey, 1977). All the nocturnal primates are small. Among the primates active during the day, the arboreal ones tend to be smaller than the terrestrial ones. Finally, species that eat mostly leaves tend to be larger than species that eat mostly fruits and seeds.

Why do these factors predict size? One important consideration is the general relationship in mammals between body weight and energy needs. In general, larger animals require more absolute energy, but smaller animals require much more energy per unit of body weight. That being so, smaller animals (and small primates) need more energy-rich food. Insects, fruits, gum, and sap are full of calories and tend to be more important in the diet of small primates. Leaves are relatively low in energy, so leaf-eaters have to consume a lot of food to get enough energy. They also need large stomachs and intestines to extract the nutrients they need, and a bigger gut, in turn, requires a

bigger skeleton and body (Jolly, 1985; Aiello, 1992). Small primates, which eat insects and other rich foods, probably would compete with birds for food. However, most very small primates are nocturnal, whereas most forest-living birds are diurnal. Energy requirements may also explain why arboreal primates are usually smaller. Moving about in trees usually requires both vertical and horizontal motion. The energy required to climb vertically is proportional to weight, so larger animals require more energy to climb. The energy for travelling horizontally, as on the ground, is not proportionate to weight, so larger animals use energy more efficiently on the ground than in the trees (Aiello, 1992). An additional consideration is the amount of weight that can be supported by small tree branches, where foods such as fruits are mostly located. Small animals can go out to small branches more safely than large animals. Also, ground dwellers might be bigger because large size is a protection against predation (Jolly, 1985).

Relative Brain Size

Larger primates usually have larger brains, but larger animals of all types generally have larger brains (see Figure 6–5). Primatologists are interested in *relative brain size*, that is, the ratio of brain size to body size.

Perhaps because human primates have relatively the largest brain size of any primate, we tend to think a larger brain is "better." However, a large brain does have "costs." From an energy perspective, the development of a large brain requires a great deal of metabolic energy; therefore, it should not be favoured by natural selection unless the benefits outweigh the costs (Parker, 1990).

Fruit-eating primates tend to have relatively larger brains than do leaf-eating primates. This difference may be due to natural selection that favours more capacity for memory, and therefore relatively larger brains, in fruit-eaters. Leaf-eaters may not need as much memory, because they depend on food that is more readily available in time and space, and therefore they may not have to remember where food might be found. In contrast, fruit-eaters may need greater memory and brain

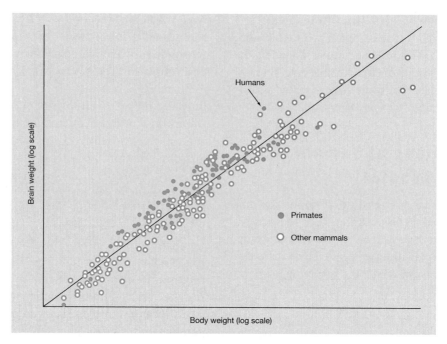

Figure 6–5

As this graph shows, larger animals generally have larger brains. Primates generally have even larger brains than we would expect from their body weight. Note that most of the primates (as indicated by the coloured circles) fall above the line showing the relationship between brain weight and body weight. The brains in primates are about twice as heavy as the brains of non-primate mammals of the same body weight.

Source: Deacon TW. 1992. Primate Brains and Senses. In: Jones S, Martin R, Pilbeam D, editors. The Cambridge Encyclopedia of Human Evolution. New York: Cambridge University Press. p 111. Copyright © 1992. Reprinted with permission of Cambridge University Press.

capacity because their foods ripen at different times and in separate places that have to be remembered (Clutton-Brock and Harvey, 1980; Milton, 1981). The brain requires large supplies of oxygen and glucose. Because leaf-eating primates do not have as much glucose in their diets as fruit-eating primates, they may also not have the energy reserves to support relatively large brains (Milton, 1988).

Group Size

Primate groups vary in size from solitary males and females with young (in orangutans) to a few individuals and young (as in gibbons) to the one hundred or so individuals in some Old World monkey troops (Jolly, 1985). What factors might account for such variation?

Nocturnal activity is an important indicator not only of small body size but also of small group size. Nocturnal primates feed either alone or in pairs (Clutton-Brock and Harvey, 1977). John Terborgh has noted that most nocturnal predators hunt by sound, so a nocturnal animal might best avoid attack by being silent (Terborgh, 1983). Groups are noisy, and therefore nocturnal animals might be more likely to survive by living alone or in pairs. On the other hand, a large group might provide advantages in the daytime. The more eyes, ears, and noses a group has, the more quickly a would-be predator might be detected—and perhaps avoided—and a larger group would have more teeth and strength to frighten or mob a predator that actually attacked (Jolly, 1985). But this line of reasoning would lead us to expect that all diurnal terrestrial species would have large groups. Yet not all do, so other factors must be taken into account. One seems to be the amount and density of food. If food occurs in small amounts and in separate places, only small groups can get enough to eat; if food occurs in large patches, there will be enough to support large groups (Jolly, 1985). An additional factor may be competition over resources. One suggestion is that substantial but separated patches of resources are likely to be fought over, and therefore individuals living in larger groups might be more likely to obtain access to them (Wrangham, 1980).

Sexual Dimorphism

Males and females of many animal species cannot readily be distinguished even though they differ in chromosome makeup and in their external and internal organs of reproduction. In contrast, many primates including humans are sexually dimorphic—that is, the females and males of the species are generally different in size and appearance. Gorillas are sexually dimorphic because there are significant differences in body size between males and females. Adult male gorillas also have much larger skulls, more dramatic musculature, and very large canine teeth relative to females.

In humans, females have proportionately wider pelvises. Males typically are taller and have heavier skeletons. A larger proportion of female body weight is fat; a larger proportion of male body weight is muscle. Males typically have greater grip strength, proportionately larger hearts and lungs, and greater aerobic capacity (greater intake of oxygen during strenuous activity). There is a tendency in our society to view "taller" and "more muscled" males as "better." Natural selection may have favoured these traits in males but different ones in females. For example, because females bear children, selection may have favoured earlier cessation of growth, and therefore less ultimate height in females so that the nutritional needs of a fetus would not compete with its mother's needs (Stini, 1971). Similarly, there is some evidence that females are less affected than males by nutritional shortages, presumably because they tend to be shorter

and have proportionately more fat (Frayer and Wolpoff, 1985). Natural selection may have favoured those traits in females because they resulted in greater reproductive success.

Distinctive Human Traits

We turn now to some of the features that distinguish humans from the other primates. Although we like to think of ourselves as unique, many of the traits we discuss here are at the extreme of a continuum that can be traced from the prosimians through the apes.

Physical Traits

Of all the primates, only humans consistently walk erect on two feet, which is known as **bipedalism**. Gibbons, chimpanzees, and gorillas (and even some monkeys and lemurs too) may stand or walk on two feet some of the time, but only for very short periods. All other primates require thick, heavy musculature to hold their heads erect; this structure is missing in humans, for our heads are more or less balanced on top of our spinal columns with the foramen magnum centred in the bottom of the skull. A dish-shaped pelvis (peculiar to humans), straight lower limbs, and arched, non-prehensile feet are all related to human bipedalism. Since we are fully bipedal, we can carry objects without impairing our locomotor efficiency. In Chapter 8 we will discuss the origins of human bipedalism in more detail and consider its effects on a diverse set of traits including toolmaking, prolonged infant dependency, and the division of labour by gender. Although many primates have opposable thumbs that enable them to grasp and examine objects, the greater length and flexibility of the human thumb allow us to handle objects with more firmness and precision.

The human brain is large and complex, particularly the **cerebral cortex**, which is the centre of speech and other higher mental activities. The brain of the average adult human measures more than 1300 cc, compared with 525 cc for the gorilla, the primate with the next largest brain. The frontal areas of the human brain are also larger than those of other primates, so that humans have more prominent foreheads than monkeys or gorillas. Human teeth reflect our completely omnivorous diet and are not very specialized, which may reflect the fact that we use tools and cooking to prepare our food. Many other primates have long lower canines, which are accommodated by a space in the upper jaw; in humans, the canines both look and act very much like incisors, and there are no spaces between the teeth. The human jaw is shaped like a parabolic arch, rather than a U shape, as in the apes, and is composed of relatively thin bones and light muscles. Humans are relatively hairless compared with other primates.

One other distinctive human trait is the sexuality of human females, who may engage in intercourse at any time throughout the year; most other primate females engage in sex only periodically, just around the time they can conceive (Thompson-Handler et al., 1984; White, 1996). Humans are also unusual among the primates in having female–male bonding. By this we mean that at least one of the sexes typically has sex with just one opposite-sex partner throughout at least one estrus or menstrual cycle. The bonding may not be monogamous—an individual may be bonded to more than one individual of the opposite sex (Ember and Ember, 1979). The importance of this trait in the evolution of modern human beings is an area of great interest to many anthropologists, and there are several theories for its development. It used to be thought that more or less continuous female sexuality may be related to female–male bonding, but comparative research on mammals and birds contradicts this idea. Those mammals and birds that have more frequent sex are not more likely to have male–female bonding (Ember and Ember, 1979; Ember and Ember, 1984).

Why, then, does human female sexuality differ from that of most other primates? One suggestion is that more or less continuous female sexuality became selectively advantageous in humans after female–male bonding developed through the growth of local groups consisting of at least several adult males and adult females (Ember and Ember,

1984). More specifically, the combination of group living and male–female bonding—a combination unique to humans among the primates—may have favoured a switch from the common higher-primate pattern of periodic female sexuality to the pattern of more or less continuous female sexuality. Such a switch may have been favoured in humans because periodic rather than continuous female sexuality would undermine female–male bonding in multimale–multifemale groups.

Field research on non-human primates strongly suggests that males usually attempt to mate with any females ready to mate. If the female (or females) a male was bonded to was not interested in sex at certain times, but other females in the group were, it seems likely that the male would try to mate with those other females. Frequent sexual relationships might jeopardize the male–female bond and thereby presumably reduce the reproductive success of both males and females. Hence, natural selection may have favoured more or less continuous sexuality in human females if humans were living in groups. If bonded adults lived alone, as do gibbons, non-continuous female sexuality would not threaten bonding, because sex with another individual would not be likely to occur. Similarly, seasonal breeding would also pose little threat to male–female bonds because all females would be sexually active at more or less the same time (Ember and Ember, 1984). So the combination of group living and male–female bonding in humans may explain why continuous female sexuality developed in humans. The bonobo, or pygmy chimpanzee, female engages in intercourse throughout the year, but bonobos do not have male–female bonding and the females are not interested in sex as often as human females (de Waal and Lanting, 1997). The difference here though is that much of bonobo sexual behaviour is not related to reproduction, but rather sex is used as a social tool to alleviate social stress and antagonism.

Behavioural Abilities

In comparison with other primates, a much greater proportion of human behaviour is learned and influenced by culture. As with many physical traits, we can trace a continuum in the learning abilities of all primates. The great apes, including orangutans, gorillas, and chimpanzees, are probably about equal in learning ability (Rumbaugh, 1970). Old and New World monkeys do much less well in learning tests, and, surprisingly, gibbons perform more poorly than most monkeys.

Toolmaking. The same kind of continuum is evident in inventiveness and toolmaking. With few exceptions, there is no evidence that any non-human primates except great apes use tools, although several species of monkeys use "weapons"—tree-dwelling monkeys have been observed dropping branches, stones, or fruit onto predators as the predators pass below them on the ground. Chimpanzees both fashion and use tools in the wild. As we have noted, they strip leaves from sticks and then use the sticks to "fish" termites from mound-shaped nests. They use leaves to mop up termites, to sponge up water, or to wipe themselves clean (Boesch and Boesch, 1990; Whiten et al., 1999). In fact, some researchers have observed Tai chimpanzees modifying tools before use, or making use of two tools at the same time to acquire a food source (Boesch and Boesch, 1990).

One example of chimpanzee tool use suggests planning. In Guinea, West Africa, observers watched a number of chimpanzees crack oil-palm nuts with two stones. The "platform" stone had a hollow depression; the other stone was used for pounding. The observers assumed that the stones had been brought by the chimpanzees to the palm trees, because no stones like them were nearby and the chimpanzees were observed to leave the pounding stone on top of or near the platform stone when they were finished (Jolly, 1985). Observers in other areas of West Africa have also reported that chimpanzees use stones to crack nuts. In one location in Liberia an innovative female appeared to have started the practice; it seems to have been imitated within a few months by others who previously showed no interest in the practice (Hannah and McGrew, 1987). Julio Mercader, a Canada Research Chair in Tropical Forest Archaeology at the University of Calgary, is opening up a new research niche he has termed "chimpanzee archaeology." His research builds upon the observation of some chimpanzees using tools to open nuts. One reason that makes this kind of research so important is that many of these instruments are similar to, though cruder than, the rough utensils that palaeoanthropologists have associated with early hominids. Mercader and his co-workers have excavated a Taï forest site called Panda 100. The site, formerly the location of so-called "Panda nut trees," revealed tree roots with pounding marks made by stones. Excavation around the roots revealed fragments of nutshells and nearly 500 stone artifacts, often including the remains of hammering stones, flakes, and pieces of shattered rock (Mercader et al., 2002).

In captivity, chimpanzees have also been observed to be inventive toolmakers. One mother chimpanzee was seen examining and cleaning her son's teeth, using tools she had fashioned from twigs. She even extracted a baby tooth he was about to lose (Anonymous, 1973).

Humans have usually been considered the only toolmaking animal, but observations such as these call for modification of the definition of toolmaking. If we define toolmaking as adapting a natural object for a specific purpose, then at least some of the great apes are toolmakers too. As far as we know, though, humans are unique in their ability to use one tool to make another.

Language. Only humans have spoken or symbolic language, but, as with toolmaking abilities, the line between human language and the communications of other primates is not as sharp as we once thought. Vocalizations in non-human primates can carry information about the sex of the animal vocalizing, group membership, social status and even an individual's identity. Many species of primates are now known to have vocalizations specific to certain kinds of threats, including different kinds of predators. There is an enormous selective advantage to those individuals that can distinguish predators by unique signalling. This advantage may have provided an evolutionary first step for the development of spoken language in humans.

How long humans have had spoken language is not known. Some think that the earliest *Homo sapiens*, perhaps 100 000 years ago, may have had the beginnings of language. Others believe that language developed more recently. One set of theoreticians of grammar suggest that there may be a language-acquisition device in the brain, as innate to humans as call systems are to other animals (Chomsky, 1975). As the forebrain evolved, this device may have become part of our biological inheritance. Whether the device in fact exists is not clear, but we do know that the actual development of individual language is not completely biologically determined. If it were, all human beings would speak the same brain-generated language. Instead, about 4000 to 5000 different and distinct languages have been identified. More than 2000 of them were still spoken as of recently, most by peoples who did not traditionally have a system of writing. Indeed, the earliest writing systems are not that old; they appeared only about 5000 years ago (Senner, 1989).

Nevertheless, the ability for language is determined partly by biology. For example, chimpanzees are physically incapable of "speaking" because of the structure of their upper respiratory system. To answer the question of when human language originated, we need to look for clues in the fossil record that show the appearance of changes in anatomical structures related to language capability. The positioning of the *larynx* is an important anatomical factor in the ability to "speak." In most mammals, the larynx is high in the throat to prevent choking—allowing animals to breathe and swallow food at the same time. The same is true of human infants (and is related to breast-feeding), but in adults the larynx drops to a position, unlike in any other animal, that allows us to speak. Since soft tissues are not preserved in the hominid record, we must look to associated skeletal evidence for these structures. This evidence includes the increased flexion of the **basicranium**—the base of the skull (Laitman et al., 1978; Laitman and Heimbuch, 1982; Leiberman, 1992; Leiberman et al., 1992). Further clues come from the structure of the brain, which can sometimes be preserved as an **endocast**—a preserved, fossilized impression of the interior braincase of a skull.

Efforts at reconstructing the skeletal anatomy associated with language in hominids suggest that Australopithecines—an earlier form of hominid—had apelike anatomy and brains that resemble living apes in both size and external form—thus, there is no apparent evidence for spoken language. However, as early as 2 million years ago, evidence from endocasts from Kenya of *Homo habilis*—the oldest species in the genus *Homo*—appear to show a more developed frontal lobe and **Broca's area**—the area that is responsible for the production of human speech (Tobias, 1987). Thus, there is some tantalizing evidence that the changes associated with speech are observed in the fossil records as early as 2 million years ago. This is not to say that spoken language existed—simply that evolutionary changes occurred in these early hominids that would allow for the development of spoken language. Further details of the evidence of language capabilities in each hominid group will be discussed in subsequent chapters.

Other Human Traits. Only humans hunt very large animals, unlike other primates. Also, humans are one of the few primates that are completely terrestrial. We do not even sleep in trees, as many other ground-living primates do. Perhaps our ancestors lost their perches when the forests receded, or cultural advances such as weapons or fire may have eliminated the need to seek nightly shelter in the trees. As well, we have the longest dependency period of any of the primates, requiring extensive parental care for well into the second decade of life.

Finally, humans are unlike almost all other primates in having a division of labour by sex in food-getting and food-sharing in adulthood. Among non-human primates, both females and males forage for themselves after infancy. Humans have more gender-role specialization, perhaps because males, unencumbered by infants and small children, were freer to hunt and chase large animals.

Having examined our distinctive traits and the traits we share with other primates, we need to ask what selective forces may have favoured the emergence of primates, and then what forces may have favoured the line of divergence leading to humans. These questions are the subjects of the next two chapters.

Summary

1. Although no living primate can be a direct ancestor of humans, we do share a common evolutionary history with the other surviving primates. Studying the behavioural and anatomical features of our closest living relatives may help us make inferences about primate evolution. Studying distinctive human traits may help us understand why the line of primates that led to humans branched away from the line leading to chimpanzees and gorillas.

2. No one trait is unique to primates. However, primates do share the following features: two bones in the lower part of the leg and in the forearm, a collarbone, flexible prehensile (grasping) hands, stereoscopic vision, a relatively large brain, only one (or sometimes two) offspring at a time, long maturation of the young, and a high degree of dependence on social life and learning.

3. The order Primates is divided into two suborders: the prosimians and the anthropoids. Compared with the anthropoids, prosimians depend more on smell for information. They have mobile ears, whiskers, longer snouts typically, and relatively fixed facial expressions. Anthropoids have rounded braincases; reduced, non-mobile outer ears; and relatively small, flat faces instead of muzzles. They have highly dextrous hands.

4. The anthropoid suborder is divided into two main groups: platyrrhines (monkeys of the New World) and catarrhines. The catarrhines are subdivided into cercopithecoids (Old World monkeys) and hominoids (apes and humans). The anthropoid apes consist of the hylobatids, or lesser apes (gibbons and siamangs), and the pongids, or great apes (orangutans, gorillas, and chimpanzees).

5. Along with the gorilla, the chimpanzee has proteins and DNA remarkably similar to that of humans, as well as anatomical and behavioural similarities to humans. Wild chimpanzees have been seen to create and use tools, modifying a natural object to fulfill a specific purpose. High conceptual ability is also demonstrated by the chimpanzee's and the gorilla's facility in learning sign language.

6. Variable aspects of the environment, differences in activity patterns, and variation in diet may explain many of the traits that vary in the primates. Nocturnal primates tend to be small and to live alone or in very small groups. Among diurnal species, the arboreal primates tend to be smaller and to live in smaller social groups than terrestrial primates. Fruit-eaters have relatively larger brains than leaf-eaters.

7. The differences between humans and the other anthropoids show us what makes humans distinctive as a species. Humans are totally bipedal; they walk on two legs and do not need the arms for locomotion. The human brain, particularly the cerebral cortex, is the largest and most complex. In contrast to females of almost all other primates, human females may engage in sexual intercourse at any time throughout the year. Human offspring have a relatively longer dependency stage. In comparison with other primates, more human behaviour is learned and influenced by culture. Spoken, symbolic language and the use of tools to make other tools are uniquely human behavioural traits. Humans also generally have a division of labour in food-getting and food-sharing in adulthood.

Glossary Terms

adaptive   (p. 124)

anthropoids   (p. 114)

arboreal   (p. 107)

basicranium   (p. 130)

bilophodont   (p. 118)

bipedalism   (p. 127)

brachiators   (p. 119)

Broca's area   (p. 130)

canines   (p. 108)

Critical Questions

1. How could you infer that a fossil primate lived in the trees?

2. Why are primates so intelligent?

3. Under what conditions would the ability to communicate be adaptive?

4. Why are humans dependent for so long?

Internet Exercises

1. Visit **www.unep-wcmc.org/** and **www.conservation.org** to see the current state of primate conservation worldwide. Which primates are currently the most endangered?

2. Visit **http://primatelit.library.wisc.edu/** for a searchable database on publications related to primate studies.

3. Visit the webpage of Canadian primatologist Dr. Anne Zeller, and view the QuickTime movies of her doing fieldwork at **www.arts.uwaterloo.ca/ANTHRO/rwpark/fac/zeller.html**. You might also want to visit her primate photo gallery at **http://artsms.uwaterloo.ca/anthropology/default.asp**.

4. Visit the Great Ape Project at **http://www.greatapeproject.org/** and click on the latest news reports. Read one of the reports of interest to you and summarize the article.

5. Want to hear some primate vocalizations? Go to **www.indiana.edu/~primate/primates.html** and listen to vocalizations from a number of different primates.

Suggested Reading

Burton FD, editor. Social Processes and Mental Abilities in NonHuman Primates: Evidences from Longitudinal Field Studies. Lewiston, NY: Edwin Mellen Press. A review of non-human primate sociality, intelligence in their behaviour, and evolutionary basis of primate behaviour by leading experts including many Canadian physical anthropologists.

Falk, D. 2000. Primate Diversity. New York: W.W. Norton and Co. A good general reference to primate studies.

Lee FC. 1999. Comparative Primate Socioecology. Cambridge Studies in Biological Anthropology 22, Cambridge University Press. An edited collection of papers that look at controversial issues surrounding the evolution of primate behavioural strategies including those of humans.

Jones S, Martin R, Pilbeam D, editors. 1992. The Cambridge Encyclopedia of Human Evolution. Cambridge: Cambridge University Press. About one-third of this comprehensive book reviews current information about primate classification, conservation, aspects of and variation in physique, physiology, behaviour, and cognitive abilities of the living primates.

Parker ST, Gibson KR, editors. 1990. "Language" and Intelligence in Monkeys and Apes: Comparative Developmental Perspectives. New York: Cambridge University Press. A volume of papers that apply frameworks from human developmental psychology and evolutionary biology to comparative studies of primate abilities.

Robbins MM, Sicotte P, and Stewart KJ, editors. 2001. Mountain Gorillas: Three Decades of Research at Karisoke. Cambridge: Cambridge University Press. A series of 15 papers on the ecology, social organization, and behaviour of mountain gorillas.

Rowe, N. 1996. The Pictorial Guide to the Living Primates. East Hampton, NY: Pogonias Press. A beautiful successor to Napier JR, Napier PH's Handbook of Living Primates, New York: Academic Press (1967), with a photograph or illustration of each of the living primates. This is the most complete collection of images yet published in a single source.

Setchell JM, Curtis DJ, editors. Field and Laboratory Methods in Primatology: A Practical Guide. Cambridge: Cambridge University Press. This manual is designed for students and researchers studying wild primates.

Smuts BB, Cheney DL, Seyfarth RM, Wrangham RW, Struhsaker TT, editors. 1987. Primate Societies. Chicago: University of Chicago Press. An extensive review, by some 50 primatologists, of primate species that have been studied in the wild.

Stanford C. 1998. Chimpanzee Hunting Behavior and Human Evolution. In: Ember CR, Ember M, Peregrine PN, editors. Research Frontiers in Anthropology. Upper Saddle River, NJ: Prentice Hall. Prentice Hall/Simon & Schuster Custom Publishing. An in-depth look at chimpanzee hunting—what goes on, what predicts it, and what implications it has for understanding human evolution.

Stier KB. 1999. Primate Behavioral Ecology. Boston: Allyn & Bacon Publishers. An in-depth look at primate behavioural ecology, comparing classic field studies with the latest information on how primates actually behave. Issues of conservation as they relate specifically to primates are also addressed.

7

PRIMATE EVOLUTION: FROM EARLY PRIMATES TO HOMINOIDS

CHAPTER OUTLINE

Primate palaeontologists and palaeoanthropologists focus on various questions about primate evolution. How far back in time did the primates emerge? What did they look like? What conditions, environmental and otherwise, favoured them? How did the early primates diverge after that point? What kinds of niches did the different primates occupy? Although our concern as anthropologists is largely with the emergence of humans, and with the primates that are in the ancestral line leading to humans, we must remember that evolution does not proceed with a purpose or to give rise to any particular species; rather, organisms adapt, or fail to adapt, to the environments in which they find themselves. Thus, the primate fossil record is full of diversity; it is also full of apparent extinctions. Most of the primate lineages of the past probably never left any currently living descendants at all (Ciochon and Etler, 1994).

The reconstruction of primate evolution depends upon the finding of fossil remains. Although many fossils have been discovered and continue to be discovered, the fossil record is still very incomplete. If geological strata are not uplifted, exposed by erosion, or otherwise accessible in the areas where ancient primates lived, palaeoanthropologists cannot recover their fossils. The fossils that are found are usually fragmented or damaged, and judgments about what the organism looked like may be based on one or just a few pieces. As we shall see, piecing together the evolutionary history of the primates requires much more than recovering fossil remains. The knowledge gained from anatomical studies of living species can allow us to make inferences about physical and behavioural traits that are likely to have been associated with the fossil features. Researchers use dating techniques developed in geology, chemistry, and physics to estimate the age of fossil remains (see Figure 7–1). Further, studies of ancient plants and animals, geography, and climate help us reconstruct the environments of ancient primates.

While there are many questions that continue to be asked about primate evolution, there are also a great many that we can answer at this point. We know that as of the early Eocene epoch, which began about 55 million years ago, primates with some of the features of modern prosimians had already emerged (see Figure 7–2 on page 137). Primates with monkey- and apelike features appeared in the Oligocene epoch, beginning about 34 million years ago. During the Miocene epoch, beginning about 24 million years ago, Old World monkeys and many different kinds of apes appeared. The ancient primates we know from fossils had some of the features of today's primates, but none of the ancient primates looked exactly like the primates of today.

In this and the following chapters we describe the main features of current theory and evidence about primate evolution, from the origin of primates to the origin of modern humans. In this chapter we deal with that part of the story before the emergence of definite bipedal hominids. Our overview covers the period from about 65 million years ago to the end of the Miocene, a little over 5 million years ago.

Interpreting the Fossil Record

How can paleoanthropologists know about what may have happened millions of years ago? There is no written record from that period from which to draw inferences. However, we do have the fossil record, and as you have seen, we have ways of "reading" the record left by fossils and of telling how old fossils are.

Much of the evidence for primate evolution comes from teeth, which along with jaws are the most common animal parts to be preserved as fossils. Animals vary in **dentition**—the number and kinds of teeth they have, their size, and their arrangement in the mouth. (See Figure 7–3 on page 138.) Dentition provides clues to evolutionary relationships because animals with similar evolutionary histories often have similar teeth. This is partly because teeth tend to change very little over time, both from an evolutionary standpoint and relative to other biological changes in a species. For example, no primate, living or extinct, has more than two incisors in each quarter of the jaw. That feature, along with others, distinguishes the primates from earlier mammals, which had three incisors in each quarter. Dentition also suggests the relative size of an animal and often offers clues about its diet. For example, comparisons of living primates suggest that fruit-eaters have flattened, rounded tooth cusps, unlike leaf- and insect-eaters, which have more pointed cusps (Kay, 1988b). CT scan methodology has helped palaeontologists image the internal parts of teeth, such as the thickness of enamel, which can also suggest the diet. Electron microscopy has revealed different patterns of growth in bones and teeth; different species have different patterns (Wood, 1994).

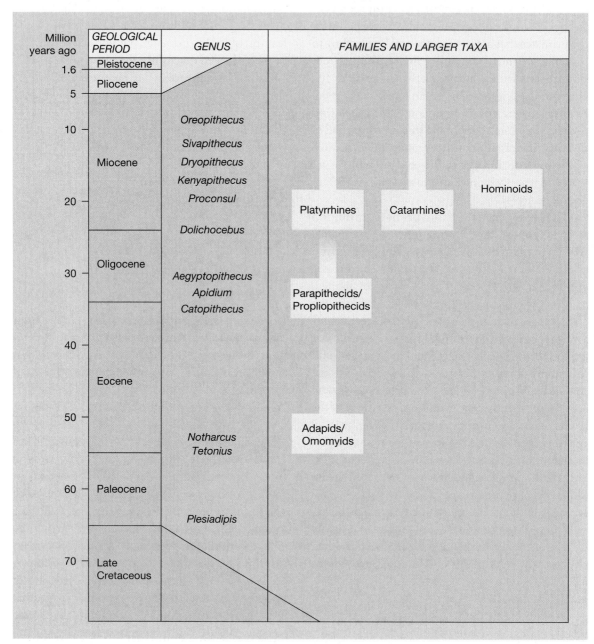

Figure 7–1 The Evolution of the Primates

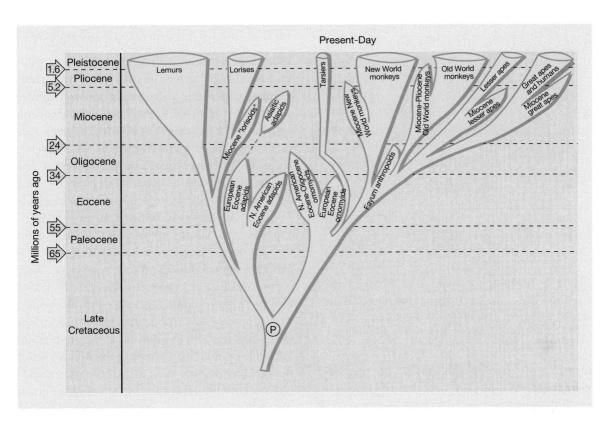

Figure 7–2

A view of the evolutionary relationships between early primates and living primates, adapted from one suggested by R. D. Martin. The primate lineages that do not extend to the present day indicate presumed extinctions. Branching from a common "stalk" suggests divergence from a common ancestor. The circled P in the figure represents the unknown common ancestor of all primates.

Sources: Martin RD and Martin AE. 1990. *Primate Origins and Evolution: A Phylogenetic Reconstruction.* Princeton, NJ: Princeton University Press.

The dates for the Paleocene, Eocene, Oligocene, and the beginning of the Miocene are from: Berggren WA, Kent DV, Obradovich JD, Swisher III, CS. 1992. Toward a Revised Paleogene Geochronology. In: Prothero DR, Berggren WA, editors. *Eocene-Oliocene Climatic and Biotic Evolution.* Princeton, NJ: Princeton University Press. p 29–45.

The dates for the end of the Miocene, Pliocene, and Pleistocene are from: Jones S, Martin R, Pilbeam D, editors. 1992. *The Cambridge Encyclopedia of Human Evolution.* New York: Cambridge University Press. p 469.

Palaeontologists can tell much about an animal's posture and locomotion from fragments of its skeleton. As you can see in Figure 7–4 (page 139), *arboreal quadrupeds* have front and back limbs of about the same length; because their limbs tend to be short, their centre of gravity is close to the branches on which they move. They also tend to have long grasping fingers and toes. *Terrestrial quadrupeds* are more adapted for speed, so they have longer limbs and shorter fingers and toes. Disproportionate limbs are more character-istic of vertical clingers and leapers, and brachia-tors. *Vertical clingers and leapers* have longer, more powerful hind limbs; *brachiators* have longer fore-limbs (Conroy, 1990). Even though soft tissues are not preserved, much can be inferred from the fossils themselves. For example, the form and size of muscles can be estimated by marks found on the bones to which the muscles were attached. The underside of the cranium may also provide infor-mation about the proportions of the brain devoted to vision, smell, or memory. The skull also reveals

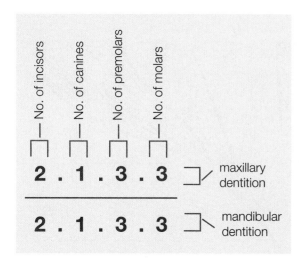

Figure 7–3 Dental Formula

Each row indicates the number of tooth types in the upper and lower jaws. From left to right the tooth types are incisors, canines, premolars, and molars.

information about characteristics of smell and vision. For example, animals that rely more on smell than on vision tend to have longer snouts; nocturnal animals tend to have larger eye sockets.

A reconstruction of smilodectes, a primate found in western North America from 50 million years ago.

The Emergence of Primates

When did the primates first emerge? This question turns out to be hard to answer from the current fossil record. Some palaeoanthropologists have suggested that fossil finds from the **Paleocene** epoch, which began about 65 million years ago, represent archaic primates, or *plesiadapiforms*. However, other palaeoanthropologists find so few similarities between them and later obvious primates that they do not include the plesiadapiforms in the order of primates (Ciochon and Etler, 1994; Fleagle, 1994; Cartmill, 1998). There is no dispute, however, about fossils dating from the early **Eocene**, about 55 million years ago. These oldest, definite primates appear in two major groups of prosimians—*adapids* and *omomyids*. The adapids led to modern lemurs and lorises (*strepsirhines*) and the omomyids led to tarsiers and anthropoids (*haplorhines*). Omomyids exhibit many characters that seem to be more anthropoid-like including a larger brain, the beginnings of postorbital closure around the eyes, and a relatively short face.

Since these two kinds of primates are different from each other in major ways, and because they both appeared rather abruptly at the border of the Paleocene and Eocene, there presumably was an earlier common primate ancestor. However, this earlier primate ancestor has not yet been identified, or at least there is no consensus about it yet among palaeoanthropologists. Even if we do not know exactly what the earliest primate looked like, the presence of the prosimians in the Eocene tells us that we need to look to an earlier time to explain the emergence of the primates. The circled P in Figure 7–2 represents the unknown common ancestor, which Robert D. Martin suggests lived in the late Cretaceous. Others think the common ancestor emerged in the Paleocene.

Now we turn to the environmental conditions in which we see the emergence of the primates.

The Environment

It is generally agreed that the earliest primate may have emerged by the Paleocene, 65 million years to

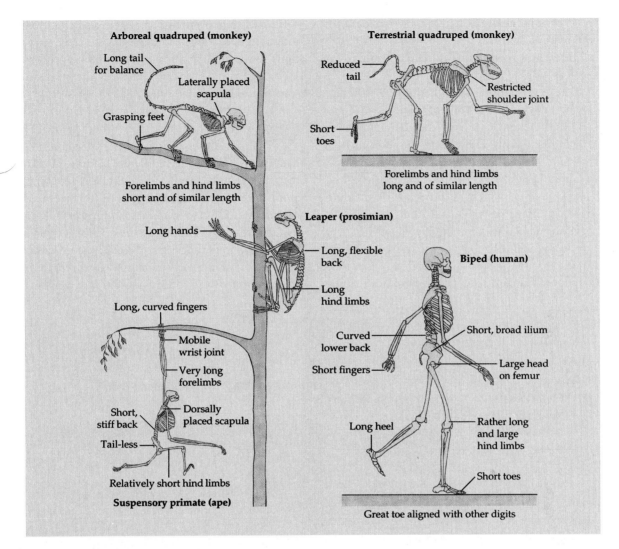

Figure 7–4 Primate Locomotion

The four major modes of primate locomotion include vertical clingers and leapers (prosimians), quadrupedalism (monkeys), brachiation (apes), and bipedalism (hominids).

Source: Fleagle JG. 1988. Primate skeletons. Primate Adaptation and Evolution. Second edition. San Diego: Academic Press. p 245–251. Reprinted with permission of Elsevier.

55 million years ago, and perhaps earlier, in the late **Cretaceous**. What was the environment like in those times? The beginning of the Paleocene marked a major geological transition, what geologists call the transition from the Mesozoic to the Cenozoic era. About 75 percent of all animal and plant life that lived in the last part of the Cenozoic (the late Cretaceous) vanished by the early Paleocene. The extinction of the dinosaurs is the most famous of these disappearances (Conroy,

1990). (See Current Issues, *Is Evolution Slow and Steady or Fast and Abrupt?* in Chapter 5.)

The climate of the Cretaceous period was almost uniformly damp and mild, but temperatures began falling at the end of the era. Around the beginning of the Paleocene epoch, both seasonal and geographic fluctuations in temperature began to develop. The climate became much drier in many areas, and vast swamplands disappeared. The climate of the Paleocene was generally somewhat cooler than in the late Cretaceous, but by no means cold. Forests and savannahs thrived in fairly high latitudes, and subtropical climates existed as far north as Alaska (Conroy, 1990).

One important reason for the very different climates of the past is **continental drift**. (See Figure 7–5.) In the early Cretaceous (ca. 135 million years ago), the continents were actually clumped into two large land masses or "supercontinents"—*Laurasia*, which included North America and Eurasia, and *Gondwanaland*, which included Africa, South America, India, Australia, and Antarctica. By the beginning of the Paleocene (ca. 65 million years ago) Gondwanaland had broken apart, with South America drifting west away from Africa, India drifting east, and Australia and Antarctica drifting

south. As the continents changed position, they moved into locations with different climatic conditions. More importantly, however, the very movement of the continents affected the climate, sometimes on a global scale (Habicht, 1979).

 Large land masses affect wind and weather patterns differently than smaller land masses, so weather patterns across Laurasia would have been different from weather in the subsequently separated continents. When continents collide, mountain ranges are formed, and mountains can also have a profound effect on weather patterns. Clouds drop their moisture as they meet a mountain range, and therefore the side away from the prevailing movement of weather systems is often very dry (a condition called a *rain shadow*),

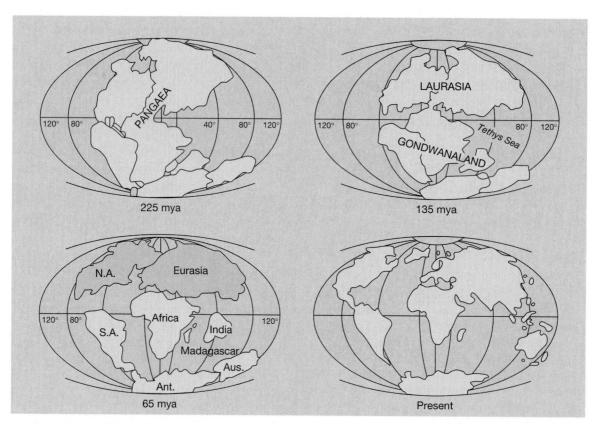

Figure 7–5 Continental Drift

The supercontinent Pangaea split into Laurasia and Gondwanaland 135 million years ago (mya). These further divided into the continents as we know them today.

whereas the other side (called the *windward side*) is often wet. When the location of continents prevents the movement of ocean currents from the tropics to the poles, the earth's climate becomes colder. Continental drift and climate change had profound effects on the evolution of the primates (Vrba, 1995).

With changes in climate came changes in vegetation. Although the first deciduous trees and flowering plants arose during the Cretaceous, it was during the late Paleocene and early Eocene that large trees with large fruits and seeds became common (Sussman, 1991). Although some mammals date from the Cretaceous, many different types of mammal evolved and diversified during the Paleocene. Primate palaeontologists think primates evolved from one of these *radiations*, or extensive diversifications, probably from the **insectivore** order of mammals, including modern shrews and moles, that is adapted to eating insects.

The new kinds of plant life opened up sources of food and protection for new forms of animals. In other words, new habitats became exploitable. Of most interest to us is that the new deciduous plant life provided an abundant food supply for insects. The result was that insects proliferated in both number and variety, and in turn there was an increase in insectivores—mammals that ate insects. The insectivores were very adaptable and were able to take advantage of many different habitats—under the ground, in water, on the ground, and above the ground, including the woody habitat of bushes, shrubs, vines, and trees. It was the last kind of adaptation, above the ground, that may have been the most important for primate evolution. The woody habitat had been exploited only partially in earlier periods. Then several different kinds, or *taxa*, of small animals, some of which may have been archaic primates, began to take advantage of the woody habitat.

What in Particular May Have Favoured the Emergence of Primates?

The traditional explanation of primate origins is called the *arboreal theory*. According to this view, the primates evolved from insectivores that took to the trees. Different palaeoanthropologists emphasized different possible adaptations to life in the trees. In 1912, G. Elliot Smith suggested that taking to the trees favoured vision over smell. Searching for food by sniffing and feeling with the snout might suit terrestrial insectivores, but vision would be more useful in an animal that searched for food in the maze of tree branches. With shorter snouts and the declining importance of the sense of smell, the eyes of the early primates would have come to face forward. In 1916, Frederic Wood Jones emphasized changes in the hand and foot. He thought that tree climbing would favour grasping hands and feet, with the hind limbs becoming more specialized for support and propulsion. In 1921, Treacher Collins suggested that the eyes of the early primates came to face forward not just because the snout got smaller. Rather, he thought that three-dimensional binocular vision would be favoured because an animal jumping from branch to branch would be more likely to survive if it could accurately judge distances across open space (Cartmill, 1974; Richard, 1985). In 1968, Frederick Szalay suggested that a shift in diet—from insects to seeds, fruits, and leaves—might have been important in the differentiation of primates from insectivores (Szalay, 1968).

In 1974 Matt Cartmill highlighted some crucial weaknesses in the arboreal theory (Cartmill, 1974; Cartmill, 1992a; Cartmill, 1998). He argued that tree living is not a good explanation for many of the primate features because there are living mammals that dwell in trees but seem to do very well without primatelike characteristics. One of the best examples, Cartmill says, is the tree squirrel. Its eyes are not front-facing, its sense of smell is not reduced in comparison with other rodents, it has claws rather than nails, and it lacks an opposable thumb. Yet these squirrels live very successfully in trees. Furthermore, other animals have some primate traits but do not live in trees or do not move around in trees as primates do. For example, carnivores, such as cats, hawks, and owls, have forward-facing eyes, and the chameleon and some Australian marsupial mammals that prey on insects in bushes and shrubs have grasping hands and feet.

Cartmill proposes that the early primates may have been insect-eaters, and that three-dimensional vision, grasping hands and feet, and reduced claws may have been advantageous for hunting insects on the slender vines and branches that filled the undergrowth of tropical forests. Three-dimensional vision would allow the insect hunter to gauge the prey's distance accurately. Grasping feet would allow the predator to move quietly up narrow supports to reach the prey, which could then be grabbed with the hands. Claws, Cartmill argues, would make it difficult to grasp very slender branches. The sense of smell would have become reduced, not so much because it was no longer useful, but because the location of the eyes at the front of the face would leave less room for a snout. (See Research Frontiers, *Matt Cartmill Re-examines His Own Theory of Primate Origins* for a discussion of his recent revision in response to criticisms.)

Robert Sussman's theory builds on Cartmill's *visual predation theory* and on Szalay's idea about a dietary shift (Sussman and Raven, 1978). Sussman accepts Cartmill's point that the early primates were likely to eat and move about mostly on small branches, not on large trunks and branches (as do squirrels). If they did, grasping hands and feet, and nails rather than claws (as squirrels have) would have been advantageous. Sussman also accepts Szalay's point that the early primates probably ate the new types of plant food (flowers, seeds, and fruits) that were becoming abundant at the time, as flowering trees and plants spread throughout the world. Sussman, however, asks an important question: if the early primates ate mostly plant foods rather than quick-moving insects, why did they become more reliant on vision than on smell? Sussman suggests it was because the early primates were probably nocturnal (as many prosimians still are): if they were to locate and manipulate small food items at the ends of slender branches in dim light, they would need improved vision. Thus, increased exploitation of flowering plants (*angiosperms*) promoted modern primate characteristics like sharp vision and the ability to distinguish colours.

We still have very little fossil evidence of the earliest primates, although the emergence of flowering plants in the Paleocene roughly coincides with the emergence of the earliest primate ancestors. When additional fossils become available, we may be better able to evaluate the various explanations that have been suggested for the emergence of primates.

The Early Primates: What They Looked Like

The earliest definite (undisputed) primates, dating back to the Eocene epoch, appeared abruptly in North America, Europe, and Asia about 55 million years ago. At that time many land masses that are now separate were connected by land bridges. North America and Europe were connected by Iceland, Greenland, and the Faeroe Islands. Europe and North America became separated later in the Eocene. The beginning of the Eocene was warmer and less seasonal than the Paleocene, and vast tropical forests abounded (Conroy, 1990).

Squirrels are arboreal, but lack many of the features that characterize primates. Matt Cartmill argued that primate features are adapted to the slender terminal branches of trees, while squirrel features are adapted to the trunks and main branches.

RESEARCH FRONTIERS

Matt Cartmill Re-examines His Own Theory of Primate Origins

Matt Cartmill originally conceived his visual predation theory to explain primate origins because he thought that the arboreal theory did not explain enough. Why do other animals, such as tree squirrels, manage very well in the trees, even though they don't have primate traits? Cartmill's theory attracted some criticism. How did he respond?

One criticism, by J. Allman, is that if visual predation is such an important predictor of forward-facing eyes, then why don't all visual predators have such eyes? Cats and owls have forward-facing eyes, but mongooses and robins do not. A second criticism, by Paul Garber, is that if claws were disadvantageous for moving on slender branches, why does at least one small primate—the Panamanian tamarin—feed on insects among small twigs and vines but have claws on four of its five digits of each paw? And Robert Sussman pointed out that most small nocturnal prosimians eat more fruit than insects. Sussman suggests that the need for precise finger manipulation to grasp small fruits and flowers at the ends of small branches, while hanging on by the hind feet, might favour both clawless digits and grasping extremities.

Cartmill acknowledged these problems and responded to them by revising his theory. He also suggests how new research could test some of the implications of his revised theory.

In regard to the problem of forward-facing eyes, Cartmill says that Allman's own research suggests a solution: namely, that forward-facing eyes are advantageous for seeing something in front more clearly in dim light. Daytime predators have eye pupils that constrict to see ahead more clearly, so fully forward-facing eyes are not necessary for daytime predation. Nocturnal predators relying on sight are more likely to have forward-facing eyes because constricting pupils would be disadvantageous. So Cartmill now believes that the earliest primates were probably nocturnal and they also probably ate fruit as well as insects, as Sussman suggests, just as many contemporary nocturnal prosimians do. If they ate fruit and insects at the ends of small branches and twigs, claws may have been disadvantageous. The Panamanian tamarin is not a case to the contrary; it has claws, but it also eats gum on the tree trunks to which it clings, using its claws as a tree squirrel does.

Cartmill thinks that his modified theory explains the changes in primate vision better than Sussman's theory does. For example, how can we explain stereoscopic, forward-facing eyes in the early primates? Sussman says that the early primates were fruit-eaters, but Cartmill points out that, although stereoscopic, forward-facing eyes are not necessary for getting fruit, they might be essential for helping to catch insects.

Cartmill suggests how future research on other arboreal mammals may help us answer some of the remaining questions about the origins of primates. Arboreal marsupials, for instance, tend to have grasping hind feet with clawless divergent first toes, and many have reduced claws on some other toes and fingers. The eyes of arboreal marsupials are also somewhat convergent (not as much, of course, as the eyes of primates). One genus of marsupial, an opposum in South America (*Caluromys*), has many additional primatelike features, including a relatively large brain, more forward-facing eyes, a short snout, and a small number of offspring at one time. Studies by Tab Rasmussen suggest that *Caluromys* fits both Cartmill's theory and Sussman's because it eats fruit on terminal branches and catches insect prey with its hands. More field research on marsupials and other animals with some primatelike habits or features could tell us a lot more. So would new fossil finds.

Sources: Cartmill M. 1992. New Views on Primate Origins. Evolutionary Anthropology 1:105–111.

Cartmill M. 1998. Explaining Primate Origins. In: Ember CR, Ember ME, Peregrine P, editors. Research Frontiers in Anthropology. Upper Saddle River, NJ: Prentice Hall/Simon & Schuster Custom Publishing.

Sussman RW. 1991. Primate Origins and the Evolution of Angiosperms. American Journal of Primatology 23:209–223.

Rasmussen T. 1990. Primate Origins: Lessons from a Neotropical Marsupial. American Journal of Primatology 22: 263–277.

The anatomy of the diverse Eocene primates suggests that they already had many of the features of modern primates—for example, nails rather than claws, a grasping, opposable first toe, and a bony bar around the side of the eye socket (Conroy, 1990). Vertical clinging and leaping was probably a common method of locomotion. Eocene prosimians not only moved around the way modern prosimians do; some were similar skeletally to living prosimians.

Two groups of prosimians appear in the early Eocene. One group, the **omomyids**, has many tarsierlike features; the other group, **adapids**, has many lemur-like features. The omomyids were very small, no bigger than squirrels; the adapids were kitten- and cat-sized.

Omomyids are considered tarsierlike because of their large eyes, long tarsal bones, and very small size. The large eyes suggest that they were active at night; the smaller-sized omomyids may have been insect-eaters and the larger ones may have relied more on fruit (Fleagle, 1994). Most of the omomyids have dental formulas characteristic of modern prosimians: two incisors and three premolars on each side of the lower jaw rather than the three incisors and four premolars of early mammals (Conroy, 1990). The importance of vision is apparent in a fossilized skull of the Eocene omomyid *Tetonius*. Imprints in the skull show that the brain had large occipital and temporal lobes—the regions associated with perception and the integration of visual memory (Radinsky, 1967).

The lemur-like adapids were more active during the day and relied more on leaf and fruit vegetation. In contrast to the omomyids, adapid remains show considerable sexual dimorphism in the canines and they retain the four premolars characteristic of earlier mammals (although there are fewer incisors) (Radinsky, 1967; Fleagle, 1994). One adapid known from its abundant fossil finds is *Notharctus*. It has a small, broad face with full stereoscopic vision and a reduced muzzle. It appears to have lived in the forest and had long and powerful hind legs for leaping from tree to tree (Conroy, 1990; Alexander, 1992).

There was a great deal of diversity among all mammals during the Eocene epoch, and the primates were no exception. Both the omomyids and adapids have a few features that suggest links between them and the anthropoids that appear later, in the Oligocene, but there is no agreement that either group gave rise to the anthropoids. Although the omomyids had some similarities to modern tarsiers and the adapids bear some resemblance to lemurs and lorises, palaeoanthropologists are not sure that either group is ancestral to

Although the Fayum depression is a desert today, it was a tropical forest in the Oligocene. The area is littered with the fossilized remains of tropical plants and the animals that fed on them, including primates.

modern prosimians. However, it is generally thought that the populations ancestral to lemurs and lorises as well as tarsiers did emerge in the Eocene or even earlier, in the late Paleocene (Conroy, 1990; Martin and Martin, 1990).

The Emergence of Anthropoids

Unfortunately, the fossil record documenting the emergence of the anthropoids is extremely spotty. The living anthropoids—monkeys, apes, and humans—have been very successful, and are represented by well over 150 species today. Who were their ancestors? There are several questions concerning the evolution of New World monkeys (platyrrhines). The first New World primates appear in the late Oligocene when South America was no closer to either Africa or North America than it is today. So the question remains, where did New World monkeys come from? The earliest fossil evidence comes from Bolivia and dates to about 35 million years ago. It is represented by a variety of genera including *Branisella, Tremacebus, Dolichocebus, Homonculus,* and *Soriacebus.*

There is no clear fossil record of the Old World forms (the catarrhines) in the two areas where they are most abundant today—the rain forests of sub-Saharan Africa and Southeast Asia (Fleagle and Kay, 1985). Some palaeoanthropologists think that recent Eocene primate finds from China, Southeast Asia, and Algeria have anthropoid affinities, but there is no clear agreement on their evolutionary status (Fleagle, 1994). Undisputed remains of early anthropoids date from a somewhat later period, the early Oligocene, about 34 million years ago, in the Fayum area, southwest of Cairo, Egypt.

A reconstruction of what two Oligocene primates might have looked like. In the foreground is a group of *Aegyptopithecus*; in the background are two individuals of Apidium. Some of the fauna that shared the Fayum region with these early primates are also shown.

The Fayum Oligocene Anthropoids

The Fayum is an uninviting area of desert badlands, but during the **Oligocene** epoch, 34 million to 24 million years ago, it was a tropical rain forest very close to the shores of the Mediterranean Sea. The area had a warm climate, and it contained many rivers and lakes. The Fayum, in fact, was far more inviting than the northern continents then, for the climates of both North America and Eurasia were beginning to cool during the Oligocene. The general cooling seems to have resulted in the virtual disappearance of primates from the northern areas, at least for a time.

As well as a prosimian family related to tarsiers, the Fayum yielded two main types of anthropoid: the monkeylike *parapithecids* and the apelike *propliopithecids.* Dating from 35 million to 31 million years ago (Fleagle, 1994), the parapithecids and the propliopithecids had enough features to be classified as anthropoids.

The monkeylike **parapithecids** had three premolars (in each quarter), as do most prosimians and the New World monkeys. They are similar to modern anthropoids in the presence of a bony partition behind the eye socket, broad incisors, projecting canines, and low, rounded cusps on their molars. But they have prosimianlike premolars and relatively small brains. The parapithecids were small, generally weighing under 1.3 kilograms; they resembled the squirrel monkeys living now in South and Central America (Kay, 1988a). Their relatively small eye sockets suggest that they were not nocturnal, and their teeth suggest that they ate mostly fruits and seeds. From the remains of one of the parapithecids, *Apidium,* an arboreal quadruped, Kay (1988a) and Conroy (1990) have inferred that this anthropoid did a considerable amount of leaping. Palaeoanthropologists still disagree as to whether the parapithecids preceded or followed the split between the New World monkeys (platyrrhines) and the Old World monkeys and apes (catarrhines). In any case, the parapithecids are the most primitive known anthropoids (Fleagle, 1988).

That parapithecids may be ancestral to New World monkeys (platyrrhines) raises an interesting puzzle in primate evolution: the origin of the New World monkeys. Anthropoidal primates such as *Dolichocebus,* a small fruit-eating monkey similar to the modern squirrel monkey (Rosenberger, 1979), appear suddenly and without any apparent ancestors in South America around 25 million years ago. Since the parapithecids predate the appearance of anthropoids in South America, and resemble them in many ways, it seems reasonable to view them as part of the population ancestral to the New World monkeys (Fleagle and Kay, 1987; Aiello, 1993; Hartwig, 1994).

But how did anthropoidal primates get from Africa to South America? Although the continents were closer together in the late Oligocene, when primates are thought to have first appeared in South America, the distance between South America and Africa was at least 3000 kilometres. An extended continental shelf and islands created by lower sea levels in the late Oligocene may have made it possible to "island-hop" from Africa to South America over ocean stretches as short as 200 kilometres, but that is still a long distance for an arboreal primate to travel.

Going from Africa to Europe and North America, which were still joined in the late Oligocene, was not likely either. North America and South America were not joined until some 5 million years ago, so even if the ancestors of the New World monkeys made it to North America, they would still have needed to cross the Atlantic Ocean to reach South America. One suggestion is that the ancestors of the New World monkeys "rafted" across the Atlantic on large mats of vegetation. Even today, such "rafts," of matted plants, roots, and soil, break away from the mouths of major rivers, and they can be quite large. It seems an unlikely scenario, but many scholars believe such drifting vegetation must have been the means of bringing anthropoids to South America (Aiello, 1993; Hartwig, 1994; Andrews, 2000).

The other type of anthropoid found in the Fayum, the **propliopithecids**, had the dental formula of modern catarrhines. This trait clearly places the propliopithecids with the catarrhines (Andrews, 1988). In contrast with the parapithecids,

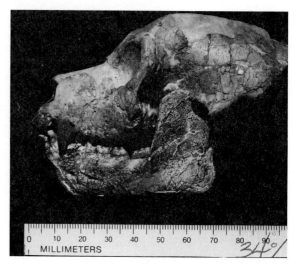

The fossil skull of an *Aegyptopithecus* from the Fayum. Its dentition, its small, bony eye sockets, and its relatively large brain make it an unambiguous ancestor of Old World monkeys and apes.

which had three premolars, the propliopithecids had only two premolars, as do modern apes, humans, and Old World monkeys. Propliopithecids shared with the parapithecids the anthropoid dental characteristics of broad lower incisors, projecting canines, and lower molars with low, rounded cusps. Like parapithecids, propliopithecids also had a bony partition behind the eye socket.

Aegyptopithecus, the best-known propliopithecid, probably moved around quadrupedally in the trees, weighed about 6 kilograms, and ate mostly fruit. It had a long muzzle and a relatively small brain and showed considerable sexual dimorphism. Although its teeth and jaws are apelike, *Aegyptopithecus* is similar in size to that of the modern South American howler monkey (Fleagle and Kay, 1985; Conroy, 1990).

Because the propliopithecids lack the specialized characteristics of living Old World monkeys and apes, but share the dental formula of the catarrhines, some palaeoanthropologists think that the propliopithecids included the ancestor of both the Old World monkeys and the hominoids—apes and humans (Fleagle and Kay, 1983; Fleagle, 1988).

Miocene Anthropoids: Monkeys, Apes, and Hominids

During the **Miocene** epoch, 24 million to 5.2 million years ago, monkeys and apes clearly diverged in appearance, and numerous kinds of apes appeared in Europe, Asia, and Africa (see Figure 7–2). In the early Miocene, the temperatures were considerably warmer than the temperatures in the Oligocene. From early to late Miocene, conditions became drier (Fleagle, 1988). We can infer that late in the Miocene, between about 8 million and 5 million years ago, the direct ancestor of humans—the first hominid—may have emerged in Africa. The inference about *where* hominids emerged is based on the fact that undisputed hominids lived in East Africa after about 5 million years ago. The inference about *when* hominids emerged is based not on fossil evidence but on comparative molecular and biochemical analyses of modern apes and humans.

One of the Miocene apes (known or unknown) was ancestral to hominids, so our discussion here deals mostly with the early hominoids or *proto-apes*, or primates that possess some but not all of the key traits shared by apes, of the early Miocene, and the *definite apes* of the middle and late Miocene. Before we get to the apes though, we should say something about monkeys and prosimians in the Miocene. Unfortunately, monkey fossils from the early Miocene are rare. In the New World, the whole Miocene fossil record is quite sparse. There have been only a few primate fossils found in Colombia and Argentina; they show close affinities with present-day South American monkeys. In the Old World, early Miocene monkey fossils have been found only in northern Africa. The situation is different for the middle and late Miocene: Old World monkey fossils are much more abundant than ape fossils (Conroy, 1990). As for prosimians, fossils from the Miocene are scarce, but we know that at least some adapids survived into the middle Miocene in India and the late Miocene in China (Conroy, 1990). Some lorislike prosimians appeared in East Africa, Pakistan, and India during the Miocene (Martin and Martin, 1990).

Gigantopithecus probably lived mostly on bamboo. It is the largest primate known to us. The genus survived for about 10 million years and only became extinct 250 000 years ago. Bill Munns is shown here with the model of "Giganto" that he reconstructed with Russell Ciochon.

Early Miocene Hominoids

Most of the fossils from the early Miocene are described as proto-apes. They have been found mostly in Africa. The best known genus is *Proconsul*, its fossils found in sites that are about 20 million years old in Kenya and Uganda (Begun, 1998). (See also Figure 7–6.)

All of the various *Proconsul* species that have been found were much bigger than any of the anthropoids of the Oligocene, ranging from about the size of a gibbon to that of a female gorilla (Conroy, 1990). *Proconsul* lacked a tail, which is one of the most definitive features of hominids. Most palaeoanthropologists now agree that *Proconsul*

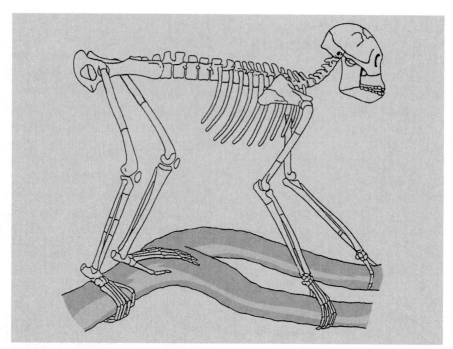

Figure 7–6

The forelimbs and hind limbs of *Proconsul africanus* (dating from about 20 million years ago) are about the same length, suggesting that it moved on all fours on the tops of branches. *Proconsul africanus* was the smallest of the *Proconsul* species, weighing about 10 to 12 kilograms.

Source: Ciochon R, Corruccini R, editors. 1983. New Interpretations of Ape and Human Ancestry. New York: Plenum. Copyright © 1983 by Plenum Publishers. Reprinted by permission of Plenum Publishers.

was definitely hominoid, but quite unlike any ape living today. Modern hominoids have many anatomical features of the shoulder, elbow, wrists, and fingers that are adapted for locomotion by suspension (brachiation). However, suspension was apparently not Proconsul's method of getting around, because its elbows, wrists, and fingers may have permitted brachiation (Begun, 1998), but, like the Oligocene anthropoids, *Proconsul* was primarily an arboreal quadruped (see Figure 7–4), although some of the larger forms may have sometimes moved on the ground. Based on dental morphology, most *Proconsul* species appear to have been fruit-eaters, but larger species may have also consumed leaves (Andrews, 1988).

Some recent finds from East Africa suggest that other types of early hominoids were also on the scene from the early Miocene, but these are quite fragmentary and not clearly classifiable. *Proconsul* may or may not have been ancestral to later apes

and humans, but given its combination of monkey-like and apelike features, it may have looked a lot like the common ancestor of apes and humans (Begun, 1998). (See also the illustration on page 134 for a reconstruction of *Proconsul africanus*.)

Middle Miocene Apes

By about 17 million years ago, a large number of distinct hominoid species emerged during the warmer Miocene epoch. These forms were distributed throughout Africa, Europe, and Asia, and included *Dryopithecus*, *Kenyapithecus*, *Oreopithecus*, *Ouranopithecus*, and *Sivapithecus*. While some of these species have been closely associated with modern forms, none of them appears to have any clear link with the earliest hominids.

The first definitely apelike finds come from East Africa in the middle Miocene, 16 million to 10 million years ago. The fossils, found on Maboko Island and nearby locations in Kenya, include

HISTORICAL PERSPECTIVES

What Happened to *Gigantopithecus*?

In studying human evolution we tend to focus on the primate lineages that presumably are ancestral to modern humans and our closest primate cousins. There were, however, other primate lineages that left no apparent descendants but were very successful in the sense that they persisted for millions of years. The first definite primates, the omomyids and the adapids, first appeared early in the Eocene and stayed for more than 20 million years, much longer than bipedal hominids have been around! Why some primates were successful for so long is an important question; so is why they became extinct. To understand evolution, we need to investigate not only why some form may have survived for a while; we need also to investigate why it died out. For example, what happened to the largest primate, *Gigantopithecus*, that ever lived?

Russell Ciochon, a palaeoanthropologist, and John Olsen, an archaeologist, have searched for clues to understanding the extinction of "Giganto," as they call it, who apparently left no descendants living in the world today. Ciochon and Olsen think that the largest form of *Gigantopithecus*, *G. blacki*, persisted for at least 5 million years and did not become extinct until about 250 000 years ago. If you count earlier *Gigantopithecus* forms, the genus may even have been around for nearly 10 million years. Ciochon and Olsen think it likely that Giganto and *Homo erectus*, a hominid that looked very much like modern humans from the head down, met up about a quarter of a million years ago in at least two Asian locations—now parts of China and Vietnam. The possible contact with *H. erectus* may have been partly responsible for the demise of Giganto.

What did Giganto look like? Reconstruction requires some guesswork, particularly with Giganto, because the only remains we have are teeth and jaw fragments. We can, however, reasonably infer some of Giganto's features and measurements from the body proportions of existing apes and the more complete fossil remains of extinct apes. Thus, it is estimated that Giganto was 3 metres tall and weighed about 545 kilograms.

What did Giganto eat? Ciochon's guess is that Giganto mostly ate bamboo from the then-plentiful bamboo forests. The large size of the jaw, the wear patterns on the teeth, and the fact that large primates eat mostly foods with a lot of cellulose all suggest a diet of bamboo or something like it. Another kind of evidence suggests a similar conclusion. A student had suggested to Ciochon that he look for phytoliths on the fossil teeth of Giganto. When the plants decompose, the phytoliths remain, so, on the chance that phytoliths were on the fossil teeth from Giganto, the researchers looked at the teeth microscopically. They found phytoliths that belong to a family of grasses as well as phytoliths from a kind of fruit. Bamboo is a kind of grass, so the phytoliths found on the Giganto teeth are consistent with both bamboo and fruit-eating. The teeth revealed something else too. Many of the teeth show pitting of the tooth enamel (*enamel hypoplasia*). This suggests that Giganto suffered periodically from malnutrition as hypoplastic lesions are produced by inadequate diet.

Bamboo forests are found almost everywhere in China and Southeast Asia, but for reasons not yet understood, they dwindle every 20 years or so. If Giganto ate bamboo, it would periodically have had a serious problem finding food, which is consistent with the hypoplasias. Could the extinction of Giganto be linked to something that happened to the bamboo forests? Perhaps. Giant pandas, which are bamboo-eaters almost exclusively, are now at risk of extinction because of the spread of humans and subsequent loss of its habitat throughout China and Southeast Asia. Bamboo is used by humans for shelter, boats, tools, and food (bamboo shoots), and the bamboo forests are now drastically reduced. In their time, *H. erectus* may also have reduced the bamboo forests, thus contributing to the demise of Giganto. It is also possible that *H. erectus* hunted Giganto for food. This possibility is very speculative, but non-human primates have been hunted for food by many recent human societies. Like the giant panda, Giganto was probably very slow-moving and easy to hunt, as are most large plant-eaters.

Humans in different places tell stories about huge, hairy, human-like creatures—"Bigfoot" or Sasquatch in northwestern North America, the "Abominable Snowman" or Yeti of the Himalayas. Is it possible that Giganto is still around? Ciochon and Olsen point out that no recent Giganto bones have been found, so it is very unlikely that Giganto is still out there. Perhaps humans continue to believe it because they encountered Giganto in the not-so-distant past. After all, Australian aborigines still tell stories referring to events that happened more than 30 000 years ago.

What we do know is that *Gigantopithecus* persisted for a very long time, until humans came on the scene. Researchers have learned a lot about Giganto from very fragmentary remains. If more fossils are found in the future, we can expect that more will come to be known about the gigantic ape.

Source: Ciochon R, Olsen J, James J. 1990. Other Origins: The Search for the Giant Ape in Human Prehistory. New York: Bantam. p 99–102. Used by permission of Bantam Books, a division of Bantam Doubleday Dell Publishing Group.

RESEARCH FRONTIERS

A New Picture of *Dryopithecus* Emerging from Rudabánya Specimens

Recent evidence from new and more complete specimens of *Dryopithecus* from Hungary are beginning to paint a better picture of the relation between these late Miocene apes and the evolution of hominoids. Dr. David Begun, a physical anthropologist at the University of Toronto, conducts palaeoanthropological research on Miocene primates in Europe. His research has focused on the excavation and analysis of fossil hominoids from Rudabánya, Hungary.

Rudabánya is a late Miocene hominoid site, dating to about 10 million years ago. All of the hominoid specimens recovered from the site have been attributed to *Dryopithecus*. Living apes and humans share many skeletal features retained from a common hominoid ancestor. One key to unravelling the question of where *Dryopithecus* fits into later hominoid evolution is to compare morphological features of fossil remains with those of living hominoids. Begun's claim that *Dryopithecus* is more closely related to African apes and humans than it

is to *Sivapithecus* and orangutans has been further supported with the reanalysis of RUD 77, the name given to the most completely preserved cranium of *Dryopithecus*. It is one of only two reasonably well-preserved and undistorted neurocranial specimens of any Miocene hominoid specimen. The new fossil evidence has shed light on the question of the evolutionary relations among living hominoids, and supports the view that humans have an evolutionary relation closest to chimpanzees, when compared with all of the other apes.

Begun continues to work on the material from Rudabánya in the hopes of finding even better preserved specimens. During the most recent field school season at Rudabánya, Begun and his crew uncovered an even more complete cranium of *Dryopithecus*. This offered not only new evidence of the connection between this fossil great ape and African apes and humans but also the possibility of reconstructing brain size and anatomy in

an early great ape. Brain evolution is critical to understanding great ape and human origins, and the new specimen promises to shed more light on this fascinating topic. In addition to his research in Hungary, he is involved in the survey, excavation, and analysis of Miocene hominoids from Turkey.

Sources: Begun DR and Kordos L. 1993. Revision of *Dryopithecus brancoi* SCHLOSSER 1901 Based on the Fossil Hominoid Material from Rudabánya. Journal of Human Evolution 25:271–286.

Begun DR. 1995. Late Miocene European Orangs, Gorillas, Humans or None of the Above? Journal of Human Evolution 29:169–180.

Begun DR. 1995. Miocene Apes. In: Ember CR, Ember M, editors. Research Frontiers in Anthropology—Advances in Archaeology and Physical Anthropology. Englewood Cliffs, NJ: Prentice Hall.

Begun DR. 1996. Events in European Hominoid Evolution. Europa 1996 23:13–22.

Kordos L, Begun DR. 1997. The Cranium of *Dryopithecus* from Rudabánya, Hungary: A New Reconstruction and Its Phylogenetic Implications. American Journal of Physical Anthropology 103:277–294.

several kinds of primate—a prosimian, several types of Old World monkeys, and a definite hominoid, *Kenyapithecus* (Begun, 1998).

Kenyapithecus has many of *Proconsul*'s features, but its molars resemble those of more modern hominoids. In contrast to *Proconsul*, *Kenyapithecus* was probably more terrestrial. It also had very thickly enamelled teeth and robust jaws, suggesting a diet of hard, tough foods, or food with a great deal of grit in it, an indicator that the food source was on the ground. Finds similar to *Kenyapithecus* appear in Europe and Turkey. Whether *Kenyapithecus* is ancestral to the later apes and humans is something of a puzzle. Its molars are more modern, but its limbs do not show the capacity for brachiation that is characteristic of all the later apes (Kelley, 1992;

A *Dryopithecus* cranium.

Begun, 1998). According to Sue Savage-Rumbaugh, knuckle walking may have evolved as a mode of terrestrial locomotion only in later apes. Because they are knuckle walkers, living apes cannot make a snapping motion with the hand (which is called "abducting the wrist"), as humans uniquely can (Savage-Rumbaugh, 1994). This last ability, along with other things hands can do if they are not involved in locomotion, may have been crucial in making complete bipedalism adaptive in the earliest humans, as we will discuss in the next chapter.

Late Miocene Apes

From the end of the middle Miocene into the late Miocene, the apes diversified and moved into many areas. Fossils are abundant in Europe and Asia, less so in Africa. This does not mean that apes were more numerous than monkeys. In fact, the fossil record suggests that monkeys in the Old World became more and more numerous than apes toward the end of the Miocene, and this trend continues to the present day. There are many more monkey than ape species now. The climate throughout the Miocene was turning cooler and drier, which probably favoured more drought-resistant plants with thicker cell walls. Modern monkeys tend to be more adapted than apes for eating leaves, so monkeys may have had an advantage in the changing environment toward the end of the Miocene, and since (Conroy, 1990).

One well-known late Miocene ape from Europe is *Oreopithecus,* which dates from about 8 million years ago. It is particularly interesting because, despite being well represented by fossils, including nearly complete ones preserved in beds of hard coal, its classification is enigmatic. *Oreopithecus* was clearly adapted to life in thickly forested marshlands. It had extremely long arms and hands and mobile joints, and was likely an agile brachiator. Its dentition suggests it had a diet that consisted mostly of leaves. However, the dentition and skull of *Oreopithecus* also had a number of unique features that suggest affinity to some Old World monkeys. In short, *Oreopithecus* had an apelike body and a monkeylike head. Because of its suspensory locomotion and other apelike features, most scholars today consider it an early, albeit specialized, ape (Fleagle, 1999).

Most palaeoanthropologists divide the later Miocene apes into at least two main groups: *Sivapithecines,* found primarily in western and southern Asia, and *Dryopithecines,* found primarily in Europe (Fleagle, 1988).

Sivapithecus, known for its thickly enamelled teeth, was remarkably similar in facial features to the modern orangutan, and is now thought to be its ancestor. Its teeth, like those of *Kenyapithecus,* suggest a diet of hard, tough, or gritty items. The closely related *Gigantopithecus* has similar dentition, but, as its name suggests, it was huge, perhaps over 3 metres if it stood erect (Begun, 1998). Some palaeoanthropologists suggest that *Gigantopithecus* weighed over 270 kilograms and became even larger over the nearly 10 million years of its existence, eventually weighing perhaps as much as 545 kilograms (Ciochon et al., 1990). (See Historical Perspectives, *What Happened to* Gigantopithecus? on page 149.)

Dryopithecines had thin tooth enamel, lighter jaws, and pointed molar cusps. In the palate, jaw, and midface, *Dryopithecines* looked like the African apes. In contrast to later hominoids, however, *Dryopithecines* had a very short face and a relatively small brow ridge (Begun, 1998).

The fingers and elbows of *Dryopithecines* and *Sivapithecines* suggest that they were quite a bit more capable of suspending themselves than were earlier hominoids, but they did not have as much of that capacity as modern hominoids. *Sivapithecines*

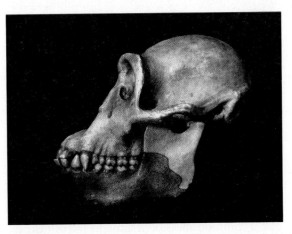

The reconstructed skull of a *Dryopithecus* strongly resembles that of modern African apes.

may have moved about more on the ground than *Dryopithecines*, but both were probably mostly arboreal (Begun, 1998).

As the climate became drier in the late Miocene, the majority of hominoid forms became extinct, leaving behind a few modern-day forms (*Pan, Gorilla,* and *Pongo*). It is still very difficult to identify the evolutionary lines leading from the Miocene apes to modern apes and humans (see Research Frontiers, *A New Picture of* Dryopithecus *Emerging from Rudabánya Specimens,* on page 150). Only the orangutans have been linked to a late Miocene ape genus, *Sivapithecus,* so presumably that lineage continued into modern times (Fleagle, 1988). *Dryopithecines* disappear from the fossil record after about 10 million years ago, leaving no known descendants, perhaps because less rainfall and more seasonality reduced the forests where they lived (Bilsborough, 1992).

The Divergence of Hominids from the Other Hominoids

The later Miocene apes are best known from fossils discovered in Europe and Asia. There has been an almost complete gap in the African fossil record between 13.5 million and 5 million years ago (Simons, 1992); however, recently, two species, *Orrorin tugenensis,* from Kenya and dated to about 6 million years ago, and *Sahelanthropus tchadensis,* from Chad and dated to perhaps 7 million years ago, have provided a glimpse of hominoid evolution during this period. Still, this scarcity of fossils from this period is unfortunate for our understanding of human evolution because the earliest known bipedal primates (hominids) appear in Africa near the beginning of the Pliocene, after 5 million years ago. To understand the evolutionary links between the apes of the Miocene and the hominids of Africa, we need more fossil evidence from late Miocene times in Africa.

However, we do have some idea about the transition to hominids. The molecular biology of the various modern primates suggests when the most recent common ancestor of humans and our closest primate relatives, the chimpanzees, probably lived.

The Molecular Clock

In 1966, on the basis of biochemical comparisons of blood proteins in the different surviving primates, Vincent Sarich and Allan Wilson estimated that gibbons diverged from the other hominoids about 12 million years ago, orangutans 10 million years ago, and the other apes (gorillas and chimpanzees) from hominids only 4.5 million years ago. These estimates depended on the assumption that the more similar in chemistry the blood proteins of different primates are, the closer those primates are in evolutionary time. In other words, the more similar the blood proteins of related species, the more recently they diverged (Sarich and Wilson, 1966; Sarich, 1968; Lewin, 1983).

This relationship between molecular closeness and evolutionary time is also based on another assumption: that molecular changes occur at a constant rate. After all, a reliable "molecular clock" should not slow down or speed up from one period of time to another. Because natural selection can speed up the rate of molecular change in the case of a characteristic that is very advantageous or very disadvantageous, researchers examine molecular characteristics that are probably neutral in terms of adaptation in order to calculate when related species might have diverged. The rate of change in a neutral characteristic is calculated from the time of some divergence that is absolutely dated. For example, if we know that two lineages split 20 million years ago, and we know the degree of molecular difference between a contemporary representative of each, we can estimate the rate of change that produced that degree of difference. Given such an estimated rate of change (in a particular characteristic), we can estimate the amount of time that has elapsed since other pairs of related species diverged from each other (Martin and Martin, 1990; Jones et al., 1992).

Subsequent comparative studies of the living primates have employed a variety of techniques, including comparisons of amino acid sequences and chromosomal structures, and the degree of matching of DNA strands from different species. These studies have confirmed the probable recent divergence of hominids from chimpanzees and gorillas. Although the different techniques yield slightly different estimates, the results are not that dissimilar. Most of the recent comparisons place the split somewhat earlier than the Sarich and Wilson estimates, but not by much. The common ancestor of chimpanzees and hominids is estimated to have lived 5 million to 6 million years ago, the common ancestor of gorillas and hominids a little farther back in time (Jones et al., 1992).

So what does the fossil evidence tell us about where and when hominids first emerged?

Unfortunately, there is no answer to this question yet. We still do not have any definite hominid fossils in Africa from the end of the Miocene (8 million to 5 million years ago), we have not found definite hominid fossils dating from the late Miocene anywhere else, nor do we know the place and time where and when hominids emerged. All we know for sure at present is that primates with indisputably hominid characteristics lived about 4 million years ago in East Africa. We turn to these hominids in the next chapter.

Summary

1. We cannot know with certainty how primates evolved. But fossils, knowledge of ancient environments, and an understanding of comparative anatomy and behaviour give us enough clues to have a tentative idea of when, where, and why primates emerged and diverged.

2. The surviving primates—prosimians, New World monkeys, Old World monkeys, apes, and humans—are thought to be descendants of small, originally terrestrial insectivores (the order, or major grouping, of mammals, including modern shrews and moles, that is adapted to feeding on insects). However, exactly who the common ancestor was and when it emerged are not yet known.

3. Fossils dating from the early Eocene, about 55 million years ago, are definitely primates. They appear to fall into two major groups of prosimians—adapids and omomyids. These two kinds of primate are different from each other in major ways, and they both appeared rather abruptly at the border of the Paleocene and Eocene, so their common ancestor would have had to emerge earlier, probably in the Paleocene.

4. What conditions may have favoured the emergence of the primates? The proliferation of insects led to an increase in insectivores— mammals that ate insects, some of which lived above ground, in the woody habitat of bushes, shrubs, vines, and trees. Eventually, trees with large flowers and fruits evolved. The exploitation of resources in the woody habitat was probably the key adaptation in the emergence of the primates.

5. The traditional view of primate evolution was that arboreal (tree) life would have favoured many of the common primate features, including distinctive dentition, greater reliance on vision over smell, three-dimensional binocular vision, and grasping hands and feet. A second theory proposes that some of the distinctive primate characteristics were selectively advantageous for hunting insects on the slender vines and branches that filled the undergrowth of forests. A third theory suggests that the distinctive features of primates (including more reliance on vision than on smell) were favoured because the early primates were nocturnal and ate flowers, fruits, and seeds, which they had to locate on slender branches in dim light.

6. Undisputed remains of early anthropoids unearthed in Egypt date from the early Oligocene (after 34 million years ago). They include the monkeylike parapithecids and the propliopithecids with apelike teeth.

7. During the Miocene epoch (24 million to 5.2 million years ago), monkeys and apes clearly diverged in appearance, and numerous kinds of apes appeared in Europe, Asia, and Africa.

Most of the fossils from the early Miocene are described as proto-apes. From the end of the middle Miocene into the late Miocene, the apes diversified and spread geographically. Most palaeoanthropologists divide the later Miocene apes into at least two main groups: *Dryopithecines*, found primarily in Europe, and *Sivapithecines*, found primarily in western and southern Asia.

8. The fossil record does not yet tell us who the first hominid was, but biochemical and genetic analyses of modern apes and humans suggest that the hominid-ape split occurred during the late Miocene (after about 6 million years ago). Because undisputed hominids lived in East Africa after about 4 million years ago, the first hominid probably emerged in Africa.

Glossary Terms

adapids   (p. 144)

continental drift   (p. 140)

Cretaceous   (p. 139)

dentition   (p. 135)

Dryopithecines   (p. 151)

Eocene   (p. 138)

insectivore   (p. 141)

Kenyapithecus   (p. 150)

Miocene   (p. 147)

Oligocene   (p. 145)

omomyids   (p. 144)

Paleocene   (p. 138)

parapithecids   (p. 145)

Proconsul   (p. 147)

propliopithecids   (p. 146)

Sivapithecus   (p. 151)

Critical Questions

1. Its skeletal anatomy suggests what an animal eats and how it gets its food. Discuss possible examples in the evolution of the primates.

2. Why do you suppose there are more monkey than ape species?

3. We like to think of the human lineage as biologically unique, which of course it is (like all evolutionary lineages). But some palaeoanthropologists say that humans, chimpanzees, and gorillas are so similar that all three should be grouped as hominids. What do you think of this reasoning, and why?

Internet Exercises

1. Mary Leakey is best known for her work at Olduvai Gorge, where early hominids were found. But she also played a role in discoveries of anthropoids from the Miocene. Read the article about her at **www.sciam.com/explorations/121696explorations.html** and summarize what those discoveries were.

2. Go to **www.bhc.edu/academics/science/harwoodr/Geol102/Study/humans.htm** to see images of many of the primates discussed in this chapter.

3. "Early Hominid Evolution: A Glossary of Terms" is illustrated and can be found at **http://anthro.palomar.edu/hominid/glossary.htm**.

4. Go to **www.wynja.com/arch/gigantopithecus.html** and review a discussion of reconstructing the biology and lifeways of *Gigantopithecus*.

Suggested Reading

Andrews P, Stringer C. 1989. Human Evolution: An Illustrated Guide. London: British Museum. A brief introduction to primate and human evolution, illustrated by reconstructions in colour of many fossil finds.

Begun DR, Ward CV, Rose MD. 1997. Function, Phylogeny and Fossils: Miocene Hominoid Origins and Adaptations. New York: Plenum Press. An up-to-date survey of the diversity among Miocene hominoids.

Cartmill M. 1998. Explaining Primate Origins. In: Ember CR, Ember M, and Peregrine P, editors.

Research Frontiers in Anthropology. Upper Saddle River, NJ: Prentice Hall, Prentice Hall/Simon & Schuster Custom Publishing. A review of the major theories of primate origins with a close look at criticisms of his own theory.

Conroy GC. 1990. Primate Evolution. New York: Norton. Conveys both the consensus and the points of disagreement in theories of primate evolution. Assumes some basic knowledge of physical anthropology or biology.

Fleagle JG. 1998. Primate Adaptation and Evolution. Second edition. San Diego: Academic Press. A textbook that examines the comparative anatomy, behavioural ecology, and palaeontology of humans and their nearest relatives. Chapters 9–14 are particularly relevant to this chapter.

Fleagle JG, Kay RF, editors. 1994. Anthropoid Origins. New York: Plenum Press. Based on a conference, this book brings together technical information about recent discoveries and current theories concerning the origin and early evolution of anthropoid primates—monkeys, apes, and humans.

Martin RD. 1990. Primate Origins and Evolution: A Phylogenetic Reconstruction. Princeton, NJ: Princeton University Press. The author draws together findings from comparisons of living primates, the fossil record, and molecular evidence to make a provisional synthesis of primate phylogeny.

8 EARLY HOMINIDS

Undisputed bipedal hominids lived in East Africa about 4 million years ago (see Figure 8–1). These hominids—meaning the bipedal ancestors of the human species—and some others who lived later in East and South Africa are generally classified in the genus **Australopithecus**. Some East African hominids, who lived nearly 2.5 million years ago, are classified in our own genus, **Homo**. In this chapter we discuss what we know or suspect about the emergence and relationship of the australopithecines and early *Homo*.

Trends in Hominid Evolution

Perhaps the most crucial change—and the defining characteristic of hominid evolution—was the development of bipedal locomotion, or walking on two legs (see Figure 8–2). We know from the fossil record that other important physical changes—including the expansion of the brain, modification of the female pelvis to allow bigger-brained babies to be born, and reduction of the face, teeth, and jaws—did not occur until about 2 million years

after the emergence of bipedalism. Other human characteristics, including an extended period of infant and child dependency and increased reliance on meat in their diet, may also have developed after that time.

Bipedalism

We do not know whether bipedalism developed quickly or gradually, because the fossil record for the period between 8 million and 4 million years ago is very sparse. We do know that many of the Miocene anthropoids, on the basis of their skeletal anatomy, were capable of assuming an upright posture. For example, brachiation (swinging by the arms through the trees) puts an animal in an upright position; so does climbing up and down trees by grasping with the hands and feet. It is also likely that the *protohominids* were capable of occasional bipedalism, just as many modern monkeys and apes are (Rose, 1984).

As we noted at the end of the last chapter, definitely bipedal hominids emerged first in Africa. About 16 million to 11 million years ago, a drying

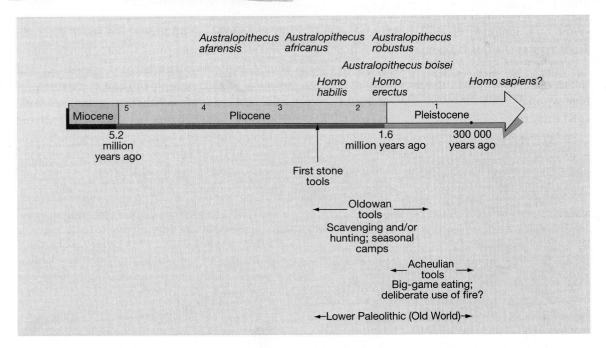

Figure 8–1 An Evolutionary Timeline

Source: Jones S, Martin R, Pilbeam D, editors. 1992. The Cambridge Encyclopedia of Human Evolution. New York: Cambridge University Press. p 454. Reprinted by permission of Cambridge University Press.

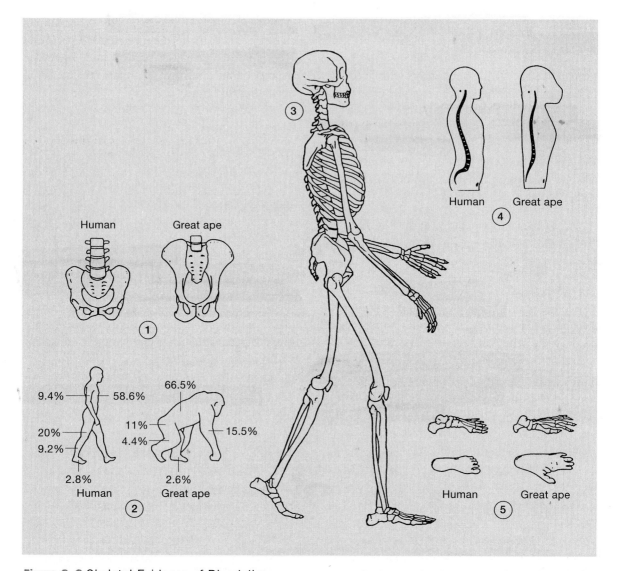

Figure 8–2 Skeletal Evidence of Bipedalism

The human skeleton differs from the skeleton of the great ape because humans move about on their legs only. The human head is more or less balanced on the backbone (see the feature marked 3 in the figure), so there is no need for powerful muscles at the back of the neck, as in the great ape. The human vertebral column (see 4 in the figure) has a forward curvature in the neck and lower back regions. These two extra curves, along with the curvature in the middle back region, allow the backbone to act more like a spring, which is advantageous given that the legs have to bear all the weight and given the need to balance on one leg with each stride. Bipedal locomotion has favoured a human pelvis (see 1 in the figure) that is lower and broader than the ape pelvis. In contrast to the apes, human legs are longer than human arms and represent a larger proportion of the body weight (see 2 in the figure); this lowers the body's centre of gravity and is advantageous for bipedalism. The most obvious adaptation to bipedalism is the human foot (see 5 in the figure). The big toe is not opposed to the other toes, as in the other primates, and the foot can no longer grasp. When we walk, the big toe is the last point of contact with the ground before the leg swings forward, which explains why the big toe has become aligned with the other toes.

Source: Jones S, Martin R, Pilbeam D, editors. 1992. The Cambridge Encyclopedia of Human Evolution. New York: Cambridge University Press. p. 78. Reprinted by permission of Cambridge University Press.

and cooling trend set in that continued into the Pliocene. The physical environment in Africa was changing from extensive tropical forest cover to more discontinuous patches of forest and open country (Bilsborough, 1992). Gradually, the African rain forests, deprived of intense humidity and rainfall, dwindled in extent; areas of **savannah** (tropical grasslands) and scattered deciduous woodlands became more common. The tree-dwelling primates did not completely lose their customary habitats because some tropical forests remained in wetter regions, and natural selection continued to favour the better-adapted tree dwellers in those forested areas. However, the more open country probably favoured characteristics adapted to ground living in some primates as well as other animals. In the evolutionary line leading to humans, these adaptations included bipedalism. Since humans are the only living primate that is habitually bipedal, the question of what factors may have led to this adaptation is of evolutionary significance. So what in particular may have favoured the emergence of bipedal hominids?

There are several possible explanations for this development. One idea is that bipedalism was the adaptive response to life amid the tall grasses of the savannahs because an erect posture may have made it easier to spot ground predators as well as potential prey (Oakley, 1964). This theory does not adequately account for the development of bipedalism, however. Baboons and some other Old World monkeys also live in savannah environments, yet, although they can stand erect, and occasionally do so, they did not develop bipedal locomotion. Recent evidence suggests that the area where early hominids lived in East Africa was not predominantly savannah; rather, it seems to have had a mix of woodland and open country (Kingston et al., 1994).

Another idea is that bipedalism may have been an adaptation that allowed for better dispersion of body heat. Because the head is raised higher, there is less surface area exposed to the sun at the hottest time of the day. This may have played a crucial role in thermoregulation of the brain in early hominids, which is important for brain development (Wheeler, 1991; Chaplin et al., 1994).

Other theories stress the importance of allowing the hands to be free while the legs are moving. If some hand activity is critical while an animal is moving, selection may favour bipedalism because it frees the hands to perform other activities at the same time while the animal is moving. What hand activities might have been so critical?

Gordon Hewes suggested that carrying food in the hands was the critical activity. If it were necessary to carry food from one locale to another, bipedal locomotion would have provided an adaptive advantage (Hewes, 1961). Hewes emphasized the importance of being able to carry hunted or scavenged meat, but many palaeoanthropologists now question whether early hominids hunted or even scavenged (Shipman, 1986; Trinkaus, 1987). Regardless, the ability to carry any food to a place safe from predators may have been one of the more important advantages of bipedalism. C. Owen Lovejoy has suggested that food-carrying might have been important for another reason. If males provided for females and their babies by carrying food back to a home base, the females would have been able to conserve energy by not travelling and therefore might have been able to produce and care for more babies (Lovejoy, 1981). Thus, whatever the advantages of carrying food, the more bipedal a protohominid was, the more it might reproduce.

Bipedalism might also have been favoured by natural selection because the freeing of the hands would allow protohominids to use, and perhaps even make, tools that they could carry with them as they moved about. Consider how advantageous such tool use might have been. Sherwood Washburn noted that some contemporary ground-living primates dig for roots to eat, "and if they could use a stone or a stick they might easily double their food supply" (Washburn, 1960:163). David Pilbeam also suggests why the use of tools by the more open-country primates may have appreciably increased the number and amount of plant foods they could eat: in order to be eaten, many of the plant foods in the grassy areas probably had to be chopped, crushed, or otherwise prepared with the aid of tools (Pilbeam, 1972). Tools may also have been used to

Many non-human primates walk upright occasionally, but the only primates that habitually walked or walk upright were our hominid ancestors and modern humans.

kill and butcher animals for food. Without tools, primates in general are not well equipped physically for regular hunting. Their teeth and jaws are not sharp and strong enough, and their speed afoot is not fast enough. So the use of tools to kill and butcher game might have increased even further their ability to exploit the available food supply.

Finally, tools may have been used as weapons against predators, which would have been a great threat to the relatively defenceless ground-dwelling protohominids. In Milford Wolpoff's opinion, it was the advantage of carrying weapons *continuously* that was responsible for transforming occasional bipedalism to a completely bipedal locomotion (Wolpoff, 1971). In particular, Sue Savage-Rumbaugh has suggested that the ability to abduct the wrist would have permitted early humans "to perfect both throwing and rock-striking skills [for tool-making] and consequently to develop throwing as

a much more effective predator defence system than apes could ever manage" (Savage-Rumbaugh, 1994).

But some anthropologists question the idea that tool use and toolmaking favoured bipedalism. They point out that our first evidence of stone tools appears perhaps a million years *after* the emergence of bipedalism. So how could toolmaking be responsible for bipedalism? Wolpoff suggests an answer. Even though bipedalism appears to be at least a million years older than stone tools, it is not unlikely that protohominids used tools made of wood and bone, neither of which would be as likely as stone to survive in the archaeological record. Moreover, unmodified stone tools discovered in the archaeological record might not be recognizable as tools (Wolpoff, 1983). This is still not a compelling argument however. Chimpanzees use unmodified wood and stones for certain tasks, and yet they did not become bipedal. The key issue for humans and their ancestors is the use of tools to modify other tools, and the earliest evidence of modified tools in the hominid record is unequivocally associated with fully bipedal hominids.

Some researchers have taken a closer look at the mechanics of bipedal locomotion to see if it might be a more efficient form of locomotion in the savannah-woodland environment, where resources are likely to be scattered. Compared with the quadrupedal locomotion of primates such as chimpanzees, bipedalism appears to be more efficient for long-distance travel. But why travel long distances? Pat Shipman suggested that bipedalism was an appropriate adaptation for hominids to scavenge food (Shipman, 1984; Shipman, 1986). While bipeds are slower and less efficient than quadrupeds when running, they are much more efficient when walking. Thus, a biped could cover large areas, although very slowly. In addition, having the head elevated would allow one to see further distances. Sinclair adds to the scavenging hypothesis by suggesting that long-distance migration may have also been important—those who were able to walk long distances, for example, to follow migrating herds, would be able to rapidly increase their numbers (Sinclair et al., 1986). Sinclair has argued that tool use developed in hominids as a response to the need to quickly butcher scavenged remains.

It is of course not clear which theories regarding the origins of bipedalism are correct. It is difficult to collect direct evidence of the factors that may have led to bipedalism. Any or all of these factors—the abilities to see farther, to carry food back to a home base, to carry tools that included weapons, or to travel long distances more efficiently—may explain the transformation of an occasionally bipedal proto-hominid to a completely bipedal hominid.

We must remember that there are also "costs" to bipedal walking. Bipedalism makes it harder to overcome gravity to supply the brain with sufficient blood, (Falk, 1988) and the weight of the body above the pelvis and lower limbs puts greater stress on the hips, lower back, knees, and feet. As Adrienne Zihlman points out, the stresses on the lower body are even greater for females. Females have to support extra weight during pregnancy, and as mothers they usually are responsible for carrying nursing infants. Thus, human bipedalism is an evolutionary compromise—a biological trade-off that was maintained through natural selection. So whatever the advantages of bipedalism, they must be greater than the disadvantages or our ancestors never would have become bipedal (Zihlman, 1992).

We must also remember that the evolution of bipedalism required some dramatic changes in the ancestral ape skeleton. While apes today can and do walk bipedally, they cannot do so efficiently or for long periods of time. To be habitually bipedal, the ancestral ape skeleton had to be modified, and the major changes that allowed the early hominids to become fully bipedal occurred primarily in the skull, pelvis, knees, and feet (Lovejoy, 1988). Let's take a look at each of these changes.

In both ancient and modern apes, the spinal column enters the skull toward the back, which makes sense because apes generally walk on all fours, with the spine roughly parallel to the ground. In bipedal hominids, the spinal column enters the skull at the bottom, through a hole called the **foramen magnum**. Thus, when hominids became bipedal, the skull ended up on top of the spinal column.

The shape of ancient and modern ape pelves is considerably different from that of a bipedal hominid. The ape pelvis is long and flat, forming a bony plate in the lower back to which the leg muscles attach. In bipedal hominids the pelvis is bowl-shaped, which supports the internal organs and also lowers the body's centre of gravity, allowing better balance on the legs. The hominid pelvis also provides a different set of muscle attachments and shifts the orientation of the femurs (the upper leg bones) from the side of the pelvis to the front. These changes allow hominids to move their legs forward in a bipedal stride (and do things like kick a soccer ball). Apes, in comparison, move their legs forward (when they walk bipedally) by shifting their pelvis from side to side, not by kicking each leg forward alternately as we do (Aiello and Dean, 1990).

Another change associated with the hominid ability to kick the leg forward is our "knock-kneed" posture. Ape legs hang straight down from the pelvis. Bipedal hominid legs, on the other hand, angle inward toward one another. This configuration not only helps us move our legs forward but also helps us maintain a centre of gravity in the midline of our bodies, so that our centre of gravity does not shift from side to side when we walk or run; the lateral gluteus medius muscles are also crucial for this motion—for example, the right gluteus medius contracts when the right leg swings forward, thus preventing the upper body from pitching to the right side.

Finally, the feet of bipedal hominids and apes are different in two major ways. First, hominid feet have an enlarged group of ankle bones forming a robust heel that can withstand the substantial forces placed on them as a result of habitual bipedalism. Second, hominid feet have an arch, which also aids in absorbing the forces endured by the feet during bipedal locomotion. We know this arch is vital to our ability to be habitually bipedal because "flat-footed" people who lack it have chronic problems in their feet, ankles, knees, and back (Aiello and Dean, 1990).

When did these changes take place? We don't know for sure, but fossils from East Africa—Ethiopia, Tanzania, and Kenya—clearly show that bipedal hominids lived there between 4 million and 5 million years ago, perhaps even earlier.

Expansion of the Brain

In the early twentieth century, the question of brain size and bipedalism in human evolution was a bit like the chicken-and-egg question—it was unclear which came first. Early palaeoanthropologists assumed that the key to human evolution was a big brain, and therefore expected that the first hominids would be large-brained apes. The evolution of upright walking followed. However, as discussed below, the discovery of the Taung fossil fuelled that debate, since it provided the evidence for the implication that early hominids were in fact bipedal "apes," with increased brain development following later in evolution. Today, it is clear that bipedalism evolved first and that increased brain development followed later.

The first definite bipedal hominids, the australopithecines, had relatively small cranial capacities, ranging from about 380 cc to 530 cc—not much larger than that of chimpanzees. Around 2 million years ago, almost half a million years after stone tools appeared, some hominids showed evidence of enlarged cranial capacity. These hominids, classified as early members of our genus, *Homo* (**Homo habilis**), had cranial capacities averaging about 630 cc to 640 cc, which is about 50 percent of the brain capacity of modern humans (the average is slightly more than 1300 cc—see Figure 8–3). A later member of our genus, **Homo erectus**, which may have first appeared about 1.8 million years ago, had a cranial capacity ranging from about 895–1040 cc, or about 70 percent of the brain capacity of modern humans (McHenry, 1998b; Tobias, 1994). *Homo erectus* is discussed in the next chapter.

The australopithecines were small and the earliest *Homo* remains indicate that they were not much bigger, suggesting that much of the increase in brain size over time might have been a result of increasing body size in *H. erectus* and *H. sapiens*. When we correct for body size, however, it turns out that brain size increased not only absolutely but also relatively after 2 million years ago. Between about 4 million and 2 million years ago, relative brain size remained just about the same. Only in the last 2 million years has the hominid brain doubled in relative size, and tripled in absolute size (McHenry, 1982).

What may have favoured the increase in brain size? Many anthropologists think that the increase

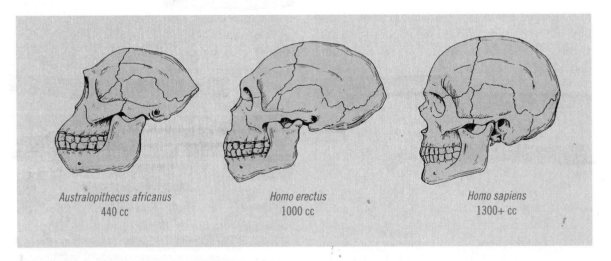

Australopithecus africanus
440 cc

Homo erectus
1000 cc

Homo sapiens
1300+ cc

Figure 8–3

Comparison of the estimated cranial capacities of *Australopithecus africanus*, *Homo erectus*, and *Homo sapiens*, demonstrating the expansion of the brain in hominid evolution.

Source: Estimated cranial capacities from: Tattersall I, Delson E, van Couvering J, editors. 1998. Encyclopedia of Human Evolution and Prehistory. New York: Garland. p 80, 263, 268.

is linked to the emergence of stone toolmaking about 2.5 million years ago. The reasoning is that stone toolmaking was important for the survival of our ancestors, and therefore natural selection would have favoured bigger-brained individuals because they had motor and conceptual skills that enabled them to be better toolmakers. According to this view, the expansion of the brain and more sophisticated toolmaking would have developed together. Other anthropologists think that the expansion of the brain may have been favoured by other factors, such as hunting, increased lifespan, and language (McHenry, 1982).

Whatever the factors favouring bigger brains, natural selection also favoured an increased breadth of the female pelvis to allow larger-brained babies to be born. But there was probably a limit to how large the pelvic outlet could be and still be adapted to bipedalism. Something had to give, and that something was the degree of physical development of the human infant at birth—for instance, the human infant is born with cranial bones so plastic that they can overlap. Because birth takes place before the cranial bones have hardened, the human infant with its relatively large brain can pass through the opening in the mother's pelvis.

Reduction of the Face, Teeth, and Jaws

As in the case of the brain, substantial changes in the face, teeth, and jaws do not appear in hominid evolution until after about 2 million years ago. We know that the australopithecines all had cheek teeth that were very large relative to their estimated body weight. The diet of the australopithecines may have been especially high in plant foods (Pilbeam and Gould, 1974), including small, tough objects such as seeds, roots, and tubers. We also know that the australopithecines had thick jawbones, probably also related to their chewing needs. So we can imagine that the earlier australopithecines had relatively large faces that projected forward below the eyes. It is particularly in the *Homo* forms that we see reduction in the size of the face, cheek teeth, and jaws. It would seem that natural selection in favour of a bigger and stronger chewing apparatus was relaxed, perhaps because human control over fire and the development of cooking made various kinds of food easier to chew. If food is cooked and easy to chew, individual humans with smaller jaws and teeth would not have been disadvantaged, and therefore the face, cheek teeth, and jaw would get smaller on average over time.

Other Evolved Traits

The fossil evidence, which we will discuss shortly, suggests when, and in which hominids, changes occurred in brain size and in the face, teeth, and jaws. Other changes in the evolution of hominids cannot yet be confidently dated with regard to time and particular hominid. For example, we know that modern humans are relatively hairless compared with the other surviving primates. We do not know though, when hominids became relatively hairless, because fossilized bones do not tell us whether their owners were hairy. On the other hand, we suspect that most of the other characteristically human traits developed after the brain began to increase in size, during the evolution of the genus *Homo*. These changes include the extension of the period of infant and child dependency, the scavenging and hunting of meat, the development of a division of labour by sex, and the sharing of food.

One of the possible consequences of brain expansion was that babies were born less developed, which may at least partly explain the lengthening of the period of infant and child dependency in hominids. Compared with other animals, we spend not only a longer proportion of our lifespan, but also the longest absolute period, in a dependent state. Prolonged infant dependency has probably been of great significance in human cultural evolution. According to Theodosius Dobzhansky,

> it is this helplessness and prolonged dependence on the ministrations of the parents and other persons that favours . . . the socialization and learning process on which the transmission of culture wholly depends. This may have been an overwhelming advantage of the human growth pattern in the process of evolution (Dobzhansky, 1962:196).

It used to be thought that the australopithecines had a long period of infant dependency, just as modern humans do, but the way their teeth apparently developed suggests that the early australopithecines followed an apelike pattern of development. Thus, prolonged maturation may be relatively recent, but just how recent is not yet known (Bromage and Dean, 1985; Smith, 1986).

Although some use of tools for digging, defence, scavenging, or hunting may have influenced the development of bipedalism, full bipedalism may have made possible more efficient toolmaking and consequently more efficient scavenging and hunting. As we shall see, there are archaeological signs that early hominids may have been scavenging and hunting animals at least as far back as the Lower Pleistocene (see Figure 8–1). As we will discuss in the next chapter, we have fairly good evidence that *H. erectus* was butchering and presumably eating big game after a million years ago. However, whether the big game were actually hunted is not yet clear.

Regardless of its timing, the development of hunting, combined with longer infant and child dependency, may have fostered a division of labour by sex. The demands of nursing might have made it difficult for women to hunt. Certainly, it would have been awkward, if not impossible, for a mother carrying a nursing child to chase animals. Alternatively, if she left the child behind, she would not have been able to travel very far to hunt. Because the men would have been freer to roam farther, they probably became the hunters. While the men were away hunting, the women may have gathered wild plants within an area that could be covered in a few hours. The division of labour by sex may have increased the likelihood of food sharing. If men primarily hunted and women primarily gathered plant foods, the only way each sex could obtain a complete diet would have been to share the results of their respective labours.

What is the evidence that the physical and cultural changes we have been discussing occurred during the evolution of the hominids? We shall now trace the sequence of known hominid fossils and how they are associated with the development of bipedalism, brain expansion, and reduction of the face, jaws, and teeth. We shall also trace the sequence

of cultural changes in toolmaking, scavenging, and hunting, and other aspects of cultural development.

The Transition from Hominoids to Hominids

The windswept deserts of western Chad don't seem a likely place to find fossil apes or hominids, but paleoanthropologist Michel Brunet thought it might be (Gibbons, 2002). Western Chad was once covered by an ancient lake, and for several million years forest-dwelling mammals, including primates, congregated there. Around 7 million years ago a primate called ***Sahelanthropus tchadensis*** lived on the shores of the lake, where its bones were fossilized and recovered by Brunet and his colleagues in 2001. *Sahelanthropus,* represented by an almost complete skull, has a unique mix of hominid and hominoid traits. While the skull itself is hominoid, with a small brain, large brow ridges, and wide face, the teeth seem more hominid-like, especially the canines, which do not project below the tooth row (Brunet et al., 2002; Wong, 2003). Unfortunately, it is unclear whether *Sahelanthropus* was bipedal. It has been tentatively suggested that the foramen magnum of *Sahelanthropus* is located relatively forward on the cranial base, suggestive of a more bipedal locomotion (Brunet et al., 2002).

There is, however, tantalizing evidence that another possible early hominid, ***Orrorin tugenensis***, was bipedal. Discovered in western Kenya by Brigitte Senut and colleagues in 1998, *O. tugenensis* consists of 19 specimens of jaw, teeth, finger, arm, and leg bones, including the top of a femur (Aiello and Collard, 2001; Pickford et al., 2002; Wong, 2003). The femur in *Orrorin,* according to Senut, shows adaptations to bipedalism, including a long, angled "head" (or top). Other scholars are not convinced. *Orrorin* dates between 5.8 and 6 million years, so if further research supports *Orrorin* bipedalism, it may turn out to be the earliest hominid.

Recently, Ethiopia has yielded a fossil find dated 4.4 million years ago that has palaeoanthropologists intrigued (Fischman, 1994). Is it a link between a Miocene ape and the australopithecines who lived about 4 million years ago? This specimen was initially classified as an early australopithecine, but has since been renamed *Ardipithecus ramidus* (White et al., 1994; White et al., 1995). Leakey and co-workers (Leakey et al., 1995; Leakey et al., 1998) suggest that *A. ramidus* is a sister species to *Australopithecus anamensis* and all later hominids (see below). However, it is difficult to tell from the few available bones whether *A. ramidus* was mostly or only intermittently bipedal. Based on the position of the foramen magnum, this species appears to have been bipedal. The central location of the foramen magnum indicates that the head was carried directly over the spine. However, contrary to expectation for the ancestral hominid, *A. ramidus* appears to have lived in the forest, not in the savannah, where popular theories for the emergence of bipedalism would anticipate. However, the remains of this specimen continue to be analyzed, so we will have to wait to see how old bipedalism really is.

Australopithecines: The Earliest Definite Hominids

Fossil finds from East Africa—Ethiopia, Tanzania, and Kenya—clearly show that bipedal hominids lived there between 4 million and 3 million years ago, perhaps even earlier. Since the 1960s, important discoveries have come mostly from the Great Rift Valley of East Africa, an area where the underlying plates of the earth are pulling away from each other. In many places the Rift Valley drops precipitously from the rim, exposing layers and layers of older rock. Figure 8–4 shows some sites where australopithecines have been found.

The current environment of a fossil site may hardly resemble the reconstructed environment of millions of years ago. For example, Hadar, in the Afar depression of north-central Ethiopia, has yielded a large number of fossil hominids. It is now one of the hottest and driest places on earth, but Hadar used to be a wooded area (Simpson, 1998) on the margin of an extensive lake (Conroy, 1990).

At Laetoli, Tanzania, more than 50 hardened human-like footprints that are estimated to be

about 3.6 million years old give striking confirmation that the hominids there were fully bipedal. Nevertheless, their bipedalism does not mean that these earliest definite hominids were completely terrestrial. All of the australopithecines, including the later ones, seem to have been capable of climbing and moving in trees, judging by arm versus leg lengths and other skeletal features (Rose, 1984; Susman et al., 1985). The South African specimen nicknamed "Little Foot" is the clearest indication yet of this—the hallux (or "big toe" of the foot, the importance of which has long been recognized in the proper function of the foot during gait) appears to have been slightly divergent, allowing good mobility of the big toe, and some prehension of the foot (Clarke and Tobias, 1995).

The australopithecines of Africa show considerable variability, and palaeoanthropologists divide the genus *Australopithecus* into at least six species (Conroy, 1990; Culotta, 1995; Wilford, 1995). Some argue that there may have been several more species. Recent finds are considered by some scholars to represent two new australopithecine species, *A. bahrelghazali* and *A. garhi*, as well as a related hominid, *Kenyanthropus platyops*, that some scholars believe is yet another australopithecine species (see Research Frontiers, *Surprising New Australopithecines* on page 171).

Australopithecus anamensis (found south of Lake Turkana in Kenya) may be 4.2 million years old. The hominids found in East Africa that lived about 4 million to 3 million years ago are classified by most palaeoanthropologists as belonging to the species *Australopithecus afarensis*. Some palaeoanthropologists do not think that these hominids should be placed in a separate species, because they resemble the later hominid species *Australopithecus africanus*, which lived between about 3 million and 2 million years ago. Another potential species of australopithecines was reported in 1995 by French researchers in Chad in north-central Africa. *Australopithecus bahrelghazali* is dated between 3.5 and 3 million years ago and is thought to be a second hominid species contemporary with *A. afarensis* (Brunet et al., 1995). Researchers who discovered the remains

Australopithecine Sites:

1. Hadar, Ethiopia
2. Laetoli, Tanzania
3. Fejej, Ethiopia
4. Lothagam, Kenya
5. Tabarin, Kenya
6. Belodelie (Middle Awash), Ethiopia
7. Kanapoi, Kenya
8. Malawi
9. Taung, South Africa
10. Sterkfontein, South Africa
11. Makapansgat, South Africa
12. Swartkrans, South Africa
13. Kromdraai, South Africa
14. Olduvai, Tanzania
15. West Turkana, Kenya
16. Omo, Ethiopia
17. East Turkana (Koobi Fora), Kenya
18. Peninj (Lake Natron), Kenya

Figure 8–4 Australopithecine Sites

Source: Ciochon RL, Fleagle JG, editors. 1993. The Human Evolution Source Book. Englewood Cliffs, NJ: Prentice Hall. p ix.

argue that their existence is important in demonstrating a wider regional spread of early hominids than had previously been thought. Critics of the taxonomic validity of *A. bahrelghazali* argue that such a widely distributed species should be expected to exhibit some morphological variability and, thus, the Bahr-el-Ghazal partial mandible may fall within the morphological range of *A. afarensis* (Suwa et al., 1997).

In 1999, the remains of **Australopithecus garhi** were discovered in the Afar region of Ethiopia, dating to about 2.5 million years ago. *Australopithecus garhi* had a projecting apelike face and small braincase, similar to *A. afarensis* but with much larger teeth, suggesting to some that it is descended from *A.*

afarensis and is a candidate ancestor for early *Homo* (Asfaw et al., 1999).

Another group of australopithecines, the robusts, lived between at least 2.5 million and 1 million years ago. Most palaeoanthropologists think that the robust australopithecines consist of two species: the East African species **Australopithecus boisei** and the South African species **Australopithecus robustus**. However, there may have been an even earlier robust australopithecine, **A. aethiopicus**.

However, which of the australopithecines was ancestral to our own genus, *Homo?* Here, too, there is controversy, as we shall see. Whatever the ancestry of *Homo*, fossils so classified date from about 2 million years ago.

Mary Leakey's expedition discovered a trail about 64 metres long of 3.6-million-year-old fossilized footprints at Laetoli, Tanzania. Shown here is one of the footprints that were left by two adults who were clearly upright walkers. The footprint shows a well-developed arch and forward-facing big toe.

Raymond Dart's Taung Child

Although the oldest australopithecine fossils come from East Africa, they were not the first australopithecine discoveries. The first finds identified as *Australopithecus* were discovered in caves in South Africa in the 1920s.

In 1925, Raymond Dart, professor of anatomy at the University of Witwatersrand in Johannesburg, South Africa, presented the first evidence that an erect bipedal hominid existed in the Pliocene epoch. As he separated bones from a matrix of material originally found in the Taung cave on the edge of the Kalahari Desert, Dart realized he was looking at more than the remains of an ape. He described the experience:

> On December 23, [1924,] the rock parted. I could view the face from the front, although the right side was still embedded. The creature that had contained

this massive brain was no giant anthropoid such as a gorilla. What emerged was a baby's face, an infant with a full set of milk teeth and its permanent molars just in the process of erupting (Dart, 1925).

From the teeth Dart identified the fossil as the remains of a 5- to 7-year-old child (although recent analysis by electron microscope suggests that the child was no more than 3.5 years old) (Bromage and Dean, 1985; Smith, 1986). He named the specimen *Australopithecus africanus*, which means "southern ape of Africa." Dart was certain the skull was that of a bipedal animal. He based his conclusion on the fact that the foramen magnum was centrally located. (In monkeys and apes, this passageway is near the back of the skull, in a position more appropriate for quadrupedal locomotion.) Furthermore, the Taung child's incisors and canine teeth were short, and therefore definitely more human than apelike.

Dart's conclusion met with widespread skepticism and opposition. Not the least of his problems was that scientists at the time believed hominids had originated in Asia. There were other reasons. Dart had found only one fossil; it was an infant rather than an adult; and no other hominid fossils had yet been found in Africa. Other australopithecines were not discovered until the 1930s, when Robert Broom recovered some fossils from the Sterkfontein cave near Johannesburg. Dart's and Broom's conclusions did not begin to be accepted until after 1945, when Wilfred Le Gros Clark, a professor of anatomy at Oxford, supported the hominid status of their finds (Eldredge and Tattersall, 1982).

Australopithecus africanus

Since the Taung child's discovery more than 75 years ago, the remains of hundreds of other similar australopithecines have been unearthed from the caves at Sterkfontein and Makapansgat in South Africa. From this abundant evidence a fairly complete picture of *A. africanus* can be drawn: "The brain case is rounded with a relatively well-developed forehead and moderate brow ridges surmount a rather projecting face" (Pilbeam,

1972:107). The estimated cranial capacity for the various finds from Taung and Sterkfontein is between 428 cc and 485 cc. In contrast, modern humans have a normal cranial capacity of between 1350 cc and 1450 cc (Holloway, 1974). *Australopithecus africanus* was very small; the adults were only about 105 to 135 centimetres tall and weighed about 20 to 40 kilograms (Szalay and Delson, 1979:504).

Australopithecus africanus retained the large, chinless jaw of the Miocene apes, but some of the dental features of *A. africanus* were similar to those of modern humans—broad incisors and non-projecting canines. Although the premolars and molars were larger than in modern humans, their form was very similar. Presumably, function and use were also similar.

The broad, bowl-shaped pelvis, which is very similar to the human pelvis in form and in areas for muscle attachments, provides corroborating evidence for bipedalism. The australopithecine spine also suggests they walked erect. The bottom part of the vertebral column forms a curve, causing the spinal column to be S-shaped (seen from the side). This **lumbar curve** and an S-shaped spinal column are found only in hominids (see Figure 8–2). Analysis of the hip-joint and femoral bone fossils also indicates that the australopithecines

A reconstruction of an *Australopithecus africanus* mother and child picking berries in a tree. Like *A. Afarensis*, *A. africanus* probably spent time in trees both feeding and avoiding predators.

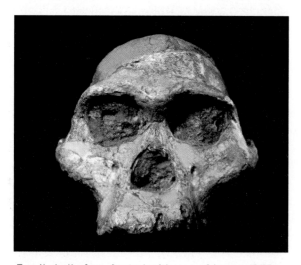

Fossil skull of an *Australopithecus africanus* (STS 5) nicknamed "Mrs. Ples," found by Robert Broom at Sterkfontein cave in 1947.

walked fully upright and that at least the later ones walked with the same direct, striding gait observed in modern humans (Lovejoy et al., 1973).

Dating of the australopithecine finds from the South African limestone caves is somewhat difficult because none of the absolute dating techniques can be applied. Relative dating is possible though. Comparisons of the fauna found in the strata with fauna found elsewhere suggest that the South African *A. africanus* lived between 3 million and 2 million years ago. The climate was probably semi-arid, not too different from the climate of today (Conroy, 1990).

Australopithecus afarensis

It appears that other bipedal australopithecines lived earlier in East Africa, before 3 million years ago. The fossils showing the clearest evidence of bipedalism come from Laetoli, Tanzania, and Hadar, Ethiopia. These finds, dated between 4 million and 3 million years ago, represent an earlier species of *Australopithecus*. The Hadar and Laetoli hominids, as well as those from some other East African sites, are classed as *A. afarensis*.

Remains from at least two dozen hominids were unearthed at Laetoli, Tanzania (Simpson, 1998). Although the remains there consisted largely of teeth and jaws, there is no question that the Laetoli hominids were bipedal, because it was at the Laetoli site that the now famous trail of footprints was found. Two hominids walking erect and side by side left their tracks in the ground 3.6 million years ago. The remains of at least 35 individuals have been found at another site, Hadar, in Ethiopia. The Hadar finds are remarkable for their completeness. Whereas palaeoanthropologists often find just parts of the cranium and jaws, many parts of the skeleton were also found at Hadar. For example, palaeoanthropologists found 40 percent of the skeleton of a female hominid they named Lucy, after the Beatles' song "Lucy in the Sky with Diamonds" (Johanson and Edey, 1981). At the time, Lucy was the most complete australopithecine specimen found. An analysis of Lucy's pelvis indicates clearly that she was a bipedal walker (Lovejoy, 1988). However, she probably spent some time in the trees, if we judge by her leg bones and joints; they are not as large proportionately as those of modern humans (Jungers, 1988).

Dating of the hominid remains at Laetoli suggests that the hominids there lived between 3.8 million and 3.6 million years ago (Johanson and White, 1979). Although Lucy and the other hominids at Hadar were once thought to be about as old as those at Laetoli, recent dating suggests that they are somewhat younger—less than 3.2 million years old. Lucy probably lived 3.2 million years ago (Walter, 1994). The environment when Lucy lived there was semi-arid, upland savannah with rainy and dry seasons (Conroy, 1990; Simpson, 1998).

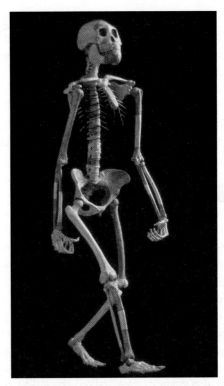

A reconstruction of a female *Australopithecus afarensis* skeleton. Note how long the arms are relative to the legs, and the long fingers. Both suggest *A. afarensis* was at least partially arboreal.

Those palaeoanthropologists, such as Donald Johanson and Tim White, who believe the Laetoli and Hadar hominids should be given the separate species name *A. afarensis*, base their decision primarily on some features of the skull, teeth, and jaws that they feel are more apelike than those of the later hominids classified as *A. africanus*. For example, the incisors and canines of the Laetoli and Hadar hominids are rather large, their tooth rows converge slightly at the back of the jaw, and the palate (roof of the mouth) is flat and narrow. Many *A. afarensis* specimens also display a **sagittal crest** (a ridge of bone along the midline of the top of the skull for muscle attachment), and some have a *temporo-nuchal* crest—a compound crest which forms at the back of the skull (Johanson and White, 1979; White et al., 1981).

In some other respects, the Laetoli and Hadar fossils resemble *A. africanus*. Like *A. africanus*, individuals were very small. Lucy, for example, was about 105 centimetres tall, and the largest individuals at these sites, presumably males, were about 150 centimetres tall (Campbell, 2001:202). The brains of the Laetoli and Hadar hominids also tend to be small; cranial capacity is estimated at 415 cc, just slightly less than that of *A. africanus* (McHenry, 1982).

Australopithecus robustus and *boisei*

There is little disagreement that the so-called "robust" species of australopithecines lived in East Africa and in South Africa from about 2.5 million to 1 million years ago. Indeed, some palaeoanthropologists think these fossils are so different that they deserve to be classified in a different genus, which they call ***Paranthropus***, literally "beside humans." Robust australopithecines were found first in South African caves, in Kromdraai and in Swartkrans, and later in East Africa, in the Omo Basin in Ethiopia, on the east and west sides of Lake Turkana in Kenya, and in the Olduvai Gorge in Tanzania (Conroy, 1990). Most palaeoanthropologists classify the South African robust australopithecines from about 1.8 million to 1 million years

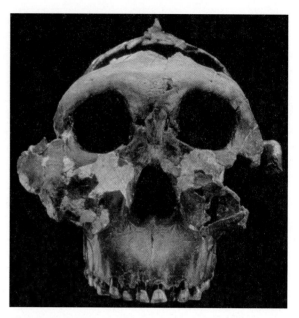

Fossil skull of *Australopithecus boisei* found by Louis and Mary Leakey in 1959. Note its huge face and teeth and its sagittal crest.

Fossil skull of *Australopithecus robustus* (SK46) found by Robert Broom at Swartkrans cave in 1949. Note its sagittal crest, massive cheekbones, and huge molars.

A reconstruction of what *Australopithecus boisei* may have looked like.

ago as *A. robustus*, and the East African robust forms from 2.2 million to 1.3 million years ago as *A. boisei* (McHenry, 1998b). There may have been another robust species even earlier, dating back more than 2.5 million years ago, but many palaeo-anthropologists classify this earlier find as *A. boisei*. Even earlier than that, another species, called *A. aethiopicus*, may have been ancestral to *A. boisei*.

RESEARCH FRONTIERS

Surprising New Australopithecines

In his description of the new species *Australopithecus garhi*, Ethiopian paleoanthropologist Berhane Asfaw explained that the word *garhi* means "surprise" in the Ethiopian language. The name is a fitting one, for neither he nor his colleagues nor the rest of the paleoanthropological community was expecting to find a new aus-tralopithecine species when they began working in the Middle Awash in 1996. In 1992, the same team had discovered *Ardipithecus ramidus*. *Australopithecus anamensis* and *Australopithecus bahrelghazali* were discovered in the following years. *Kenyanthropus platyops*, which many identify as australopithecine rather than a new genus, was found in 1998. Within a decade, four to five new hominids had been discovered, essentially doubling the number known from the previous 30 years.

Surprising, too, were the skeletal and dental traits of *A. garhi*, which was found in rock dating to approximately 2.5 million years ago. Asfaw and his colleagues expected the new find to resemble one of the previously known australopithecine species, but it did not. While clearly not *Homo*, the teeth and jaws were also clearly not like those of *A. afarensis* or any of the robust australopithecines. *A. garhi* has larger molars than does *A. afarensis*, yet does not have the huge face and jaws of the robust aus-tralopithecines. It also lacks the enlarged brain of early *Homo*. Several limb bones were found in the same rock layers, and these do resemble those of *A. afarensis*. *A. garhi*, then, looks to be an afarensis-like creature but with greatly enlarged molars.

Most surprising of all, however, was the fact that the remains of butchered animals were found in the same rock layer as the *A. garhi* remains. Several bones found near the *A. garhi* fossils show unambigu-ous cut marks and signs of having been broken with a stone tool. Unfortunately, no stone tools have been found, but the evidence for butchery suggests they must have been used. And since no other species of hominid have been found in the area, it is reasonable to think that *A. garhi* was the toolmaker and butcher. Asfaw and his colleagues suggest that *A. garhi* is in the right place, at the right time, and has the right physical and behavioural traits to be the direct ancestor of early *Homo*.

Equally surprising is *Australo-pithecus bahrelghazali*, not so much because of its physical features, but because it was found further west, in what is now central Chad. *A. bahrel-ghazali* is the first early hominid to be found outside of the Rift Valley (in East Africa), and until *A. bahrelghaz-ali* surfaced, few thought early hominids were present anywhere else. *A. bahrelghazali* dates to about 3 mil-lion years ago, and is very similar to contemporary *A. afarensis* fossils from the Rift Valley. It differs from *A. afarensis* in some distinct ways (its premolars, for example, have thinner enamel and more well-defined roots), but the important difference is where *A. bahrelghazali* lived. Most scholars assume the early hominids represent a specific adaptation to the Rift Valley. The discovery of an early australo-pithecine some 2500 kilometres west of the Rift Valley calls this assump-tion into question.

Australopithecus bahrelghazali is represented by a single, frag-mentary jaw, and only a handful of skull and limb fragments represent *A. garhi*. While the finds are intrigu-ing, we will not know how important either species is, or how they may change our understanding of early hominid evolution, until more fos-sils from them are found.

Finally, the nearly complete skull of *Kenyanthropus platyops*, dated at 3.5 million years ago, from west-ern Kenya shows traits that Meave Leakey and her colleagues suggest separate it from the australo-pithecines that lived at the same time. Its face is smaller and flatter, and its molars are smaller than the australopithecines. Leakey believes *Kenyanthropus* may be a direct link to *Homo*, but others are not so sure. The skull is distorted, and scholars are not convinced that its features lie outside the range of the aus-tralopithecines. With such surprises appearing in the last decade of the twentieth century, one can only wonder what surprises the first decade of this century will bring.

Sources: Asfaw B, White T, Lovejoy O, Latimer B, Simpson S, Suwa G. 1999. *Australopithecus garhi:* A New Species of Early Hominid from Ethiopia. Science 284:629–635.

Brunet M, Beauvilain A, Coppens Y, Heintz E, Moutaye AHE, Pilbeam D. 1995. The First Australopithecine 2,500 Kilometers West of the Rift Valley. Nature 378:273–275.

Leakey M, Spoor F, Brown F, Gathogo P, Kiarie C, Leakey L, McDougall I. 2001. New Hominid Genus from Eastern Africa Shows Diverse Middle Pliocene Lineages. Nature 410:433–451.

In contrast to *A. africanus*, the robust australopithecines generally had thicker jaws, with larger molars and premolars but smaller incisors, more massive muscle attachments for chewing, and well-developed sagittal crests to support heavy chewing (Szalay and Delson, 1979; Wood, 1992), although this has been suggested to be a sexually dimorphic trait among males. In addition, *A. robustus* and *A. boisei* have somewhat larger cranial capacities (about 490 cc to 530 cc) than *A. africanus*. Compared with *A. robustus*, *A. boisei* has even more extreme features that reflect a huge chewing capability—enormous molar teeth and expanded premolars that look like molars, a massive thick and deep jaw, thick cheekbones, and a more pronounced sagittal crest (McHenry, 1998b).

It used to be thought that the robust australopithecines were substantially bigger than the other australopithecines—hence, the use of the word *robust*. Recent calculations though suggest that these australopithecines were not substantially different in body weight or height as compared with the other australopithecines. The robustness is primarily in the skull and jaw, most strikingly in the teeth. If the robust forms were larger in body size, their slightly bigger brain capacity would not be surprising, since larger animals generally have larger brains. However, the body of the robust forms is similar to that of *A. africanus*, so the brain of the robust australopithecines was relatively larger than the brain of *A. africanus* (Jungers, 1998; McHenry, 1998a).

In 1954, John T. Robinson proposed that *A. africanus* and *A. robustus* had different dietary adaptations—*A. africanus* was an omnivore (dependent on meat and plants) and *A. robustus* was a vegetarian with a need for heavy chewing. Robinson's view was hotly debated for many years. Evidence from electron microscopy supports Robinson's view that

RESEARCH FRONTIERS

New Finds of Early "Robust" Australopithecines Are Puzzling

Where do the robust australopithecines, with their big jaws and bony skull ridges, fit into the evolution of humans? The very early date of some robust australopithecine fossils in East Africa presents a puzzle, according to palaeoanthropologist Henry McHenry. (These fossils, classified by some as belonging to a new species, *Australopithecus aethiopicus*, date apparently from about 2.5 million years ago.) If the late robust forms (*A. robustus* and *A. boisei*) descend from *A. aethiopicus* and if the line leading to *Homo* had already split off from an earlier australopithecine, then why do the late robust australopithecines resemble *Homo erectus* more than they resemble the australopithecines, who were their presumed ancestors?

The late robust australopithecines are like *H. erectus* in having a relatively large brain (as compared with *A. africanus*), reduced *prognathism* (lower face projection), and a deep jaw joint. If they diverged earlier from the *Homo* line, similarity to *Homo* would not present a puzzle. But if the robust line diverged much earlier, as the 2.5-million-year-old *A. aethiopicus* suggests, the late robust forms should be much more divergent from *Homo*. After all, the further back in time two lines diverge, the more you would expect the later examples in each to differ.

What could explain some of the similarities between the late robust australopithecines and the *Homo* line? McHenry suggests two possible explanations, both involving convergence. McHenry points out that *convergence*, the independent appearance of similar structures in different lines of descent, can obscure the issue of how far back there was common ancestry. As such, one explanation of the similarities between the late robust australopithecines and the *Homo* line is that the late robust forms descend from the early robust forms but resemble *H. erectus* because of convergence. A second possibility is that the late robust forms and *Homo* share a not yet found recent ancestor; if they do, then the early robust forms were not ancestral to the late robust forms.

On the basis of his analysis of trait similarities, McHenry thinks that the two late robust australopithecine species (*A. robustus* and *A. boisei*) share a common ancestor but that ancestor was not the early robust form, *A. aethiopicus*. In many ways, the late robust forms are not that similar to *A. aethiopicus*. *A. aethiopicus* is represented by a nearly complete skull (the "Black Skull") and a mandible from Omo, previously assigned to *A. robustus*. It is no doubt robust. It has huge premolars and molars and a cranial crest. In other ways though, it resembles *A. afarensis*: protruding muzzle, shallow jaw joint, and small

A. robustus ate mostly small hard objects such as seeds, nuts, and tubers. But how different was *A. africanus* in this respect? Recent analyses suggest that *A. africanus* also did fairly heavy chewing (McHenry, 1998b).

The idea that *A. robustus* was only vegetarian is also questioned by a relatively new chemical technique that analyzes strontium-calcium ratios in teeth and bones to estimate the proportions of plant versus animal food in the diet. This new kind of analysis suggests that *A. robustus* was an omnivore (McHenry, 1998b). Thus, *A. robustus* may have needed large teeth and jaws to chew seeds, nuts, and tubers, but that does not mean that it didn't eat other foods.

Was *A. robustus* adapted then to a drier, more open environment than *A. africanus*? This is a possibility, but the evidence is somewhat controversial. At any rate, most palaeoanthropologists think that

A. robustus died out shortly after 1 million years ago (Grine, 1998) and therefore could not be ancestral to our own genus, *Homo* (Stringer, 1985).

One Model of Human Evolution

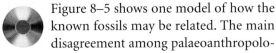

Figure 8–5 shows one model of how the known fossils may be related. The main disagreement among palaeoanthropologists concerns which species of *Australopithecus* were ancestral to the line leading to modern humans. For example, the model shown in Figure 8–5 suggests that *A. africanus* is not ancestral to *Homo*, only to one line of robust australopithecines. *Australopithecus afarensis* is viewed as ancestral to both lines of robust australopithecines and to the line leading to modern humans. Those who think that *A. afarensis* was the last common ancestor of all the hominid lines shown in Figure 8–5 also think

braincase, as well as the presence of a temporo-nuchal crest (compound crest). McHenry thinks that convergent evolution produced the resemblances between the early and late robust australopithecines and the convergence happened because of strong selective pressure for heavy chewing. Features associated with heavy chewing have evolved in other primates as well, in evolutionary lines far removed from the human line—*Gigantopithecus*, with its enormous premolars and molars, was one such primate. Thus, although McHenry still considers the late robust australopithecines to constitute a side branch to the *Homo* line, his analysis suggests that *A. robustus* and *A. boisei* were not as far from *Homo* as previously thought (McHenry, 1998b).

Timothy Bromage, who has studied fossil facial growth, and Randall Susman, who has studied the hominid thumb, have other suggestions about the robust australopithecines. Bromage has used the

scanning electron microscope to study images of fossil faces, particularly to see how the face would have grown from infancy to adulthood. The maturing face changes in shape by a combination of deposition of bone in some locations and removal of bone in other locations. So, for instance, a jaw becomes more protruding when bone is deposited on the forward-facing surfaces and is *resorbed* on the opposite surfaces. Scanning electron microscopy can reveal whether bone is deposited or resorbed. Bromage found differences between the growth patterns of the robust australopithecines and *A. africanus*. *Australopithecus africanus* and even early *Homo* finds are more apelike in their growth pattern than the later robust australopithecines (Bromage, 1998).

Susman has studied thumb bones and the attached musculature to see what traits would be needed to make tools. Modern humans have longer but stouter thumbs than apes do, so they can perform the kind of precise

grasping needed for toolmaking. Did any early hominids have such precise grasping ability? Susman thinks that all the australopithecines after about 2.5 million years ago, including the robust ones, were capable of making tools with their hands (Susman, 1994). This doesn't mean that they made tools, only that they could have.

The robust australopithecines with their small foreheads, extremely flat cheeks, and enormous jaws may have looked very different from the forms in the *Homo* line, but they could be closer to us evolutionarily than we once thought.

Sources: McHenry HM. "Robust" Australopithecines, Our Family Tree, and Homoplasy; Bromage TG. Palaeoanthropology and Life History, and Life History of a Palaeoanthropologist. Both in: Ember CR, Ember M, Peregrine PN, editors. 1998. Research Frontiers in Anthropology. Upper Saddle River, NJ: Prentice Hall. Prentice Hall/Simon & Schuster Custom Publishing.

Susman RL. 9 September 1994. Fossil Evidence for Early Hominid Tool Use. Science 1570–1573.

the split to *Homo* occurred over 3 million years ago (Wood, 1992). Despite the uncertainty and disagreements about what species was ancestral to the *Homo* line, there is widespread agreement among palaeoanthropologists about other aspects of early hominid evolution: (1) There were at least two separate hominid lines between 3 million and 1 million years ago; (2) the robust australopithecines were not ancestral to modern humans but became extinct by 1 million years ago; and

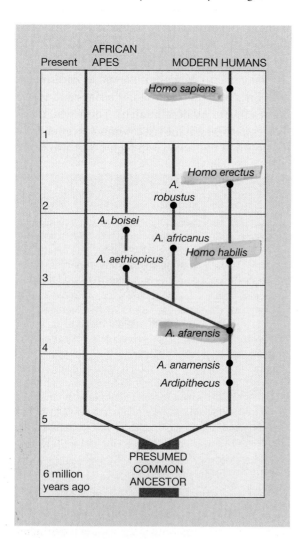

Figure 8–5 Phylogenetic Timelines

Source: Adapted from Leakey M, Tattersall I. 5 September 1995. The Fossil Trail. New York Times C9. Dates changed slightly to reflect recent redating. Copyright © 1995 by the New York Times Company. Reprinted by permission of the New York Times.

(3) *Homo habilis* (and successive *Homo* species) were in the direct ancestral line to modern humans.

Early Species of *Homo*

Hominids with a brain absolutely and relatively larger than that of the australopithecines appeared about 2.5 million years ago. These hominids, classified in our own genus, *Homo*, are generally divided into two species: *Homo habilis* and **Homo rudolfensis**. Fossils of both were primarily found in the western parts of Kenya and Tanzania, but remains have been found elsewhere in eastern and southern Africa, including the Omo Basin of Ethiopia and Sterkfontein cave in South Africa (Conroy, 1990). Both lived in the same place and time as the robust australopithecine *Australopithecus boisei*, and may have lived at the same time as *Homo erectus* (Simpson, 1998).

Homo habilis appears to be the earlier of these two species, appearing around 2.3 million years ago. Compared with the australopithecines, *H. habilis* had a significantly larger brain, averaging 630–640 cc (Tobias, 1994; McHenry, 1998b), and reduced molars and premolars (Simpson, 1998). The rest of the skeleton is similar to the australopithecine skeleton, including the presence of powerful hands and relatively long arms, suggesting that *H. habilis* was at least partially arboreal. *H. habilis* might also have been sexually dimorphic like the australopithecines, as individuals seem to have greatly differed in size.

Homo rudolfensis is roughly contemporary with *H. habilis*, and shares many of its features. In fact, many palaeoanthropologists make no distinction between the two species, putting them both together as *H. habilis*. Those who do not see them as distinct species point to the larger and more thickly enamelled cheek teeth of *H. rudolfensis*, its flatter and broader face, and its more modern-like limb proportions. Even with its large teeth and broad face, the dentition of *H. rudolfensis* is considerably reduced compared with that of the australopithecines and, like *H. habilis*, its brain is at least a third larger.

 We have few postcranial skeletal remains for either of these early species of *Homo*, so it is impossible to tell whether the female pelvis had changed. But, with the brains averaging a third larger than the australopithecines', it seems likely that some modifications must have developed to allow for larger-brained offspring to be born. We do know though that changes in the female pelvis to accommodate larger-brained babies can be seen in *Homo erectus*, discussed in the next chapter.

 Early Hominid Cultures

Tool Traditions

Because stone tools found at various sites in East Africa date to about the time of *H. habilis*, some anthropologists surmise that *H. habilis*, rather than the australopithecines, made those tools. After all, *H. habilis* had the greater brain capacity. But the fact is that none of the earliest stone tools are clearly associated with *H. habilis*, so it is impossible as yet to know who made them. All the hominids that lived from at least 2.5 million years ago had a thumb capable of toolmaking, so all of them may have been toolmakers (Susman, 1994). We turn now to those tools and what archaeologists infer about the lifestyles of their makers, the hominids (whoever they were) who lived between about 2.5 million and 1.5 million years ago.

The earliest identifiable stone tools found so far come from various sites in East Africa and date from about 2.5 million years ago (Susman, 1994), and maybe earlier. The oldest tools, some 3000 in number, were discovered recently at Gona, Ethiopia. The tools range from very small flakes (thumb-size) to cobble or core tools that were fist-size (Anonymous, 1997c). These early tools were apparently made by striking a stone with another stone, a technique called **percussion flaking**. Both the sharp-edged flakes and the sharp-edged cores (the pieces of stone left after flakes are removed) were probably used as tools. Archaeologists consider a pattern of behaviour, such as a particular way to make a tool that is shared and learned by a group of individuals, to be a sign of some cultural behaviour. To be sure, toolmaking does not imply that early humans had anything like the

complex cultures of humans today, because, as we noted in Chapter 6, chimpanzees have patterns of tool use and toolmaking that appear to be shared and learned, but they do not have that much in the way of cultural behaviour. On the basis of their toolmaking, early hominids had some cultural behaviour, but we cannot tell yet how much culture they had.

What were those earliest stone tools used for? What do they tell us about early hominid culture? Unfortunately, little can be inferred about lifestyles from the earliest tool sites because little else was found with the tools. In contrast, finds of later tool assemblages at Olduvai Gorge in Tanzania have yielded a rich harvest of cultural information. The Olduvai site was uncovered accidentally in 1911, when a German entomologist followed a butterfly into the gorge and found fossil remains. Beginning in the 1930s, Louis and Mary Leakey searched the gorge for clues to the evolution of early humans. Of the Olduvai site, Louis Leakey wrote,

> [It] is a fossil hunter's dream, for it shears 300 feet [91.4 metres] through stratum after stratum of earth's history as through a gigantic layer cake. Here, within reach, lie countless fossils and artifacts that but for the faulting and erosion would have remained sealed under thick layers of consolidated rock (Leakey, 1960).

The oldest cultural materials from Olduvai (Bed I) date from the Lower Pleistocene. The stone artifacts include core tools and sharp-edged flakes, but flake tools predominate. Among the core tools, so-called *choppers* are common. A chopper is a core tool that has been partially flaked and has a side that might have been used for chopping. Other core tools, with flaking along one side and a flat edge, are called *scrapers*. Whenever a stone has facets removed from only one side of the cutting edge, we call it a **unifacial tool**. If the stone has facets removed from both sides, we call it a **bifacial tool**. Although there are some bifacial tools in the early stone tool assemblages, they are neither as plentiful nor as elaborated as in later tool traditions. The kind of tool assemblage found in Bed I and to some extent in later (higher) layers is referred to as **Oldowan** (see Figure 8–6) (Clark, 1970; Schick and Toth, 1994).

Lifestyles

Archaeologists have long speculated about the lifestyles of early hominids from Olduvai and other sites. Some of these speculations come from analysis of what can be done with the tools, microscopic analysis of wear on the tools, and examination of the marks the tools make on bones; other speculations are based on what is found in association with the tools.

Archaeologists have experimented with what can be done with Oldowan tools. The flakes appear to be very versatile; they can be used for slitting the hides of animals, dismembering animals, and whittling wood into sharp-pointed sticks (wooden spears or digging sticks). The larger stone tools (choppers and scrapers) can be used to hack off branches or cut and chop tough animal joints (Schick and Toth, 1994). Those who have made and tried to use the stone flake tools for various purposes are so impressed by the sharpness and versatility of flakes that they wonder whether the core tools were really routinely used as tools. The cores could mainly be what remained after flakes were struck off (Schick and Toth, 1994:129). Archaeologists surmise that many early tools were also made of wood and bone, but these do not survive in the archaeological record. For example, present-day populations use sharp-pointed digging sticks for extracting roots and tubers from the ground; stone flakes are very effective for sharpening wood to a very fine point (Schick and Toth, 1994).

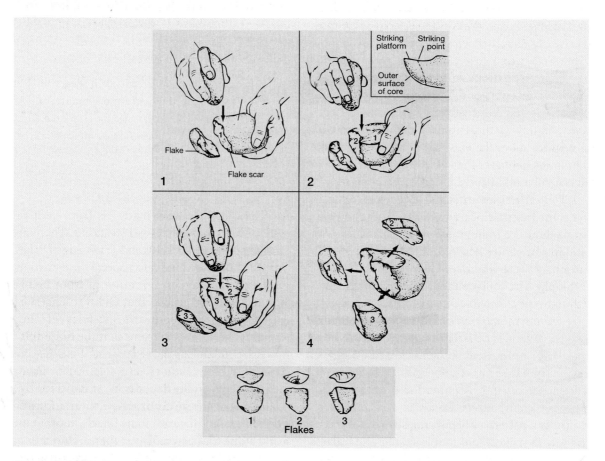

Figure 8–6 The Production of a Simple Oldowan Chopper Core and the Resultant Flakes

Source: Freyman R. The First Technology. Scientific American. © *Scientific American*, Inc. Reprinted by permission of Ed Hanson, artist.

None of the early flaked stone tools can plausibly be thought of as weapons. So if the toolmaking hominids were hunting or defending themselves with weapons, they had to have used wooden spears, clubs, or unmodified stones as missiles. Later Oldowan tool assemblages also include stones that were flaked and battered into a rounded shape. The unmodified stones and the shaped stones might have been lethal projectiles (Isaac, 1984).

Experiments may tell us what can be done with tools, but they cannot tell us what was actually done with them. Other techniques, such as microscopic analysis of the wear on tools, are more informative. Early studies focused on the microscopic scratches formed when a tool was used in different ways. Scratches parallel to the edge of a tool often occur when a tool is used in a sawing motion; perpendicular scratches suggest whittling or scraping (Whittaker, 1994). Lawrence Keeley used high-powered microscopes in his experimental investigations of tools and found that different kinds of "polish" develop on tools when they are used on different materials. The polish on tools used for cutting meat is different from the polish on tools used for woodworking. On the basis of microscopic investigation of the 1.5-million-year-old tools from the eastern side of Lake Turkana, Keeley and his colleagues concluded that at least some of the early tools were probably used for cutting meat, others for cutting or whittling wood, and others for cutting plant stems (Schick and Toth, 1994).

In the 1950s and 1960s, Olduvai Gorge revealed the presence of both Oldowan tools and the remains of broken bones and teeth from many different animal species. For many years it seemed plausible to assume that hominids were the hunters and the animals their prey. However, archaeologists had to re-examine this assumption with the emergence of the field of *taphonomy*, which is the study of the processes that can alter and distort a sample of bones. So, for example, flowing water can bring bones and artifacts together, which may have happened at Olduvai Gorge about 1.8 million years ago. (The area of what is now the gorge bordered the shores of a shallow lake at that time.) Also other animals such as hyenas could have brought carcasses to some of the same places that hominids frequented. Taphonomy requires archaeologists to consider all the possible reasons that might explain why things may be found together (Speth, 1998).

Regardless there is little doubt that hominids shortly after 2 million years ago were cutting up animal carcasses for meat. Microscopic analyses show that cut marks on animal bones were unambiguously created by stone flake tools, and microscopic analyses of polish on stone tools show the polish to be consistent with butchering. We still do not know for sure whether the hominids around Olduvai Gorge were just scavenging meat (taking meat from the kills of other animals) or hunting the animals. On the basis of her analysis of cut marks on bone from Bed I in Olduvai Gorge, Pat Shipman suggested that scavenging, not hunting, was the major meat-getting activity of the hominids living there between 2 million and 1.7 million years ago. For example, the fact that cut marks made by stone tools usually (but not always) overlie teeth marks made by carnivores suggests that the hominids were often scavenging the meat of animals killed and partially eaten by non-hominid predators. The fact that the cut marks were sometimes made first, however, suggested to Shipman that the hominids were also sometimes the hunters (Szalay, 1975; Shipman, 1986). On the other hand, prior cut marks may indicate only that the hominids scavenged before carnivores had a chance to.

The artifact and animal remains from Bed I and the lower part of Bed II at Olduvai suggest a few other things about the lifestyles of the hominids there. First, it seems that the hominids moved around during the year; most of the sites in what is now the Olduvai Gorge appear to have been used only in the dry season, as indicated by an analysis of the kinds of animal bones found there (Speth and Davis, 1976). Second, whether the early Olduvai hominids were hunters or scavengers, they apparently exploited a wide range of animals. Although most of the bones are from medium-sized antelopes and wild pigs, even large animals such as elephants and giraffes seem to have been eaten (Isaac, 1971). It is clear, then, that the Olduvai hominids scavenged or hunted for meat, but we cannot tell yet how important meat was in their diet.

There is also no consensus yet about how to characterize the Olduvai sites. In the 1970s, there was a tendency to think of these sites (which contain tools and animal bones) as home bases to which hominids (presumably male) brought meat to share with others (presumably nursing mothers and young children). In short, the scenario involved a home base, a division of labour by sex, and food-sharing. Archaeologists now are not so sure. For one thing, carnivores also frequented these sites. Places with meaty bones lying around may not have been so safe for hominids to use as home bases. Second, the animal remains at the sites had not been completely dismembered and butchered. If the sites had been hominid home bases, we would expect more complete processing of carcasses (Potts, 1988).

If these sites were not home bases, what were they? Some archaeologists are beginning to think that these early sites with many animal bones and tools may just have been places where hominids processed food but did not live. Why would the hominids return to a particular site? Richard Potts suggests one possible reason—that hominids left caches of stone tools and stones for toolmaking at various locations to facilitate their food-collecting and food-processing activities (Potts, 1988). Future research may tell us more about early hominid life. Did they have home bases, or did they just move from one processing site to another? How did they protect themselves from predators? They apparently did not have fire to keep the predators away. Did they climb trees to get away from predators or to sleep safely?

Regardless of the answers to these questions, the presence of patterned stone tools means that these early hominids had probably developed culture. What exactly makes human culture so different from other forms of animal behaviour? Anthropologists have spent more than a century trying to answer this question, and there is still no widely accepted answer. One thing is clear, however.

Culture must be understood as a set of interrelated processes, not as a thing (Wolf, 1984). What are the processes that make up culture? Let's consider some of the more important ones.

First, culture is learned and shared. That is the fundamental difference between culture and most other forms of animal behaviour. Culture is not a set of innate behaviours but rather a set of learned ones. Culture is something individuals acquire during their lifetimes as they mature and interact with others. Interaction is key here, because not only are cultural behaviours learned, they are learned through interaction with others and through education and shared experiences. Culture, then, is a social process, not an individual one.

Second, culture is generally adaptive. What this means is that most of the learned and shared behaviours that make up a culture are thought to have developed and spread through a group of people because they help that group of people to survive in a given environment. Thus, cultural behaviour may be favoured by natural selection just as genes are. The extent to which human culture is a product of natural selection is hotly debated, but few anthropologists would argue that culture is not a key aspect of human adaptation. What makes culture quite different from the behavioural systems of other animals is that, because culture is learned and shared rather than innate, humans can develop new behaviours quickly and adapt to diverse and changing conditions with relative ease. Adaptation, therefore, is perhaps the most significant process of culture.

Change is the third major process of culture, for culture is always changing. Culture change regularly occurs as new and beneficial means of adaptation are developed and shared. However, anthropologists also assume that when new behaviours are developed, they tend to become integrated within existing behaviours. That is, new behaviours that conflict with established ones may lead to one or the other changing. For example, a group of early humans could not have both scavenged meat and, at the same time, prohibited eating meat that they themselves did not kill. Such a situation would create a contradiction, and something would have to change.

Working out contradictions between new, highly beneficial behaviours and established but less beneficial behaviours may be one of the reasons that cultures are so dynamic.

It seems clear that early hominids, like other primates, were social beings. It also seems clear from the archaeological record that early hominids were making and using stone tools. Tools are frequently found in discrete concentrations, and often in association with animal bones and other debris from activity. As has already been suggested, therefore, these concentrations may reflect campsites or small shelters, implying that home bases may have been a part of early hominid culture.

Whether they reflect home bases or not, these accumulations of tools and other artifacts suggest that the areas were being used by groups of individuals over periods of time. In such a situation, sharing of food is very likely. It seems counterintuitive to think that individuals would have purposely brought food to a common location only to keep it to themselves. While this is only speculation, it does not seem unreasonable to think that closely related individuals, such as families, would be more likely to associate and share food with one another than more distantly related individuals. This speculation is supported by the fact that when food-sharing takes place among chimpanzees it is usually among closely related individuals (Boyd and Silk, 2000). Thus, the ancient locations of early hominid social activity may be evidence for family groups.

Language

As discussed briefly in Chapter 6, the evidence for language capabilities among hominids comes from skeletal evidence like the increased flexion of the basicranium. Other evidence comes from endocasts that can give us clues as to the structure of the brain. Through the reconstruction of the skeletal anatomy associated with language in hominids, australopithecines appear to have had apelike anatomy and brains that resemble the living apes in both size and external form—thus, there is no apparent evidence for spoken language. Similarly, there is no strong evidence in support of language capabilities for *H. habilis*, with the exception of a 2-million-year-old endocast that shows a more developed frontal lobe and Broca's area—the area that is responsible for human speech (Tobias, 1987).

However, some have argued that bipedalism, which allowed for the freeing of the hands, may have also provided the ability for increased communication by gestures among the earliest hominids—to a much greater extent than non-human primates (Corballis, 1999). Merlin Donald, a researcher in the Department of Psychology at Queen's University, has suggested that early forms of communication involved the whole body rather than just the hands and arms. There is debate about whether this form of "body language" is distinct from language proper, or whether it is a precursor to the development of spoken language (Corballis, 1999). The earliest hominids appear not to have developed spoken language capabilities, although there may be evidence for selection favouring those features that would be important for spoken language in later hominids.

In the next chapter we will discuss the appearance of *H. erectus*, the first hominid to leave Africa, and early *H. sapiens* populations, including Neandertals.

Summary

1. The drying trend in climate that began about 16 million to 11 million years ago diminished the extent of African rain forests and gave rise to areas of savannah (tropical grasslands) and scattered deciduous woodlands. The more open country probably favoured characteristics adapted to ground living in some primates. In the evolutionary line leading to humans, these adaptations included bipedalism.

2. One of the crucial changes in early hominid evolution was the development of bipedalism. There are several theories for this development. It may have increased the emerging

hominid's ability to see predators and potential prey while moving through the tall grasses of the savannah; by freeing the hands for carrying, it may have facilitated transferring food from one place to another; tool use, which requires free hands, may have favoured two-legged walking; and bipedalism may have made long-distance travelling more efficient.

3. Other important physical changes—including the expansion of the brain, modification of the female pelvis to allow bigger-brained babies to be born, and reduction of the face, teeth, and jaws—did not begin until about 2 million years after the emergence of bipedalism. By that time (about 2 million years ago) hominids had come to depend to some extent on scavenging and possibly hunting meat.

4. The remains of undisputed hominids dating back to between 4 million and 3 million years ago have been found in East Africa. These definitely bipedal hominids are now generally classified in the genus *Australopithecus*. Most palaeoanthropologists divide the genus *Australopithecus* into at least four species. Some East African hominids that lived nearly 2 million years ago are classified as an early species of our own genus, *Homo habilis*.

5. The earliest stone tools found so far come from various sites in East Africa and date from about 2.5 million years ago. We do not yet know who made them. These tools were made by striking a stone with another stone to remove sharp-edged flakes. Both the flakes and the sharp-edged cores were used as tools. This early tool tradition is called Oldowan.

Glossary Terms

Ardipithecus ramidus   (p. 165)

Australopithecus   (p. 157)

Australopithecus aethiopicus   (p. 166)

Australopithecus afarensis   (p. 165

Australopithecus africanus   (p. 165)

Australopithecus anamensis   (p. 165)

Australopithecus bahrelghazalia   (p. 165)

Australopithecus boisei   (p. 166)

Australopithecus garhi   (p. 166)

Australopithecus robustus   (p. 166)

bifacial tool   (p. 175)

foramen magnum   (p. 161)

Homo   (p. 157)

Homo erectus   (p. 162)

Homo habilis   (p. 162)

Homo rudolfensis   (p. 174)

lumbar curve   (p. 168)

Oldowan   (p. 176)

Orrorin tugenensis   (p. 164)

Paranthropus   (p. 170)

percussion flaking   (p. 175)

sagittal crest   (p. 169)

Sahelanthropus tchadensis   (p. 164)

savannah   (p. 159)

unifacial tool   (p. 175)

Critical Questions

1. How could there have been more than one species of hominid living in East Africa at the same time?

2. What may have enabled australopithecines to survive in the face of many ground predators?

3. What is the evidence for language among the earliest hominids?

Internet Exercises

1. Visit **www.talkorigins.org/faqs/homs/specimen.html** to view some prominent hominid fossils. Write a brief summary of your findings pertaining to *Australopithecus afarensis* and Donald Johanson.

2. Go to **www.cruzio.com/~cscp/maps.htm** to view maps of sites where fossil hominids have been found in China.

3. Explore a site devoted to stone tool technology at **www.hf.uio.no/iakn/roger/lithic/**. Look in particular for earlier stone tool technologies, and draw a rough progression of technologies.

4. Test your knowledge by viewing the online quizzes at **www.sscnet.ucla.edu/classes/fall97/ anthro7/new/flashcard.pl?quiz=fossils**.

5. Review the classification of early hominid fossils at **www.d.umn.edu/cla/faculty/troufs/ anth1602/pchomini.html**.

Suggested Reading

Conroy GC. 1990. Primate Evolution. New York: Norton. Chapter 6 summarizes the fossil record for the australopithecines and early *Homo*, discusses the geography and climate of the early sites, and explains the bio-mechanical principles of bipedalism.

Ember CR, Ember M, and Peregrine PN, editors. 1998. Research Frontiers in Anthropology. Upper Saddle River, NJ: Prentice Hall. Prentice Hall/Simon & Schuster Custom Publishing. Several chapters in this series deal with the evolution of early hominids and their cultures, for example, Bromage TG, Paleoanthropology and Life History, and Life History of a Paleoanthropologist; Kramer A, The Natural History and Evolutionary Fate of *Homo erectus*; McHenry HM, "Robust" Australopithecines, Our Family Tree, and Homoplasy; Simpson SW, *Australopithecus afarensis* and Human Evolution; Speth JD, Were Our Ancestors Hunters or Scavengers?

Grine FE, editor. 1988. Evolutionary History of the "Robust" Australopithecines. New York: Aldine. A great deal of controversy has surrounded the "robust" australopithecines. In a 1987 workshop, participants from many different fields were asked to summarize recent knowledge of this group of australopithecines.

Phillipson DW. 1993. African Archaeology. Second edition. Cambridge: Cambridge University Press. A summary and interpretation of the archaeological evidence in Africa and what it tells us about human history from its beginnings to historic times. Chapters 2 and 3 are particularly relevant to this chapter.

Schick K, Toth N. 1994. Making Silent Stones Speak. New York: Simon & Schuster. A large part of understanding past tool traditions is making them and using them. The authors describe their experimental work and relate it to the archaeologically recovered tool traditions of the past.

9

HOMO ERECTUS AND ARCHAIC *HOMO SAPIENS*

In this chapter, we examine the expansion of early Palaeolithic populations out of Africa and their transition to Middle Palaeolithic Archaic *Homo sapiens*. The fossil remains of all hominids more than 2 million years old were found only in Africa. With the emergence of *Homo erectus*, we see the movement of hominid populations off the African continent. *Homo erectus* flourished in Africa, Europe, and Asia from over 1.5 million years ago.

In the Middle Palaeolithic we see changes in the fossil evidence that reflect the emergence of Archaic *Homo sapiens*. This chapter discusses the evidence and controversies surrounding this transition. Evidence shows that toolmaking skills became more sophisticated; hominids now cooked their foods and lived in caves and campsites. The first signs of funeral rituals and altruism appear in the archaeological record. The chapter ends with consideration of the relationship between Neandertals and modern humans.

Homo erectus

Homo erectus is the first hominid to be found outside of Africa, with fossil specimens found in both Europe and Asia, dating to about 2 million years ago. Prior to the emergence of *Homo erectus*, neither *Homo habilis* nor the australopithecines are known to have inhabited areas outside of the African continent. Evidence that *H. erectus* was the first hominid to leave Africa comes from a variety of finds distributed throughout the Old World (see Figure 9–1). Examples of *H. erectus* were found first in Java, later in China, and still later in Africa. Most palaeoanthropologists agree that some human ancestor moved from Africa to Asia at some point. Until recently it was assumed that it was *H. erectus* who moved, because *H. erectus* lived in East Africa about 1.6 million years ago but not until after about 1 million years ago in Asia (Rightmire, 1988). Recent discoveries of *H. erectus* skulls in the Republic of Georgia have been dated

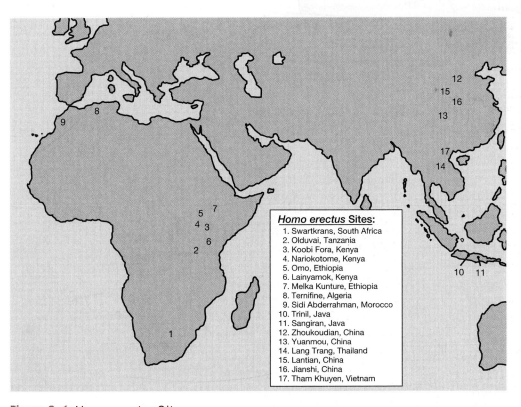

Figure 9–1 *Homo erectus* Sites

Source: Chiochon RL, Fleagle JG, editors. 1993. The Human Evolution Source Book. Englewood Cliffs, NJ: Prentice Hall. p x.

to 1.7 million years ago (Gabunia et al., 2000). If these dates are accurate, then these specimens would represent some of the earliest hominids outside of the African continent. One well-preserved skull from Dmanisi has features that are reminiscent of *H. habilis*—a capacity of only about 600 cc, relatively large canines, and a relatively thick brow ridge (Gabunia et al., 2000). While the excavator classes these remains as *H. erectus*, it does make one wonder if *H. habilis* or transitional species between *H. habilis and H. erectus* individuals were the first to leave Africa.

Nevertheless, for reasons that still remain speculative, *H. erectus* is thought to be the first hominid to move out of Africa. As we have mentioned, all of these specimens from the Old World are broadly classed as *H. erectus*. However, some suggest that the African version appears to have a larger cranial capacity and smaller facial bones. Thus, an alternative scheme has been proposed in which the African remains are classed as **Homo ergaster,** with the East Asian forms remaining *H. erectus*, and later European specimens being classed as *Homo heidelbergensis* (see also Research Frontiers, *Homo erectus: One or More Species?*). Other palaeoanthropologists think that the finds in Europe thought to be *H. erectus* are actually early examples of *H. sapiens*, as are some of the finds in southern Africa and the Near East that were previously thought to be *H. erectus* (Rightmire, 1985; Wolpoff and Nkini, 2001). As we shall see in the next chapter, the evolutionary scheme in which these remains are classed depends greatly on how one views the origins of modern humans.

It is also interesting to consider that in eastern Africa *H. erectus* coexisted with at least one other species of hominid (*A. boisei*) and possibly with as many as three (*A. boisei, A. africanus,* and *H. habilis/rudolfensis*). Why did *H. erectus* survive and flourish while these other species went extinct? Again, culture may be the answer. *A. boisei* seems to have been a specialized grasslands species. Their large molars and powerful dental architecture allowed them to eat hard grass seeds and other coarse materials that other hominids could not chew. However, they had to compete with the many

other grassland animals that also relied on these plants, but reproduced faster and could move quickly enough to escape from predators. Early *Homo* apparently used tools and relied at least in part on scavenging and hunting, but compared with that of *H. erectus*, early *Homo* technology was crude and *Homo* social organization was less complex. As we will discuss below, *H. erectus* appears to have been better organized to scavenge and hunt and to defend themselves against predators. These differences in culture may have provided advantages to *H. erectus* that drove early *Homo* to extinction.

The Discovery in Java and Later Finds

In 1891, Eugene Dubois, a Dutch anatomist digging in Java, found what he called *Pithecanthropus erectus*, meaning "erect ape man." (We now refer to this hominid as *Homo erectus*.) The discovery was not the first human-like fossil found; Neandertals, which we discuss later in the chapter, were known many years earlier. However, no one was certain, not even Dubois himself, whether the fossil he found in Java represented an ape or a human.

The actual find consisted of a cranium and a thigh bone. For many years it was thought that the fragments were not even from the same animal. The skull was too large to be that of a modern ape but was smaller than that of an average human, having a cranial capacity between the average ape's 500 cc and the average modern human's 1300 cc or more. The thigh bone, however, matched that of a modern human. Did the two fragments in fact belong together? The question was resolved many years later by fluorine analysis. As mentioned in Chapter 2, if fossils from the same deposit contain the same amount of fluorine, they are the same age. The skull fragment and thigh bone found by Dubois were tested for fluorine content and found to be the same age.

A discovery by G. H. R. von Koenigswald in the mid-1930s, also in Java, not only confirmed Dubois's earlier speculations and extended our knowledge of the physical characteristics of *H. erectus* but also gave us a better understanding of this

RESEARCH FRONTIERS

Homo erectus: One or More Species?

In living populations, it is possible to tell whether two different primates belong to different species. Can they interbreed? And are the offspring fertile? If the answer to either question is no, we are dealing with different species. The question is, how can we tell species apart in the fossil record? Palaeoanthropologists must judge by the degree of difference between them. Once two populations stop interbreeding, they will begin to develop divergent traits. But how different do they have to be for us to call them different species?

Because the fossil record does not reveal mating patterns, it is not surprising that palaeoanthropologists have differences of opinion about whether two fossils represent the same species or not. In addition, palaeoanthropologists have different predispositions; some tend to be "splitters," identifying more different species; and others tend to be "lumpers," identifying fewer different species. In the 1920s and 1930s, splitting was common; almost every new find of what we now call *H. erectus* was assigned to a different species or even a different genus. For example, *Pithecanthropus erectus* is now called *H. erectus* from Java, and *Sinanthropus pekinensis* is now *H. erectus* from near Peking (now Beijing). Franz Weidenreich in the 1940s suggested this lumping, which dominated classification through the 1960s and 1970s. However, in the 1980s, Peter Andrews, Christopher Stringer, and

Bernard Wood proposed that the Asian and African fossils previously grouped as *H. erectus* were different enough to be split into two separate species—one Asian and one African. So once again there were opposing hypotheses about those fossils. Was *H. erectus* one or two species?

To discover which hypothesis is more likely to be correct, Andrew Kramer analyzed various skull measurements for the Asian and African fossils and two other groups—modern humans, who we know belong to the same species, and a mixed set of early hominids, who are conventionally classified as belonging to two or three different species. Kramer reasoned that if the African and Asian fossils are not more variable than the modern humans, we can conclude that those fossils belong to one species, *H. erectus*. Further, the mixed set of ancient hominids should be more variable than the modern humans.

Kramer analyzed 16 Asian and African skulls that were supposed to have been from a single species, *H. erectus*. They ranged in dating from 1.8 million to half a million years ago; other things being equal, such a great range in time should have made for more variability and therefore more likelihood that the 16 supposed *H. erectus* skulls would show more variability than the sample of modern humans. Kramer wanted to compare these 16 skulls with the same number of modern skulls. But how does one

choose a representative sample of 16 modern skulls from a population of billions in the world? Certainly one random sample would not be sufficient. So Kramer used 1000 different random samples of 16 each from a set of 2533 modern skulls. For each trait he wished to compare between samples, he computed a measure of variability for each sample of 16. What were the results of the comparisons? The 16 supposed *H. erectus* skulls were not more variable than most of the modern human samples, strongly suggesting that they did come from the same species. To test this conclusion further, Kramer compared the modern samples with the mixed sample of ancient hominids (on the basis of the same traits). Because the mixed ancient sample presumably came from more than one species, it should have been more variable than the modern human samples, and in fact, it was. As it turns out, almost all of the modern human samples were less variable than the mixed ancient sample.

So Kramer's research strongly suggests that the hominids in Asia and Africa between 1.8 million years and 500 000 years ago were all *H. erectus*.

Source: Kramer A. 1998. The Natural History and Evolutionary Fate of *Homo erectus*. In: Ember CR, Ember E, Peregrine PN, editors. Research Frontiers in Anthropology. Volume 3. Physical Anthropology. Upper Saddle River, NJ: Prentice Hall. Prentice Hall/Simon & Schuster Custom Publishing. p 133–150.

early human's place in time. Since then, many more *H. erectus* fossils have been found in Java. However, dating of *H. erectus* remains in Java remain unclear, with estimates from more than 1 million years old

(Rightmire, 1990; Swisher III et al., 1994) to less than 55 000 years old (Swisher et al., 1996).

Between the times of Dubois's and von Koenigswald's discoveries, Davidson Black, a

Canadian anatomy professor teaching in Peking (now Beijing), China, set out to investigate a large cave at nearby Zhoukoudian where a fossilized tooth had been found. Confident that the tooth came from a hitherto unknown hominid genus, he obtained funds to excavate the area extensively. After two years of excavation, he and his colleagues found a skull in limestone whose owner was dubbed "Peking Man" (see Historical Perspectives, *Davidson Black*). Black died in 1934, and his work was carried on by Franz Weidenreich. Dubois never acknowledged the relationship between the *H. erectus* finds from Java and those from China.

It was not until the 1950s that *H. erectus* fossils were uncovered in northern Africa. Many finds since then have come from East Africa, particularly from two sites—Olduvai Gorge in Tanzania and the Lake Turkana region of Kenya. An almost complete skeleton of a boy was found at Nariokotome, on the western side of Lake Turkana, dating from about 1.6 million years ago. The Olduvai finds are from about 1.2 million years ago (Rightmire, 1988).

The oldest known specimen of *H. erectus*, KNM-ER 3733, is a cranium found by Richard Leakey in 1975 on the shore of Lake Turkana, Kenya, that dates to about 1.78 million years ago (Feder and Park,

HISTORICAL PERSPECTIVES

Davidson Black

Davidson Black was born in Toronto in 1884. He obtained a medical degree in 1906 from the University of Toronto, after which he studied comparative anatomy and began working as an anatomy instructor in 1909. Black taught at Western Reserve University in Cleveland, and in 1914, he spent six months in England working under the famous anatomist G. Elliot Smith. At the time, Smith was working on the Piltdown material—later shown to be a hoax combining bones from a human and an ape—and Black became intensely interested in the problem of human origins. In 1917 he left Cleveland to join the Canadian army medical corps.

In 1919 Black accepted an invitation to work at the Peking Union Medical College in China. At that time, it was widely believed that the earliest humans evolved in Asia, and Black saw the position as an opportunity to search for early human ancestors. He searched unsuccessfully for the remains of early hominids in northern China, and later in Thailand. However, in 1926, while planning a journey to central Asia, he heard of two human fossil teeth that had been found near Peking. In 1927, with the

aid of the Rockefeller Foundation, he began a large excavation there.

In 1927 Birger Bohlin, a member of Black's team, discovered another fossil hominid tooth at Dragon Bone hill in Zhoukoudian, 48 kilometres from Beijing. He recognized immediately the evolutionary importance of the specimen, from which he inferred the existence of a previously unknown hominid genus and species—*Sinanthropus pekinensis*. While Black was travelling in 1928 trying to convince others of the find's validity, a portion of lower jaw with three teeth in place was found. Finally, in 1929, Black got the evidence he was looking for when the first "Peking Man" skull was discovered. A second skull was also discovered in 1929, but only recognized in 1930. Later excavations yielded 14 skullcaps, several mandibles, facial bones and limb bones, and the teeth of about 40 individuals.

The Zhoukoudian hominid fossils are dated to the Middle Pleistocene, from about 900 000 to 130 000 years ago, although a more exact date has not been determined. For the next few years, Black published descriptions of the Peking Man fossils. When he travelled to Europe

in 1930 to present his new evidence, the reception was much more favourable, and in 1932 he was elected a Fellow of the Royal Society for his efforts. Davidson Black died suddenly in 1934.

The original "Peking Man" fossils were under study at the Peking Union Medical College in 1941, when, with the threat of Japanese invasion on the cusp of World War II, an attempt was made to smuggle them out of China and to the United States. The bones never made it to their destination and have never been recovered, leaving only plaster casts for study. Renewed excavation in the caves, beginning in 1958, brought new specimens to light.

Sources: Shapiro HL. 1981. Davidson Black: An Appreciation. In: Sigmon B, Cybulski J. *Homo erectus:* Papers in Honor of Davidson Black. Toronto: University of Toronto Press. p 21–26.

Swinton WE. 18 December 1976. Physician Contributions to Non-medical Science: Davidson Black, Our Peking Man. Canadian Medical Association Journal 115(12): 1251–1253.

von Koenigswald GHR. 1981. Davidson Black, Peking Man, and the Chinese Dragon. In: Sigmon B, Cybulski J. *Homo erectus*: Papers in Honor of Davidson Black. Toronto: University of Toronto Press. p 27–40.

1997:241). The specimen, with pronounced brow ridges and a *sagittal keel* (a pronounced flattening of the skull toward the midline) has a cranial capacity of about 850 cc. Leakey later found a similar specimen named KNM-ER 3883. It is somewhat less complete, being slightly more rugged in appearance and with a slightly smaller cranial capacity. It has been suggested that 3883 is a male and 3733 is a female (Tobias, 1994; Feder and Park, 1997).

Physical Characteristics of *Homo erectus*

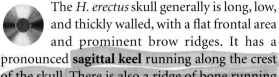 The *H. erectus* skull generally is long, low, and thickly walled, with a flat frontal area and prominent brow ridges. It has a pronounced **sagittal keel** running along the crest of the skull. There is also a ridge of bone running horizontally along the back of the skull called the **occipital torus**, which adds to the skull's overall long shape (see Figure 9–2).

Compared with *H. habilis*, *H. erectus* had relatively small teeth. *H. erectus* was the first hominid to have third molars that were smaller than the second or first molars, as in modern humans. The molars also had an enlarged pulp cavity, called

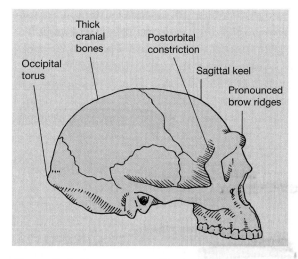

Figure 9–2 *Homo erectus* Features

taurodontism, which may have allowed teeth to withstand harder use and wear than the teeth of modern humans. However, the *H. erectus* jaw was lighter and thinner than in either early *Homo* or the australopithecines, and the face was less **prognathic**, or forward thrusting, in the upper and lower jaw.

The brain, averaging 895 cc to 1040 cc, was larger than that found in any of the australopithecines or *H. habilis* but smaller than the average

Homo erectus, seen in this skull and facial reconstruction, had prominent brow ridges, a thickly walled skull, and a low forehead. Its brain capacity was about 70 percent of that of modern humans. *H. erectus* was hardly distinguishable from modern humans.

brain of a modern human (Tobias, 1994; Feder and Park, 1997). While the increased brain size could be related to an increase in overall body size, the skull was proportioned differently—suggesting that the brain too was structured differently than the *H. habilis* brain.

Homo erectus had a prominent, projecting nose, in contrast to the australopithecines' flat, non-projecting noses (Franciscus and Trinkaus, 1988). From the neck down, *H. erectus* was practically indistinguishable from *H. sapiens*, although the *femoral cortex*—the thick dense bone that forms the shaft of the thigh bone—is very thick. In general, their ability to walk upright and manipulate objects was fully modern. In contrast to the much smaller australopithecines and *H. habilis*, who lived in East Africa around the same time, *H. erectus* was comparable to modern humans in size.

The discovery of KNM-WT 15000 by the Leakey team at Nariokotome, on the west side of Lake Turkana, is important because it is of the nearly complete remains of an adolescent. The remains date to about 1.6 million years ago. At this time, the Nariokotome region was probably open grassland, with trees mostly along rivers (Feibel and Brown, 1993). *Homo erectus* in East Africa was similar in size to Africans today who live in a similarly open, dry environment (Ruff and Walker, 1993). Reconstruction of KNM-WT 15000 suggests that he was 1.6 metres tall when he died at between 11 and 12 years of age; the researchers estimate that he would have been 1.85 metres tall if he had lived to maturity (Brown et al., 1985). This is important because in most other animals, a 12-year-old would be fully grown. This specimen may provide evidence for a prolonged developmental period in *H. erectus*. This is also supported by analyses of *H. erectus* hipbones that have suggested that *H. erectus* babies would have smaller heads relative to adult brain size. The implication is that, like modern humans, *H. erectus* babies would have been more immature when they were born so as to allow the head to pass through the bipedal pelvic outlet (Bogin, 1997; Nelson and Thompson, 1999).

Those scholars who group the African populations into a distinct species, *H. ergaster*, point to several differences between them and other *H. erectus* populations. The cranial proportions differ in *H. ergaster*; the brow ridge is thinner and is arched above each of the eye sockets; the eye sockets are more rounded; and the face is oriented more vertically. On the other hand, some scholars believe that the differences between *H. erectus* and modern humans are not large enough to call us different species, and argue that *H. erectus* populations should be lumped into *H. sapiens* (Wolpoff et al., 1994).

The evolution of *H. erectus* reflects a continuation of the general evolutionary trends we discussed previously. The brain continued to expand, its capacity increasing more than a third over that of the early *Homo* brain (just as the early *Homo* brain's capacity had increased more than a third over that of the australopithecines). The face, teeth, and jaws continued to shrink, moving toward a more modern form. An increasing use and variety of tools may have led to a further development of the brain. *Homo erectus* was eating and probably cooking meat, and this may have led to further reduction in the teeth and jaws.

One additional change in *H. erectus* is an apparent reduction in the extent of sexual dimorphism to almost modern levels. Recall that the australopithecines and early *Homo* were quite sexually dimorphic. *Homo erectus* does not appear to be as sexually dimorphic as these earlier hominids. What might have caused this change? In other primates, sexual dimorphism appears to be linked to social systems in which males are at the top of dominance hierarchies and dominant males control sexual access to multiple females. In contrast, lack of sexual dimorphism seems most pronounced in the few primates and other animals where *pair bonding* exists—that is, where one male and one female form a breeding pair that last for a long period of time (Fleagle, 1988). Could pair bonding have developed in *H. erectus*? It seems possible.

Homo erectus Culture

The archaeological finds of tools and other cultural artifacts dating from 1.8 million years ago to about 200 000 years ago are assumed to have been produced by *H. erectus*. Unfortunately, fossils are not usually associated with these materials. Therefore, it is possible that some of the tools were produced by hominids other than *H. erectus*, such as *H. habilis* earlier and *H. sapiens* later. *Homo erectus* continued to use the Oldowan chopper tool technology, but also developed a more sophisticated tool tradition called **Acheulian**. The Acheulian tool assemblages dating from 1.5 million years ago to more than a million years later are very similar to each other. *Homo erectus* is the only hominid that spans the entire period, so it is conventionally assumed that *H. erectus* was responsible for most if not all of the Acheulian tool assemblages we describe below (Phillipson, 1993:57).

The Acheulian Tool Tradition

The Acheulian stone toolmaking tradition was named after the site at St. Acheul, France, where the first examples were found. However, the oldest Acheulian tools, dating back about 1.5 million years, have been recovered from East Africa, on the Peninj River, Tanzania (Schick and Toth, 1994). In contrast to Oldowan, the Acheulian tools were larger, with a set of typical designs or shapes. Oldowan tools have sharp edges, made by a few blows. Acheulian toolmakers shaped the stone by knocking more flakes off most of the edges. Many of these tools were made from very large flakes that had been struck from very large cores or boulders. One of the most characteristic and prevalent tools in the Acheulian tool kit is the so-called "hand axe," which is a teardrop-shaped bifacially flaked tool with a thinned sharp tip. Other large tools resemble cleavers and picks. There were also many other kinds of flake tools, such as scrapers with a wide edge. Early Acheulian tools appeared to have been made by blows with a hard stone, but later tools are wider and flatter and may have been made with a soft "hammer" of bone or antler (Schick and Toth, 1994; Whittaker, 1994).

Were hand axes made for chopping trees, as their name suggests? We cannot be sure what they were used for, but experiments with Acheulian hand axes suggest that they are not good for

An Acheulian hand axe. Lawrence Keeley examined the edge wear on hand axes to determine how they were used.

cutting trees; they seem more suited for butchering large animals (Schick and Toth, 1994; Whittaker, 1994). Lawrence Keeley microscopically examined some Acheulian hand axes, and the wear on them is consistent with animal butchery. The picks may have been used for woodworking, particularly hollowing and shaping wood, and they are also good for digging (Schick and Toth, 1994:260).

Acheulian tools are found widely in Africa, Europe, and western Asia, but bifacial hand axes, cleavers, and picks are not found as commonly in eastern and southeastern Asia. Because *H. erectus* has been found in all areas of the Old World, it is puzzling why the tool traditions seem to differ from west to east. Older arguments suggested differences in technological sophistication between eastern and western populations. However, some archaeologists have suggested that large bifacial tools may be lacking in eastern and southeastern Asia because *H. erectus* there had a better material for making tools—bamboo. Bamboo is used today in Southeast Asia for many purposes, including the making of incredibly sharp arrows and sticks for digging and cutting. Geoffrey Pope showed that bamboo is found in those areas of Asia where hand axes and other large bifacial tools are missing (Pope, 1989; Ciochon et al., 1990). Recent evidence shows the presence of Acheulian hand axes over 800 000 years ago in southern China (Yamei et al., 2000).

Big-Game Eating

Some of the Acheulian sites have produced evidence of big-game eating. F. Clark Howell, who excavated sites at Torralba and Ambrona, Spain, found a substantial number of elephant remains and unmistakable evidence of human presence in the form of tools. These sites are situated strategically on two hilltops flanking a mountain pass. Howell suggests that the humans at those sites used fire to frighten elephants into muddy bogs, from which they would be unable to escape (Howell, 1966). To hunt elephants in this way, the humans would have had to plan and work co-operatively in fairly large groups.

But do these finds of bones of large and medium-sized animals, in association with tools, tell us that the humans definitely were big-game hunters? Some archaeologists who have reanalyzed the evidence from Torralba think that the big game may have been scavenged. Because the Torralba and Ambrona sites are near ancient streams, many of the elephants could have died naturally, their bones accumulating in certain spots because of the flow of water (Binford, 1987; Klein, 1987). It is still unclear whether *H. erectus* deliberately butchered different kinds of game. While different types of tools are found with different types of animal (Freeman, 1994), reanalysis by Pat Shipman and Jennie Rose of the cut marks on the remains has cast new doubt on this evidence. Over 95 percent of the bones present were too poorly preserved to clearly identify stone tool cut marks. Of those that could be clearly identified, only 16 cut marks have been confirmed on four bones (Shipman and Rose, 1983). Thus, whether the humans hunted big game at Torralba and Ambrona is debatable; all we can be sure of, as of now, is that they consumed big game and probably hunted smaller game.

Other sites that may represent evidence of co-operative hunting include BK II in Tanzania, which dates to at least 400 000 years ago. Here there are the remains of wild cattle that may have been driven into the swamp and then killed and butchered by *H. erectus* (Howell, 1966; Butzer, 1982a). At Olorgesailie in Kenya, there is possible evidence of co-operative hunting by *H. erectus*. On the lake edge at this site more than 60 individuals of extinct baboons have been excavated. K/Ar dates for this site suggest it may be as old as 700 000 to 900 000 years (Isaac, 1977). It is worth noting that these are not the savannah baboons with which we are familiar today, but rather an extinct "giant" baboon, *Theropithecus oswaldi*, which could be as big as a female gorilla. Given an animal of this size and power, the argument for some sort of co-operative hunting is strengthened that much more. At both these sites the animal remains have been excavated in association with cobbles and stone tools.

Control of Fire

Because *H. erectus* was the first hominid to be found throughout the Old World and in areas with freezing winters, most anthropologists presume that *H. erectus* had learned to control fire, at least for warmth. There is archaeological evidence of fire in some early sites, but fires can be natural events. Thus, whether fire was under deliberate control by *H. erectus* is difficult to establish.

Suggestive but not conclusive evidence of the deliberate use of fire comes from Kenya in East Africa and is over 1.4 million years old (Isaac, 1984; Brain and Sillen, 1988) and from the Swartkans cave in South Africa dated to between 1.5 and 1 million years ago (Brain and Sillen, 1988). More persuasive, but still not definite, evidence of human control of fire, dating from nearly 500 000 years ago, comes from the cave at Zhoukoudian in China where *H. erectus* fossils have been found (Klein, 1989:171). In that cave are thousands of splintered and charred animal bones, apparently the remains of meals. There are also layers of ash, suggesting human control of fire.

But recent analysis raises questions about these finds. The most serious problem is that human remains, tools, and ash rarely occur together in the same layers. In addition, there are no hearths at the Zhoukoudian site. Fires can spontaneously occur with heavy accumulation of organic matter, so clear evidence of human control of fire is still not definitely attested. Even the inference that humans brought the animals to the cave for butchering is only possibly a correct guess. Throughout the cave

Homo erectus ate—and probably hunted—large game animals, and probably also learned to control fire.

there is evidence of hyenas and wolves, and they, not the humans, may have brought many of the animal parts to the cave (Binford and Ho, 1985).

Better evidence of the deliberate use of fire comes from Europe somewhat later. Unfortunately, the evidence of control of fire at these European sites is not associated with *H. erectus* fossils either, so the link between deliberate use of fire and *H. erectus* cannot be definitely established yet. The lack of clear evidence does not, of course, mean that *H. erectus* did not use fire. After all, *H. erectus* did move into cold areas of the world, and it is hard to imagine how that could have happened without the deliberate use of fire.

Fire would be important not only for warmth; cooking would also be possible. The control of fire was a major step in increasing the energy under human control. Cooking made all kinds of food (not just meat) more safely digestible and therefore more usable. Fires would also have kept predators away, a not inconsiderable advantage given that there were a lot of them around.

Campsites

Acheulian sites were usually located close to water sources, lush vegetation, and large stocks of herbivorous animals. Some camps have been found in caves, but most were in open areas surrounded by rudimentary fortifications or windbreaks. Several African sites are marked by stony rubble brought there by *H. erectus*, possibly for the dual purpose of securing the windbreaks and providing ammunition in case of a sudden attack (Clark, 1970).

The presumed base campsites display a variety of tools, indicating that the camps were the centre of many group functions. More specialized sites away from camp have also been found. These are marked by the predominance of a particular type of tool. For example, a butchering site in Tanzania contained dismembered hippopotamus carcasses and rare heavy-duty smashing and cutting tools. What appear to have been workshops are another kind of specialized site encountered with some regularity. They are characterized by tool debris and are located close to a source of natural stone suitable for toolmaking (Clark, 1970).

A camp has been excavated at the Terra Amata site near Nice, on the French Riviera. The camp appears to have been occupied in late spring or early summer, judging by the pollen found in fossilized human feces. The excavator describes stake holes driven into the sand, associated with parallel lines of stones, presumably marking the spots where the people constructed huts of roughly 4.5 metres by 9 metres (see Figure 9–3). A basic feature of each hut was a central hearth that

Figure 9–3 A Reconstruction of the Oval Huts Built at Terra Amata

These huts were approximately 4.5 metres by 9 metres.

seems to have been protected from drafts by a small wall built just outside the northeast corner of the hearth. The evidence suggests that the Terra Amata occupants gathered seafood such as oysters and mussels, did some fishing, and hunted in the surrounding area. The animal remains suggest that they obtained both small and large animals but mostly got the young of larger animals such as stags, elephants, boars, rhinoceroses, and wild oxen. Some of the huts contain recognizable toolmakers' areas, scattered with tool debris; occasionally, the impression of an animal skin shows where the toolmaker actually sat (de Lumley, 1969). The site at Terra Amata, which is geologically dated between 400 000 and 200 000 years ago, has been interpreted as possibly one of the earliest identified hominid shelters (de Lumley, 1969).

Religion and Ritual

Did *H. erectus* take part in rituals? Did *H. erectus* have religion? The data we have to answer these questions are limited, but there are some hints that ritual may have been part of Lower Palaeolithic culture.

Remains of red ochre (oxidized clay) have been found on a number of Lower Palaeolithic sites (Dickson, 1990). This may be significant because in many later cultures, even modern ones, red ochre has been used in rituals of various types to represent blood, or more generally, life. Ochre seems to be particularly important in burial rituals, and human remains sprinkled with red ochre have been found in many parts of the world and dating back as far as the Middle Palaeolithic (about 200 000 years ago). However, there is no evidence to suggest that *H. erectus* buried their dead, nor any evidence that red ochre was used in rituals. It may have been used for body decoration, or simply for protection against insects or sunburn.

More significant, and even more controversial, is the suggestion made by the excavators of Zhoukoudian in northern China that some of the *H. erectus* remains there showed evidence of ritual cannibalism (Dickson, 1990; Tattersall and Schwartz, 2000). The foramen magnum of some specimens had been deliberately enlarged and the facial bones had been deliberately broken away from the cranium on others. A possible reason may have been to remove the brain for ritual consumption. Ritual cannibalism has been widely reported among living peoples, so its presence among ancient peoples is not impossible. But scholars point out that the parts of the skull that seem to have been purposely enlarged to remove the brain are those that are also the weakest points of the skull, and may have broken away because of decay or disturbance over time. Therefore, at this time we cannot say with any certainty what role, if any, religion or ritual played in Lower Palaeolithic culture.

Language

We use the same skeletal evidence to determine whether *H. erectus* had developed language that we used to examine language development in earlier hominids. As noted above, while an increased cranial capacity in *H. erectus* could be related to an increase in overall body size, it appears that the skull was proportioned differently than in earlier hominids. This suggests a remodelling of the brain, in particular the differential growth of the frontal and posterior portion of the brain. In other words, the *H. erectus* brain is more similar in form to the modern brain. Analysis of endocasts of *H. erectus* specimens from Ngandong and Sangiran in Java have suggested that hemispheric specialization—the idea that the right and left halves of the brain control different aspects of behaviour, as in modern humans—is present in *H. erectus* (Holloway, 1980; Holloway, 1981). This has been interpreted by some to suggest that by 1.7 million years ago *H. erectus* would have possessed linguistic skills and the ability to manipulate symbols (Holloway, 1980; Holloway, 1981). Other evidence from the basicranial remains of *H. erectus* also supports a modern capability for language. It is suggested that *H. erectus* had the ability for language at the level of a modern 6-year-old (Laitman and Heimbuch, 1984).

Archaic *Homo sapiens*

The cultures of early hominids are traditionally classified as Lower Palaeolithic or early Stone Age. In this section we discuss the fossil evidence as well as the controversies about the transition from *H. erectus* to Archaic *Homo sapiens*, which may have begun 500 000 years ago. We also discuss what we know archaeologically about Middle Palaeolithic cultures of the early *H. sapiens* that lived between about 300 000 and 40 000 years ago.

Most palaeoanthropologists agree that *H. erectus* evolved into *H. sapiens*, but they disagree about how and where the transition occurred. There is also disagreement about how to classify some fossils from 400 000 to about 200 000 years ago that have a mix of *H. erectus* and *H. sapiens* traits (Stringer, 1985). A particular fossil might be called *H. erectus* by some anthropologists and "archaic" *Homo sapiens* by others. As we shall see, still other anthropologists see so much continuity between *H. erectus* and *H. sapiens* that they think it is completely arbitrary to call

Early renditions of Neandertals portrayed them as brutish and very non-human-like.

them different species. According to these anthropologists, *H. erectus* and *H. sapiens* may just be earlier and later varieties of the same species and therefore all should be called *H. sapiens*. (*Homo erectus* would then be *H. sapiens erectus*.)

There seems to be a fair degree of homogeneity in *H. erectus* specimens, both geographically and temporally, over the 1 million years or so of their successful existence. While there are regular anatomical changes over time, like a reduction in the size of the rear teeth, an associated decrease in the size of the face and lower jaw, and an increase in incisor size, other features remain relatively constant. Similarly there is also a small increase in cranial capacity over time, but for the most part, even this feature is relatively consistent. Archaeologically, the Acheulian tool kit also seems to remain relatively consistent over time, although later hand axes do appear to be more refined than earlier ones. However, around 400 000 years ago there is a substantial increase in cranial capacity in the fossil hominid record. These new specimens are classed as early *Homo sapiens*. These early *H. sapiens* are not exactly like anatomically modern humans, so they are distinguished as **Archaic Homo sapiens**. While modern people are classed in the subspecies *sapiens* (that is, **Homo sapiens**

sapiens), Archaic *H. sapiens* are believed to represent one or several ancient and extinct subspecies.

Archaic *H. sapiens* fossils have been found in Africa, Europe, and Asia. In recent years some scholars have suggested that the "transitional" fossils share common traits and may actually represent a separate species—***Homo heidelbergensis***, named after a jaw found in 1907 in the village of Mauer near Heidelberg, Germany (Rightmire, 1998; Fleagle, 1999). For example, a specimen from the Broken Hill mine in Zambia, Africa, dates from about 200 000 years ago. Its mixed traits include a cranial capacity of over 1200 cc (well within the range of modern *H. sapiens*), together with a low forehead and large brow ridges, which are characteristic of earlier *H. erectus* specimens (Rightmire, 1984:303). Other fossils with mixed traits have been found at Bodo, Hopefield, Ndutu, Elandsfontein, and Rabat in Africa; Heidelberg, Bilzingsleben, Petralona, Arago, Steinheim, and Swanscombe in Europe; and Dali and Solo in Asia.

Homo heidelbergensis differs from *H. erectus* in having smaller teeth and jaws, a much larger brain (on the order of 1300 cc), a skull that lacks a sagittal keel and occipital torus, a brow ridge that divides into separate arches above each eye, and a more robust skeleton. *Homo heidelbergensis* differs

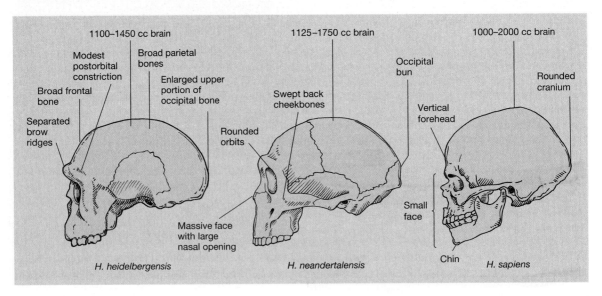

Figure 9–4 Comparison of the Crania of *Homo heidelbergensis*, *Homo neandertalensis*, and *Homo sapiens*, Showing Important Differences

from *H. sapiens* in retaining a large and prognathic face with relatively large teeth and jaws, a brow ridge, and a long, low cranial vault with a sloping forehead, and in its more robust skeleton (Fleagle, 1999; Rightmire, 1998).

Many scholars question whether *H. heidelbergensis* represents one or several species of Middle Pleistocene hominid, or whether it is indeed a separate species at all. Many would argue that *H. heidelbergensis* should be considered an Archaic *H. sapiens*. As noted, some scholars also argue that *H. erectus* should be included in the *H. sapiens* species (see Figure 9–4).

Neandertals

There may be disagreement about how to classify the mixed-trait fossils from 400 000 to 200 000 years ago, but there is hardly any disagreement about the fossils that are less than 200 000 years old. Nearly all anthropologists agree that they were definitely *H. sapiens*. These early definite *H. sapiens* did not look completely like modern humans, but they were not so different from us either—not even the ones called **Neandertals**, after the valley in Germany where the first evidence of them was found. Somehow through the years the Neandertals have become the victims of their cartoon image, which usually misrepresents them as burly and more ape than human. Actually, they might go unnoticed in a cross-section of the world's population today.

In 1856, three years before Darwin's publication of *The Origin of Species*, a skullcap and other fossilized bones were discovered in a cave in the Neander Valley (*tal* is the German word for "valley"), near Düsseldorf, Germany. The fossils in the Neander Valley were the first that scholars could tentatively consider an early hominid. (The fossils classified as *H. erectus* were not found until later in the nineteenth century, and the fossils belonging to the genus *Australopithecus* not until the twentieth century.) After Darwin's revolutionary work was published,

Boule's reconstruction of Neandertal (left) as displayed at Chicago's Field Museum in 1929, and a more recent construction (right). The recent reconstruction makes Neandertal seem more like modern humans.

the Neandertal find aroused considerable controversy. A few evolutionist scholars, such as Thomas Huxley, thought that the Neandertal was not that different from modern humans. Others dismissed the Neandertal as irrelevant to human evolution; they saw it as a pathological freak, a peculiar, disease-ridden individual. However, similar fossils turned up later in Belgium, Yugoslavia, France, and elsewhere in Europe, which meant that the original Neandertal find could not be dismissed as an oddity (Spencer, 1984).

The predominant reaction to the original and subsequent Neandertal-like finds was that the Neandertals were too "brutish" and "primitive" to have been ancestral to modern humans. This view prevailed in the scholarly community until well into the 1950s. A major proponent of this view was French anatomist Marcellin Boule, who claimed between 1908 and 1913 that the Neandertals would not have been capable of complete bipedalism. Boule's reconstruction of the La Chapelle-aux-Saints Neandertal remains emphasized the minor differences rather than the remarkable similarities between the Neandertal and modern skeletons. Further, Boule's reconstruction was based on an older male, who suffered from severe arthritis. Despite the fact that Boule seemed to have ignored two other healthy skeletons on which to reconstruct the Neandertals, Boule's biased view was maintained in popular culture for a considerable time.

Since the 1950s, however, a number of studies have disputed Boule's claim, and it is now generally agreed that the skeletal traits of the Neandertals are completely consistent with bipedalism. Perhaps more important, when the much more ancient australopithecine and *H. erectus* fossils were accepted as hominids in the 1940s and 1950s, anthropologists realized that the Neandertals did not look that different from modern humans—despite their sloping foreheads, large brow ridges, flattened braincases, large jaws, and nearly absent chins (Trinkaus, 1985). After all, they did have larger brains (averaging more than 1450 cc) than modern humans (slightly more than 1300 cc) (Stringer, 1988b). Some scholars believe that the large brain capacity of Neandertals suggests that they were capable of the full range of

behaviour characteristic of modern humans. Their skeletons did, however, attest to one behavioural trait markedly different from that of most modern humans: Neandertals had much more robust and more heavily muscled bodies (Trinkaus and Shipman, 1993).

It took almost 100 years for scholars to accept the idea that Neandertals were not that different from modern humans and therefore should be classified as **Homo sapiens neandertalensis.** As we shall discuss later though, there is still debate over whether the Neandertals in western Europe were ancestral to modern-looking people who lived later in western Europe, after about 40 000 years ago. In any case, Neandertals lived in other places besides western Europe. A large number of fossils from central Europe strongly resemble those from western Europe, although some features, such as a projecting midface, are less pronounced (Smith, 1984:187). Neandertals have also been found in southwestern Asia (Israel, Iraq) and Central Asia (Uzbekistan). One of the largest collections of Neandertal fossils comes from Shanidar Cave in the mountains of northeastern Iraq, where Ralph Solecki unearthed the skeletons of nine individuals (see site 31 in Figure 9–5) (Trinkaus, 1984).

The Neandertals have received a great deal of scholarly and popular attention, probably because they were the first pre-modern humans to be found. We now know though, that other pre-modern *H. sapiens*, some perhaps older than Neandertals, lived elsewhere in the Old World—in East, South, and North Africa, as well as in Java and China (Smith and Spencer, 1984). These other pre-modern but definite *H. sapiens* are sometimes considered Neandertal-like, but more often they are named after the places where they were first found, as indeed the original Neandertal was. For example, the cranium from China called *Homo sapiens daliensis* was named after the Chinese locality, Dali, in which it was found in 1978 (Xinzhi and Maolin, 1985).

What has changed scholars' opinions of the Neandertals so that they are now most commonly seen as not belonging to the *H. sapiens* group?

In 1997, a group of researchers from the United States and Germany published findings that forced

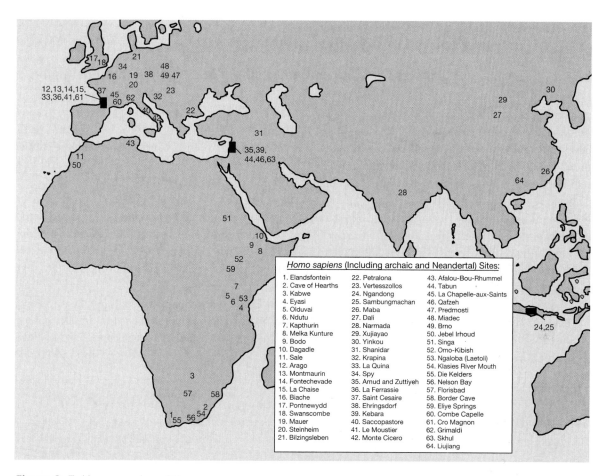

Figure 9–5 *Homo sapiens* Sites

Source: Ciochon RL, Fleagle JG, editors. 1993. The Human Evolution Source Book. Englewood Cliffs, NJ: Prentice Hall. p xi.

a reconsideration of the Neandertals and their relationship to modern humans. These scholars reported that they had been able to extract DNA from the original Neandertal specimen found in 1856 (Krings et al., 1997, 1999). The DNA they extracted was not nuclear DNA—the material that makes up the human genome. Rather, it came from a tiny structure found in all eukaryotic cells (that is, cells with a membrane-bound nucleus and DNA in the chromosomes) called *mitochondria*. Mitochondria produce enzymes needed for energy production, and they have their own DNA, which replicates when a cell replicates but is not thought to be under any pressure from natural selection (Cann, 1988).

The only source of change in mitochondrial DNA (usually referred to as *mt*DNA) is random mutation. Mitochondrial DNA is inherited only from mothers in animals; it is not carried into an egg cell by sperm, but is left with the sperm's tail on the outside of the egg. These unique characteristics make it possible to use mtDNA to measure the degree of relatedness between two species, and even to say how long ago those species diverged (Cann, 1988). The longer two species have been separated, the more differences there will be in their mtDNA, which is thought to mutate at a fairly constant rate of about 2 percent per million years. Thus, the number of differences between the mtDNA of two organisms can be converted into an estimated date in the past when those organisms stopped being part of the same breeding population. While controversy remains over many of the details of how and why mtDNA mutates and about its accuracy for determining absolute dates of divergence, most scholars agree that it is a powerful tool for examining relative degrees of relatedness between species (Vigilant et al., 1991).

How similar is Neandertal mtDNA to modern human DNA? Not as similar as many scholars would have expected. Among individual modern humans, there are usually five to ten differences in the sequence of mtDNA examined by the U.S. and German researchers. Between modern humans and the Neandertal specimen, there tend to be about 25 differences—more than three times that among modern humans (see Figure 9–6). This suggested to the researchers that the ancestors of modern humans and the Neandertal must have diverged about 600 000 years ago (Krings et al., 1997, 1999). If the last common ancestor of ours and the Neandertal lived that long ago, the Neandertal would be a much more distant relative than previously thought. This research has since been replicated with mtDNA from other Neandertal fossils (Ovchinnikov et al., 2000; Scholz et al., 2000).

Recent archaeological findings from Europe and the Near East may also indicate that Neandertals and the modern human were different species. It has been known for decades that both modern human and Neandertal fossils are found in the same locations in parts of the Levant, but recent improvements in dating technology and newly discovered fossils have even more clearly demonstrated that the two kinds of hominid co-existed. In fact, several caves in the Mount Carmel region of Israel contain evidence of both modern human and Neandertal occupations. The fact that these two groups of hominids co-inhabited the Near East for perhaps as much as 30 000 years and did not interbreed or share much in the way of tool technology strongly suggests that the two are different species (Tattersall, 1999; Gibbons, 2001).

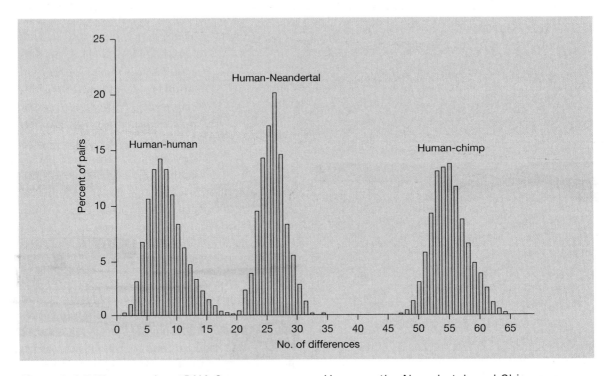

Figure 9–6 Differences in mtDNA Sequences among Humans, the Neandertal, and Chimpanzees

The x-axis shows the number of sequence differences; the y-axis shows the percent of individuals that share that number of sequence differences.

Source: 1997. Cell (90):25. Reprinted with permission from Elsevier Science.

In addition, finds in Europe seem to corroborate that assessment. As early modern humans began moving into Europe, they appear to have displaced populations of Neandertals already living there. Sites with tools thought to be associated with

Neandertals become less frequent throughout Europe as sites with tools thought to be associated with modern humans expand their range (Mellars, 1996). Significantly, the area of Europe (Iberia) last colonized by modern humans contains the very

RESEARCH FRONTIERS

Neandertal Growth and Development

One of the reasons many scholars think the Neandertals did not belong to the *Homo sapiens* species is that their material culture was less sophisticated than that of early modern humans who lived at the same time. Since much of contemporary human behaviour is dependent on learning that takes place during our long period of infant dependency, could it be that Neandertals matured more rapidly than modern humans and thus had a shorter period in which to learn cultural behaviours?

Paleoanthropologist Nancy Minugh-Purvis decided to test this idea by examining growth and development of the skull and face in Neandertals. Minugh-Purvis's study of Neandertal growth and development was feasible largely because Neandertals may have buried their dead. Juvenile and infant skeletons are rare in the archaeological record and often do not preserve well. In juveniles and infants, many of the bones are still growing and thus are relatively delicate. They are also smaller than adult bones, and a wider variety of scavengers can consume them. But because Neandertals may have buried their dead, a number of well-preserved juvenile and infant skeletons are available for study. Indeed, Minugh-Purvis was able to locate more than 100 Neandertal skeletons, ranging in age from newborn to young adult.

To chart the way the skull and face of Neandertals grew from infancy to adulthood, Minugh-Purvis measured the available fossils on a set of standard anthropometric

indices—indices that are widely used in physical anthropology to compare the size and shape of bones. She found that newborn Neandertals and modern humans do not differ very much, but that Neandertal infants tend to have thicker cranial bones than modern humans and perhaps heavier musculature. Many of the more striking features of adult Neandertals—a large face with a protruding nose, brow ridges, and a long skull—are not present in infants. These typical Neandertal characteristics begin to appear in children. For example, a 4-year-old Neandertal from the site of Engis, Belgium, already had brow ridges. A 7-year-old from the site of La Quinta in France not only had brow ridges but also a large, protruding nose and face and a long skull. Finally, a 10-year-old from the site of Teshik-Tash in Uzbekistan had all of the typical Neandertal features, and is basically identical to an adult Neandertal except in size.

In short, Neandertals are born similar to modern humans, but by the age of about 10 have developed all of the striking physical features that differentiate Neandertals from modern humans. What does this tell us about Neandertal growth and development? Minugh-Purvis suggests that it was much like our own. Indeed, she argues that many of the physical differences between the Neandertal face and skull and those of modern humans might be due not to genetic differences but rather to behavioural ones. Neandertal teeth show wear patterns that suggest

they were used as tools, particularly to hold objects while working on them with the hands. The teeth and jaws were apparently placed under tremendous stress from these uses. Minugh-Purvis suggests that the prognathic face and heavy musculature may be a result of the teeth and jaws being used as tools from a young age, rather than from developmental differences between modern humans and Neandertals.

However, there are other differences between Neandertals and modern humans that cannot be explained by behaviour. The overall picture that appears from Minugh-Purvis's study is that Neandertals did indeed mature slightly faster than modern humans. But was their maturation fast enough to account for the lack of cultural elaboration among the Neandertals? Did Neandertals grow so fast they had no time to learn? Minugh-Purvis suggests the differences are not that significant, and that other factors must be sought to explain the differences in cultural elaboration between Neandertals and modern humans.

Sources: Minugh-Purvis N. 2002. Neandertal Growth: Examining Developmental Adaptations in Earlier *Homo sapiens*. In: Peregrine PN, Ember CR, Ember M, editors. Physical Anthropology: Original Readings in Method and Practice. Upper Saddle River, NJ: Prentice Hall. Also in: Ember CR, Ember M, editors. 2003. New Directions in Anthropology. Upper Saddle River, NJ: Prentice Hall. CD-ROM.

Stringer C, Gamble C. 1993. In Search of the Neanderthals. New York: Thames and Hudson.

Trinkaus E. 1987. The Neandertal Face: Evolutionary and Functional Perspectives on a Recent Hominid Face. Journal of Human Evolution 16:429–443.

latest Neandertal fossils yet found, dating to some 30 000 years ago (Mellars, 1998).

With all this evidence pointing to Neandertals not being part of the modern human species, why is there an ongoing debate? In part this is because none of the evidence is conclusive, and much of it can be interpreted in alternative ways. There is also evidence suggesting that Neandertals were not all that different physically from modern humans (see Research Frontiers, *Neandertal Growth and Development*). Perhaps more important, however, Neandertal culture, typically referred to as Middle Paleolithic after the predominant tool technology, has some features that make it seem similar to the culture of early modern humans.

Middle Palaeolithic Cultures

The period of cultural history associated with the Neandertals is traditionally called the **Middle Palaeolithic** in Europe and the Near East and dates from about 300 000 years ago to about 40 000 years ago (Strauss, 1989). For Africa, the term *Middle Stone Age* is used instead of *Middle Palaeolithic*. The tool assemblages from this period are generally referred to as *Mousterian* in Europe and the Near East and as *post-Acheulian* in Africa. (See the timeline in Figure 9–7.)

Tool Assemblages

The Mousterian. The Mousterian type of tool complex is named after the tool assemblage found in a rock shelter at Le Moustier in the Dordogne region of southwestern France. Compared with an Acheulian assemblage, a **Mousterian tool assemblage** has a smaller proportion of large core tools such as hand axes and cleavers and a bigger proportion of small flake tools such as scrapers (Schick and Toth, 1994). Although many flakes struck off from a core were used "as is," the Mousterian is also characterized by flakes that were often altered or "retouched" by striking small flakes or chips from one or more edges (see Figure 9–8) (Klein, 1989). Studies of the wear on scrapers suggest that many were used for scraping hides or working wood. The fact that some of the tools, particularly projectile points, were thinned or shaped on one side suggests that they were hafted or attached to a shaft or handle (Schick and Toth, 1994; Whittaker, 1994).

Toward the end of the Acheulian period, toolmakers developed a technique to produce flake tools of a predetermined size instead of simply chipping flakes away from the core at random. In this **Levalloisian method**, the toolmaker first shaped the core and prepared a "striking platform" at one end. Flakes of predetermined and standard sizes could then be detached by percussion flaking. Although some Levallois flakes date as far back as 400 000 years ago, they are found more frequently in Mousterian tool kits (Klein, 1989).

The tool assemblages in particular sites may be characterized as Mousterian, but one site may have more or fewer scrapers, points, and so forth, than

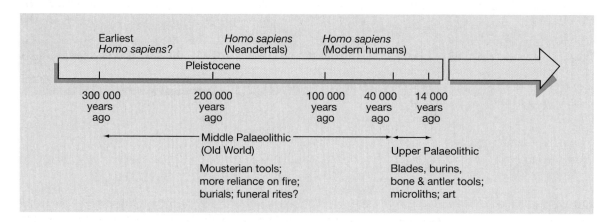

Figure 9–7 An Evolutionary Timeline

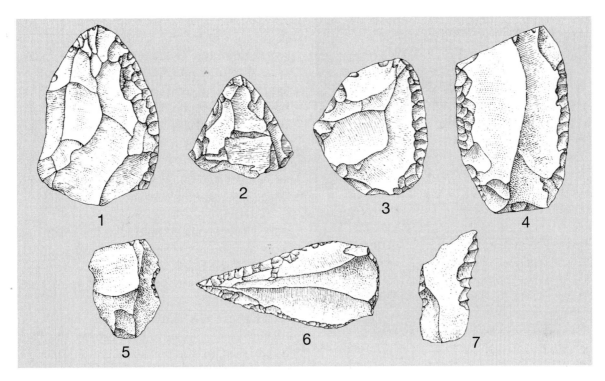

Figure 9–8 A Typical Mousterian Tool Kit

A Mousterian tool kit emphasized sidescrapers (1–4), notches (5), points (6), and sawtoothed denticulates (7). How these stone artifacts were actually used is not known, but the points may have been joined to wood shafts, and denticulates could have been used to work wood. The tools illustrated here are from Mousterian sites in Western Europe.

Source: Klein RG. June 1974. Ice-Age Hunters of the Ukraine. Scientific American 96–105. Reprinted with permission of Nelson H. Prentiss.

another site. A number of archaeologists have suggested possible reasons for this variation. For example, Sally Binford and Lewis Binford suggested that different activities might have occurred in different sites. Some sites may have been used for butchering and other sites may have been base camps; hence, the kinds of tools found in different sites should vary as a reflection of the range of specialized activities carried out there (Binford and Binford, 1969). And Paul Fish has suggested that some sites may have more tools produced by the Levalloisian technique because larger pieces of flint were available (Fish, 1981).

The Post-Acheulian in Africa. Like Mousterian tools, many of the post-Acheulian tools in Africa during the Middle Stone Age were struck off prepared cores in the Levalloisian way. The assemblages consist mostly of various types of flake tools. A well-described sequence of such tools comes from the area around the mouth of the Klasies River on the southern coast of South Africa. This area contains rock shelters and small caves in which early and later *H. sapiens* lived. The oldest cultural remains in one of the caves may date back 120 000 years (Butzer, 1982b). These earliest tools include parallel-sided flake **blades** (probably used as knives), pointed flakes (possibly spear points), **burins** or gravers (chisel-like incising tools), and scrapers. Similar tools discovered at Border Cave, South Africa, may have been used almost 200 000 years ago (Phillipson, 1993).

Homesites

Most of the excavated Middle Palaeolithic homesites in Europe and the Near East are located in caves and rock shelters. The same is true for the excavated

Archaeologist Hilary Deacon at the mouth of the Klasies River in South Africa, where early modern humans have been found.

Middle Stone Age homesites in sub-Saharan Africa. We might conclude, therefore, that Neandertals and other early *H. sapiens* lived mostly in caves or rock shelters, although this conclusion could be incorrect. Caves and rock shelters may be overrepresented in the archaeological record because they are more likely to be found than are sites that originally were in the open but now are hidden by thousands of years, and many metres, of sediment. **Sediment** is the dust, debris, and decay that accumulates over time; when we dust the furniture and vacuum the floor, we are removing sediment.

Still, we know that many early *H. sapiens* lived at least part of the year in caves. This was true, for example, along the Dordogne River in France. The river gouged deep valleys in the limestone of that area. Below the cliffs are rock shelters with overhanging roofs and deep caves, many of which were occupied during the Middle Palaeolithic. Even if the inhabitants did not stay all year, the sites do seem to have been occupied year after year (Binford, 1973). Although there is evidence of some use of fire in earlier cultures, Middle

Palaeolithic humans seem to have relied more on fire. There are thick layers of ash in many rock shelters and caves, and also evidence that hearths were used to increase the efficiency of the fires (Schick and Toth, 1994).

Quite a few homesites of early *H. sapiens* were in the open. In Africa, open-air sites were located on floodplains, at the edges of lakes, and near springs (Klein, 1977). Many open-air sites have been found in Europe, particularly eastern Europe. The occupants of the well-known site at Moldova in western Russia lived in river-valley houses framed with wood and covered with animal skins. Bones of mammoths (huge elephants now extinct) surround the remains of hearths and were apparently used to help hold the animal skins in place. Even though the winter climate near the edge of the nearby glacier was cold at that time, there would still have been animals to hunt because the plant food for the game was not buried under deep snow.

The hunters probably moved away in the summer to higher land between the river valleys. In all likelihood, the higher ground was grazing land for the large herds of animals the Moldova hunters depended on for meat. In the winter river-valley sites, archaeologists have found skeletons of wolf, arctic fox, and hare with their paws missing. These animals probably were skinned for pelts that were made into clothing (Klein, 1974).

Getting Food

How early *H. sapiens* got their food probably varied with their environment. In Africa, they lived in savannah and semi-arid desert. In western and eastern Europe, they had to adapt to cold; during periods of increased glaciation, much of the environment was steppe grassland and tundra.

The European environment during this time was much richer in animal resources than the tundra of northern countries is today. Indeed, the European environment inhabited by Neandertals abounded in game, both big and small. The tundra and alpine animals included reindeer, bison, wild oxen, horses, mammoths, rhinoceroses, and deer, as well as bears, wolves, and foxes (Bordes, 1961). Some European sites have also yielded bird and

RESEARCH FRONTIERS

Re-examining Middle Palaeolithic Hunting

The extent and level of hominid hunting during the Middle Palaeolithic has been widely debated. There is a growing realization of the importance of faunal analyses for reconstructing complex behaviour in Middle Palaeolithic hominid populations. Dr. Ariane Burke is an archaeologist at the Université de Montréal. Much of her research has focused on the analysis of faunal remains from Middle Palaeolithic sites in western Crimea in Ukraine. This research has enabled Burke to develop a hypothesis of land use and resource exploitation among Neandertal populations in the Crimea.

One of the issues emerging from this kind of research is that Neandertal resource strategies (getting food and using the land) are far more complicated than have been previously thought. In particular, recent research from a variety of areas in the Old World have emphasized the importance of Neandertal flexibility in their food-gathering activities in response to changes in the seasons and possible different sources of food. For example, studies have implied a mixture of both seasonally focused hunting of specific animals, intermixed with opportunistic hunting of animals that are encountered unintentionally. Further, periods of climatic crisis show a greater variety of foods being utilized by Neandertal populations, which suggests flexibility in hunting strategies during these hard times.

Burke and others, through research at a variety of Middle Palaeolithic sites, have begun to challenge the traditional notion of a lack of forethought and planning among Neandertal populations. The capacity for complex planning is abundantly demonstrated by Middle Palaeolithic patterns of land-use and subsistence strategies. This of course is important with respect to defining "modern" humans. The idea of a "Neandertal niche"—whereby Neandertals were over-specialized to very specific environmental conditions—implies that Middle Palaeolithic populations were biologically and culturally distinct from anatomically modern Upper Palaeolithic populations. Renewed research in this area brings a greater understanding of what it is to be truly "modern," and helps us to understand both the evolution of modern cultures and why Neandertal populations disappeared.

Source: Burke AM, editor. 2000. Hunting in the Middle Palaeolithic. Special Issue of the International Journal of Osteoarchaeology 10(5):281–406.

---

fish remains. For example, people in a summer camp in northern Germany apparently hunted swans and ducks and fished for perch and pike (Patterson, 1981). Little, however, is known about the particular plant foods the European Neandertals may have consumed; the remains of plants are unlikely to survive thousands of years in a non-arid environment.

In Africa, too, early *H. sapiens* got food in different ways. For example, we know that the people living at the mouth of the Klasies River in South Africa ate shellfish as well as meat from small grazers such as antelopes and large grazers such as eland and buffalo (Phillipson, 1993). But archaeologists disagree about how the Klasies River people got their meat when they began to occupy the caves in the area.

Richard Klein thinks they hunted the large as well as small game. Klein speculates that because the remains of eland of all ages have been found in Cave 1 at this site, the people there probably hunted the eland by driving them into corrals or other traps, where animals of all ages could be killed. Klein thinks that buffalo were hunted differently. Buffalo tend to charge attackers, which would make it difficult to drive them into traps. Klein believes that, because bones from mostly very young and very old buffalo were found in the cave, the hunters were able to stalk and kill only the most vulnerable animals (Klein, 1983).

Lewis Binford thinks the Klasies River people hunted only small grazers and scavenged the eland and buffalo meat from the kills of large carnivores. He argues that sites should contain all or almost all of the bones from animals that were hunted. According to Binford, since more or less complete skeletons were found only from small animals, the Klasies River people were not at first hunting all the animals they used for food (Klein, 1983; Binford, 1984).

But there is new evidence suggesting that people were hunting big game as much as 400 000 years ago. Wooden spears that old were recently found in Germany in association with stone tools and the butchered remains of more than 10 wild horses. The heavy spears resemble modern aerodynamic javelins, which suggests they would have been thrown at large animals such as horses, not at small animals. This new evidence strongly suggests that hunting, not just scavenging, may be older than archaeologists used to think (Wilford, 1997). (See also Research Frontiers, *Re-examining Middle Palaeolithic Hunting,* on page 203).

Funeral Rituals?

Some Neandertals were deliberately buried. At Le Moustier, the skeleton of a boy 15 or 16 years old was found with a beautifully fashioned stone axe near his hand. Near Le Moustier, graves of five other children and two adults, apparently interred together in a family plot, were discovered. These finds, along with one at Shanidar Cave in Iraq, have aroused speculation about the possibility of funeral rituals.

The evidence at Shanidar consists of pollen around and on top of a man's body. Pollen analysis suggests that the flowers included ancestral forms of modern grape hyacinths, bachelor's buttons, hollyhocks, and yellow flowering groundsels. John Pfeiffer speculated about this find:

> A man with a badly crushed skull was buried deep in the cave with special ceremony. One spring day about 60 000 years ago, members of his family went out into the hills, picked masses of wild flowers, and made a bed of them on the ground, a resting place for the deceased. Other flowers were probably laid on top of his grave; still others seem to have been woven together with the branches of a pinelike shrub to form a wreath (Pfeiffer, 1978).

Can we be sure? Not really. All we really know is that there was pollen near and on top of the body. It could have been deposited there because humans put flowers in the grave, or perhaps through other, even accidental, reasons.

As this reconstruction illustrates, Neandertals may have been the first humans to purposely bury their dead.

Neandertals may have taken part in other rituals as well, but, as with funeral rituals, the evidence is ambiguous. At Drachenloch cave in the Swiss Alps, for example, a stone-lined pit holding the stacked skulls of seven cave bears was found in association with a Neandertal habitation. Why preserve these skulls? One reason might be for rituals intended to placate or control bears. Cave bears were enormous—some nearly 2.7 metres tall—and competed with Neandertals for prime cave-living sites. Perhaps the Neandertals preserved the skulls of bears they killed in the cave as a way of honouring or appeasing either the bears or their spirits. But, as with funeral rituals, the evidence is not completely persuasive. In our own society some may hang a deer or moose head on the wall without any associated ritual. At this point we cannot say for certain whether or not Neandertals engaged in ritual behaviour (Chase and Dibble, 1987).

Altruism

Another aspect associated with Neandertals is the evidence for **altruism**—the concept of caring for and sustaining members of the group who may no longer contribute to the group's survival. The interpretation of altruism among the Neandertals comes from the La Chapelle-aux-Saints and the Shanidar I skeletons that implicitly demonstrate the Neandertals' capacity to care for the sick and aged. For example, the La Chapelle-aux-Saints finds included the remains of a middle-aged male suffering from arthritis. Whether or not this individual could care for himself has been debated, and while it is probable that he was able to interact with the group until his death, it is possible that his survival was in part due to the aid of other members of the group. Better evidence comes from the Shanidar I remains, which include the skeleton of an individual with healed injuries that would have left him blind with a paralyzed right arm (Trinkaus, 1983). In this case it certainly seems likely that the individual's survival, at least during the period of recovery from his injuries, would have been possible only with the support of other members of the group (Trinkaus, 1983).

Cannibalism

Another area of interest for Neandertals that has re-emerged in the news is the possibility of cannibalism. Recent research by Tim White and colleagues suggests that the site of Moula-Guercy—a Neandertal cave site in France dating to 100 000 years ago—contains evidence of cannibalism. The site includes 78 bone fragments representing the remains of at least six individuals including two adults, two adolescents, and two young children. Tim White has suggested that the cut marks on these bones could have been caused by sharp flints, and that the skulls were smashed and long bones broken open, presumably to extract the marrow. Further, there was no evidence of animals gnawing on the bones (Defleur et al., 1999).

Language

Recall from earlier discussions that the basicranium of the australopithecines is apelike while that of H.

erectus is more reminiscent of modern humans. Similarly, the basicrania of Archaic H. sapiens appears modern, with specimens from Petralona, Steinheim, Kabwe, and other sites implying a modern ability for language by about 250 000 years ago (Laitman and Heimbuch, 1984). However, there is ongoing debate as to whether Neandertals may have been different. Neandertal specimens do show a greater degree of flexion of the basicranium than those of H. erectus, but less so than other Archaic H. sapiens. This has led some researchers to suggest that Neandertals had a more constricted range of vocalization than other archaic populations. This notion has been challenged from an analysis of a fully modern-looking hyoid bone from Kebara, Israel (Arensburg et al., 1990).

Evolutionary Relations

One of the primary questions concerning the Neandertals is, what is their evolutionary relationship to modern humans? For a long time it was assumed that modern H. sapiens had evolved directly from Archaic populations like Neandertals. However, as we have already discussed, new evidence has emerged with the advent of molecular anthropology, implying that this may not be the case. We also now know from the archaeological record that some Neandertal populations lived at the same time and in some cases in the same place as anatomically modern humans. The question now becomes, what is the evolutionary relation of Neandertals to modern human populations? In the next chapter, we will discuss in further detail the two prevailing models of the origins of modern humans. Regardless of either model, it is clear that the Neandertals disappear from the archaeological record and are replaced, either biologically or culturally, by anatomically modern humans. Whether or not Neandertal genes are incorporated into the modern human genome remains to be debated.

Summary

1. *Homo erectus*, with a larger brain capacity than *H. habilis*, emerged about 1.8 million to 1.6 million years ago. *Homo erectus* was the first hominid species to be widely distributed in the Old World. The tools and other cultural artifacts from about 1.6 million to about 200 000 years ago were probably produced by *H. erectus*; *Acheulian* is the name given to the tool tradition of this period. Acheulian tools include both small flake tools and large tools, but hand axes and other large bifacial tools are characteristic. Although it is presumed that *H. erectus* had learned to use fire to survive in areas with cold winters, there is no definite evidence of the control of fire by *H. erectus*. There is evidence in some sites of big-game eating, but whether *H. erectus* hunted those animals is debated.

2. Most anthropologists agree that *H. erectus* began to evolve into *H. sapiens* after about 500 000 years ago. But there is disagreement about how and where the transition occurred. The mixed traits of the transitional fossils include large cranial capacities (well within the range of modern humans), together with low foreheads and large brow ridges, which are characteristic of *H. erectus* specimens. The earliest definite *H. sapiens*, who did not look completely like modern humans, appeared after about 200 000 years ago.

3. Remains of Archaic *H. sapiens* have been found in many parts of the Old World—in Africa and Asia as well as in Europe. Some of these *H. sapiens* may have lived earlier than the Neandertals of Europe, who were the first premodern humans to be found. There is still debate over whether the Neandertals in western Europe became extinct, or survived and were the ancestors of the modern-looking people who lived in western Europe after about 40 000 years ago.

4. The period associated with the Neandertals is traditionally called the Middle Palaeolithic in Europe and the Near East and dates from about 300 000 to about 40 000 years ago. For Africa, the term *Middle Stone Age* is used. The assemblages of flake tools from this period are generally referred to as *Mousterian* in Europe and the Near East and as *post-Acheulian* in Africa. Compared with an Acheulian assemblage, a Mousterian tool assemblage has a smaller proportion of large hand axes and cleavers and a larger proportion of small flake tools such as scrapers. Some Mousterian sites show signs of intentional burial.

Glossary Terms

Acheulian   (p. 189)

altruism   (p. 204)

Archaic *Homo sapiens*   (p. 194)

blades   (p. 201)

burins   (p. 201)

Homo ergaster   (p. 184)

Homo heidelbergensis   (p. 194)

Homo sapiens neandertalensis   (p. 196)

Homo sapiens sapiens   (p. 194)

Levalloisian method   (p. 200)

Middle Palaeolithic   (p. 200)

Mousterian tool assemblage   (p. 200)

Neandertal   (p. 195)

occipital torus   (p. 187)

prognathic   (p. 187)

sagittal keel   (p. 187)

sediment   (p. 202)

taurodontism   (p. 187)

Critical Questions

1. *Homo erectus* lived in many places in the Old World. What enabled them to spread so widely?

2. Why do you think Neandertals became extinct?

3. Archaic *H. sapiens* including Neandertals show evidence of some key cultural differences from earlier hominids. What are they, and how might they have developed?

Internet Exercises

1. Go to **www.modernhumanorigins.com/erectus.html** and review the important characteristics that are attributed to *H. erectus* specimens. Hyperlinks at the site connect to illustrations of fossil remains. Review the importance of these remains for understanding the evolution of *H. erectus*.

2. Read all about Neandertals at this site: **www.modernhumanorigins.com/neanderthalensis.html**
Using the resources that you will find there, pick a global location and season, pretend you are a Neandertal, and list "what I did today, what I ate today, and where I slept last night."

3. Go to **www.dnalc.org/neandertal.html** and explore an interactive overview of the reconstruction of Neandertal fossils.

Suggested Reading

Ciochon RL, Fleagle JG, editors. 1993. The Human Evolution Source Book. Upper Saddle, NJ: Prentice Hall. A collection of original articles about human evolution. Parts VI and VII are particularly relevant to this chapter.

Dibble HL, Mellars P, editors. 1992. The Middle Paleolithic: Adaptation, Behavior, and Variability. Philadelphia: University Museum. A collection of papers that present new data and whose authors rethink the variability in behaviour during the Middle Palaeolithic. The focus is on Europe and the Near East.

Ember CR, Ember M, Peregrine P, editors. 1998. Research Frontiers in Anthropology. Upper Saddle River, NJ: Prentice Hall: Simon & Schuster Custom Publishing. Especially relevant to this chapter are the following: Fryer DW, Testing Theories and Hypotheses about Modern Human Origins; Kramer A, The Natural History and Evolutionary Fate of *Homo erectus*; Minugh-Purvis N, Neandertal Growth: Examining Developmental Adaptations in Earlier *Homo sapiens*; and Tattersall I, Paleoanthropology and Evolutionary Theory.

Fagan BM. 1989. People of the Earth: An Introduction to World Prehistory. Sixth edition. Glenview, IL: Scott, Foresman. Chapters 5 to 8 survey the fossil and archaeological evidence on *H. sapiens* in different parts of the world.

Sigmon BA, Cybulski JS, editors. 1981. *Homo erectus*: Papers in Honor of Davidson Black. Toronto: University of Toronto Press. A series of biographical and historical papers on Davidson Black and his discoveries derived from a symposium at the Canadian Association for Physical Anthropology meetings held in 1976.

Trinkaus E, editor. 1989. The Emergence of Modern Humans: Biocultural Adaptations in the Later Pleistocene. Cambridge: Cambridge University Press. Physical anthropologists and archaeologists review and debate what is known, and not known, about the Neandertals and the transition to modern humans.

Wenke RJ. 1999. Patterns in Prehistory: Humankind's First Three Million Years. Fourth edition. New York: Oxford University Press. A summary of cultural development that focuses on why various crucial changes may have occurred. Chapter 4 is particularly relevant to this chapter.

10 MODERN *HOMO SAPIENS*

Until recently, palaeoanthropologists thought that modern-looking people evolved about 50 000 years ago in Europe. Now we know that they appeared earlier. Recent finds in southern Africa and elsewhere indicate the presence of modern-looking people perhaps as much as 100 000 or even 200 000 years ago. In this chapter we examine the major theories regarding the emergence of anatomically modern humans. The two major theories involve the question "Did modern humans evolve from a single population in a single location, or did they evolve from multiple locations throughout the Old World?"

We examine evidence from various sources—fossils, genetics, and archaeological discoveries—to better understand this period. We also discuss the movement of modern human populations into the New World.

The Emergence of Modern Humans

The skeletal resemblances between those humans and recent people are so great that most palaeo-anthropologists consider them all to be "anatomically modern humans," *Homo sapiens sapiens*. One palaeoanthropologist, Christopher Stringer, characterizes anatomically modern human, *H. sapiens sapiens*, as having "a domed skull, a chin, small eyebrows, brow ridges, and a rather puny skeleton"(Stringer, 1985). Some of us might not like to be called puny, but except for our larger brain, most modern humans definitely are small compared with *H. erectus* and even with earlier forms of our own species, *H. sapiens*. This smallness is true in many respects including our thinner and lighter bones as well as our smaller teeth and jaws.

Cro-Magnon humans, who appeared in western Europe about 35 000 years ago, were once thought to be the earliest specimens of modern humans, or *H. sapiens sapiens*. The Cro-Magnons are named after the rock shelter in France where their remains were first found in 1868 (Stringer et al., 1984). As of now, the oldest known fossils classified as *H. sapiens sapiens* came from Africa. Some of these fossils,

discovered in one of the Klasies River Mouth caves, are possibly as old as 100 000 years (Singer and Wymer, 1982). Other modern-looking fossils of about the same age have been found in Border Cave in South Africa, and a find at Omo in Ethiopia may be an early *H. sapiens sapiens* (Bräuer, 1984; Rightmire, 1984). Remains of anatomically modern humans found at two sites in Israel, at Skhul and Qafzeh, which used to be thought to date back 40 000 to 50 000 years, may be 90 000 years old (Valladas et al., 1988; Schwarcz and Grun, 1992). There are also anatomically modern human finds in Borneo, at Niah, from about 40 000 years ago and in Australia, at Lake Mungo, from about 30 000 years ago (Stringer et al., 1984).

These modern-looking humans differed from the Neandertals and other early *H. sapiens* in that they had higher, more bulging foreheads, thinner and lighter bones, smaller faces and jaws, chins, and slight bone ridges (or no ridges at all) over the eyes and at the back of the head.

Theories about the Origins of Modern Humans

Two hypotheses about the origins of modern humans continue to be debated among anthropologists. We will first consider the **single-origin hypothesis**. This suggests that modern humans emerged in just one part of the Old World (Africa is generally thought to be the place of origin for modern humans) and then spread to other parts, replacing Neandertals and other pre-modern *H. sapiens*.

Single-Origin Hypothesis. According to the single-origin hypothesis, most of the Neandertals and other Archaic *H. sapiens* did not evolve into modern humans. Instead, anatomically modern humans evolved in a limited geographic area. From there they migrated and either physically replaced the indigenous Archaic populations, or genetically replaced them through interbreeding. So, according to this model, the earliest fossil and cultural evidence for modern humans should have first appeared in a single location and Archaic *H. sapiens* (including Neandertals) and anatomically modern populations should have coexisted in some areas for at least some time. If the single-origin hypothesis is correct, modern genetic diversity should be small, since all modern groups would have descended from a single population relatively recently. Further, genetic diversity should be the greatest in populations from the region where modern humans emerged, because this single population would be the oldest and therefore the most genetically diverse.

The presumed place of origin of the first modern humans for the single-origin hypothesis has varied over the years as new fossils have been discovered. In the 1950s the source population was presumed to be the Neandertals in the Near East, who were referred to as "generalized" or "progressive" Neandertals. Later, when earlier *H. sapiens sapiens* were found in Africa, palaeoanthropologists postulated that modern humans emerged first in Africa and then moved to the Near East and from there to Europe and Asia. Single-origin theorists think that the originally small population of *H. sapiens sapiens* had some biological advantage or cultural advantage, or both, that allowed them to spread and replace Archaic *H. sapiens*.

Multiregional Hypothesis. The second hypothesis has been called the **multiregional hypothesis**. This suggests that modern humans evolved in various parts of the Old World after *H. erectus* spread out of Africa (see Figure 10–1). According to the multiregional hypothesis, *H. erectus* populations in various parts of the Old World gradually evolved into anatomically modern-looking humans. This hypothesis supports the idea of gradual, "in place" evolution of regional populations of ancient hominids into modern humans. If this hypothesis is correct, we should be able to trace regional morphological traits through the evolutionary record, and we should see the simultaneous evolution toward

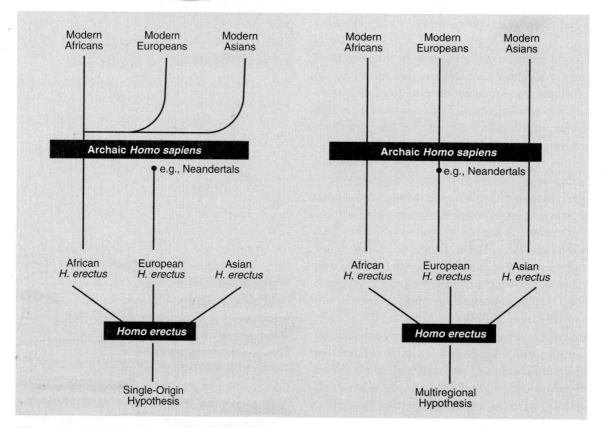

Figure 10–1 Two Possible Evolutionary Models for the Origins of Modern Humans

all needed in the same direction

anatomically modern humans in Europe, Asia, and Africa. It is also assumed that there is sufficient gene flow—movement of genetic material among populations—to maintain a single species.

To explain why human evolution would proceed gradually and in the same direction in various parts of the Old World, multiregional theorists point to cultural improvements in cutting-tool and cooking technology that occurred all over the Old World. These cultural improvements may have relaxed the prior natural selection for heavy bones and musculature in the skull. The argument is that unless many plant and animal foods were cut into small pieces and thoroughly cooked in hearths or pits that were efficient thermally, they would be hard to chew and digest. Thus, people previously would have needed robust jaws and thick skull bones to support the large muscles that enabled them to cut and chew their food. However, robust bone and muscle would no longer be needed after people began to cut and cook more effectively (Trinkaus, 1986).

Alternative Theories. The single-origin and multiregional hypotheses are not the only possible interpretations of the available fossil record. There is also the alternative interpretation that there may have been some replacement of one population by another, some local continuous evolution, and some interbreeding between early modern humans, who spread out of Africa, and populations encountered in North Africa, Europe, and Asia (Trinkaus, 1986). As the biologist Alan Templeton has noted, the debates over a single-origin versus multiregional evolution of *Homo sapiens* "are based on the myth that replacement of one physical feature in a fossil series with another feature can only be created by one population replacing another (either biologically or culturally), but such fossil patterns could be a reflection of one genotype replacing another through gene flow and natural selection. Morphological replacement should not be equated with population replacement when one is dealing with populations that can interbreed" (Templeton, 1996:1363). The next chapter discusses how modern human populations may also vary in physical features because

natural selection favours different features in different environments.

Genetic Evidence

The single-origin (sometimes called the "out of Africa" or "replacement") hypothesis first emerged from studies where diversity in mitochondrial DNA (mtDNA) in modern human populations was used for estimating the timing of divergence between various regional populations (see Research Frontiers, *DNA Evidence and the "Out of Africa" Hypothesis of Modern Human Origins*). The question of modern human relations is based on the notion that mtDNA is inherited from the mother only and that mutation rates remain constant over time. The single-origin hypothesis implies little genetic diversity among modern populations, whereas the multiregional hypothesis implies greater genetic diversity since the genetic makeup of populations in different regions would change relatively independently of one another. Early studies of mtDNA demonstrated that the greatest variation was in African populations, implying that they represented the oldest modern human lineage. Using this information as a "molecular clock" (see Chapter 7), the time of "divergence" for modern humans from their archaic ancestral population was estimated at about 200 000 years ago (Cann et al., 1987). However, a reanalysis of the mtDNA data from the original study that suggested this so-called "Eve hypothesis" is more critical, showing that the computer models could support either model (Excoffier and Langaney, 1989; Stoneking, 1994; Ayala, 1995).

Additional genetic evidence continues to corroborate the mtDNA studies. For example, the analysis of microsatellite segments of nuclear DNA imply an African origin of modern humans from about 150 000 years ago (Seielstad et al., 1999). Like the original mtDNA support for the "Eve" hypothesis, Y-chromosome studies (genetic material passed from males to males only) have implied a common male ancestor to modern living populations who lived about 270 000 years ago (Dorit et al., 1995).

Another issue to keep in mind for these studies however is the concept of *genetic bottlenecks* in

RESEARCH FRONTIERS

DNA Evidence and the "Out of Africa" Hypothesis of Modern Human Origins

Palaeoanthropologists used to believe that humans (hominids) diverged from apes (pongids) more than 10 million years ago. Then molecular biologists started comparing the blood proteins and DNA of living primate species. These comparisons indicated that the probable time of divergence should be pushed up to between 5 million and 6 million years ago. Molecular biology now has entered another palaeoanthropological debate—this time about the origin of modern-looking humans. On the basis of comparisons of mitochondrial DNA in various populations of living humans, molecular biologists generally support the "out of Africa" hypothesis—the view that modern-looking humans emerged first in Africa and then spread throughout the world, replacing premodern *Homo sapiens*.

Mitochondrial DNA (mtDNA) is found in the mitochondrion, a part of the cell that converts food into energy for the cell. There are three advantages to using mtDNA over other kinds of DNA found in cell nuclei. The first is that mtDNA comprises only 37 genes; the fewer the genes, the easier the comparisons. Second, many neutral mutations accumulate rapidly and steadily in mtDNA, making it easier to find markers of similarity and difference in recent populations. (The more similar the mutations, the closer are two populations to a common ancestor.) The third advantage of mitochrondrial DNA is that it is inherited only from the mother, making it less complicated to trace evolutionary lines. Because mtDNA is passed on through the maternal line, molecular biologists refer to the ancestor of all modern humans as "Eve." Of course, there wasn't just one "Eve"; there must have been more than one of her generation with similar mtDNA.

Comparing the mtDNA of humans from different geographic regions and using computer software to create branching "tree" diagrams, the molecular researchers claim that the simplest or most parsimonious of the possible solutions traces modern human mtDNA back to females who lived some 200 000 years ago. They also suggest that the mtDNA evidence is consistent with palaeoanthropological evidence indicating that modern-looking humans appeared first in Africa, somewhat later in the Near East, and later still in Europe and Asia.

Critics of the out-of-Africa hypothesis point out that the acceptability of the model depends on dubious assumptions. For example, it's possible to construct thousands of tree diagrams from mtDNA data. Those already obtained may point to an African origin of modern humans, but other possibilities may suggest other scenarios. Why should we assume that the current results cover all the reasonable possibilities?

A second criticism of the out-of-Africa hypothesis points to fossil evidence suggesting continuous

human evolution. Genetic bottlenecks, which can result from *demographic collapse*, can make human populations appear evolutionarily "younger" than they actually are. The reason is that demographic collapse results in the subsequent populations descending from a reduced gene pool, and therefore showing reduced genetic diversity from a relatively recent period (Harpending et al., 1998). Just as the term *demographic collapse* implies, imagine a wine bottle filled with pebbles of various colours. If you were asked to pick any coloured pebbled from that bottle, you could choose from a wide range. However, if you were asked to choose from only those colours that fall though the neck of the bottle immediately after tipping it over, your current selection, despite the original diversity of the bottle's contents, would be severely limited by the reduced flow of pebbles through the constricted neck of the bottle. Thus, the term *genetic bottleneck* refers to a rapid reduction in gene flow. Genetic bottlenecks among hominoid groups have been implied by various studies, and in some cases may be the result of infectious disease (Harpending et al., 1998). In general though, the molecular anthropological data continues to provide support for the "out of Africa" hypothesis, although the question now remains as to the degree of gene flow and local evolution in other areas. To address this, we must look more closely at the fossil evidence.

Fossil Evidence

As we noted earlier, the oldest known fossils attributed to anatomically modern humans come from Africa. Sites that are dated to around 100 000

evolution toward modern-looking traits in various regions of the world. In other words, the fossil record is not consistent with the idea that modern-looking traits were introduced from outside those regions. The out-of-Africa hypothesis must be wrong, critics argue, if physical traits persist in even just one region other than Africa, from the time of early humans to modern humans. For the out-of-Africa hypothesis assumes that humans from southern Africa completely *replaced* early *H. sapiens*, with no gene flow between them. If this is what happened, the fossil record should show some discontinuity over time. However, in Southeast Asia and Australia the fossils spanning 700 000 years (from *H. erectus* to modern-looking humans) have similar features throughout that time span. For instance, they have sloping rather than vertical frontal bones (foreheads), in contrast to early modern skulls in South Africa (such as at Border Cave), which have more vertical foreheads. In China there are shovel-shaped incisors from ancient

times to modern times; African populations, early and late, lack this trait. So the persistence of distinctive traits in different regions (shovel-shaped incisors in China and sloping foreheads in Southeast Asia and Australia) is not consistent with the idea that modern-looking humans completely replaced previous *H. sapiens* in those regions.

There is also a lack of archaeological evidence to support the idea that an invading modern population came out of southern Africa. An invading population might have a very different tool kit, but in the Near East, where both Neandertal and modern human fossils are found with tools, the two have similar tool kits. In Asia, too, there is no discontinuity in technology, as we might expect with an invading population.

We would expect an invading population that replaced all other *H. sapiens* populations to have had some significant superiority. If not technological, then what? Some out-of-Africa theorists have suggested that the earliest modern

humans had language, whereas previous *H. sapiens* did not. The evidence from anatomy regarding capacity for spoken language, however, remains controversial.

As with most controversies, this one may be resolved with additional fossil evidence and more deliberate hypothesis tests of alternative interpretations.

Sources: For support of the out-of-Africa hypothesis, see: Vigilant L, Stoneking M, Harpending H, Hawkes K, Wilson AC. 27 September 1991. African Populations and the Evolution of Human Mitochondrial DNA. Science 1503.

Wilson AC, Cann RL. April 1992. The Recent African Genesis of Humans. Scientific American 68–73.

For critiques of the out-of-Africa hypothesis, see: Frayer DW. Testing Theories and Hypotheses about Human Origins. Weller S. The Research Process. Both in: Ember CR, Ember M, Peregrine PN, editors. Research Frontiers in Anthropology. Upper Saddle River, NJ: Prentice Hall, 1998, Prentice Hall/Simon & Schuster Custom Publishing.

Thorne AG, Wolpoff MH. April 1992. The Multiregional Evolution of Humans. Scientific American 76–83.

years ago include the Klasies River Mouth, the Border Cave in South Africa, and Omo in Ethiopia (Singer and Wymer, 1982; Bräuer, 1984; Rightmire, 1984). Found at the Klasies River Mouth, a modern upper jaw and a lower jaw (mandible) with distinct chin have been dated to 90 000 years ago (Grun et al., 1990). From the Border Cave we have a near complete cranium, a mandible, and partial infant skeleton dating between 60 000 and 80 000 years ago (Grun et al., 1990). The Omo 1 skull dates to 130 000 years ago and the Mumba teeth have been dated as 110 000 years old (Feder and Park, 1997:310). More transitional specimens have been found at the sites of Florisbad, Jebel Irhoud, Omo (Omo 2), and Ngaloba (Laetoli Hominid 18) (Smith et al., 1989). These specimens all have larger, more rounded crania, and smaller brow

ridges than do older African archaic populations and are somewhat older than the modern-looking material discussed above.

The Cro-Magnon fossils discovered in 1868 in France remain the oldest evidence of anatomically modern populations in western Europe. They have modern-looking skulls with vertical foreheads, small brow ridges, and a large cranial capacity. Cro-Magnons date to less than 30 000 year ago, and until recently there have been no intermediate forms observed in western Europe. In 1999, a multinational team of anthropologists published the discovery of an early Upper Palaeolithic human burial from Portugal. They argued that this provided evidence of a transitional Neandertal–early modern human, a conclusion that remains debated (Duarte et al., 1999; Tattersall and Schwartz, 1999). The remains are that of a young child (approximately 4 years old) with an associated date of about 24 500 years ago. The skeleton presents a "mosaic of European early modern human and Neandertal features" (Duarte et al., 1999; Tattersall and Schwartz, 1999). In eastern Europe, however, there is some evidence that has been interpreted as being transitional (Neandertal to modern). Material found in the Czech Republic dates to between 35 000 and 45 000 years ago (Omoto and Tobias, 1998). More recently, radiocarbon dates taken directly on Neandertal remains from the sites of Vindija and Velika Pecina in Croatia have suggested that this group of Archaic *H. sapiens* may have survived until as recently as 28 000 to 29 000 years ago (Smith et al., 1999).

Based on the range of recent dates noted above, it seems clear that both Neandertals and modern humans (*H. sapiens sapiens*) coexisted in Europe and the Near East for at least 20 000 years, and maybe as long as 60 000 years. But what happened to the Neandertals? Three answers have generally been considered. First, they interbred with modern humans and the unique Neandertal characteristics slowly disappeared from the interbreeding population. Second, they were killed off by modern humans. Third, they were driven to extinction due to competition with modern humans.

The interbreeding scenario seems the most probable, yet evidence supporting it is weak. If modern humans and Neandertals interbred, we should be able to find "hybrid" individuals in the fossil record. In fact, a group of scholars has argued that an Upper Palaeolithic skeleton from Portugal demonstrates a combination of modern human and Neandertal features (Duarte et al., 1999). The finding remains controversial, however, because it is a child's skeleton (approximately 4 years old) and its Neandertal-like features have not been corroborated by other scholars. More significantly, if the interbreeding hypothesis is correct, then the mtDNA analysis we have discussed several times in this chapter must be wrong. On the other hand, recent research on Neandertal tools suggests that some Neandertal groups adopted new techniques of tool manufacture that are thought to be uniquely

associated with modern humans (Bahn, 1998). If Neandertals were learning from modern humans, then the idea that they could have interbred and perhaps been absorbed within the modern human population gains credibility.

The genocide scenario, that modern humans killed off Neandertals, has appeal as a sensational story, but little evidence. Not a single "murdered" Neandertal has ever been found, and one might wonder, in a fight between the powerful Neandertals and the more gracile modern humans, who might get the better of whom.

Finally, it may have been that Neandertals simply could not compete with modern humans. Physical anthropologist Erik Trinkaus has argued, based on both physical characteristics of the Neandertal skeleton and their apparent patterns of behaviour, that Neandertals were less efficient hunters and gatherers than modern humans (Trinkaus, 1986). If this is true, a modern human group would have been able to live and reproduce more easily than a Neandertal group in the same territory, and this would likely drive the Neandertals away. When there were no new territories to run to, the Neandertals would go extinct—precisely what the archaeological record seems to suggest (Klein, 2003). However, as we discussed in the last chapter (see Research Frontiers, *Re-examining Middle Palaeolithic Hunting* in Chapter 9), archaeological evidence has suggested that Neandertal hunting strategies were more complex than previously demonstrated (Burke 2000). Thus, it remains that some additional cultural forces were being selected for in anatomically modern humans.

In southwest Asia anatomically modern specimens have been excavated from regions where Neandertals have also been discovered. Modern remains from Skhul and Qafzeh in Israel predate Neandertal remains discovered there (Stringer, 1988a). Similarly, some have argued that fossils from the Levant show Neandertals lived there at the same time as anatomically modern human populations from about 120 000 years ago, although others use the same evidence to suggest a continuum of rather than distinct populations (Corruccini, 1992; Sohn and Wolpoff, 1993). In

East Asia there does appear to be some continuity in regional traits from *H. erectus* to Archaic to modern populations. Traits like shovel-shaped incisors, extra cranial sutures, and a mandibular torus that are more common in modern populations from this area seem to imply at least some level of long-term regional continuity.

The fossil evidence does seem to suggest the presence of anatomically modern populations in many areas that would be suggestive of the single-origin model. However, despite many areas having overlap between both Archaic and anatomically modern populations, other regions like eastern Europe show evidence of transitional forms that would seem to support the multiregional hypothesis.

Cultural Evidence

Artifacts found in association with early modern sites do seem to be more sophisticated than other assemblages of the same period from Europe and Asia, including the blade technology. Sites from southern Africa dating to 90 000 years ago have shown worked bone, harpoons, and other tools that are not seen at Archaic sites anywhere (Yellen et al., 1995). Outside of Africa, however, the evidence is problematic. In areas like the Middle East there are few differences in the tool assemblages of Neandertal and Archaic populations from those associated with early modern populations in Africa and southwest Asia (Thorne and Wolpoff, 1992). In Europe, others see a clear increase in sophistication of later Mousterian tools after Neandertals came into contact with modern populations and their more sophisticated tool technology, called Aurignacian. **Aurignacian tools**—a stone tool technology that began in Europe around 35 000 years ago—included the production of long, narrow blade tools.

Upper Palaeolithic Cultures

The period of cultural history in Europe, the Near East, and Asia known as the **Upper Palaeolithic** dates from about 40 000 years ago to the period known as the **Mesolithic** (about 14 000 to about 10 000 years ago, depending on the area). In Africa,

the cultural period comparable to the Upper Palaeolithic is known as the Later Stone Age and may have begun much earlier. To simplify terminology, we use the term *Upper Palaeolithic* in referring to cultural developments in all areas of the Old World during this period.

In many respects, lifestyles during the Upper Palaeolithic were similar to lifestyles before. People were still mainly hunters and gatherers and fishers who probably lived in highly mobile bands. They made their camps out in the open in skin-covered huts and in caves and rock shelters, and continued to produce smaller and smaller stone tools.

The Upper Palaeolithic is also characterized by a variety of new developments. One of the most striking is the emergence of art—painting on cave walls and stone slabs and carving tools, decorative objects, and personal ornaments out of bone, antler, shell, and stone. (Perhaps for this as well as other purposes, people began to obtain materials from distant sources.) Because more archaeological sites date from the Upper Palaeolithic than from any previous period and some Upper Palaeolithic sites seem larger than any before, many archaeologists think that the human population increased considerably during the Upper Palaeolithic (White, 1982). At the same time new inventions, such as the bow and arrow, the spear-thrower, and tiny replaceable blades that could be fitted into handles, appear for the first time (Strauss, 1982).

The Last Ice Age

The Upper Palaeolithic world had an environment very different from today's. The earth was gripped by the last ice age, with glaciers covering Europe as far south as Berlin and Warsaw, and North America as far south as Chicago. To the south of these glacial fronts was a tundra zone extending in Europe to the Alps and in North America to the Ozarks, Appalachians, and well out onto the Great Plains (see Figure 10–2). Environmentally, both Europe and North America probably resembled contemporary Siberia and northern Canada. Elsewhere in the world conditions were not as extreme, but were still different from conditions today (Dawson, 1992).

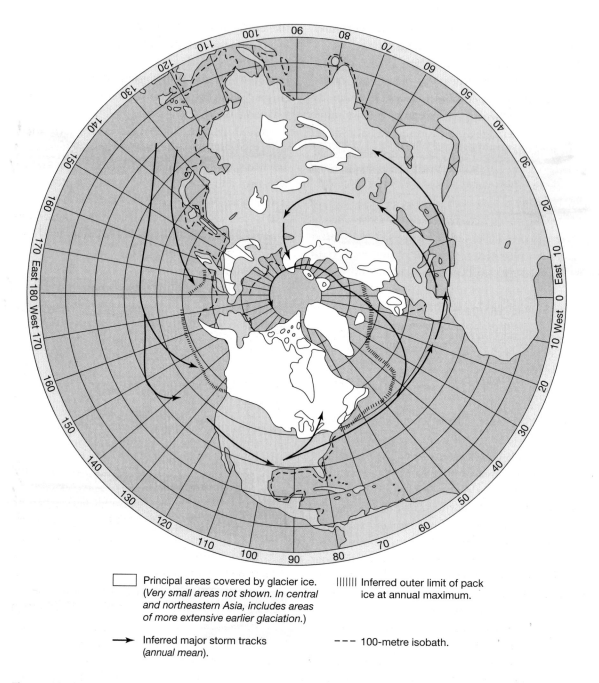

Principal areas covered by glacier ice. (*Very small areas not shown. In central and northeastern Asia, includes areas of more extensive earlier glaciation.*)

|||||| Inferred outer limit of pack ice at annual maximum.

→ Inferred major storm tracks (*annual mean*).

- - - 100-metre isobath.

Figure 10–2 The Extent of Glaciation during the Upper Palaeolithic

Source: Stein P, Rowe B. 2000. Physical Anthropology. Seventh edition. Boston: McGraw-Hill. Copyright © 2000. Reprinted by permission of The McGraw-Hill Book Company.

For one thing, the climate was different. Average annual temperatures were as much as 10 degrees Celsius below today's, and changes in ocean currents would have made temperature contrasts (that is, the differences between summer and winter months) more extreme as well. The changing ocean currents also changed weather patterns, and Europe experienced heavy annual snowfall. Not all the world was cold, however; still, the presence of huge ice sheets in the north changed the climate throughout the world. North Africa, for example, appears to have been much wetter than today, and South Asia was apparently drier. And everywhere the climate seems to have been highly variable.

The plants and animals of the Upper Palaeolithic world were adapted to these extreme conditions. Among the most important, and impressive, were the large game animals collectively known as *Pleistocene megafauna* (Martin and Wright, 1967). These animals, as their name suggests, were huge compared with their contemporary descendants. In North America, for example, giant ground sloths stood some 2.5 to 3 metres tall and weighed a few thousand kilograms. Siberian mammoths were the largest elephants ever to live—some standing more than 4 metres tall. In East Asia, species such as the woolly rhinoceros and giant deer were present.

Homesites

As was the case in the known Middle Palaeolithic sites, most of the Upper Palaeolithic remains that have been excavated were situated in caves and rock shelters. In southwestern France, some groups seem to have paved parts of the floor of the shelter with stones. Tent-like structures were built in some caves, apparently to keep out the cold (Patterson, 1981). Some of what were formerly open-air sites have also been excavated.

The site at Dolni Vestonice in what is now the Czech Republic dates to about 25 000 years ago. It is one of the first for which there is an entire settlement plan (Klima, 1962). The settlement seems to have consisted of four tent-like huts, probably made from animal skins, with a great open hearth in the centre. Around the outside were mammoth bones, some rammed into the ground, which suggests that the huts were surrounded by a wall. All told, there were bone heaps from about 100 mammoths. Each hut probably housed a group of related families—about 20 to 25 people. (One hut was approximately 8 by 14 metres and had five hearths distributed inside it, presumably one for each family.) With 20 to 25 people per hut, and

assuming that all four huts were occupied at the same time, the population of the settlement would have been 100 to 125.

Up a hill from the settlement was a fifth and different kind of hut. It was dug into the ground and contained a bake oven and more than 2300 small, fired fragments of animal figurines. There were also some hollow bones that may have been musical instruments. Another interesting feature of the settlement was a burial find of a woman with a disfigured face. She may have been a particularly important personage, because her face was found engraved on an ivory plaque near the central hearth of the settlement.

Tools: New Techniques

Upper Palaeolithic toolmaking appears to have had its roots in the Mousterian and post-Acheulian traditions, because flake tools are found in many Upper Palaeolithic sites. The Upper Palaeolithic, however, is characterized by a preponderance of blades; there were also burins, bone and antler tools, and *microliths* (see Figure 10–3).

In addition, two new techniques of toolmaking appeared—*indirect percussion* and *pressure flaking*. Blades were found in Middle Palaeolithic assemblages, but they were not widely used until the Upper Palaeolithic. Although blades can be made in a variety of ways, **indirect percussion** using a hammer-struck punch was commonly used in the Upper Palaeolithic. After shaping a core into a pyramidal or cylindrical form, the toolmaker put a punch of antler or wood or another hard material into position and struck it with a hammer. Because the force is directed, the toolmaker was able to strike off consistently shaped blades, which are more than twice as long as they are wide (Schick and Toth, 1994; Whittaker, 1994) (see Figure 10–4).

The Upper Palaeolithic is also noted for the production of large numbers of bone, antler, and ivory tools; needles, awls, and harpoons made of bone appear for the first time (Whittaker, 1994). The manufacture of these implements may have been made easier by the development of many varieties of burins. **Burins** are chisel-like stone

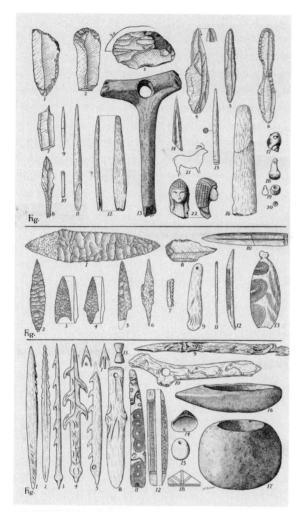

Figure 10–3

Upper Palaeolithic tools. Upper Palaeolithic peoples made a much wider variety of tools than their predecessors.

Source: American Museum of Natural History.

tools used for carving (see Figure 10–3); bone and antler needles, awls, and projectile points could be produced with them (Bordaz, 1970). Burins have been found in Middle and Lower Palaeolithic sites but are present in great number and variety only in the Upper Palaeolithic.

Pressure flaking also appeared during the Upper Palaeolithic. Rather than using percussion to strike off flakes as in previous technologies, pressure flaking works by employing pressure with a bone, wood, or antler tool at the edge of the tool to remove small flakes. Pressure flaking would usually be used in the final stages of retouching a tool (Whittaker, 1994).

As time went on, all over the Old World smaller and smaller blade tools were produced. The very tiny ones, called **microliths**, were often hafted or fitted into handles, one blade at a time or several blades together, to serve as spears, adzes, knives, and sickles. The hafting required inventing a way to trim the blade's back edge so that it would be blunt rather than sharp. In this way the blades would not split the handles into which they might be inserted; the blunting would also prevent the users of an unhafted blade from cutting themselves (Phillipson, 1993).

Some archaeologists think that the blade technique was adopted because it made for more

Figure 10–4

One way to remove blades from a core is to hit them with a punch using indirect percussion. The object being struck is the punch, which is made of bone or horn.

Source: Fagan BM. 1972. In the Beginning. Boston: Little, Brown. p 195.

economical use of flint. André Leroi-Gourhan of the Musée de l'Homme in Paris calculated that with the old Acheulian technique, a 1-kilogram lump of flint yielded 40 centimetres of working edge and produced only two hand axes. If the more advanced Mousterian technique were used, a lump of equal size would yield 1.8 metres of working edge. The indirect percussion method of the Upper Palaeolithic would yield as much as 22.8 metres of working edge (Bordaz, 1970). With the same amount of material, a significantly greater number of tools could be produced. Getting the most out of a valuable resource may have been particularly important in areas lacking large flint deposits.

Jacques Bordaz suggested that the evolution of toolmaking techniques, which continually increased the amount of usable edge that could be derived from a lump of flint, was significant because people could then spend more time in regions where flint was unavailable. Another reason for adopting the blade toolmaking technique may have been that it made for easy repair of tools. For example, the cutting edge of a tool might consist of a line of razor-like microliths set into a piece of wood. The tool would not be usable if just one of the cutting edge's microliths broke off or was chipped. If, however, the user carried a small, prepared core of flint from which an identical-sized microlith could be struck off, the tool could be repaired easily by replacing the lost or broken microlith. A spear whose point was lost could be similarly repaired. Thus, the main purpose of the blade toolmaking technique may not have been to make more economical use of flint, but rather to allow easy replacement of damaged blades (Clark, 1977).

How Were the Tools Used?

The tools made by Upper Palaeolithic people suggest that they were much more effective hunters and fishers than their predecessors (Klein, 1994). During the Upper Palaeolithic, and probably for the first time, spears were launched with a spear-thrower rather than thrown with the arm. We know this because bone and antler **atlatls** (the Aztec word for "spear-thrower") have been found in some sites. A spear propelled off a grooved board could be sent through the air with increased force, causing it to travel farther and hit harder, and with less effort by the thrower. The bow and arrow was also used in various places during the Upper Palaeolithic; and harpoons, used for fishing and perhaps for hunting reindeer, were invented at this time.

These new tools and weapons for more effective hunting and fishing do not rule out the possibility that Upper Palaeolithic people were still scavenging animal remains. Olga Soffer suggests that Upper Palaeolithic people may have located their settlements near places where many mammoths died naturally in order to use the bones for building (see Figure 10–5). For example, in Moravia the mammoths may have come to lick deposits of calcite and other sources of magnesium and calcium, particularly during the late spring and early summer when food resources were short and mortality was high. Consistent with the idea that humans may not have killed all the enormous mammoths found there is the fact that in some places there are few human-made cut marks on mammoth bones. For example, at Dolni Vestonice, where bones of 100 mammoths were found, few bones show cut marks from butchering and few bones were found inside the huts. In contrast, the living floors are littered with bison, horse, and reindeer bones, suggesting that these other animals were deliberately killed and eaten by humans. If the people had actually killed all the mammoths that we find the remains of, why would they have hunted so many other animals (Soffer, 1993)?

Art

The earliest discovered traces of art are beads and carvings, and then paintings, from Upper Palaeolithic sites. We might expect that early artistic efforts were crude, but the cave paintings of Spain and southern France show a marked degree of skill. So do the naturalistic paintings on slabs of stone excavated in southern Africa. Some of those slabs appear to have been painted as much as 28 000 years ago, which suggests that painting in Africa is as old as painting in Europe (Phillipson, 1993). In fact, painting may be even

Figure 10–5

Here we see the type of mammoth-bone shelters constructed about 15 000 years ago on the East European Plain. Often mammoth skulls formed part of the foundation for the tusk, long bone, and wooden frame, covered with hide. As many as 95 mammoth mandibles were arranged around the outside in a herringbone pattern. Ten men and women could have constructed this elaborate shelter of 24 square metres in six days, using 20 800 kilograms of bone.

older than that. The early Australians may have painted on the walls of rock shelters and cliff faces at least 30 000 years ago and maybe as much as 60 000 years ago (Morell, 1995).

Peter Ucko and André Rosenfeld identified three principal locations of paintings in the caves of western Europe: (1) in obviously inhabited rock shelters and cave entrances—art as decoration or "art for art's sake"; (2) in "galleries" immediately off the inhabited areas of caves; and (3) in the inner reaches of caves, whose difficulty of access has been interpreted by some as a sign that magical-religious activities were performed there (Ucko and Rosenfield, 1967).

The subjects of the paintings are mostly animals. The paintings rest on bare walls, with no backdrops or environmental trappings. Perhaps, like many contemporary peoples, Upper Palaeolithic men and women believed that the drawing of a human image could cause death or injury. If that were indeed their belief, it might explain why human figures are rarely depicted in cave art. Another explanation for the focus on animals might be that these people sought to improve their luck at hunting. This hypothesis is suggested by evidence of chips in the painted figures, perhaps made by spears thrown at the drawings. However, if hunting magic was the chief motivation for the paintings, it is difficult to explain why only a few show signs of having been speared. Perhaps the paintings were inspired by the need to increase the supply of animals. Cave art seems to have reached a peak toward the end of the Upper Palaeolithic period, when the herds of game were decreasing.

The particular symbolic significance of the cave paintings in southwestern France is more explicitly revealed, perhaps, by the results of Patricia Rice and Ann Paterson's statistical study (Rice and Paterson, 1985; Rice and Paterson, 1986). The data suggest that the animals portrayed in the cave paintings were mostly the ones that the painters preferred for meat and for materials such as hides. For example, wild cattle (bovines) and horses are portrayed more often than we would expect by chance, probably because they were larger and heavier (meatier) than the other animals in the environment. In addition, the paintings mostly portray animals that the painters may have feared the most because of their size, speed, natural weapons such as tusks and horns, and unpredictability of behaviour. That is, mammoths, bovines, and horses are portrayed more often than deer and reindeer. Thus, the paintings are consistent with the idea that "the art is related to the importance of hunting in the economy of Upper Palaeolithic people" (Rice and Paterson, 1985:98). Consistent with this idea, according to the investigators, is the fact that the art of the cultural period that followed the Upper Palaeolithic also seems to reflect how people got their food. However, in that period, when getting food no longer depended on hunting large game (because they were becoming extinct), the art ceased to focus on portrayals of animals.

Upper Palaeolithic art was not confined to cave paintings. Many shafts of spears and similar objects were decorated with figures of animals. Alexander Marshack has an interesting interpretation of some of the engravings made during the Upper Palaeolithic. He believes that as far back as 30 000 B.C., hunters may have used a system of notation, engraved on bone and stone, to mark the phases of the moon. If this is true, it would mean that Upper Palaeolithic people were capable of complex thought and were consciously aware of their environment. In addition, figurines representing the human female in exaggerated form have been found at Upper Palaeolithic sites. Called *Venuses*, these figurines portray women with broad hips and large breasts and abdomens. It has been suggested that the figurines were an ideal type or an expression of

The Venus of Willendorf, one of the most famous Venus figurines.

a desire for fertility. Most of these figurines were made during the Gravettian period from about 25 000 to 23 000 years ago. Clive Gamble argues that the Venus figurines were religious in nature. As such, their presence in the archaeological record implies a widespread belief system shared between geographically isolated groups. From her analysis of the shape, size, and form of almost 200 figurines, Patricia Rice concluded that the figurines reflect a distribution of ages similar to the demographic profiles seen in contemporary foraging groups. A number of questions remain unanswered, however, particularly regarding the general featureless style of the figures. LeRoy McDermott suggests they are a reflection of how a woman represents herself through self-observation, including the absence of anatomical features and distortions in the bodily proportions. However, more recent exploration of these artifacts by Sofer and colleagues suggests that

A piece of three-dimensional Upper Palaeolithic art from France. This depiction of a bison licking itself is both accurate and beautifully executed, clearly showing the skill of Upper Palaeolithic artists.

a variety of aspects of these figurines have been missed or misinterpreted by past investigations. In particular, these researchers have argued that a number of the figurines are depicted wearing clothing that demonstrates considerable craftsmanship and knowledge of woven fabric (Marshack, 1972). In addition to the Venus figurines, there are other depictions of women in Upper Palaeolithic art (see New Perspectives on Gender, *Depictions of Women in Upper Palaeolithic Art*).

What the Venus figurines symbolized remains controversial. As is usually the case in current scholarly controversies, there is little or no evidence available now that might allow us to accept or reject a particular interpretation. But not all controversies in anthropology continue because of lack of evidence. Sometimes a controversy continues because there is some, usually disputed evidence on all sides. This was the case until recently with the controversy to which we now

NEW PERSPECTIVES ON GENDER

Depictions of Women in Upper Palaeolithic Art

Image of four women from Gönnersdorf cave.

Source: Duhard JP. 1993. Upper Paleolithic Figures as a Reflection of Human Morphology and Social Organization. Antiquity 67:86.

It is a common misperception that depictions of the human form in Upper Palaeolithic art are restricted to Venus figurines. To the contrary, there are many other depictions of humans, both female and male, running the whole range of ages from infants to old people. For women, figures of obese or pregnant women, like those sometimes depicted in Venus figurines, appear to be only one type in a wide range of images, many of which offer accurate rather than stylized representations.

In a survey of Upper Palaeolithic art, Jean-Pierre Duhard found that all shapes and sizes of women as well as all age ranges were present. Indeed, he argued that a range of female body

types can be seen. One engraved figure from Gönnersdorf cave on the Rhine River, for example, depicts four women. Three are the same size, but one is smaller and has small breasts—she may be an adolescent. Of the three larger figures, one appears to have a child tied to her back, and she also has large, rounded breasts, as opposed to the flat and pointed breasts of the other two. Duhard argued that this is an accurate depiction of four women, one with a child she is breast-feeding.

Duhard suggested that women's roles as mothers may have given them a privileged status in Upper Palaeolithic life, which may be why that status is the most frequently depicted subject in Upper Palaeolithic art. In a similar way, Patricia Rice has argued that Venus figurines accurately reflect the social importance of women in Upper Palaeolithic society. She demonstrated that a range of body types and ages are represented in Venus figurines, and argued that, since the Venuses depict real women of all ages, not just pregnant women, they should be seen as symbols of "womanhood" rather than "motherhood." The wide distribution of Venus figurines and their apparent importance to Upper Palaeolithic peoples reflect, according to Rice, the recognized

importance of women in Upper Palaeolithic society.

Arguing along similar lines, Olga Soffer examined the clothing worn by some Venus figures. Soffer and her colleagues show that woven items are the most frequently depicted, and argue that, since these woven items would have been highly valued in Upper Palaeolithic society, their presence on some Venus figurines suggests that some women held positions of high status in Upper Palaeolithic society.

Duhard also argued that while depictions of women are common in Upper Palaeolithic art, similar depictions of men and children are comparatively rare. He suggested this disparity may reflect women's status in Upper Palaeolithic societies. Most depictions of women show them in some motherhood role—pregnant, in childbirth, or carrying an infant (and perhaps walking with older children).

Sources: Duhard J-P. 1993. Upper Palaeolithic Figures as a Reflection of Human Morphology and Social Organization. Antiquity 67:83–91.

Rice P. 1981. Prehistoric Venuses: Symbols of Motherhood or Womanhood? Journal of Anthropological Research 37:402–414.

Soffer O, Adovasio JM, Hyland DC. 2000. The "Venus" Figurines: Textiles, Basketry, Gender, and Status in the Upper Palaeolithic. Current Anthropology 41:511–537.

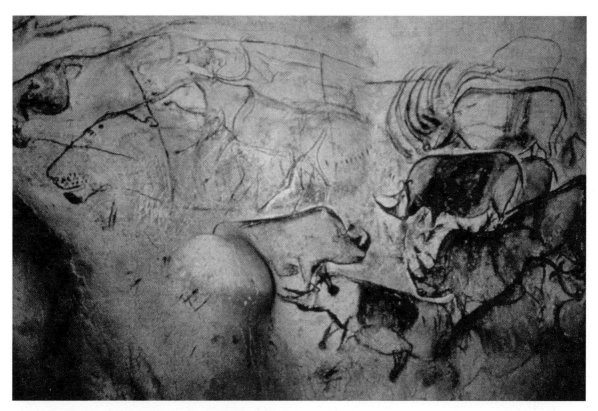

Cave paintings from the Upper Palaeolithic discovered in 1995 in a grotto in Vallon-Pont-D'Arc, Ardech, France. Statistical research on cave paintings suggests that artists tended to portray animals that were meatier as well as more fearsome.

turn—whether there were people in the Americas before about 11 500 years ago.

The Earliest Humans in the New World

So far in this chapter we have dealt only with the Old World—Africa, Europe, and Asia. What about the New World—North and South America? How long have humans lived there, and what were their earliest cultures like?

Because only *H. sapiens sapiens* fossils have been found in North and South America, migrations of humans to the New World had to have taken place sometime after the emergence of *H. sapiens sapiens*. When exactly these migrations occurred is subject to debate, particularly about when people got to areas south of Alaska. At the Old Crow site on the

Porcupine River in the Yukon Territory, a possible early human occupation site has been dated to between 12 000 and 27 000 years ago (Morlan et al., 1990). If the site is indeed that old, it represents the oldest known human habitation site in the New World. Nearby, the Bluefish Caves site in the Yukon Territory revealed the faunal remains of mammoth, horse, bison, and caribou. Stone tools, including some microblades, were discovered at the site. Radiocarbon dating on bone collagen from the faunal remains suggests a date of between 15 000 and 12 000 years ago (Harington and Cinq-mars, 1995; Burke and Cinq-mars, 1998). Because of a lack of archaeological evidence in the northwest Arctic, the prevailing view has been that humans were not present south of Alaska until after 15 000 years ago. However, evidence from an archaeological site called Monte Verde in Chile suggests that modern humans might have been living in southern South America at least 12 500 years ago, and maybe as much as 33 000 years ago. (See Research Frontiers, *When and How Did Humans Populate the New World?* on page 226.) The Monte Verde site contains more than 700 stone tools, the remains of hide-covered huts, and a child's footprint next to a hearth (McDonald, 1998).

The people there may or may not have hunted big game, but just a little while later there were people living in the tropical rain forest of the Amazon basin in what is now Brazil who were definitely not hunters of mammoths and other big game, as their contemporaneous North American counterparts were. In other words, it looks like the earliest inhabitants of the New World—in what is now Chile and Brazil, and in North America—varied in culture. The people in the Amazon lived by collecting fruits and nuts, fishing, and hunting small game. They lived in caves with painted art on the walls and left 30 000 stone chips from making tips of spears, darts, or harpoons (Gibbons, 1995; Roosevelt et al., 1995).

According to the comparative linguists Joseph Greenberg and Merritt Ruhlen, there were three waves of migration into the New World (Greenberg and Ruhlen, 1992). They compared hundreds of languages in North and South America, grouping them into three different language families. Because each of these language families has a closer relationship to an Asian language family than to the other New World language families, it would appear that three different migrations came out of Asia. The first arrivals spoke a language that diverged over time into most of the languages found in the New World—the Amerind family of languages; the speakers of these related languages came to occupy all of South and Central America as well as most of North America. Next came the ancestors of the people who speak languages belonging to the Na-Dené family, which today includes Haida on the northwest coast of Canada, Navaho and Apache in the southwestern United States, and various Athapaskan languages. Finally, perhaps 4000 years ago, came the ancestors of the Inuit and Aleut (the latter came to occupy the islands southwest of Alaska and the adjacent mainland), who speak languages belonging to the Inuit-Aleut family.

Christy Turner's study of New World teeth supports the Greenberg and Ruhlen proposal of three separate migrations. Turner looked at the proportions of shovel-shaped incisors, a common Asian trait, in New World populations. The varying proportions fall into three distinct groupings, the same three suggested by the linguists (Turner II, 1989) (see Figure 10–6). In contrast, genetic analysis suggests that Inuit-Aleut may have split from Na-Dené in the New World (Szathmáry, 1993). The peopling of the New World may have been even more complicated. There could have been four separate migrations from the Old World, from different regions of Asia (McDonald, 1998).

Archaeological remains of early New World hunters have been found in the United States, Mexico, and Canada. For example, just south of the

A jury of visiting archaeologists at the Monte Verde site in Chile confirmed that modern humans arrived in southern South America at least 12 500 years ago.

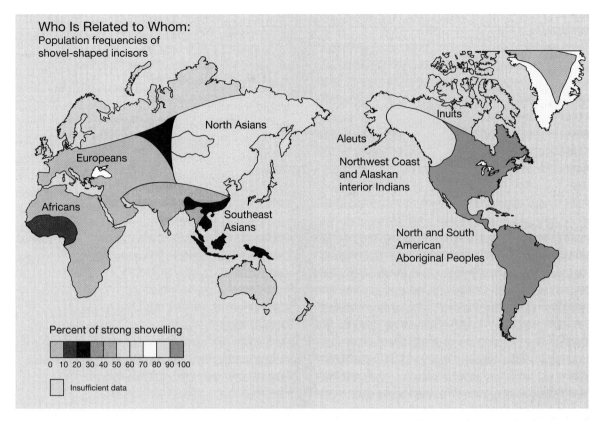

Who Is Related to Whom:
Population frequencies of
shovel-shaped incisors

North Asians

Europeans

Africans

Southeast
Asians

Inuits

Aleuts

Northwest Coast
and Alaskan
interior Indians

North and South
American
Aboriginal Peoples

Percent of strong shovelling

0 10 20 30 40 50 60 70 80 90 100

Insufficient data

Figure 10–6

Inuit and Aleuts, speakers of Na-Dené languages, and other Native American language groups differ in the frequency of shovel-shaped incisors. These genetic differences seem to reflect three waves of migration into the New World.

Source: Turner II CG. January 1987. Telltale Teeth. **Natural History** 8. Courtesy of *Natural History* magazine.

farthest reaches of the last glaciation, the area east of the Rocky Mountains known as the High Plains abounded with mammoths, bison, wild camels, and wild horses. The tools found with mammoth kills are known as the Clovis complex, which includes the Clovis projectile point as well as stone scrapers and knives and bone tools. The Clovis projectile point is large and leaf-shaped, flaked on both sides. These tools are characterized by the removal of a flake that runs longitudinally up the centre of each side. These flakes were removed by very sophisticated flaking of the base of the points, presumably to facilitate hafting to a wooden spear shaft (Wheat, 1967). Because one mammoth was found with eight Clovis points in it, there is little dispute that Clovis people hunted large game such as the mammoth (Fagan, 1991).

Recent dating places most Clovis sites in the range of 11 200 to 10 900 years ago (Hoffecker et al., 1993).

Clovis points.

The mammoth disappeared in North America about 10 000 years ago (for possible reasons, see Chapter 11), and the now-extinct large, straight-horned bison became the largest prey species of humans. The hunters of that bison used a projectile point called the Folsom point, which was much smaller than the Clovis point. Tools are also found with many other kinds of animal remains, including wolf, turtle, rabbit, horse, fox, deer, and camel, so the bison hunters obviously depended on other animals as well (Jennings, 1968). In the Rio Grande valley, the Folsom toolmakers characteristically established a base camp on low dune ridges overlooking both a large pond and broad, open grazing areas. If we assume that the pond provided water for the grazing herds, the people in the camp would have been in an excellent position to watch the herds (Judge and Dawson, 1972).

As the climate of what is now the American Southwest became drier, the animals and the cultural adaptations changed somewhat. About 9000 years ago the earlier straight-horned bison

RESEARCH FRONTIERS

When and How Did Humans Populate the New World?

On the basis of similarities in biological traits such as tooth forms and blood types, and on possible linguistic relationships, anthropologists agree that Native Americans originally came from Asia. The traditional assumption is that they came to North America from Siberia, walking across a land bridge (Beringia) that is now under water (the Bering Strait) between Siberia and Alaska. The ice sheets or glaciers that periodically covered most of the high latitudes of the world contained so much of the world's water (the ice sheets were thousands of metres thick in some places) that **Beringia** was dry land in various periods. For example, there was a land bridge for a while until the last 10 000 years or so. Since then, the glaciers have mostly melted, and the Bering "bridge" has been completely covered by a higher sea level. We now know that the Monte Verde site in Chile was occupied at least 12 500 years ago, so it would seem that there was at least one wave of human migration into the New World before then, by walking and/or perhaps in boats. Even when the last glaciers were at their fullest extent, there was still a small ice-free corridor through which people could have walked (see the diagram in this box).

It was geologically possible then for humans to have walked into the New World at various times, and they could have travelled by boat too. Parts of the Beringia land bridge were exposed from about 60 000 to 25 000 years ago. It wasn't until between 20 000 and 18 000 years ago that the land bridge was at its maximum. When did the last land bridge disappear? Until recently, it was widely believed that the land bridge was flooded around 14 000 years ago, but recent evidence suggests that walking across Beringia was still possible until about 10 000 years ago. An ice-free corridor between the Laurentide and Cordilleran ice sheets may have been present after 25 000 years ago, but that corridor is not likely to have supported big game, and permitted humans to hunt enough, until after about 14 000 years ago. So some investigators suggest that moving through the ice-free corridor to what is now south of Canada was not likely until after that time.

There is no disagreement that humans were living south of Canada around 11 000 years ago. The Clovis people, as they are called (after an archaeological site near Clovis, New Mexico), left finely shaped spear points in many locations in North America. We also have the presence of human skeletal remains after 11 000 years ago. Now that the Monte Verde site has been reliably dated, we know that there were people south of Canada earlier than the Clovis people were in New Mexico. There are other possible sites of pre-Clovis occupation as well, although many archaeologists do not agree that the presumed tools at these sites were made by humans (they could have been made by rockfalls or other natural forces) or that the sites are accurately dated. One site that may be another pre-Clovis site is the Meadowcroft Rockshelter in western Pennsylvania.

In the bottom third of a stratum that seems to date from 19 600 to 8000 years ago, the Meadowcroft site shows clear signs of human occupation—a small fragment of human bone, a spear point, and chipped knives and scrapers. If the dating is accurate, the tools would be about 12 800 years old. William Parry suggests we need to date the human bone found in the site. If the bone turns out to date from before 12 000 years ago, few anthropologists would question the conclusion that humans occupied the Meadowcroft site before the time of the Clovis people.

variety became extinct and were replaced by smaller modern forms (Wheat, 1967). Base camps began to be located farther from ponds and grazing areas and closer to streams. If the ponds were no longer reliable sources of water during these drier times, the animals probably no longer frequented them, which would explain why the hunters had to change the sites of their base camps. Not that much is known about the plant foods these people may have exploited, but on the desert fringes plant gathering may have been vital.

In Nevada and Utah, archaeologists have found milling stones and other artifacts for processing plant food (Fagan, 1989).

The Olsen-Chubbuck site, a kill site excavated in Colorado, shows the organization that may have been involved in hunting bison (Wheat, 1967). In a dry gulch dated to 6500 B.C. were the remains of 200 bison. At the bottom were complete skeletons and at the top, those of completely butchered animals. This find clearly suggests that hunters deliberately stampeded the animals into a natural

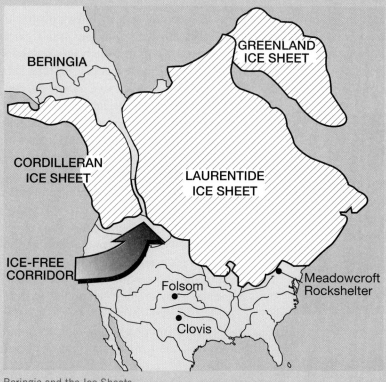

Beringia and the Ice Sheets

Source: Meltzer DK. 1993. Pleistocene Peopling of the Americas. Evolutionary Anthropology. Vol. 1. Copyright © 1993. Reprinted by permission of Wiley-Liss, Inc. a subsidiary of John Wiley and Sons, Inc.

that humans came very early to the New World by water, but there is as yet no evidence of that under water along the coast. Even if people did come early to the New World by water, they might not have survived long enough and spread widely enough to give archaeologists a chance to find their remains. There might be some remains somewhere, but that has not yet been definitely established.

Exactly when humans first came into the New World, how many migrations there were, and how they spread south of Canada are questions to which we still have only tentative answers. New evidence continues to surface regularly, so we should have firmer answers to these questions before too long. That is part of what makes research exciting. There is always something new to look for.

Sources: Hoffecker JF, Powers WG, Goebel T. 1 January 1993. The Colonization of Beringia and the Peopling of the New World. Science 46–53.

McDonald KA. 13 March 1998. New Evidence Challenges Traditional Model of How the New World Was Settled. Chronicle of Higher Education A22ff.

Parry WJ. 1998. When and How Did Humans Populate the New World? In: Ember CR, Ember M, Peregrine PN, editors. Research Frontiers in Anthropology. Upper Saddle River, NJ: Prentice Hall. Prentice Hall/Simon & Schuster Custom Publishing.

People now cross the Bering Strait by water. Could earlier humans have come to the New World the same way, before a land bridge existed? If they had come by water, instead of by walking over a land bridge and down through an ice-free corridor, there would be coastal sites with evidence of humans who travelled by water. Such sites would now be covered by water because the sea level is higher. It is conceivable then

trapùan arroyo, or steep-sided dry gully. The animals in front were probably pushed by the ones behind into the arroyo. Joe Wheat estimated that the hunters might have obtained 25 000 kilograms of meat from this one kill. If we judge from the habits of nineteenth-century Plains Indians, who could prepare bison meat to last a month, and estimate that each person would eat half a kilogram a day, the kill at the Olsen-Chubbuck site could have fed more than 1800 people for a month (they probably did not all live together throughout the year).

The hunters must have been highly organized, not only for the stampede itself, but also for butchering. It seems that the enormous carcasses had to be dragged to flat ground for that job. In addition, the 25 000 kilograms of meat and hides had to be carried back to camp (Wheat, 1967). Since a dead bison is too bulky and heavy to move whole, the kill site is usually the scene of primary butchering. This involves cutting manageable

The "river of bones" at the Olsen-Chubbuck site. These are the remains of bison that Palaeo-Indian hunters stampeded into an arroyo.

portions off the carcass and removing them for secondary butchering and processing elsewhere. The low-value portions of the skeleton are abandoned in the "kill floor," perhaps to be exposed later by the archaeologist. In this case they are overlying the unbutchered animals that got trampled under by the stampede into the trap. There are important social implications associated with all the processes required for an undertaking of this magnitude. In particular it requires large groups and thorough political integration to organize these kills and subsequently distribute the meat and hides among participants.

Although big game may have been most important on the High Plains, other areas show different adaptations. For example, Paleo-Indian people in woodland regions of what is now the United States seem to have depended more heavily on plant food and smaller game. In some woodland areas, fish and shellfish may have been a vital part of the diet (Fagan, 1989). On the Pacific coast, some Paleo-Indian people developed food-getting strategies more dependent on fish (Fagan, 1991). And in other areas, the lower Illinois River valley being one example, Palaeo-Indian people who depended on game and wild vegetable foods managed to get enough food to live in permanent villages of perhaps 100 to 150 people (Fagan, 1989).

As the climate became warmer and drier, the flora and fauna of North America changed. Megafauna, as elsewhere in the world, went extinct, and were replaced by smaller mammals, particularly deer. The availability of meat was greatly reduced—hunters could count on coming home with kilograms, not tonnes, of meat. Warmer adapted plants replaced cold adapted plants, and were used for food to replace the meat that was no longer available. Warmer adapted plants had advantages as food resources for humans over cold adapted ones because edible seeds, fruits, and nuts were more common, and often more plentiful and accessible, on the warmer adapted plants. Thus a much greater diversity of plants and animals came to be used by the Archaic peoples (Daniel, 2001).

The Archaic peoples of North America began to follow a more sedentary lifestyle. Two forms of

Archaic settlement appear to have been typical. One was a residential base camp, which would have been inhabited seasonally by several, probably related families. The other was a special-purpose camp, which would have been a short-term habitation near a particular resource or perhaps used by a group of hunters for a short period (Sassaman, 1996). On the Atlantic coast, for example, individual groups apparently moved seasonally along major river valleys, establishing summer base camps in the piedmont and winter camps near the coast. Special-purpose camps were created year-round as groups went out from the base camp to hunt and collect particular resources, such as stone for making tools (Sassaman, 1996).

One of the innovations of the Archaic peoples was the development of ground stone woodworking tools. Axes, adzes, and tools for grinding seeds and nuts become more and more common in the tool kit (Brown, 1983). This probably reflects the emergence of greater areas of forest following the retreat of the glaciers from North America, but it also demonstrates a greater reliance on forest products and, most likely, a greater use of wood and wood products. Fish and shellfish also came to be relied upon in some areas, and this too reflects the adjustment made by the Archaic peoples to the changing conditions they faced at the end of the last ice age.

Early Arctic Populations

The **Palaeo-Arctic tradition** represents the first undisputed cultural development in the Arctic, after the more tentative early occupation sites associated with the peopling of the New World. The earliest well-documented Palaeo-Arctic sites are dated from 8000 B.C. to 5000 B.C., and are identified by stone tools, including microblades and small bifaces—no bone artifacts have been found (McGhee, 1996). The Palaeo-Arctic tradition is present throughout Alaska, east into the southwestern Yukon and south to the Queen Charlotte Islands in British Columbia. Following the Palaeo-Arctic tradition comes the **Arctic Small Tool tradition**, representing the first humans to move into the eastern Canadian Arctic and Greenland. In Alaska the Arctic Small Tool tradition evolved into

the *Norton tradition,* while in the eastern Arctic it became the *Dorset culture.* The later Thule tradition developed from the Norton tradition in the area around Bering Strait and subsequently spread throughout the entire Arctic region with the exception of the Aleutian Islands (see Figure 10–7).

Arctic Small Tool Tradition

The Arctic Small Tool tradition represents a widespread phenomenon in the North American Arctic that occurred between approximately 2000 B.C. and 800 B.C. It is characterized by finely made microblades, burins, scrapers, and blades, and, more important, the bow and arrow. The Arctic Small Tool tradition does not appear to be related to the preceding Palaeo-Arctic tradition, but is most likely the product of a rapid migration of people from eastern Siberia.

Dorset. The Dorset culture was an incredibly stable Arctic culture, surviving longest in the eastern Arctic regions (Maxwell, 1985; McGhee, 1996). The Dorset subsistence pattern depended mostly on seal, caribou, muskox, and fish, but bones of walrus, polar bear, and some bird species have also been found (Maxwell, 1985; McGhee, 1996). Seal was probably primarily hunted on the sea ice or by hunting along the edge of ice floes; the Dorset do not appear to have had the equipment necessary for open-water hunting, as they probably made only small kayaks. Caribou hunting was a group effort as the herds were channelled into a small area bounded by previously constructed rows of rock piles.

Dorset technology was somewhat limited when compared with the later Thule culture. Although the Dorset possessed the kayak, they lacked the larger seagoing umiak and flotation gear of the Thule. This gear included the toggling harpoon head (that would fix the removable head into the flesh of the animal) and the bladder balloons, which enabled the Thule to hunt sea mammals on open water and to prevent the loss of their prey underwater once it had been killed. The general lack of dog bones found on Dorset sites implies that the Dorset did have sleds but that they

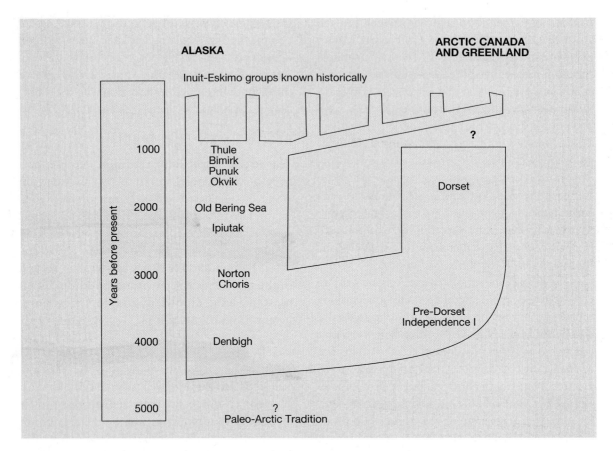

Figure 10–7 A Model of the Cultural Relationships between Early Arctic Peoples in North America

This model, proposed by Robert Park, shows the relationship between modern Inuit populations and a variety of archaeologically defined Arctic populations over the past 5000 years. In particular note that it is the Thule rather than the Dorset tradition that is the precursor to modern Arctic populations.

Source: Robert Park's webpage (**arts.uwaterloo.ca/ANTHRO/rwpark/ArcticArchStuff/ArcticIntro.html**). Reprinted with permission of Robert Park.

were pulled by hand rather than by dogs like the later Thule sleds. There are snow knives found on Dorset sites that would indicate that they did make winter snow houses like the later Thule. Other Dorset winter dwellings were probably structures built of sod blocks and roofed with skins.

Thule. The Thule represent a population migration from Alaska that brought with it a whole new technology. These included the use of metals including iron (the Dorset had made use of some cold-worked copper), which came through contact with Siberia in their Alaskan homeland (Maxwell, 1985; McGhee, 1996). In the west, some Thule groups also made use of crude ceramics, but in the eastern Arctic soapstone was utilized for bowls and cooking pots. It is from the Thule population that the modern Inuit peoples derive (Park, 1993; Park, 2000). (See Research Frontiers, *Reconstructing Thule Life: Bob Park*.)

RESEARCH FRONTIERS

Reconstructing Thule Life: Bob Park

Robert W. Park is an anthropological archaeologist at the University of Waterloo interested in the past cultures of the Far North (including the Canadian Northwest Territories, Nunavut, Greenland, and Alaska). Archaeological research in the Arctic presents a number of unique challenges, including short field seasons and excavation into permafrost (permanently frozen ground). These difficulties are compensated for by the richness of the Inuit ethnographic record, the complexity of their material culture, and the marvellous preservation of evidence sometimes provided by permafrost. The Arctic is also an incredibly vast region. Due to the large area involved and the small number of researchers working there, Arctic archaeology was until very recently mostly exploratory, trying to fill in gaps in the region's cultural history. Archaeologists rarely had the luxury of completely excavating sites, or of testing more than a very few sites within a region. When archaeologists were able to begin asking more complex questions concerning the ancient peoples of the Arctic, they had to adopt new, very different research strategies for reconstructing Arctic life.

Early in his career, Park became interested in the social and demographic characteristics of the Thule people, the immediate ancestors of the Inuit. From historic records we know that when Europeans arrived in the Arctic, large groups of Inuit would spend the winter together in a series of mobile snow-house (igloo) camps out on the sea ice. From archaeological evidence, we know that their Thule ancestors spent the winter in a quite different fashion, passing the entire winter in semi-subterranean houses on the Arctic coasts. Thule winter house sites are the most prominent archaeological remains in the Canadian Arctic, and can contain from two to more than 50 houses. However, over one-third of all known sites have three or fewer houses, and thus would have had no more than a very small population. Some archaeologists are convinced that at the larger sites the Thule wintered in comparably larger groups but, by coming up with a way of demonstrating that the Thule recycled building materials from abandoned houses into newly constructed ones, Park was able to show that only a few of the 14 houses at a site he was investigating would have been occupied during any given winter. Thus, the site was never the winter home to more than a few families. He hopes to explore further the reasons for this pronounced difference between Thule and historic Inuit settlement patterns.

In an attempt to go beyond cultural history in Arctic archaeology, Park compared the abundance of Thule toys—miniature versions of specific tools, such as hunting implements, with the proportion of full-sized, functional versions of the same types. He found that the miniature and full-sized versions of several classes of artifacts occurred in strikingly similar proportions, but with a few significant exceptions. Studying these patterns allowed him to explore differences in gender roles between children and adults in Thule culture. He was able to demonstrate that the historic Inuit practice of treating

children as "miniature adults" was practised by the Thule people as well. Intriguingly, there are hints that children in the Dorset culture did not have the same types of toys, suggesting that the experience of childhood may have been different in that earlier culture.

Sources: Park RW. 1997. Thule Winter Site Demography in the High Arctic. American Antiquity 62:2:273–284.

Park RW. 1998. Current Research and the History of Thule Archaeology in Arctic Canada. In: Smith PJ, Mitchell D, editors. Bringing Back the Past: Historical Perspectives on Canadian Archaeology. Mercury Series Paper 158. Hull: Canadian Museum of Civilization, Archaeological Survey of Canada. p 191–201.

Park RW. 1998. Size Counts: The Miniature Archaeology of Childhood in Inuit Societies. Antiquity 72:269–281.

Summary

1. Fossil remains of fully modern-looking humans have been found in Africa, the Near East, Asia, and Australia, as well as in Europe. The oldest of these fossils have been found in South Africa and may be 100 000 years old.

2. Two theories about the origins of modern humans continue to be debated among anthropologists. One, the *single-origin* hypothesis (among other names), suggests that modern humans emerged in just one part of the Old World—the Near East and, more recently, Africa have been the postulated places of origin—and spread to other parts of the Old World, superseding Neandertals and other pre-modern *H. sapiens*. The second hypothesis, the *multiregional* hypothesis, suggests that modern humans emerged in various parts of the Old World, becoming the varieties of humans we see today.

3. The period of cultural history known as the Upper Palaeolithic in Europe, the Near East, and Asia, or the Later Stone Age in Africa, dates from about 40 000 years ago to about 14 000 to 10 000 years ago. The Upper Palaeolithic is characterized by the preponderance of blades; there were also burins, bone and antler tools, and (later) microliths. In many respects, lifestyles were similar to lifestyles before. People were still mainly hunters and gatherers and fishers who probably lived in highly mobile bands. They made their camps out in the open and in caves and rock shelters.

4. The Upper Palaeolithic is also characterized by a variety of new developments: new techniques of toolmaking, the emergence of art, population growth, and new inventions such as the bow and arrow, the spear-thrower (atlatl), and the harpoon.

5. Only *H. sapiens* remains have been found in the New World. The prevailing opinion is that humans migrated to the New World over a land bridge between Siberia and Alaska in the area of what is now the Bering Strait. The prevailing view until recently was that humans were not present south of Alaska until after 15 000 years ago. Now it appears from an archaeological site called Monte Verde in Chile that modern humans got to southern South America by at least 12 500 years ago, and perhaps as much as 33 000 years ago.

6. The Palaeo-Arctic tradition represents the first undisputed cultural development in the Arctic. The earliest well-documented Palaeo-Arctic sites occur throughout Alaska, east into the southwestern Yukon and south to the Queen Charlotte Islands in British Columbia from 8000 B.C. to 5000 B.C. Following this comes the Arctic Small Tool tradition, representing the first humans to migrate into the eastern Canadian Arctic and Greenland. In Alaska, the Arctic Small Tool tradition evolved into the Norton tradition, while in the eastern Arctic it becomes the Dorset culture. The Thule tradition developed from the Norton tradition in the area around Bering Strait and later spread throughout most of the Arctic.

Glossary Terms

Arctic Small Tool tradition   (p. 229)

atlatls   (p. 219)

Aurignacian tools   (p. 215)

Beringia   (p. 226)

burin   (p. 217)

indirect percussion   (p. 217)

Mesolithic   (p. 215)

microliths   (p. 218)

mitochondrial DNA   (p. 212)

multiregional hypothesis   (p. 210)

Palaeo-Arctic tradition   (p. 229)

pressure flaking   (p. 218)

single-origin hypothesis   (p. 209)

Upper Palaeolithic   (p. 215)

Critical Questions

1. If the single-origin or "out of Africa" hypothesis is correct, by what mechanisms could one

group of *H. sapiens* have been able to replace another?

2. If modern human traits emerged in *H. erectus* populations in different areas more or less at the same time, what mechanisms would account for similar traits emerging in different regions?

3. Upper Palaeolithic cave paintings arouse our imaginations. We have described some research that tested ideas about what these paintings might mean. Can you think of other ways to understand the significance of cave art?

4. The peopling of the New World continues to be debated by archaeologists. A variety of different kinds of evidence can be used to understand how various populations are related to one another in the New World. Given the different kinds of evidence available, why is there so much debate regarding this issue?

Internet Exercises

1. Out of Africa ... or elsewhere ... or everywhere? Read the essay by the discoverer of "Lucy" at **www.actionbioscience.org/ evolution/johanson.html** and compare the out-of-Africa model with the multiregional model also presented. To what extent could there be truth to both theories, or must they conflict?

2. Take a virtual tour through the cave of Lascaux at **www.culture.gouv.fr/culture/arcnat/lascaux/ en/**. View the remarkable paintings made by Upper Palaeolithic peoples and learn how they were made. When you are done, test your knowledge with the site's questionnaire.

3. A team of experts has endorsed the findings from a site in Chile named Monte Verde suggesting that humans were in the New World earlier than traditionally thought. Look at the press release at **www.nationalgeographic.com/ society/ngo/events/97/monteverde/dallas .html**. Then visit **www.civilization.ca/archeo/ hnpc/npvol21e.html** to view a presentation on the Paleo-Eskimos. Compare the information, particularly the dates, found at the two sites.

4. Stone tools played an important role in human cultural evolution. Visit **http://rubens.anu.edu .au/student.projects/tools/homepage.html** to see the various forms of Australian stone tools and summarize your findings.

Suggested Reading

A special edition of Scientific American, "A New Look at Human Evolution" (August 2003), presents a variety of papers by various experts on the latest controversies in human evolution.

Lahr MM. 1996. The Evolution of Modern Human Diversity. Cambridge: Cambridge University Press. This book looks at the evolution of anatomically modern humans and how earlier Archaic populations differ from modern *H. sapiens* populations. The multiregional and single-origin models are discussed in light of the current evidence.

Maxwell MS. 1985. Prehistory of the Eastern Arctic. Orlando, FL: Academic Press. A classic examination of the archaeological evidence for the distribution and development of populations in the eastern Arctic.

McGhee R. 1996. Ancient People of the Arctic. Vancouver: University of British Columbia Press. This book examines the life of the first peoples to enter and inhabit the North American Arctic. It uses an analysis of hundreds of artifacts, including art and tools, to paint a picture of Palaeo-Eskimo life.

Schledermann P. 1996. Voices in Stone: A Personal Journey into the Arctic Past. Komatik Series, No. 5. Calgary: The Arctic Institute of North America of the University of Calgary. A personal account of the discovery of archaeological materials in the High Arctic, examining not only the archaeology of Arctic populations but also recounting life in the field with constant threats of sudden, violent storms or curious polar bears.

11 HUMAN VARIATION

CHAPTER OUTLINE

In the preceding chapter we discussed the emergence of people like ourselves, *Homo sapiens sapiens*. Just as the cultures of those human beings differed in some respects, so do the cultures of peoples in recent times, as we will see in the chapters that follow. But anthropologists are also concerned with how recent human populations physically resemble or differ from each other, and why.

In any given human population, individuals vary in external features such as skin, hair, and eye colour, or height, and in internal features such as blood type or susceptibility to a disease. If you measure the frequencies of such features in different populations, you will typically find differences on average from one population to another. So, for example, some populations are typically darker in skin colour than other populations.

Why do these physical differences exist? They may be largely the product of differences in genes. Or they may be largely due to growing up in a particular environment, physical and cultural. Or perhaps they are the result of an interaction between environmental factors and genes.

We turn first to the processes that may singly or jointly produce the varying frequencies of physical traits in different human populations. Then we discuss specific differences in external and internal characteristics and how they might be explained. Finally, we close with a critical examination of racial classification and whether it helps or hinders the study of human variation.

Processes in Human Variation

Natural Selection

Mutations, or changes in the structure of a gene, are the ultimate source of all genetic variation. Because different genes make for greater or lesser chances of survival and reproduction, natural selection results in genes associated with increased survival becoming more frequent in a population over time. How adaptive a gene or trait is depends on the environment; what is adaptive in one environment may not be adaptive in another. For example, in the chapter on evolution, we discussed the advantage that dark moths had over light moths when certain areas of England became industrialized. Predators could not easily see the darker moths against the newly darkened trees, and these moths soon outnumbered the lighter variety. Similarly, human populations live in a great variety of environments, so we would expect natural selection to favour different genes and traits in those different environments. As we shall see, variations in skin colour and body build are among the many features that can be at least partly explained by how natural selection works in different environments.

The type of natural selection in the moth example is called **directional selection** because a particular trait seems to be positively favoured and the average value shifts over time toward the adaptive trait. Figure 11–1 shows the effects of directional selection over time. But there can also be **normalizing selection**. In this type of selection the average value does not change, but natural selection removes the extremes (Harrison et al., 1988). An example is the birth weight of babies. Both very low birth weights and very high birth weights are disadvantageous and would be selected against. Directional selection and normalizing selection both assume that natural selection will either favour or disfavour genes, but there is a third possibility—balancing selection (Durham, 1991:122). **Balancing selection** occurs when a heterozygous combination of alleles is positively favoured even though a homozygous combination is disfavoured. Later in this chapter we discuss a trait that apparently involves balancing selection—sickle-cell anemia—which is found in persons of West African ancestry, among other populations.

Natural selection does not account for variation in frequencies of neutral traits—that is, traits that do not seem to confer any advantages or disadvantages on their carriers. The sometimes different and sometimes similar frequencies of neutral traits in human populations may result, then, from genetic drift or gene flow.

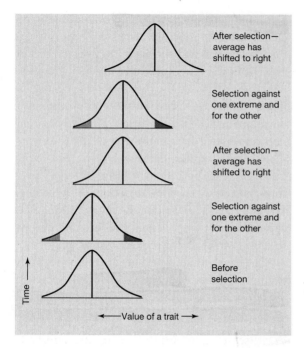

Figure 11–1

Directional selection shifts the average value of a continuous trait (such as darkness of skin colour) in a population over time. The shaded grey area represents the individuals who are selected against in a particular environment; the blue represents the individuals who are selected for in that same environment. So, for example, in a very sunny environment, light skin colour would be selected against and dark skin colour would be selected for. Gradually, darker skin would become more common.

Source: Relethford J. 1990. The Human Species: An Introduction to Biological Anthropology. Mountain View, CA: Mayfield. p 130, 132.

Genetic Drift

The term **genetic drift** refers to various random processes that affect gene frequencies in small, relatively isolated populations. Genetic drift is the result of *population fission*—that is, the breaking apart of a previously large population into smaller, distinct groups. Thus, genetic drift may be the result of natural barriers (such as mountain ranges or oceans) or, in humans, cultural barriers (such as religious practices, or marriage rules). In a small population, over time genetic drift may result in a neutral or nearly neutral gene becoming more or less frequent simply by chance (Harrison et al., 1988).

One variety of genetic drift, called *founder effect*, occurs when a small group recently derived from a larger population migrates to a relatively isolated location (Harrison et al., 1988). If a particular gene is absent just by chance in the migrant group, the descendants are likely also to lack that gene, assuming that the group remains isolated. Similarly, if all members of the original migrant group carried a particular gene just by chance, their descendants would also be likely to share that gene. Isolation can occur for physical reasons, such as when a group moves to a previously uninhabited place and does not return. The populations that travelled over the Bering land bridge from Asia to North America could not readily return when the sea level rose. Or the isolation can occur for cultural reasons. For example, in 1918, there was a mass migration of Hutterites to Alberta and Manitoba by the descendants of the 100 Hutterite families who had settled in South Dakota by 1879. The fact that the families kept to themselves probably explains why some of their gene frequencies differ from what is found in both Germany and the broader population of both Canada and the United States.

Gene Flow

Gene flow is the process whereby genes pass from one population to another through mating and reproduction. Unlike the other processes of natural selection and genetic drift, which generally increase the differences between populations in different environments, gene flow tends to work in the opposite direction—it decreases differences between populations. Two populations at opposite ends of a region may have different frequencies of a particular gene, but the populations located between them have an intermediate gene frequency because of gene flow between them. The variation in gene frequency from one end of the region to the other is called a **cline**. In Europe, for example, there is a cline in the distribution of blood type B, which gradually diminishes in frequency from east to west (Harrison et al., 1988:198).

Gene flow may occur between distant as well as close populations. Long-range movements of people, to trade or raid or settle, may result in gene flow. But they do not always do so.

Influence of the Physical Environment

Natural selection may favour certain genes because of certain physical environmental conditions, as in the case of the moths in England. But the physical environment can sometimes produce variation even in the absence of genetic change. As we shall see, climate may influence the way the human body grows and develops, and therefore some kinds of human variation may be explainable largely as a function of environmental variation. Moreover, access to certain nutrients and exposure to certain diseases may vary from one physical environment to another, and this variation may also influence how one population differs physically from another. But the influence of the physical environment might also be modified by the cultural environment.

Influence of the Cultural Environment

Culture may allow humans to modify their environments to some extent, and such modifications may lessen the likelihood of genetic adaptation. For example, the effects of cold may be modified by the cultural traits of living in houses, harnessing energy to create heat, and clothing the body to insulate it. In these cultural ways, we alter our "microenvironments." Iron deficiency may be overcome by the cultural trait of cooking in iron pots. If a physical environment lacks certain nutrients, people may get them by the cultural trait of trading for them; for example, trading for salt has been common in world history. Culture can also influence the direction of natural selection. For example, the cultural practice of dairying seems to have increased the frequency of genes that allow adults to digest milk (Durham, 1991).

In the next section we discuss some aspects of human (biological) variation that involve one or more of the processes responsible for human variation.

Biological Diversity in Human Populations

While human adaptability to varying environmental conditions is a long-standing theme in anthropology, it is difficult to adequately define the term. In the broadest sense of the word, *adaptation* can refer to the basic biocultural flexibility of humans in responding to their environment. Ways in which humans adapt are through learned behaviours, species-wide physiological changes, and population-specific genetic characteristics (Harrison et al., 1988; Stinson, 1992).

The most noticeable physical variations among populations are those that are external, on the surface—body build, facial features, skin colour, and height. No less important are internal variations, such as variation in susceptibility to different diseases and differences in the ability to produce certain enzymes.

We begin our survey with some physical features that appear to be strongly linked to variation in climate, particularly variation in temperature, sunlight, and altitude.

Body Build and Facial Construction

Scientists have suggested that the body build of many birds and mammals may vary according to the temperature of the environment in which they live. Bergmann and Allen, two nineteenth-century naturalists, suggested some general rules for animals, but it was not until the 1950s that researchers began to examine whether these rules applied to human populations (Harrison et al., 1988; Hanna et al., 1989). **Bergmann's rule** describes what seems to be a general relationship between body size and temperature: The more slender populations of a species inhabit the warmer parts of its geographic range, and the more robust populations inhabit the cooler areas.

D. F. Roberts's studies of variation in mean body mass of human populations in regions with widely differing temperatures have provided support for Bergmann's rule (Roberts, 1953; Garn, 1971; Roberts, 1978). Roberts discovered that the

Jumping Samburu dancers in northern Kenya have the long-limbed, lean body type that is often found in equatorial regions. Such a body type provides more surface area in relation to body mass, and thus may facilitate the dissipation of body heat.

relatively shorter in the cooler areas of a species's range than in the warmer areas. Research comparing human populations tends to support Allen's rule (Roberts, 1953).

The rationale behind these theories is that the long-limbed, lean body type often found in equatorial regions provides more surface area in relation to body mass and thus facilitates the dissipation of body heat. In contrast, the shorter-limbed body type found among residents of cold regions promotes retention of body heat because the surface area relative to body mass is less. The build of the Inuit appears to exemplify Bergmann's and Allen's rules. The relatively large bodies and short legs of the Inuit may be adapted to the cold temperatures in which they live.

It is not clear whether differences in body build between populations are due solely to natural selection of different genes under different conditions of cold or heat. Some of the variation may be induced

lowest body mass was found among residents of areas with the highest mean annual temperatures, and vice versa. Figure 11–2 shows the relationship between body mass of males and average annual temperature for four different geographic populations. Although the slope of the relationship is slightly different for each group, the trend is the same—with colder temperatures, mass is greater. Looking at the general trend across populations (see the "Total" line), we see that where the mean annual temperatures are about freezing (0°C; 32°F), the average body mass for males is about 65 kilograms; where the mean annual temperatures are about 25°C (77°F), male body mass is, on average, about 50 kilograms.

Allen's rule refers to another kind of variation in body build among birds and mammals: Protruding body parts (for example, limbs) are

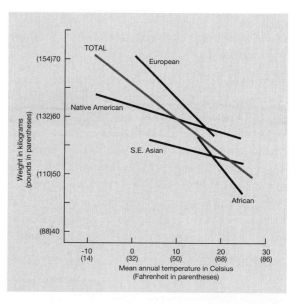

Figure 11–2 Relationship between Body Mass (Weight) of Males and Average Annual Temperature for Four Major Population Groups

Source: Roberts DF. 1953. Body Weight, Race, and Climate. Figure 2. *American Journal of Physical Anthropology* 11:553–538. In: Jones S, Martin R, Pilbeam D. 1992. *The Cambridge Encyclopedia of Human Evolution*. New York: Cambridge University Press. p 47. Reprinted with the permission of Cambridge University Press.

This Inuit father and son illustrate Allen's rule. Both have relatively large bodies and short limbs, which help them maintain body heat in the cold climate they inhabit.

during the life span of individuals (Harrison et al., 1988). Alphonse Riesenfeld provided experimental evidence that extreme cold can affect body proportions during growth and development. Rats raised under conditions of extreme cold generally showed changes that resemble characteristics of humans in cold environments. These cold-related changes included shortening of the long bones, consistent with Allen's rule (Riesenfeld, 1973).

Like body build, facial structure may also be affected by environment. Riesenfeld found that the facial width of rats increased in cold temperatures and their nasal openings grew smaller (Riesenfeld, 1973). Because the rats raised in cold environments were genetically similar to those raised in warmer environments, we can confidently conclude that environment, not genes, brought about these changes in the rats. How much the environment directly affects variation in the human face is not clear. We do know that variation in climate is associated with facial variation. For example, people living in the humid tropics tend to have broad, short, flat noses, whereas people living in climates with low humidity (with cold or hot temperatures) tend to have long, thin noses. A narrow nose may

be a more efficient humidifier of drier air than a broad nose (Weiner, 1954; Steegman Jr., 1975; Larsen, 1998).

Skin Colour

Human populations obviously differ in average skin colour. Many people perceive skin colour as reflecting "racial" differences and sometimes treat others differently solely on this basis. But anthropologists, in addition to being critical of prejudice, also note that skin colour is not a good indicator of ancestry. For example, extremely dark skin is found most commonly in Africa. However, there are natives of southern India whose skin is as dark as or darker than that of many Africans. Yet these people are not closely related to Africans, either genetically or historically.

How can we explain the wide range of skin colours among the peoples of the world? The colour of a person's skin depends on both the amount of dark pigment, or melanin, in the skin and the amount of blood in the small blood vessels of the skin (Harrison et al., 1988). Despite the fact that there is still much to understand about the genetics of skin colour, we do have some theories that may partly account for variation in skin colour.

The amount of melanin in the skin seems to be related to the climate in which a person lives. **Gloger's rule** states that populations of birds and mammals living in warmer climates have more melanin, and therefore darker skin, fur, or feathers, than do populations of the same species living in cooler areas. On the whole, this association with climate holds true for people as well as for other mammals and birds.

The populations of darker-skinned humans do live mostly in warm climates, particularly sunny climates (Figure 11–3). Dark pigmentation seems to have at least one specific advantage in sunny climates. Melanin protects the sensitive inner layers of the skin from the sun's damaging ultraviolet rays. In fact, when someone gets a suntan, this is a product of the body's natural defence mechanism to produce more melanin to protect the skin from damage by solar radiation. Therefore, dark-skinned people living in sunny areas are safer from sunburn and skin cancers than are light-skinned people. Dark skin may also confer other important biological advantages in tropical environments, such as greater resistance to tropical diseases (Polednak, 1974; Branda and Eaton, 1978).

What, then, might be the advantages of light-coloured skin? Presumably, there must be some benefits in some environments; otherwise, human populations would all tend to have relatively dark skin. Although light-skinned people are more susceptible to sunburn and skin cancers, the ultraviolet radiation that light skin absorbs also facilitates the body's production of vitamin D. Vitamin D helps the body incorporate calcium and thus is necessary for the proper growth and maintenance of bones. Too much vitamin D, however, can cause illness. Thus, the light-coloured skin of people in temperate latitudes maximizes ultraviolet penetration, perhaps ensuring production of sufficient amounts of vitamin D for good health, whereas the darker skin of people in tropical latitudes minimizes ultraviolet penetration, perhaps thereby preventing

These women in Kerala, India, have a great deal of melanin in their skin. Similar skin colouring is found in people in much of Africa and the Pacific, areas close to the equator. This suggests that skin colour is an adaptation to the amount of sunlight in the locality.

illness from too much vitamin D (Loomis, 1967). Light skin may also confer another advantage in colder environments: It is less likely to be damaged by frostbite (Post et al., 1975).

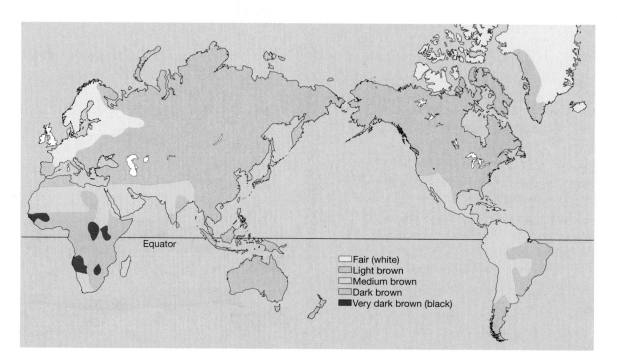

Figure 11–3 Variation in Skin Colour

Adaptation to High Altitude

Oxygen constitutes 21 percent of the air we breathe at sea level. At high altitudes, the percentage of oxygen in the air is the same, but because the barometric pressure is lower, we take in less oxygen with each breath (Stini, 1975). We breathe more rapidly, our hearts beat faster, and all activity is more difficult. The net effects are discomfort and a condition known as **hypoxia**, or oxygen deficiency.

If high altitude presents such difficulties for many human beings, how is it that populations numbering in the millions can live out their lives, healthy and productive, at altitudes of 2000 metres, 3000 metres, or even 5000 metres? Populations in the Himalayas and the Andes have adapted to their environments and do not display the symptoms suffered by low-altitude dwellers if and when they are exposed to high altitudes. Moreover, high-altitude dwellers have also come to terms physiologically with extreme cold, deficient nutrition, strong winds, rough countryside, and intense solar radiation (Mazess, 1975).

Early studies of Andean high-altitude dwellers found that they differed in certain physical ways from low-altitude dwellers. Compared with low-altitude dwellers, high-altitude Andean Indians had larger chests and greater lung capacity, as well as more surface area in the capillaries of the lungs (which was believed to facilitate the transfer of oxygen to the blood) (Greksa and Beall, 1989). Early researchers thought that genetic changes had allowed the Andeans to maximize their ability to take in oxygen at the lower barometric pressure of their high-altitude environment. Recent research, however, has cast some doubt on this conclusion. It appears now that other populations living at high altitudes do not show the Andean pattern of physical differences. In the Himalayas, for example, low-altitude dwellers and high-altitude dwellers do not differ in chest size or lung size, even though both groups show adequate lung functioning (Greksa and Beall, 1989).

Thus, current research does not suggest that high-altitude living requires biological adaptations that are purely genetic. In fact, some evidence suggests that humans who grow up in a high-altitude environment may adapt to hypoxia during their lifetimes, as they mature. For example, Peruvians who were born at sea level but who grew up at high altitudes developed the same amount of lung capacity as people who spent their entire lives at high altitudes (Frisancho and Greksa, 1989). Consistent with a presumed environmental effect, the children of high-altitude Peruvians who grow up in the lowlands do not develop larger chests. As with other traits that have been studied, it appears that life experiences can have profound effects on how the body grows.

Height

Studies of identical twins and comparisons of the height of parents and children suggest that heredity plays a considerable role in determining height (Eveleth and Tanner, 1990), so genetic differences must at least partly explain average height differences between populations. For example, Figure 11–4 shows the pattern of height versus age for Toronto schoolchildren, from the late nineteenth century to the early and middle twentieth century (Hoppa and Garlie, 1998). The data clearly show a positive **secular trend**—change over time—toward increased attained height for age from the earliest to most recent data, reflective of a global trend toward increased height and reduced age of sexual maturity over the last several centuries.

The considerable variation in average height among human populations may be partly explained by temperature differences. The Dutch of Europe are among the tallest populations in the world on average, and the Mbuti in central Africa are among the shortest (Bogin, 1988). We already know that mass is related to mean annual temperature (Bergmann's rule). Body mass is also related to height (taller people are likely to be heavier). So, since the taller (heavier) Dutch live in a cooler climate, some of the population variation in height would appear to involve adaptation to heat and cold (Harrison et al., 1988). Other factors besides heat and cold must also be operating, however, because tall and short peoples can be found in most areas of the world.

Many researchers think that poor nutrition and disease lead to reduced height and body mass. In many parts of the world, children in higher social

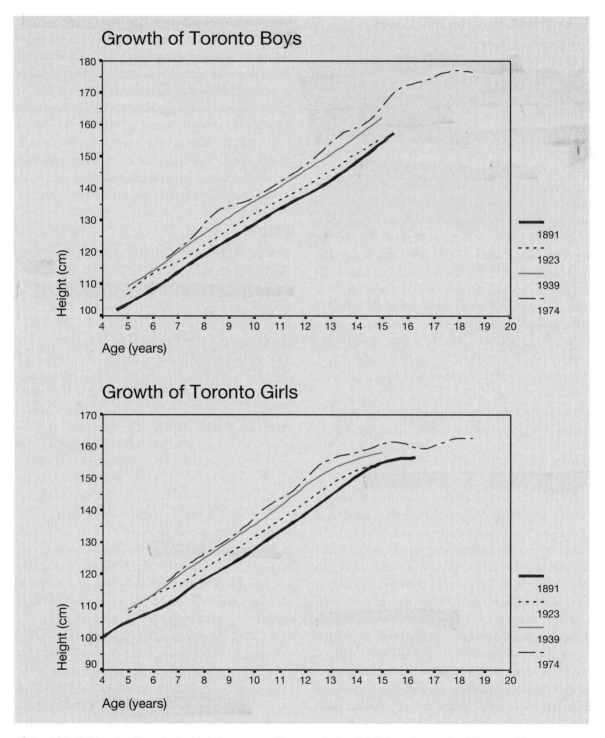

Figure 11–4 Secular Trends in Height among Toronto Schoolchildren from the Nineteenth to Twentieth Centuries

Source: Hoppa RD, Garlie TN. 1998. Secular Trends in Heights of Children during the Last Century. *Annals of Human Biology* 25(6): 553–561. Published by Taylor and Francis Ltd. **www.tandf.co.uk/journals.**

In recent times there has been a dramatic increase in average height, which may be due to one or more environmental factors. Here we see a Chinese American girl who is taller than her mother and almost as tall as her father.

classes are taller on the average than children in lower social classes (Harrison et al., 1988) and this difference is more marked in economically poorer countries (Huss-Ashmore and Johnston, 1985) where the wealth and health differences between the classes are particularly large. During times of war and poor nutrition, children's stature often decreases. For example, in Germany during World War II, the stature of children 7 to 17 years of age declined (as compared with similar data over previous periods), despite the fact that stature had generally increased over time (Harrison et al., 1988).

More persuasive evidence for the effects of poor nutrition and disease comes out of longitudinal studies of the same individuals over time. For example, Reynaldo Martorell found that children in Guatemala who had frequent bouts of diarrhea were on the average over 3 centimetres shorter at 7 years of age than children without frequent

diarrhea (1980). Although malnourished or diseased children can catch up in their growth, follow-up research on Guatemalan children suggests that if stunting occurs before 3 years of age, stature at age 18 will still be reduced (Martorell et al., 1991).

As we noted earlier, in several areas of the world, people have been getting taller. What accounts for this recent trend toward greater height? Several factors may be involved. Researchers have generally agreed that improvements in health and nutrition in communities have likely contributed to the observed changes in patterns of growth (Tanner, 1966, 1992; Hauspie et al., 1996). Tanner's extensive review concluded that the positive secular trend in growth for many countries began in the nineteenth century, during the period of increased industrialization and subsequent improvements in socioeconomic conditions (Tanner, 1966). However, others have noted that there are secular changes in height that predate the health and nutritional improvements of this time. Further, some studies have observed no secular shifts in the height of populations even where such improvements have occurred (Meredith, 1976). In short, both genetic and environmental factors seem to be responsible for differences in human size.

Susceptibility to Infectious Diseases

Certain populations seem to have developed inherited resistances to certain infectious diseases; that is, populations repeatedly decimated by certain diseases in the past now have a high frequency of genetic characteristics that ameliorate the effects of these diseases. As Arno Motulsky (1971) pointed out, if there are genes that protect people from dying when they are infected by one of the diseases prevalent in their area, these genes will tend to become more common in succeeding generations.

Infectious diseases seem to follow this pattern among human populations. When a disease enters a population that has not been previously exposed to it, or has not had exposure for a considerably long time, this often results in what is called a **virgin soil epidemic**. In other words, because there is no previous immunity within a portion of the population, the disease tends to affect all members of the group equally, and can be extremely dangerous. The 1918 influenza *pandemic* that affected populations around the world is a good example. Other examples include new diseases brought by the explorers to the New World. We tend to think of measles as a childhood disease that kills virtually no one, and we now have a vaccine against it. But when first introduced into populations, the measles virus can kill large numbers of people. In 1949, the Tupari of Brazil numbered about 200 people. By 1955, two-thirds of the Tupari had died of measles introduced into the tribe by rubber gatherers in the area (Motulsky, 1971). Large numbers of people died of measles in epidemics in the Faeroe Islands in 1846, in Hawaii in 1848, in the Fiji Islands in 1874, and among the Canadian Inuit very recently. It is possible that where mortality rates from measles are low, populations have acquired a genetic resistance to death from this disease (Motulsky, 1971).

More recently diseases like the West Nile virus and SARS have had similar impacts on many populations. In North America, Toronto had the largest outbreak of SARS (severe acute respiratory syndrome) in the spring of 2003 (Naylor et al., 2004; Svoboda et al., 2004). In Toronto, 225 residents met the case definition of SARS, and all but three travel-related cases were linked to the original patient, who had returned to Toronto from a trip to Hong Kong (Svoboda et al., 2004). The disease spread to more than half of Toronto's acute care hospitals, and undiagnosed cases among patients caused a resurgence, or a second phase, of the outbreak. In total, Toronto Public Health investigated 2132 potential cases of SARS, identified 23 103 contacts of SARS patients as requiring quarantine, and logged 316 615 calls on its SARS hotline (Svoboda et al., 2004). Despite the relatively low and restricted spread among the Canadian population, the SARS outbreak had a significant psychological and economic impact (Blendon et al., 2004).

But why is a population susceptible to a disease in the first place? The epidemiologist Francis Black suggests that lack of genes for resistance is not the whole answer. A high degree of

Permanent settlements and high population densities allow diseases to spread rapidly and produce epidemics. Here shoppers at a supermarket in China wear masks in the hope of preventing the spread of SARS.

genetic homogeneity in the population may also increase susceptibility (Black, 1992). A virus grown in one host is pre-adapted to a genetically similar new host and is therefore likely to be more virulent in the new host. For example, the measles virus adapts to a host individual; when it replicates, the forms that the host cannot kill are those most likely to survive and continue replicating. When the virus passes to a new host *with similar genes*, the pre-adapted virus is likely to kill the new host. If, on the other hand, the next host is very different genetically, the adaptation process starts all over; the virus is not so virulent at first because the host can kill it. Populations that recently came to an area, and that had a small group of founders (as was probably true for the first Native Americans and the Polynesian seafarers who first settled many islands in the Pacific), tended to have a high degree of genetic homogeneity. Therefore, epidemic diseases introduced by Europeans (such as measles) would be likely to kill many of the natives within the first few years after contact. It is estimated that 56 million people died in the New World after contact with Europeans, mostly because of introduced diseases such as smallpox and measles.

Most researchers agree that non-genetic factors may also partly explain differential resistance to infectious disease. Increasingly, anthropologists have become aware that human behaviour plays an important role in the distribution and spread of infectious diseases. Differences in most disease patterns are, in fact, largely the result of cultural differences in behaviours and not biological variation (Dunn and Janes, 1986; Inhorn and Brown, 1990; Sattenspiel, 1990). For example, Ann Herring and colleagues have been exploring the impact of socio-cultural behaviours associated with changing patterns of disease and mortality in central Canadian subarctic Cree populations during the nineteenth and early twentieth centuries. Among the Western James Bay Cree at Moose Factory, a clearly seasonal pattern of epidemic diseases in this period can be observed. This reflects the seasonal socio-economic pattern of life that existed among these people. In the winter, the community dispersed in the small family units to trap furs, with population density reduced and contact among individuals minimized. However, during the summer, families congregated around the Hudson's Bay Company post, and increased population numbers and density, coupled with more inter-community travel, led to epidemic outbreaks of a variety of diseases like measles, whooping cough, and influenza (Hoppa, 1998; Herring and Hoppa, 1999). In fact, in modelling the patterns of travel—where people travelled to and when, how often, and how long they stayed—between communities during the 1918 influenza pandemic, Lisa Sattenspiel and Ann Herring observed that social organization and responses to the epidemic were more important than movement patterns between communities for explaining the differences in the impact of this virgin soil epidemic on the three study communities (Sattenspiel and Herring, 1998). Epidemics of infectious disease may occur only if many people live near each other.

Early hunters and gatherers lived in small, mobile bands that seldom came into contact with other human groups. While they would have been susceptible to parasitic infections as well as non-specific infections, the high mobility of these groups would have made them relatively safe from diseases transmitted by humans. With little contact between the different groups, it would have been difficult for any human-transmitted disease to

survive and spread. With the domestication of plants and animals, increase in sedentary life, and increased overall population size and density (discussed in the next chapter), human beings became susceptible to a new range of diseases that they had been able to avoid in the past. Infectious diseases that required large populations to maintain themselves were now able to do so. As a consequence of humans and animals living in close proximity to each other and domesticated animals, easy transmission of diseases between both humans and animals alike was facilitated.

Sickle-Cell Anemia

Another biological variation is an abnormality of the red blood cells known as **sickle-cell anemia**, or **sicklemia**. This is a condition in which normal, disk-shaped red blood cells assume a crescent (sickle) shape when deprived of oxygen. The sickle-shaped red blood cells do not move through the body as readily as normal cells, and thus cause more oxygen deficiency and damage to the heart, lungs, brain, and other vital organs. In addition, the red blood cells tend to "die" more rapidly, and the anemia worsens still more (Durham, 1991).

Sickle-cell anemia is caused by a variant form of the genetic instructions for hemoglobin, the protein that carries oxygen in the red blood cells (Durham, 1991). Individuals who have sickle-cell anemia have inherited the same allele (Hb^S) from both parents and are therefore *homozygous* for that gene. Individuals who receive this allele from only one parent are *heterozygous*; they have one Hb^S allele and one allele for normal hemoglobin (Hb^A). Heterozygotes generally will not show the full-blown symptoms of sickle-cell disease, although in some cases a heterozygous individual may have a mild case of anemia. A heterozygous person has a 50 percent chance of passing on the sickle-cell allele to a child. And if the child later mates with another person who is also a carrier of the sickle-cell allele, the statistical probability is that 25 percent of their children will develop sickle-cell anemia. Without advanced medical care, most individuals with two Hb^S alleles are unlikely to live more than a few years (Durham, 1991).

Why has the allele for sickle-cell persisted in various populations? If people with sickle-cell anemia do not usually live to reproduce, we would expect a reduction in the frequency of Hb^S to near zero through the process of *normalizing selection.* But the sickle-cell allele occurs fairly often in some parts of the world, particularly in the wet tropical belt of Africa, where frequencies may be between 20 and 30 percent, and in Greece, Sicily, and southern India (Harrison et al., 1988).

Because the sickle-cell gene occurs in these places much more often than expected, researchers in the 1940s and the 1950s began to suspect that heterozygous individuals (who carry one Hb^S allele) might have a reproductive advantage in a malarial environment (Durham, 1991). If the heterozygotes were more resistant to attacks of malaria than the homozygotes for normal hemoglobin (who get the Hb^A allele from both parents), the heterozygotes would be more likely to survive and reproduce, and therefore the recessive Hb^S allele would persist at a higher than expected frequency in the population. This kind of outcome is an example of *balancing selection* (Madigral, 1989).

A number of pieces of evidence support the "malaria theory." First, geographic comparisons show that the sickle-cell allele tends to be found where the incidence of malaria is high (see Figure 11–5). Second, as land in the tropics is opened to yam and rice agriculture, the incidence of the sickle-cell allele also increases. The reason seems to be that malaria, carried principally by the *Anopheles gambiae* mosquito, becomes more prevalent as tropical forest gives way to more open land where mosquitoes can thrive in warm, sunlit ponds. Indeed, even among peoples of similar cultural

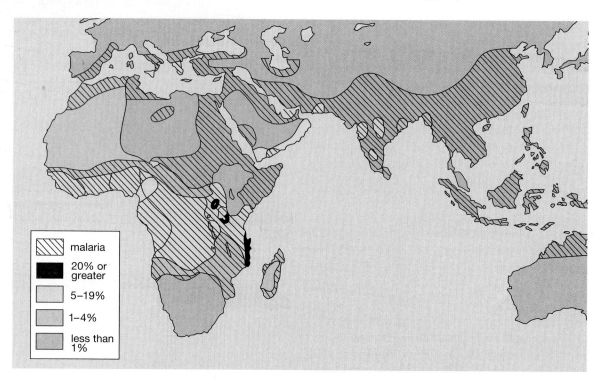

Figure 11–5 Geographic Distribution of Sicklemia and Its Relationship to the Distribution of Malaria

This map shows the percentage of the population infected with sickle-cell anemia, and the areas where malaria is found.

Source: Buettner-Janusch J. 1973. Physical Anthropology: A Perspective. New York: Wiley. © 1973 by John Wiley & Sons, Inc. Reprinted by permission of John Wiley & Sons, Inc.

👀

backgrounds, the incidence of the sickle-cell allele increases with greater rainfall and surpluses of water. Third, children who are heterozygous for the sickle-cell trait tend to have fewer malarial parasites in their bodies than do homozygous normal individuals, and they are more likely to survive (Madigral, 1989). The sickling trait does not necessarily keep people from contracting malaria, but it greatly decreases the rate of mortality from malaria—and in evolutionary terms, the overall effect is the same (Motulsky, 1971). Fourth, if there is no balancing selection because malaria is no longer present, we should find a rapid decline in the incidence of the sickle-cell allele. Indeed, we find such a decline in populations with African ancestry. Those who live in malaria-free zones of the New World have a much lower incidence of sickle-cell anemia than do those who live in malarial regions of the New World (Diamond, 1993).

Hb^S is not the only abnormal hemoglobin to have a distribution related to malaria. It seems that a number of abnormal hemoglobins may be much more widespread because of the advantage heterozygotes have against the disease. For example, another abnormal hemoglobin, Hb^E, occurs in populations from India through to Southeast Asia and New Guinea where malaria occurs, but Hb^S is not that common. Why should heterozygotes have resistance to malaria? One possibility is that malarial parasites are less able to survive in an individual's blood with some normal and some abnormal hemoglobin. Abnormal hemoglobin cells are more delicate and don't live as long, so they cannot readily support malarial parasites (Molnar, 1998).

Type II Diabetes

Type II diabetes or *non-insulin-dependent diabetes mellitus (NIDDM)*, unlike insulin-dependent diabetes, tends to manifest itself in adult patients as a result of a sedentary lifestyle, chronic obesity, and excess sugar intake. The disease is particularly common in certain Aboriginal populations, including First Nations people in Canada. In 1962 J. V. Neel suggested that a "thrifty gene" might exist in greater proportion in certain human populations (Neel, 1962). This gene may have held survival value

in periods of food shortage, but under a modern westernized lifestyle characterized by food abundance, high carbohydrate intake, and sedentary living patterns, it would lead to increased obesity and diabetes incidence (see Research Frontiers, *Obesity, Hypertension, and Diabetes: Health Consequences of Modernization?*). Critics have noted that this theory assumes that carbohydrate intake exceeds daily energy requirements. The early occupants of North America subsisted in Arctic or subarctic environments, living on protein- and fat-based diets with few carbohydrates (Ritenbaugh and Goodby, 1989; Szathmáry, 1990; Szathmáry, 1994). Alternative metabolic pathways to provide energy may have been favoured in them by natural selection (Young et al., 2000b). Other explanations continue to be offered. Hegele observed the presence of a genetic mutation among Aboriginal people in northern Ontario that is highly predictive of Type II diabetes (Hegele, 2001). Alternatively, it has been suggested that Type II diabetes is the result of fetal malnutrition (Benyshek et al., 2001).

Of all the chronic conditions, Type II diabetes (NIDDM) has been prominent in the epidemiological literature because of its high prevalence among many Canadian and other Aboriginal populations (see Figure 11–6). According to a report from Statistics Canada in 1991, the prevalence of diabetes among native groups in Canada is as follows: 8.5 percent of North American Aboriginal peoples on reserves and settlements; 5.3 percent of North American Aboriginal peoples off reserves; 5.5 percent of Métis people; and 1.9 percent of Inuit people (MacMillan et al., 1996). Of those with the disease, about two-thirds are women (Health Canada, 1997). Compared with non-Aboriginal rates in Canada, diabetes is between two and five times more prevalent among Aboriginal people (Young et al., 1990; Waldram et al., 1995). Inuit people are an exception to this pattern, with rates that are currently below the national average. However, there is some evidence that these rates may be on the rise, and that over time may be comparable to other Aboriginal groups (Health Canada, 1997).

Up until the 1940s, diabetes was virtually unknown among Aboriginal populations (Chase,

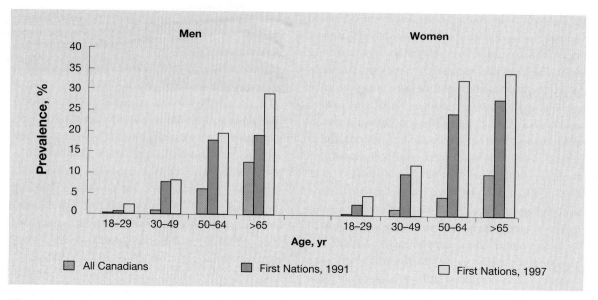

Figure 11–6 Prevalence of Type II Diabetes, by Age Group, among All Canadians (1994), and First Nations People (1991 and 1997)

Source: Young TK, Reading J, Elias B, O'Neil JD. 2000. Type 2 Diabetes Mellitus in Canada's First Nations: Status of an Epidemic in Progress. Canadian Medical Association Journal 163(5):561–566. Copyright © Canadian Medical Association; reprinted with permission.

1937; Szathmáry, 1994; MacMillan et al., 1996). However, in 1983 a study in the Sioux Lookout Zone observed a prevalence rate of 2.8 percent for the disease. A decade later, it had risen to 3.8 percent, a pattern of increase that has been observed by a variety of studies (Young et al., 1985; Fox et al., 1994). For chronic illnesses of long duration, such as diabetes, the prevalence can be expected to increase over time as a function of survival of people with diabetes, and aging of the population (Health Canada, 1997).

Although Type II diabetes is classed as "adult-onset," concern has been raised by researchers who have observed increased incidence of the disease in recent years in Aboriginal children as young as 5 to 8 years of age (Dean et al., 1992; Harris et al., 1996; Harris et al., 1997; Young et al., 2000a). According to Health Canada, the number of Aboriginal children in Manitoba with a diagnosis of diabetes rose from 20 in 1990 to 51 in 1995. A similar pattern was observed in the Sioux Lookout Zone, with diagnoses in children rising from 18 in 1994 to 52 in 1997 (Health Canada, 1997). In both instances, girls outnumbered boys by more than

five to one among the children with this condition (Health Canada, 1997).

Diabetes, and in particular Type II diabetes (NIDDM), has become perhaps one of the most important health concerns of First Nations people today. Understanding the impact (Daniel et al., 1999; Rodrigues et al., 1999; Bruce, 2000; Jacobs et al., 2000; Young et al., 2000b) and addressing perception of health and disease among Aboriginal communities (Daniel et al., 1999; Bruce, 2000) are a critical facet of dealing with this disease. In addressing the health problems associated with diabetes, the First Nations have increased their leadership role in the First Nations and Inuit Health Programs (FNIHP). In 1994, the National Aboriginal Diabetes Association (NADA) was created, bringing together representatives of First Nations and Inuit national, regional, and tribal organizations.

Race and Racism

For as long as any of us can remember, countless aggressive actions—from fistfights to large-scale riots and civil wars—have stemmed from tensions

RESEARCH FRONTIERS

Obesity, Hypertension, and Diabetes: Health Consequences of Modernization?

Contact with the West first brought medical devastation to many populations previously unexposed to European illnesses. However, with the acceptance of modern medical care throughout much of the developing world, infant mortality has declined and life expectancies have gone up. These achievements have largely come about because of the control of major epidemic diseases, such as smallpox (now eradicated), cholera, yellow fever, syphilis, and tuberculosis, as well as the inoculation of children against childhood diseases. Improvements in medical health are by no means uniform. The AIDS epidemic, which we discuss in Chapter 14, is spreading throughout much of the world. Overall deaths from infectious diseases may have declined, but other health problems have increased. As more people survive into older ages, problems of hypertension, heart disease, cancer, and diabetes increase. Some of the increase in these chronic diseases is due to the aging of populations, but much of it appears to be due to changes in lifestyle that accompany modernization.

A good deal of research has focused on the Samoans of the South Pacific who traditionally depended on root and tree crop horticulture. As did many other people in the modern world, Samoans increasingly moved to urban areas, worked for wages, and started buying most of their food. Researchers reported substantial increases, within a relatively short time, in rates of hypertension, diabetes, and obesity across a wide range of age groups. For example, in 1990 about two-thirds of American Samoans were severely overweight, up substantially from the situation in the 1970s. And Samoans from more

rural areas show less hypertension and physiological signs of stress. Among the lifestyle changes thought to be responsible are less physical activity and changes in diet to low-fibre, high-calorie foods. Stress may also increase as more individuals buy material things and status goods without having the economic resources to support them.

What about genetic factors? Could some genetic predisposition be interacting with modernization to create obesity in the Samoan population? One possibility is referred to as the "thrifty" gene. The geneticist James Neel suggested that individuals who have very efficient metabolisms and who can store calories in fatty tissue are most apt to survive and reproduce in environments with frequent famines or chronic food shortages. In time, populations in such environments would have a high prevalence of individuals with "thrifty" genes. What happens though when such individuals no longer need to exercise much or have access to high-calorie foods? Neel suggested that adult-onset diabetes might result, a scenario that is consistent with the increase in diabetes in Samoa and other parts of Polynesia. It is also consistent with the increase in obesity and hypertension.

The "thrifty" gene theory does not pertain just to the Samoans and other Polynesian populations. Probably most human populations used to have to cope with food uncertainty in the past. If the food supply increases with modernization, but it is accompanied by a reduction in physical activity and a switch to high-calorie diets, then increases in obesity, diabetes, and hypertension may frequently accompany modernization. Understanding

When food is not plentiful, the "thrifty gene" helps people survive on less. But when the food supply becomes plentiful and reliable, people may become overweight, as in the Marquesas.

both biological and cultural factors is essential in helping populations adapt to conditions of urban life.

Sources: Allen JS, Cheer SM. 1996. The Non-Thrifty Genotype. Current Anthropology 37:831–842.

Bindon JR, Crews DE. 1993. Changes in Some Health Status Characteristics of American Samoan Men: Preliminary Observations from a 12-Year Follow-up Study. American Journal of Human Biology 5:31–37.

Bindon JR, Knight A, Dressler WW, Crews DE. 1997. Social Context and Psychosocial Influences on Blood Pressure among American Samoans. American Journal of Physical Anthropology 103:7–18.

McGarvey ST. 1994. The Thrifty Gene Concept and Adiposity Studies in Biological Anthropology. Journal of the Polynesian Society 103:29–42.

Pearson JD, James GD, Brown DE. 1993. Stress and Changing Lifestyles in the Pacific: Physiological Stress Responses of Samoans in Rural and Urban Settings. American Journal of Human Biology 5:49–60.

World Bank. World Development Report 1995. Workers in an Integrating World. Oxford: Oxford University Press.

and misunderstandings between various groups commonly referred to by many as races. Race has become such a common term that most of us take the concept for granted, not bothering to consider what it does, and does not, mean. We may talk about the "human race," which means that all humans belong to the same breeding population. Yet we are often asked to check a box to identify our particular "race." We discuss first how biologists sometimes use the term *race*; then we turn to why many biological anthropologists and others now conclude that the concept of race does not usefully apply to humans. We discuss how racial classifications are largely social constructions that have been used to justify the exploitation and even execution of certain categories of people.

The Biological Fallacy of Race

Biological variation is not uniformly distributed in any species. While all members of a species can

"We don't consider ours to be an underdeveloped country so much as we think of yours as an overdeveloped country."

Source: 10 January 1970. Saturday Review. Courtesy of *Saturday Review*.

potentially interbreed with others, most matings take place within smaller groups or breeding populations. Through the processes of natural selection and genetic drift, populations inhabiting different geographic regions will exhibit some differences in biological traits. When differences within a species become sufficiently noticeable, biologists may classify different populations into different *varieties*. Unfortunately, as applied to humans, racial classifications are the product of social and cultural beliefs that some certain groups of people (often classed as different "races") are innately inferior to others. Historically, a number of populations have been subjected to discrimination on the basis of this concept, which unfortunately continues to be prevalent among many members of today's populations. However, biological anthropologists and others have argued that the concept cannot be applied to human biological differences.

A second reason for not applying racial classification to humans is that humans have exhibited so much interbreeding that different populations are not clearly classifiable into discrete groups that can be defined in terms of the presence or absence of particular biological traits (Marks, 1994; Shanklin, 1994). In fact, racial classification is extremely problematic because we know there is more physical, physiological, and genetic diversity *within* a single geographic group that might be called a race (for example, Africans) than there is *between* such supposed groups. For example, sub-Saharan Africans vary more among themselves than they do in comparison with people elsewhere (Brooks et al., 1993). It is for this very reason that recent criticisms of the Human Genome Project have emerged. These critics assert that the project has failed to adequately sample from populations that contain a large proportion of total human genome diversity (Dukepoo, 1998). Therefore, many argue that the concept of race is not scientifically useful for describing human biological variation.

Race as a Social Construct

If race is not a useful device for classifying humans, why is it so widely used? Racial classifications should be recognized for what they are—

social categories to which individuals are assigned, by themselves and others, on the basis of supposedly shared biological traits.

If racial categories are just social categories, we need to ask why they were invented. Part of the answer may be a desire to separate "my" group from others. People tend to be ethnocentric, to view their culture as better than other cultures. Therefore, racial classifications reflect the same tendency to divide "us" from "them." For example, when German-speaking Hutterites settled in parts of Canada in the early twentieth century, they were viewed with suspicion when World War I broke out. Similarly, Japanese Canadians became "the enemy" in World War II, even though many of them were second-generation Canadians.

We do know that racial classifications have often been, and still are, used by certain groups to justify discrimination, exploitation, or genocide. Recent examples include the campaigns of "ethnic cleansing" in the Balkans. The most heinous twentieth-century example, of course, was Hitler's vision of the blond-haired, blue-eyed, white-skinned "Aryan race" dominating the world, to which end he and others committed mass genocide. It is estimated that 65 million Jews, Slavs, and others were murdered in the Holocaust (Friedman, 1980). But who are the Aryans? Technically, Aryans are any people, including the German-speaking Jews in Hitler's Germany, who speak one of the Indo-European languages. The Indo-European languages include such disparate modern tongues as Greek, Spanish, Hindi, Polish, French, Icelandic, German, Gaelic, and English. And many Aryans speaking these languages have neither blond hair nor blue eyes. Similarly, all kinds of people may be Jews, whether or not they descend from the ancient Near Eastern population that spoke the Hebrew language. There are light-skinned Danish Jews and darker Jewish Arabs. One of the most orthodox Jewish groups in the United States is based in New York City and is composed entirely of African Americans.

The arbitrary and social basis of most racial classifications becomes apparent when you compare how they differ from one place to another. Consider, for example, what used to be thought about the races in South Africa. Under apartheid, the system of racial segregation and discrimination, someone with mixed "white" and "black" ancestry was considered "coloured." However, when important people of African ancestry from other countries would visit South Africa, they were often considered "white." Chinese were considered "Asian" but the Japanese, who were important economically to South Africa, were considered "white" (Ross, 1998). Biologically speaking, this makes no sense, but socially it was another story (Marks, 1994).

The Myths of Racism

Race and Civilization. Many persons hold the racist viewpoint that the biological inferiority of certain groups, which they call "races," is reflected in the supposedly "primitive" quality of their cultures. They argue that the "developed" nations are "white" and the "developing" nations are not. (We put terms like "white," which are used as racial categories, in quotes to indicate the problematic nature of the categories.) But to make such an argument ignores much of history. As will be discussed in Chapter 13, many of today's so-called "developing nations"—primarily in Asia, Africa, and South America—had developed complex and sophisticated civilizations long before European nations expanded and acquired considerable power. The advanced societies of the Shang dynasty in China, the Mayans in Mesoamerica, and the African empire of Ghana were all founded and developed by "non-whites."

Between 1523 and 1028 B.C., China had a complex form of government, armies, metal tools and weapons, and production and storage facilities for large quantities of grain. The early Chinese civilization also had writing and elaborate religious rituals (Carrington Goodrich, 1959). From A.D. 300 to 900, the Mayans were a large population with a thriving economy. They built many large and beautiful cities in which were centred great pyramids and luxurious palaces (Coe, 1966). According to legend, the West African civilization of Ghana was founded during the second century A.D. By A.D. 770, the time of the Sonniki rulers, Ghana had developed two capital cities—one Muslim and the other non-Muslim—each with its own ruler and both supported largely by Ghana's lucrative gold market (Bartlett Thompson, 1966).

Considering how recently northern Europeans developed cities and central governments, it seems odd that some "whites" should label others as backward in terms of historical achievement, or biologically inferior in terms of capacity for civilization. But racists, both "white" and "non-white," choose to ignore the fact that many populations have achieved remarkable advances in civilization. Most significant, racists refuse to believe that they can acknowledge the achievements of another group without in any way downgrading the achievements of their own.

Race, Conquest, and the Role of Infectious Disease.
There are those who would argue that Europeans' superiority accounted for their ability to colonize much of the world during the last few hundred years. But it now appears that Europeans were able to dominate at least partly because many native peoples were susceptible to diseases brought by the Europeans (McNeill, 1976). Earlier, we discussed how continued exposure to epidemics of infectious diseases, such as tuberculosis and measles, can cause succeeding generations to acquire a genetic resistance to death from such diseases. Smallpox had a long history in Europe and Africa; genetic resistance eventually made it mostly a survivable childhood disease. But in the New World it was quite another story. Cortés and the conquistadors were inadvertently aided by smallpox in their attempt to defeat the Aztecs of Mexico. In 1520, a member of Cortés's army unwittingly transmitted smallpox to the natives. The disease spread rapidly, killing at least 50 percent of the population, and so the Aztecs were at a considerable disadvantage in their battle with the Spaniards (Motulsky, 1971).

It is also known that there are associations between some infectious diseases and different blood types. For example, for the ABO blood system, certain disease organisms have ABO antigens on their cell walls, conferring some resistance on individuals who manufacture the appropriate antibodies, and increasing the susceptibility of people whose blood type matches the antigens.

Examples include antigen A for syphilis and smallpox, and antigen O for bubonic plague.

Race and Intelligence.
In the nineteenth century, European white supremacists tried to find scientific justification for what they felt was the genetically inherited mental inferiority of "blacks." They did this by measuring skulls. It was believed that the larger the skull, the greater the cranial capacity and the bigger (hence, also better) the brain. However, we know that cranial capacity alone is not an appropriate measure of intellectual ability. For example, as discussed in Chapter 9, Neandertals had a cranial capacity that exceeded the modern range. Although the skull-measuring mania quickly disappeared and is no longer considered as a way to measure intelligence, other "facts" have been used to imply intellectual superiority of certain groups of people. Attempts to document differences in intelligence among the so-called "races" have a fairly long history. Two of the most recent attempts are the 1994 book *The Bell Curve*, by Americans Charles Murray and Richard Herrnstein (see Current Issues, *Differences in Average IQ Scores—What Do They Mean?* on page 254), and the publications of Philippe Rushton, a professor of psychology at the University of Western Ontario.

Rushton has proposed a genetic evolutionary theory for what he claims are consistent observations for East Asians and their descendants having larger brains, greater intelligence, more sexual restraint, slower rates of maturation, and a greater propensity to abide by the law and mores of social organization than do Europeans and their descendants, who in turn have higher scores on those "traits" than do Africans and their descendants (Rushton, 1995; Rushton, 1996). These observations are based on his synthesis of the international literature. One of the fundamental flaws in Rushton's arguments is, of course, his reliance on dividing the human species into three simple biological groups. As we have discussed earlier, these so-called "races" cannot be applied universally, and the biological and cultural diversity that is represented in each of these three groups makes any kind of comparison useless. Finally, while brain size and maturity can be readily quantified, the other traits are at best difficult to quantify, and would be highly ethnocentric in their construction.

To test Rushton's ideas, Peregrine, Ember, and Ember (2000) used information about the 186 cultures composing the Standard Cross-Cultural Sample (Peregrine et al., 2000). They examined 26 separate behaviours that Rushton predicted would differ among the "races." Contrary to Rushton's predictions, there were no differences between supposed "racial" groups for the most part. For only one behaviour were there the differences that Rushton predicted (frequency of homicide, which Rushton predicted would be higher among "Negroids" and lower among "Mongoloids," does indeed show this pattern), and the results for five behaviours (sexual restraint, acceptance of rape, degree of political integration, level of social stratification, and level of technological specialization) demonstrated a pattern that was the *opposite* of what Rushton predicted. So Rushton's gross division of humans into these "races" does not generally predict variation in human behaviour. His ideas appear plainly wrong and do not support the concept that it is scientifically useful to distinguish human "races" (Lieberman, 1999).

Despite his occasional media attention, Rushton's work has been dismissed by the general anthropological and broader scientific community. Unfortunately, it continues to be exploited by groups interested in promoting racist sociopolitical agendas, and therefore needs to be continually addressed within the public arena.

Critics of genetic predisposition to intelligence within the so-called "races" point to at least two problems. First, there is widespread recognition now that IQ tests are probably not accurate measures of "intelligence" because they are probably biased in favour of the subculture of those who construct the tests. That is, many of the questions on the test refer to things that middle-class children are familiar with, thus giving such children an advantage (Smith, 1974). So far, no one has come up with a "culture-fair," or bias-free, test. There is more agreement that, although the IQ test may not measure "intelligence" well, it may predict scholastic success or how well a

child will do in the primarily "middle-class"-oriented school system (Dobzhansky, 1973).

A second major problem with a purely genetic interpretation of the IQ difference is that many studies also show that IQ scores can be influenced by the social environment. Economically deprived children, regardless of skin colour, will generally score lower than affluent middle-class children. And training of children with low IQ scores clearly improves their test scores (Dobzhansky, 1973).

The geneticist Theodosius Dobzhansky has reminded us that conclusions about the causes of different levels of achievement on IQ tests cannot be drawn until all people have equal opportunities to develop their potentials. He stressed the need for an open society operating under the democratic ideal, where all persons are given an equal opportunity to develop whatever gifts or aptitudes they possess and choose to develop (Boyd and Richerson, 1985).

Cultural Diversity and Adaptation

Even though culture is learned and not genetically inherited like biological evolution, cultural practices can influence the evolution of a population. The frequency of certain genetic alternatives is likely to increase over time if those genetic traits increase their carriers' chances of survival and reproduction. Similarly, the frequency of a new learned behaviour will increase over time and become customary in a population if the people with that behaviour are most likely to survive and reproduce. Thus, if a culture is adapted to its environment, culture change should also be adaptive—not always, to be sure, but commonly.

One of the most important differences between cultural evolution and genetic evolution is that individuals often can decide whether or not to accept and follow the way their parents behave or think, whereas they cannot decide whether or not to inherit certain genes. When enough individuals change their behaviour and beliefs, we say that the culture has changed. Therefore, it is possible for culture change to occur much more rapidly than genetic change. It is particularly when circumstances change that individuals are likely to try new ideas or behaviours.

Whatever the motives for humans to change their behaviour, the theory of natural selection suggests that new behaviour is not likely to become cultural or remain cultural over generations if it has harmful reproductive consequences, just as a genetic mutation with harmful consequences is not likely to become frequent in a population (Campbell, 1965; Boyd and Richerson, 1985; Durham, 1991). Still, we know of many examples of culture change that seem maladaptive—the switch to bottle-feeding rather than nursing infants, which may spread infection because contaminated water is used, or the adoption of alcoholic beverages, which may lead to alcoholism and early death. In the last few hundred years, the major stimulus to culture change, adaptive and maladaptive, has been the new social environment produced by the global spread of people from western European societies and the new globalization that is spreading American cultural values around the world.

Many of the cultural changes in the world from A.D. 1500 to the present have been caused, directly or indirectly, by the dominance and expansion of Western societies (McNeill, 1967). Thus, much of the cultural change in the modern world has been externally induced, if not forced. This is not to say that cultures are changing now only because of external pressures; but externally induced changes have been the changes most frequently studied by anthropologists and other social scientists. Most of the external pressures have come from Western societies, but not all. Eastern societies, such as Japan and China, have also stimulated culture change. And the expansion of Islamic societies after the eighth century A.D.

CURRENT ISSUES

Differences in Average IQ Scores—What Do They Mean?

In late 1994, a new American book reignited controversy about the relationship between "race" and intelligence. It seemed to give evidence of African American "inferiority," but there were problems with the evidence. The book was *The Bell Curve*, by Charles Murray and Richard Herrnstein. It purported to show that the intelligence of an individual was largely inherited and unchangeable throughout the lifespan, that an individual's success was largely based on intelligence, and that African Americans were likely to remain at the bottom of society because they had less intelligence than European Americans. Herrnstein and Murray appealed to a lot of studies to buttress their argument, but their argument was still faulty.

If you look at the average scores on many standard intelligence tests, you might conclude, as racists have, that African Americans are less intelligent than European Americans. The average scores are different between the two groups; African Americans typically have lower scores. But what does this average difference mean? Herrnstein and Murray, like many before them, fail to distinguish between a measure, such as a particular IQ test, and what is supposedly being measured, intelligence. If a test only imperfectly measures what it purports to measure, lower average IQ scores merely mean lower scores on that particular IQ test; they do not necessarily reflect lower intelligence. There are many reasons why some people might not do well on particular kinds of IQ tests. For example, the way the tests are administered may affect performance, as may lack of familiarity with the format or the experiences and objects referred to. The test might also not measure particular kinds of intelligence such as social "smarts" and creativity.

If African Americans were really less intelligent, more than their average IQ scores would be lower. The whole frequency distribution of their individual scores should also be lower—they should have fewer geniuses and more retarded individuals. That is, the bell-shaped curve showing how their scores are distributed should range lower than the curve for other Americans, and African Americans should also have proportionately fewer scores at the very high end of the scale. But neither expectation is confirmed. According to research by Henry Grubb, the proportion of African Americans at the low end of the scale is not significantly different from the proportion of European Americans. And Grubb and Andrea Barthwell report that, on the basis of IQ tests administered by Mensa (a high-IQ society), the proportion of African Americans at the high end of the scale is not different from the proportion of European Americans. So the available evidence suggests that African Americans have lower average test scores, but not fewer

made for an enormous amount of culture change in the Near East, Africa, Europe, and Asia.

Measured in terms of travel time, the world today is much smaller than it has ever been. It is now possible to fly halfway around the globe in the time it took people less than a century ago to travel to the next province. In the realm of electronic communications, the world is even smaller. Although modern transportation and communications facilitate the rapid spread of some cultural characteristics to all parts of the globe, it is highly unlikely that all parts will end up the same. Cultures are bound to retain some of their original characteristics or develop some distinctive new adaptations. Even though television has diffused around the world, local people prefer to watch local programming when it is available. And even when people all over the world watch the same program, they may interpret it in very different ways. People are not just absorbing the messages they get; they may resist them or rework them (Kottak, 1996).

Future research on contemporary culture change should increase our understanding of how and why various types of change are occurring. And if we can increase our understanding of culture change in the present, we should be better able to understand similar processes in the past. Another lead to understanding change in the past is the large number of cross-cultural correlations between a cultural variation and its presumed causes that have been discovered since the 1970s (Ember and Levinson, 1991). All cultures have changed over time. Therefore, the variations we see are the products of change, and the "predictors" of

very high scores or more very low scores (proportionately). Why, then, might their average scores be lower?

Grubb and Barthwell point out that the average scores are not lower on all IQ tests. One test that shows no significant difference is an untimed version of an intelligence test using pictures (the pictorial reasoning test). You can administer the pictorial reasoning test in one of two ways—timed or untimed. A person must finish the test by the end of a prescribed, relatively short time; or the test-taker can respond to the questions without any time limit. African Americans have lower average scores than European Americans on the timed version of the pictorial reasoning test (although not as much lower as on other tests) but not on the untimed version. This finding suggests that a timed test measures or reflects more than just intelligence. What else besides intelligence might affect performance on a timed IQ test?

Familiarity with a particular format or the content could increase performance on a timed test. So could familiarity or comfort with speed. Although they do not have evidence for how African Americans feel about speed, Grubb and Barthwell cite a study that shows that discomfort with speed can affect performance on an IQ test. The study cited was conducted by A. Lieblich and S. Kugelmass and compared Jewish and Arab children in Israel. The Arab children scored lower than the Jewish children on the parts of a standard Wechsler intelligence test that were timed, but the Arab children scored the same or even higher on the parts that were untimed. Lieblich and Kugelmass concluded that the Arabs' poorer performance on the timed tests might reflect a cultural abhorrence of speed; "Time is of the Devil" is an Arab saying. Speed is not highly valued in some cultures. If unfamiliarity or discomfort with speed can affect performance on an IQ test, then clearly the test is not measuring intelligence only.

Critics have pointed to many other problems with the evidence presented in *The Bell Curve*. But the fundamental problem is the same as with all attempts to use differences in average IQ scores to make judgments about the capability of different groups. IQ tests may not adequately measure what they purport to measure. If they do not—and there are good reasons to think they do not—it is scientifically and morally incorrect to conclude that differences in average scores are caused by genetic differences in intelligence.

Sources: Grubb HJ. 1987. Intelligence at the Low End of the Curve: Where Are the Racial Differences? Journal of Black Psychology 14:25–34.

Grubb HJ, Barthwell AG. 1996. Superior Intelligence and Racial Equivalence: A Look at Mensa. Paper presented at 1996 annual meeting of the Society for Cross-Cultural Research.

Herrnstein RJ, Murray C. 1994. The Bell Curve: Intelligence and Class Structure in American Life. New York: Free Press.

Kamin LJ. February 1995. Behind the Curve. Scientific American 99–103.

those variations may suggest how and why the changes occurred.

The Future of Human Variation

Laboratory fertilization of an ovum, subsequent transplantation of the resulting embryo, and successful birth have been accomplished with humans and non-humans. *Cloning*—the exact reproduction of an individual from cellular tissue—has been achieved with frogs and sheep. And *genetic engineering*—the substitution of some genes for others—is increasingly practised on non-human organisms. Indeed, as we discussed in the chapter on evolution, genetic engineering is now used on humans to eliminate certain disorders that are produced by defective genes. What are the implications of such practices for the genetic future of humans? Will it really be possible someday to control the genetic makeup of our species? If so, will the effects be positive or negative?

It is interesting to speculate on the development of a "perfect human." Aside from the serious ethical question of who would decide what the perfect human should be like, there is the serious biological question of whether such a development might in the long run be detrimental to the human species, for what is perfectly suited to one physical or social environment may be totally unsuited to another. The collection of physical, emotional, and intellectual attributes that might be "perfect" in the early twenty-first century might be inappropriate by the end of the century (Haldane, 1963). Even defects such as the sickle-cell trait may confer advantages under certain conditions, as we have seen.

In the long run, the perpetuation of genetic variability is probably more advantageous than the creation of a "perfect" and invariable human being. In fact, biodiversity is crucial to the survival of all organisms. In the event of dramatic changes in the world environment, absolute uniformity in the human species might be an evolutionary dead end. Such uniformity might lead to the extinction of the human species if new conditions favoured genetic or cultural variations that were no longer present in the species. Perhaps our best hope for maximizing our chances of survival is to encourage the persistence of many aspects of human variation, both biological and cultural (Simpson, 1971).

Summary

1. Physical variation—variation in the frequencies of physical traits—from one human population to another is the result of one or more of the following factors: natural selection, genetic drift, gene flow, the influence of the physical environment, and the influence of the social or cultural environment.

2. Some physical variations in human populations involve genetic variation; other variations, including body build, facial construction, and skin colour, may be adapted to variation in climate. Still other variations may be adapted partially to variation in cultural environment.

3. Most biological anthropologists today agree that race is *not* a useful way of referring to human biological variation because human populations do not unambiguously fall into discrete groups defined by a particular set of biological traits. Physical traits that are adaptive vary *clinally*, which makes it meaningless to divide humans into discrete racial entities. Rather it is suggested that racial classifications are mostly social categories that are presumed to have a biological basis.

4. Perhaps the most controversial aspect of racial discrimination is the relationship supposed between racial categories and intelligence. Attempts have been made to show, by IQ tests and other means, the innate intellectual superiority of one racial category over another. But there is doubt that IQ tests measure intelligence fairly. Because evidence indicates that IQ scores are influenced by both genes and environment, conclusions about the causes of

differences in IQ scores cannot be drawn until all the people being compared have equal opportunities to develop their potentials.

5. Even though customs are not genetically inherited, cultural adaptation may be somewhat similar to biological adaptation. Traits (cultural or genetic) that are more likely to be reproduced (learned or inherited) are likely to become more frequent in a population over time. And if culture is generally adapted to its environment, then culture change should also be generally adaptive.

Glossary Terms

Allen's rule   (p. 238)

balancing selection   (p. 235)

Bergmann's rule   (p. 237)

cline   (p. 236)

directional selection   (p. 235)

gene flow   (p. 236)

genetic drift   (p. 236)

Gloger's rule   (p. 239)

hypoxia   (p. 241)

normalizing selection   (p. 235)

secular trend   (p. 241)

sickle-cell anemia (sicklemia)   (p. 245)

Type II diabetes   (p. 247)

virgin soil epidemic   (p. 243)

Critical Questions

1. Why is skin colour used more often than hair or eye colour or body proportions in "racial" classifications?

2. If Europeans had been more susceptible to New World and Pacific diseases, how might the world be different today?

3. What kinds of cultural items might most easily be borrowed by another culture, and why do you think so?

4. Why might an increasing understanding of cultural variation also provide an increasing understanding of culture change in the past?

5. How might studies of natural selection help increase tolerance of other populations?

Internet Exercises

1. Explore **www.ghr.nlm.nih.gov/ghr/disease/sicklecellanemia** to find out what groups are most likely to have sickle-cell anemia (a group of inherited red blood cell disorders). Briefly discuss the cause and symptoms of this inherited disorder.

2. The site on Genetics and Public Issues (**www.csu.edu.au/learning/ncgr/gpi/about_gpi.html**) contains information on current issues. If humans were cloned, how similar do you think the clones would be to each other? Using the search words "nature" and "nurture," find an article that explores this question and summarize its position.

3. Use the Human Genome Site at **www.ornl.gov/TechResources/Human_Genome/home.html** to either review your knowledge of molecular genetics or explore some of the ethical issues that may arise.

Suggested Readings

Bogin B. 1999. Patterns of Human Growth. Second edition. Cambridge: Cambridge University Press. A new, revised edition of this classic monograph, providing a synthesis of the evolution of the human growth pattern. Chapters explore the physiological, environmental, and cultural factors related to population variation in growth, and the genetic and endocrine factors that regulate individual growth patterns.

Cavalli-Sforza LL, Menozzi P, Piazza A. 1994. The History and Geography of Human Genes. Princeton, NJ: Princeton University Press. The first full-scale attempt at mapping the global distribution of genes in over 1800 populations. The authors use genetic data integrated with data from geography, ecology, archaeology, physical anthropology, and linguistics to address a range of issues in human history that have been long debated.

Durham WH. 1991. Coevolution: Genes, Culture, and Human Diversity. Stanford, CA: Stanford University Press. Intended as an update of Dobzhansky's *Mankind Evolving*, this book discusses recent theory and research on how the interaction of genes and culture helps determine human diversity.

Frisancho AR. 1993. Human Adaptation and Accommodation. Revised edition. Ann Arbor: University of Michigan Press. A survey of research on human adaptations to heat, cold, humidity, high altitude, solar radiation, under- and over-nutrition, and the westernization of dietary habits.

Gould SJ. 1996. The Mismeasure of Man. New York: W.W. Norton and Company. This revised edition of the problems of categorizing biological diversity includes a critique of Herrnstein and Murray's *The Bell Curve*.

Mascie-Taylor CGN, Lasker GW. 1991. Applications of Biological Anthropology to Human Affairs. New York: Cambridge University Press. This book discusses how biological anthropologists study fertility, childhood development, adult health, degenerative diseases, and aging.

McNeill WH. Plagues and Peoples. 1976. Garden City, NY: Doubleday Anchor. A historian suggests that epidemics have crucially affected the history of various societies all over the world.

Molnar S. 1998. Human Variation: Races, Types, and Ethnic Groups. Fourth edition. Upper Saddle River, NJ: Prentice Hall. A basic text on human biological diversity. Considers the biological principles underlying human variation and various aspects of that variation.

Molnar S, Molnar IM. 2000. Environmental Change and Human Survival. Upper Saddle River, NJ: Prentice Hall. Ecological perspective on the interactions of human behaviour and the environment, tracing demographic and cultural developments through a series of demographic landmarks.

Moran EF. 2000. Human Adaptability: An Introduction to Ecological Anthropology. Second edition. Boulder, CO: Westview Press. This revised edition covers non-genetic strategies of human adaptation to a variety of environments, and addresses the impact of political economy, global environment change, demography, and health in the study of human ecology.

Waldram JB, Herring DA, Young TK. 1995. Aboriginal Health in Canada: Historical, Cultural and Epidemiological Perspectives. Toronto: University of Toronto Press. This book explores the historical development of contemporary health issues among Canadian Aboriginal populations, arguing that health is a product of a complex bio-cultural web of factors.

ORIGINS OF FOOD PRODUCTION AND SETTLED LIFE

12

Toward the end of the Upper Palaeolithic, people seem to have obtained most of their food from hunting migratory herds of large animals, such as wild cattle, antelope, bison, and mammoths. These hunter-gatherers were probably highly mobile in order to follow the migrations of the animals. Beginning about 14 000 years ago, people in some regions began to depend less on big-game hunting and more on relatively stationary food resources, such as fish, shellfish, small game, and wild plants (see Figure 12–1). In some areas, particularly Europe and the Near East, the exploitation of local, relatively permanent resources may account for an increasingly settled way of life. The cultural period in Europe and the Near East during which these developments took place is called the *Mesolithic*. Other areas of the world show a similar switch to what is called *broad-spectrum* food collecting, but they do not always show an increasingly settled lifestyle.

We see the first clear evidence of a changeover to food production—the cultivation and domestication of plants and animals—in the Near East, about 8000 B.C. (Miller, 1992). This shift, called the "Neolithic revolution," occurred, probably independently, in other areas of the Old and New Worlds within the next few thousand years. In the Old World there were independent centres of domestication in China, Southeast Asia (what is now Malaysia, Thailand, Cambodia, and Vietnam), and Africa around 6000 B.C. (MacNeish, 1991; Crawford, 1992; Phillipson, 1993). In the New World there were centres of cultivation and domestication in the highlands of Mesoamerica

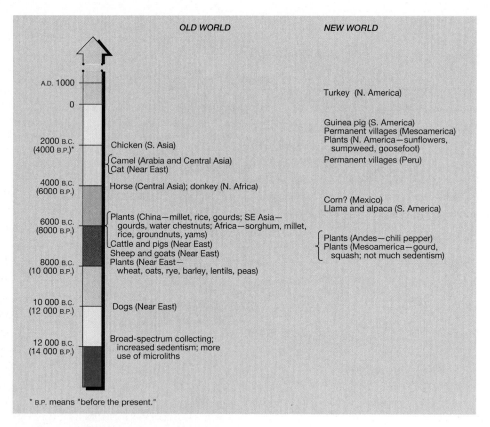

Figure 12–1 The Evolution of Domestication

Source: Dates for animal domestication are from Clutton-Brock J. 1992. Domestication of Animals. In: Jones J, Martin R, Pilbeam D, editors. The Cambridge Encyclopedia of Human Evolution. New York: Cambridge University Press. p 384. Copyright © 1992. Reprinted by permission of Cambridge University Press.

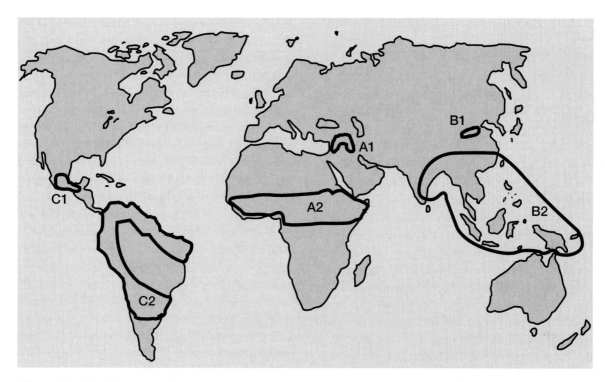

Figure 12–2 Original Locations of the World's Main Food Crops

The world's main food crops were originally domesticated in different regions: (A1) barley, wheat, peas, lentils, and chickpeas in the Near East; (A2) various millets, sorghum, groundnuts, yams, dates, coffee, and melons in Africa; (B1) various millets and rice in north China; (B2) rice, bananas, sugar cane, citrus fruits, coconuts, taro, and yams in Southeast Asia; (C1) maize or corn, squash, beans, and pumpkins in Mesoamerica; (C2) lima beans, potatoes, sweet potatoes, manioc, and peanuts in lowland and highland South America. There was also independent domestication in North America, but (except for the sunflower) the plants domesticated there are not common crops today.

Source: Hole F. 1992. Origins of Agriculture. In: Jones S, Martin R, Pilbeam D, editors. The Cambridge Encyclopedia of Human Evolution. New York: Cambridge University Press. p 376. Reprinted with permission of Cambridge University Press.

(about 7000 B.C.), the central Andes around Peru (about 7000 B.C.), and the Eastern Woodlands of North America (about 2000 B.C.) (Flannery, 1986; Pearsall, 1992; Smith, 1992a). Most of the world's major food plants and animals were domesticated well before 2000 B.C. Also developed by that time were techniques of plowing, fertilizing, fallowing, and irrigation (Hole, 1992). Figure 12–2 shows the regions of the world that domesticated today's main food crops.

In this chapter we discuss what is believed about the origins of food production and settled life, called **sedentism**—how and why people in different places may have come to cultivate and domesticate plants and animals and to live in permanent villages. Agriculture and a sedentary life did not necessarily go together. In some regions of the world, people began to live in permanent villages before they cultivated and domesticated plants and animals, whereas in other places people planted crops without settling down permanently. Much of our discussion focuses on the Near East and Europe, the areas we know best archaeologically for the developments leading to food production and settled life. As much as we can, however, we try to indicate how data from other areas appear to suggest patterns different from, or similar to, those in Europe and the Near East.

Food Collection and Production

Food collection may be generally defined as all forms of **subsistence technology** in which food-getting is dependent on naturally occurring resources, that is, wild plants and animals. Although this was the way humans got their food for most of human history, the few remaining food collectors in the world today, also referred to as **foragers**, live in what have been called the *marginal areas* of the earth—deserts, the Arctic, and dense tropical forests—habitats that do not allow easy exploitation by modern agricultural technologies.

Anthropologists are interested in studying the relatively few food-collecting societies still available for observation because these groups may help us understand some aspects of human life in the past when all people were foragers. Ethnographic analogy from contemporary or recent historic hunter-gatherer and foraging populations can also provide us with models for prehistoric populations (Fix, 1977; Howell, 1979; Ray and Roth, 1984; Bogerhoff Mulder, 1992; Early and Peters, 1992). The basic premise underlying ethnographic data is that recent foragers and hunter-gatherers are like prehistoric populations in the same kinds of environments in terms of the ways in which they get food and therefore similar in terms of demographic structure, mobility patterns, social networks, etc. However, the range of fertility (the number of births per mother) and mortality among different hunter-gatherer, forager, and sedentary populations is so diverse that ethnographic analogy from subsistence base and mobility is extremely problematic (Harpending and Pennington, 1991; Pennington and Harpending, 1991; Pennington, 1992).

We must be cautious in drawing inferences about the past from our observations of contemporary food collectors for three reasons. First, early foragers lived in almost all types of environments, including some very bountiful ones. Therefore, what we observe among recent and contemporary food collectors may not be comparable to what would have been observable in more favourable environments in the past (Ember, 1978). Second, contemporary foragers are not relics of the past. Like all contemporary societies, they have evolved and are still evolving. Indeed, recent research suggests considerable variation in economic behaviour as well as in social structure in foraging groups that share common ancestry. This implies that recent foragers have responded to differences in local environmental conditions (Kent, 1996). Third, recent and contemporary foragers have been interacting with kinds of societies that did not exist until after 10 000 years ago—agriculturalists, pastoralists (groups who maintain and/or follow grazing herd animals), and intrusive powerful state societies (Schrire, 1984; Myers, 1988). So what we see in intersociety relations recently may be different from intersociety relations in the past. As a result, we must be careful not to automatically assume that similar subsistence strategies necessarily reflect social or cultural similarities between past and present societies.

Is there a typical pattern of food-getting among food collectors? Many anthropologists have assumed that foragers typically get their food more from gathering than from hunting, and that women contribute more than men to subsistence, because women generally do the gathering (Lee and DeVore, 1968). (See New Perspectives on Gender, *From Man the Hunter, to Woman the Gatherer, to . . . ?*)

Beginning about 10 000 years ago, certain peoples in widely separated geographic locations made the revolutionary changeover to **food production**. That is, they began to cultivate and then domesticate plants and animals. (Domesticated plants and animals are different from the ancestral wild forms.) With domestication of these food sources, people acquired control over certain natural processes, such as animal breeding and plant seeding. Today, most peoples in the world depend for their food on some combination of domesticated plants and animals.

Horticulture

The word **horticulture** may conjure up visions of people with "green thumbs" growing orchids and other flowers in greenhouses. To anthropologists though, the word means the growing of crops of all kinds with relatively simple tools and methods, in the absence of permanently cultivated fields. The tools are usually hand tools, such as the digging stick or hoe, not plows or other equipment pulled by animals or tractors. Nor do the methods used include fertilization, irrigation, or other ways to restore soil fertility after a growing season.

There are two kinds of horticulture. The more common one involves a dependence on **shifting cultivation**. The land is worked for short periods and then left idle for some years. During the years when the land is not cultivated, wild plants and brush grow up; when the fields are later cleared by **slash-and-burn** techniques, nutrients are returned to the soil. The other kind of horticulture involves a dependence on long-growing tree crops. The two kinds of horticulture may be practised in the same society, but in neither case is there permanent cultivation of field crops.

Most horticultural societies do not rely on crops alone for food. Many also hunt or fish; a few are nomadic for part of the year. For example, the northern Kayapo of the Brazilian Amazon leave their villages for as long as three months at a time to trek through the forest in search of game. The entire village participates in a trek, carrying large quantities of garden produce and moving their camp every day (Werner, 1978). Other horticulturalists raise domestic animals, but these are

NEW PERSPECTIVES ON GENDER

From Man the Hunter, to Woman the Gatherer, to . . . ?

Anthropologists know it is important to understand the food-collecting way of life, for all humans were food collectors until 10 000 years ago. An important conference was held in 1966 to bring together anthropologists of all types to discuss what was known about food collectors. Organized by Richard B. Lee and Irven DeVore, the conference and the resulting book were called *Man the Hunter*. At the time, the word *man* was used widely in anthropology as a way of referring to humans in general. But referring to "man the hunter" appeared to ignore women, since women rarely do the hunting among recent foragers. It was not that women's contribution was entirely ignored by the participants in the conference. Indeed, Richard Lee pointed out that some food collectors such as the !Kung of southwest Africa depended mostly on gathering, which was mainly women's work. Even so, the title of the conference and of the resulting book conveyed that hunting and the work of men were most important among food collectors.

With the growing women's movement in North America, thinking in anthropology subsequently began to change. New questions began to be asked. What were women doing? How much did they contribute to subsistence and to other essential economic activities? How much time did they work? What were their views of the world? What kinds of mate choices do women have? What kinds of decisions did they make? How much influence did women have?

In 1981, a book edited by Frances Dahlberg appeared. It was titled *Woman the Gatherer*. The editor was well aware that gathering is not usually the most important subsistence activity among food collectors. It may be more important among contemporary foragers such as the !Kung and Australian aborigines, who live in warmer climates, but gathering is less important in colder climates, where most recent foragers have lived. Indeed, if we look at a large sample of recent foragers, we discover that fishing is more often the most important subsistence activity, more important (providing more calories) than either gathering or hunting. Why the title *Woman the Gatherer* then? Although the editor did not say so explicitly, we suggest that the title was intended to raise consciousness about the importance of women. We now know that food-collecting societies show considerable variability in how they get their food, so neither "Man the Hunter" nor "Woman the Gatherer" describes most foragers accurately.

Sources: Dahlberg F, editor. 1981. Woman the Gatherer. New Haven, CT: Yale University Press.

Ember CR. 1978. Myths about Hunter-Gatherers. Ethnology 18:439–448. Reprinted in: Ember M, Ember CR. 1983. Marriage, Family, and Kinship: Comparative Studies of Social Organization. New Haven, CT: HRAF Press. p 313–331.

Lee RB, DeVore I, editors. 1968. Man the Hunter. Chicago: Aldine.

usually not large animals, such as cattle and camels (Anonymous, 1967). More often than not, the animals raised by horticulturalists are smaller ones, such as pigs, chickens, goats, and sheep.

In most horticultural societies, simple farming techniques have tended to yield more food from a given area than is generally available to food collectors. Consequently, horticulture is able to support larger, more densely populated communities. The way of life of horticulturalists is more sedentary than that of food collectors, although communities may move after some years to farm a new series of plots. (Some horticulturalists have permanent villages because they depend mostly on food from trees that keep producing for a long time.) In contrast with most recent food-collecting groups, horticultural societies exhibit the beginnings of *social differentiation*. For example, some individuals may be part-time craft workers or part-time political officials, and certain members of a kin group may have more status than other individuals in the society.

Intensive Agriculture

People engaged in **intensive agriculture** use techniques that enable them to cultivate fields permanently. Essential nutrients may be put back in the soil through the addition of fertilizers, which may be organic material (most commonly dung from humans or other animals) or inorganic (chemical) fertilizers. There are, however, other ways to restore nutrients. The Luo of western Kenya plant beans around corn plants. Bacteria growing around the roots of the bean plant replace lost nitrogen, and the corn plant conveniently provides a pole for the bean plant to wind around as it grows. Some intensive agriculturalists use irrigation from streams and rivers to ensure an adequate supply of waterborne nutrients. Crop rotation—using different fields from year to year—and plant stubble that has been plowed under also restore nutrients to the soil.

Pre-Agricultural Developments

Europe

After about 10 000 years ago in Europe, the glaciers began to disappear. With their disappearance came other environmental changes. The melting of the glacial ice caused the oceans to rise, and, as the seas moved inland, the waters inundated some of the richest fodder-producing coastal plains, creating islands, inlets, and bays. Other areas, particularly in Scandinavia, were opened up for human occupation as the glaciers retreated and the temperatures rose (Collins, 1976). The cold, treeless plains, tundra, and grasslands eventually gave way to dense mixed forests, mostly birch, oak, and pine, and the mammoths became extinct. The warming waterways gradually cleared of glacial sediment, and began to be filled with fish and other aquatic resources (Chard, 1969).

Archaeologists believe that these environmental changes induced some populations in Europe to alter their food-getting strategies. When the tundra and grasslands disappeared, hunters could no longer obtain large quantities of meat simply by remaining close to large migratory herds of animals, as they probably did during Upper Palaeolithic times. Even though deer and other game were available, the number of animals per square kilometre (density) had decreased, and it became more difficult to stalk and kill animals sheltered in the thick woods. Thus, in many areas of Mesolithic Europe people seem to have turned from a reliance on big-game hunting to the intensive collecting of wild plants, molluscs, fish, and small game to make up for the extinction of the mammoths and the northward migration of the reindeer.

The Maglemosian Culture of Northern Europe.

Some adaptations to the changing environment can be seen in the cultural remains of the settlers in northern Europe who are called Maglemosians by archaeologists. Their name derives from the peat bogs (*magle mose* in Danish means "great bog") where their remains have been found.

To deal with the new, more forested environment, the Maglemosians made stone axes and adzes to chop down trees and form them into various objects. Large timbers appear to have been split for houses; trees were hollowed out for canoes; and smaller pieces of wood were made into paddles. The canoes presumably were built for travel and perhaps for fishing on the lakes and rivers that abounded in the postglacial environment.

We do not know to what extent the Maglemosians relied on wild plant foods, but there were a lot of different kinds available such as hazelnuts. However, we do know many other things about the Maglemosians' way of life. Although fishing was fairly important, as suggested by the recovery of fish hooks, and the frequent occurrence of bones from pike and other fish, these people apparently depended mainly on hunting for food. Game included elk, wild ox, deer, and wild pig. In addition to many fishing implements and the adzes and axes, the Maglemosians' tool kit included the bow and arrow. Some of their tools were ornamented with finely engraved designs. Ornamentation independent of tools also appears in amber and stone pendants and small figurines such as the head of an elk (Clark, 1975).

Like the Maglemosian finds, many of the European Mesolithic sites are along lakes, rivers, and marine shorelines. But these sites probably were not inhabited year-round; there is evidence that at least some groups moved seasonally from one place of settlement to another, perhaps between the coast and inland areas (Petersen, 1973). Finds such as kitchen middens with piles of shells that centuries of Mesolithic seafood-eaters had discarded and remains of fishing equipment, canoes, and boats indicate that Mesolithic people depended much more heavily on fishing than had their ancestors in Upper Palaeolithic times. The very fact that this domestic waste accumulated in middens is indicative of the growing degree of sedentism associated with the Mesolithic.

The Near East

Cultural developments in the Near East seem to have paralleled those in Europe (Binford, 1971).

With the disappearance of mammoths in the northern hemisphere, hunter-gatherers had to change how they got their food. They began to rely more on smaller game and marine resources.

Here, too, there seems to have been a shift from mobile big-game hunting to the utilization of a broad spectrum of natural resources. There is evidence that people subsisted on a variety of resources, including fish, molluscs, and other water life; wild deer, sheep, and goats; and wild grains, nuts, and legumes (Flannery, 1973a). The increased utilization of stationary food sources such as wild grain may partly explain why some people in the Near East began to lead more sedentary lives during the Mesolithic.

Even today, a traveller passing through the Anatolian highlands of Turkey and other mountainous regions in the Near East may see thick stands of wild wheat and barley growing as densely as if they had been cultivated. Wielding flint sickles, Mesolithic people could easily have harvested a bountiful crop from such wild stands. Just how productive these resources can be was demonstrated in a field experiment duplicating prehistoric conditions. Using the same kind of flint-blade sickle that a Mesolithic worker would have used, researchers were able to harvest a little over 1 kilogram of wild grain in an hour. A Mesolithic family of four, working only during the few weeks of the harvest season, probably could have reaped more wheat and barley than they needed for the entire year (Harlan, 1967).

The amount of wild wheat harvested in the experiment prompted Kent Flannery to conclude, "Such a harvest would almost necessitate some degree of sedentism—after all, where could they go with an estimated metric ton of clean wheat?" (Flannery, 1971). Moreover, the stone equipment used for grinding would have been a clumsy burden to carry. Part of the harvest would probably have been set aside for immediate consumption, ground, and then cooked either by roasting or boiling. The rest of the harvest would have been stored to supply food for the remainder of the year. A grain diet, then, could have been the impetus for the construction of roasters, grinders, and storage pits by some Mesolithic people, as well as for the construction of solid, fairly permanent housing. Once a village was built, people may have been reluctant to abandon it. We can visualize the earliest pre-agricultural settlements clustered around such naturally rich regions, as archaeological evidence indeed suggests they were.

The Natufians of the Near East. Eleven thousand years ago the Natufians, a people living in the area that is now Israel and Jordan, inhabited caves and rock shelters and built villages on the slopes of Mount Carmel in Israel. At the front of their rock shelters they hollowed out basin-shaped depressions in the rock, possibly for storage pits. Examples of Natufian villages are also found at the Eynan site in Israel.

Eynan is a stratified site containing the remains of three villages in sequence, one atop another. Each village consisted of about 50 circular pit houses. The floor of each house was sunk a few metres into the ground, so that the walls of the house consisted partly of earth, below ground level, and partly of stone, above ground level. Pit houses had the advantage of retaining heat longer than houses built above the ground. The villages appear to have had stone-paved walks; circular stone pavements ringed what seem to be permanent hearths; and the dead were interred in village cemeteries.

The tools suggest that the Natufians harvested wild grain intensively. Sickles recovered from their villages have a specific sheen, which experiments have shown to be the effect of flint striking grass stems, as the sickles would have been used in the cutting of grain. The Natufians are the earliest Mesolithic people known to have stored surplus crops. Beneath the floors of their stone-walled houses, they constructed plastered storage pits. In addition to wild grains, the Natufians exploited a range of other resources (Mellaart, 1961). The remains of many wild animals are found in Natufian sites; Natufians appear to have concentrated on hunting gazelle, which they would take by surrounding whole herds (Henry, 1989).

The Natufians, as well as food collectors in other areas at the time, show many differences as compared with food collectors in earlier periods (Brown and Price, 1985). Not only was Natufian food collection based on a more intensive use of stationary resources such as wild grain, but the archaeological evidence suggests increasing social complexity. Natufian sites were, on average, five times larger than those of their predecessors. Communities were now occupied for most of the year, if not year-round. Burial patterns suggest more social differences between people. Although wild cereal resources appear to have enabled the Natufians to live in relatively permanent villages, their diet seems to have suffered. Their tooth enamel shows signs of nutritional deficiency, and their stature declined over time (Henry, 1989; Henry, 1991; Olszewski, 1991).

Mesoamerica

A similar shift toward more broad-spectrum hunting and gathering occurred in the New World at the end of the Palaeo-Indian period, about 10 000 years ago. Climate change seems to have been vital here too, as it was in the Old World. The retreat of glacial ice from North America and overall warmer and wetter climate brought dramatic changes to plant and animal communities throughout North America and Mesoamerica. Pleistocene megafauna, such as mammoths, mastodon, rhinoceros, giant ground sloth, and others, as well as a variety of smaller game animals, such as the horse, all went extinct in a relatively short period of time (Martin and Wright, 1967). Hunting strategies shifted toward a broader range of game species, particularly deer, antelope, bison, and small mammals. At the same time, deciduous woodlands and grasslands expanded, providing a range of new plants to exploit. Ground-stone woodworking tools such as axes and adzes first appeared, as did nut-processing tools such as mortars and pestles. Shellfish began to be exploited in some areas. Throughout North America and Mesoamerica people began to expand the range of plants and animals they relied upon (Brown, 1985; Keuhn, 1998).

The Archaic Peoples of Highland Mesoamerica.
In Highland Mesoamerica, that is, the mountainous regions of central and southern Mexico, we also see a shift from big-game hunting to a broader use of resources, in part due to a change in climate more

like today's. Altitude became an important factor in the hunting and collecting regime, as different altitudes have different plant and animal resources. Valleys tend to have scrubby, grassland vegetation, whereas foothills and mountains have "thorn forests" of cactuses and succulents giving way to oak and pine forests at higher altitudes, where there is more moisture. This vertical zonation means that a wide range of plants and animals were available in relatively close proximity—different environments were close by—and the Archaic peoples took advantage of these varied conditions to hunt and collect a range of resources (Marcus and Flannery, 1996).

About 8000 years ago the Archaic peoples in Mesoamerica appear to have moved seasonally between communities of two different sizes: camps with 15 to 30 residents (*macrobands*) and camps with only 2 to 5 residents (*microbands*). Macroband camps were located near seasonally abundant resources, such as acorns or mesquite pods. Several families would have come together when these resources were in season, both to take advantage of them and to work together to harvest them while they were plentiful, to perform rituals, and simply to socialize. Microband camps were also inhabited seasonally, probably by a single family, when groups were not assembled into macroband camps. Remains of these microband camps are often found in caves or rock shelters from which a variety of environments could be exploited by moving either upslope or downslope from the campsite (Marcus and Flannery, 1996).

Unlike the Natufians of the Near East, there is no evidence of social differences among the Archaic peoples of Highland Mesoamerica. The largest social unit, the macroband camp, was probably composed of related family groups, and leadership in these groups was probably informal. There is little evidence of ritual behaviour beyond the presence of what may have been a ceremonial dance floor at Gheo-Shih, a macroband campsite in the Valley of Oaxaca. In short, lifestyles remained much like the simple and egalitarian ones of the Palaeo-Indians, despite the transition to a much broader strategy of food collection.

Other Areas

People in other areas in the world also shifted from hunting big game to collecting many types of food before they apparently began to practise agriculture. The still-sparse archaeological record suggests that such a change occurred in Southeast Asia, which may have been one of the important centres of original plant and animal domestication. The faunal remains recovered from inland sites in the region indicate that many different sources of food were being exploited from the same base camps. For example, these base camps yield the remains of animals from high mountain ridges as well as lowland river valleys, birds and primates from nearby forests, bats from caves, and fish from streams. The few coastal sites indicate that many kinds of fish and shellfish were collected and that animals such as deer, wild cattle, and rhinoceros were hunted (Gorman, 1970). As in Europe, the pre-agricultural developments in Southeast Asia probably were responses to changes in the climate and environment, including a warming trend, more moisture, and a higher sea level (Chang, 1970; Gorman, 1970).

In Africa, too, the pre-agricultural period was marked by a warmer, wetter environment. The now-numerous lakes, rivers, and other bodies of water provided fish, shellfish, and other resources that apparently allowed people to settle more permanently than they had before. For example, there were lakes in what is now the southern and central Sahara desert, where people fished and hunted hippopotamuses and crocodiles. This pattern of broad-spectrum food-collecting seems also to have been characteristic of the areas both south and north of the Sahara (Clark, 1970). One area showing increased sedentism is the Dakhleh Oasis in the Western Desert of Egypt. Between 9000 and 8500 years ago, the inhabitants lived in circular stone huts on the shores of rivers and lakes. Bone harpoons and pottery are found there and in other areas from the Nile Valley through the central and southern Sahara westward to what is now Mali. Fishing seems to have allowed people to remain along the rivers and lakes for much of the year (Phillipson, 1993).

At about the same time in the Americas, people were beginning to exploit a wide variety of wild food resources. For example, evidence from present-day Alabama and Kentucky shows that, by about 5000 B.C., people had begun to collect freshwater mussels as well as wild plants and small game. In the Great Basin of what is now the United States, people were beginning to spend longer and longer periods each year collecting the wild resources around and in the rivers and glacial lakes (Patterson, 1973).

Why Did Broad-Spectrum Collecting Develop?

It is apparent that the pre-agricultural switch to broad-spectrum collecting was fairly common throughout the world. Climate change was probably at least partly responsible for the exploitation of new sources of food. For example, the worldwide rise in sea level may have increased the availability of fish and shellfish. Changes in climate may have also been partly responsible for the decline in the availability of big game, particularly the large herd animals. In addition, it has been suggested that another possible cause of that decline was human activity, specifically overkilling of some of these animals. The evidence suggesting overkill is that the extinction in the New World of many of the large Pleistocene animals, such as the mammoth, coincided with the movement of humans from the Bering Strait region to the southern tip of South America (Martin, 1973).

The overkill hypothesis has been largely discredited on the basis of the breadth of extinctions that includes bird as well as mammal species in the Americas. An enormous number of bird species also became extinct during the last few thousand years of the North American Pleistocene, and it is difficult to argue that human hunters caused all of those extinctions. Because the bird and mammal extinctions occurred simultaneously, it is likely that most or nearly all the extinctions were due to climatic and other environmental changes (Grayson, 1977, 1989; Guthrie, 1984; Marshall, 1984).

The decreasing availability of big game may have stimulated people to exploit new food resources, but they may have turned to a broader spectrum of resources for another reason—population growth (see Figure 12–3). As Mark Cohen has noted, hunter-gatherers were "filling up" the world, and they may have had to seek new, possibly less desirable sources of food (Cohen, 1977a). (We might think of shellfish as more desirable than mammoths, but only because we don't have to do the work to get such food. A lot of shellfish have to be collected, shelled, and cooked to obtain about the same amount of protein obtainable from one large animal.) Consistent with the idea that the world was filling up around this time is the fact that not until after 30 000 years ago did hunter-gatherers begin to move into previously uninhabited parts of the world, such as Australia and the New World (Cohen, 1977a; Hassan, 1981; Bailey et al., 1989).

Broad-spectrum collecting may have involved exploitation of new sources of food, but that does not necessarily mean that people were eating better. A decline in stature often indicates a poorer diet. During the Mesolithic, height apparently declined by as much as 5 centimetres in many parts of the Old World (Greece, Israel, India, and northern and western Europe) (Cohen, 1989). This decline may have been a result of decreasing nutrition, but it could also be that natural selection for greater height was relaxed because leverage for throwing projectiles such as spears was not so favoured after the decline of big-game hunting. (Greater limb-bone length, and therefore greater height, would enable you to throw a spear with more force and farther [Frayer, 1981].) In other areas of the world, such as Australia and what is now the midwestern United States, skeletal evidence also suggests a decline in the general level of health with the rise of broad-spectrum collecting (Cohen, 1989).

Broad-Spectrum Collecting and Sedentism

Does the switch to broad-spectrum collecting explain the increasingly sedentary way of life we see

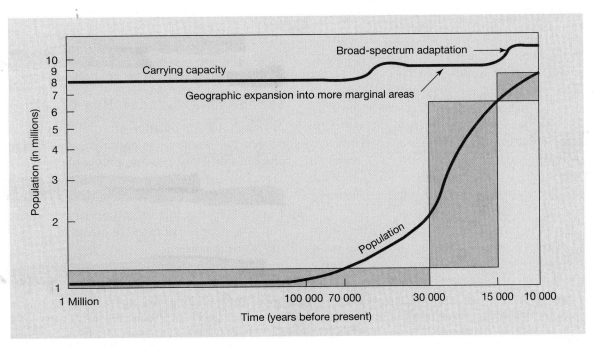

Figure 12–3 Reconstructed Increases in World Population and Carrying Capacity for Humans during the Pleistocene
Estimates of human population suggest that substantial increases preceded the movement of humans into more marginal areas. Further population increase preceded the emergence of broad-spectrum collecting.

Source: Adapted from Hassan FA. 1981. Demographic Archaeology. New York: Academic Press. p 207.

The !Kung of the Kalahari Desert on the move. Spacing births an average of four years apart helps to ensure that a woman will not have to carry more than two children at a time. The woman in front is carrying both a large and a small child.

in various parts of the world in pre-agricultural times? The answer seems to be both yes and no. In some areas of the world—some sites in Europe, the Near East, Africa, and Peru—settlements became more permanent. In other areas, such as the semi-arid highlands of Mesoamerica, the switch to broad-spectrum collecting was not associated with increasing sedentism. Even after the highland Mesoamericans began to cultivate plants, they still did not live in permanent villages (Flannery, 1973b). The question is why.

It would seem that it is not simply the switch to broad-spectrum collecting that accounts for increasing sedentism in many areas. Rather, a comparison of settlements on the Peruvian coast suggests that the more permanent settlements were located nearer (within 6 kilometres) than were temporary settlements to most, if not all, of the diverse food resources exploited during the year. The community that did not have a year-round settlement seems to have depended on more widely distributed resources. What accounts for sedentism may thus be the nearness (Patterson, 1971) or the high reliability and yield (Harris, 1977; Johnson, 1977) of the broad-spectrum resources, rather than the broad spectrum itself.

Sedentism and Population Growth

Although some population growth undoubtedly occurred throughout the hunting and gathering phase of world history, some anthropologists have suggested that populations would have increased dramatically when people began to settle down. The evidence for this suggestion comes largely from a comparison of recent nomadic and sedentary !Kung populations.

The settling down of a nomadic group may reduce the typical spacing between births (Lee, 1972; Sussman, 1972). Nomadic !Kung have children about every four years; in contrast, recently settled !Kung have children about every three years. Why might birth spacing change with settling down? There are several possibilities.

Regulating the spacing of childbirths can occur in a number of ways. One way, if effective contraceptives are not available, is prolonged sexual abstinence after the birth of a child—the postpartum sex taboo—that is common in recent human societies. Another way is abortion or infanticide (Harris, 1977). Nomadic groups may be motivated to have children farther apart because of the problem of carrying small children. Carrying one small child is difficult enough; carrying two might be too burdensome. Thus, sedentary populations could have children spaced more closely because carrying children would not always be necessary.

It is possible that intensive collectors and early horticulturalists may have seen advantages to having larger families (more individuals could contribute to labour). It may be that women, who were likely doing much of the plant foraging and early horticulture, saw an advantage from having more children as a means of improving the efficiency of the group.

Although some nomadic groups may have deliberately spaced births by abstinence or infanticide, there is no evidence that such practices explain why there is typically four years between births among nomadic !Kung. There may be another explanation, involving an unintended effect of how babies are fed. Nancy Howell and Richard Lee have suggested that the presence of baby foods other than mother's milk may be responsible for the decreased birth spacing in sedentary agricultural !Kung groups (Howell, 1979; Lee, 1979). It is now well established that the longer a mother nurses her baby without supplementary foods, the longer it is likely to be before she starts ovulating again. Nomadic !Kung women have little to give their babies in the way of soft, digestible food, and the babies depend largely on mother's milk for two to three years. Sedentary !Kung mothers can, however, give their babies soft foods such as cereal (made from cultivated grain) and milk from domesticated animals. Such changes in feeding practices may shorten birth spacing by shortening the interval between birth and the resumption of ovulation. In pre-agricultural sedentary communities, it is possible that baby foods made from wild grains might have had the same effect. For this reason alone, therefore, populations may have grown even before people started to farm or herd.

Another reason sedentary !Kung women may have more babies than nomadic !Kung women has to do with the ratio of body fat to body weight. Some investigators suspect that a critical minimum of fat in the body may be necessary for ovulation. A sedentary !Kung woman may have more fatty tissue than a nomadic !Kung woman, who walks many kilometres daily to gather wild plant foods, often carrying a child around with her. Thus, sedentary !Kung women might resume ovulating sooner after the birth of a baby and so may be likely for that reason alone to have more closely spaced children. If some critical amount of fat is necessary for ovulation, that would explain why in our own society many women who have little body fat—long-distance runners, gymnasts, and ballet dancers are examples—do not ovulate regularly (Howell, 1979; Frisch, 1980).

Mesolithic Technology

Technologically, Mesolithic cultures did not differ radically from Upper Palaeolithic cultures (Phillipson, 1993). (*Mesolithic*, like the term *Upper Palaeolithic*, properly applies only to cultural developments in the Old World. However, we use the term *Mesolithic* here to represent some general pre-agricultural trends.) The trend toward smaller and lighter tools continued. Microliths, small blades 1.2 centimetres to 5 centimetres long, which were made in late Upper Palaeolithic times, were now used in quantity. In place of the one-piece flint implement, Mesolithic peoples in Europe, Asia, and Africa equipped themselves with composite tools—that is, tools made of more than one material.

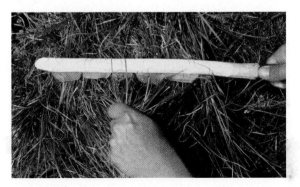

A sickle made with microliths.

Microliths, too small to be used one at a time, could be fitted into grooves in bone or wood to form arrows, harpoons, daggers, and sickles. A sickle, for example, was made by inserting several microliths into a groove in a wooden or bone handle. The blades were held in place by resin. A broken microlith could be replaced like a blade in a modern razor. Besides being adaptable for many uses, microliths could be made from many varieties of available stone; Mesolithic people were no longer limited to flint. Since they did not need the large flint nodules to make large core and flake tools, they could use small pebbles of flint to make the small blades (Semenov, 1970; Whittaker, 1994).

The Domestication of Plants and Animals

Neolithic means "of the new stone age"; the term originally signified the cultural stage in which humans invented pottery and stone tools with ground edges. We now know, however, that both were present in earlier times, so we cannot define a Neolithic state of culture on the basis of the presence of pottery and ground-stone tools. At present, archaeologists generally define the Neolithic in terms of the presence of domesticated plants and animals. In this type of culture, people began to produce food rather than merely collect it.

The line between food-collecting and food-producing occurs when people begin to plant crops and to keep and breed animals. How do we know when this transition occurred? In fact, archaeologically we do not see the beginning of food production; we can see signs of it only after plants and animals show differences from their wild varieties. When people plant crops, we refer to the process as *cultivation*. It is only when the crops cultivated and the animals raised are modified—and become different from wild varieties—that we speak of plant and animal **domestication**. A domesticated plant or animal is one that depends upon human intervention for its continued survival.

We know, in a particular site, that domestication occurred if plant remains have characteristics different from those of wild plants of the same types. For example, wild grains of barley and wheat have a fragile **rachis**—the seed-bearing part of the stem—which shatters easily, releasing the seeds. Domesticated grains have a tough rachis, which does not shatter easily. Similarly, domesticated plants tend to have larger seeds than their wild ancestors. In addition, plants found in areas for which there is no naturally growing ancestral form are assumed to have been brought there by humans, and are therefore, by definition, domesticates.

How did the domesticated plants get to be different from the wild varieties? Artificial or human selection, deliberate or accidental, obviously was required. Consider how the rachis of wheat and barley may have changed. As we said, when wild grain ripens in the field, the rachis shatters easily, scattering the seed. This trait is selectively advantageous under wild conditions; it is nature's method of propagating the species. Plants with a tough rachis, therefore, have only a slight chance of reproducing themselves under natural conditions, but they are more desirable for maximizing yield during harvesting. When humans arrived with sickles and flails to collect the wild stands of grain, the seeds harvested probably contained a high proportion of tough-rachis mutants, because these could best withstand the rough treatment of harvest processing. If planted, the harvested seeds would be likely to produce tough-rachis plants (see Figure 12–4). If in each successive harvest seeds from these plants were the least likely to be lost, tough-rachis plants would come to predominate (Zohary, 1969).

Domesticated species of animals also differ from the wild varieties. For example, the horns of wild goats in the Near East are shaped differently from those of domesticated goats (Flannery, 1965). Differences in physical characteristics may not be the only indicators of domestication. Some archaeologists believe that imbalances in the sex and age ratios of animal remains at particular sites also suggest that domestication had occurred. For example, at Zawi Chemi Shanidar in Iraq, the proportion of young to mature sheep remains was much higher than the ratio of young to mature sheep in wild herds. One possible inference to be

Figure 12–4 Seed Heads of Wild and Domesticated Wheat
Note the larger and more numerous seeds on domesticated wheat.

Source: Feder K. 2000. Past in Perspective. Second edition. Mountain View, CA: Mayfield. Copyright © 2000 by Mayfield Publishing Company. Reprinted by permission of The McGraw-Hill Book Company.

drawn is that the animals were domesticated, the adult sheep being saved for breeding purposes while the young were eaten. (If mostly young animals were eaten, and only a few animals were allowed to grow old, most of the bones found in a site would be from the young animals that were killed regularly for food [Flannery, 1965; Collier and White, 1976].)

Domestication in the Near East

For some time most archaeologists have thought that the arc of land stretching up from Israel and the Jordan Valley through southern Turkey and then downward to the western slopes of the Zagros Mountains in Iran (see Figure 12–5) was one of the earliest centres of plant and animal domestication. We know that several varieties of domesticated wheat were grown there after about 8000 B.C., as were oats, rye, barley, lentils, peas, and various fruits and nuts (apricots, pears, pomegranates, dates, figs, olives, almonds, and pistachios) (MacNeish, 1991; Hole, 1992). It appears that the first animals were domesticated in the Near East. Dogs were first

domesticated before the rise of agriculture, around 10 000 B.C. (see Research Frontiers, *Did Dogs [and Cats] Domesticate Themselves?* on page 276), goats and sheep around 7000 B.C., and cattle and pigs around 6000 B.C. (Clutton-Brock, 1988).

Let us look at two early Neolithic sites in the Near East to see what life there may have been like after people began to depend on domesticated plants and animals for food.

Ali Kosh. At the stratified site of Ali Kosh in what is now southwestern Iran (see Figure 12–5), we see the remains of a community that started out about 7500 B.C. living mostly on wild plants and animals. Over the next 2000 years, until about 5500 B.C., agriculture and herding became increasingly important. After 5500 B.C. we see the appearance of two innovations—irrigation and the use of domesticated cattle—that seem to have stimulated a minor population explosion during the following millennium.

From 7500 to 6750 B.C., the people at Ali Kosh cut small slabs of raw clay out of the ground to build small multi-room structures. The rooms excavated by archaeologists are small, seldom more than 2.1 metres by 3 metres, and there is no evidence that the structures were definitely houses where people actually spent time or slept. Instead, they may have been storage rooms. On the other hand, house rooms of even smaller size are known in other areas of the world, so it is possible that the people at Ali Kosh in its earliest phase were actually living in those tiny, unbaked "brick" houses. There is a bit of evidence that the people at Ali Kosh may have moved over the course of the summer with their goats to nearby mountain valleys (just a few days' walk away), perhaps in search of more grassy habitats.

We have a lot of evidence about what the people at Ali Kosh ate. They got some of their food from cultivated emmer wheat and a barley variety. However a considerable amount of protein was derived from domesticated goats. We know the goats were domesticated because wild goats do not seem to have lived in the area. Also, the fact that virtually no bones from elderly goats were found in the site suggests that the goats were domesticated

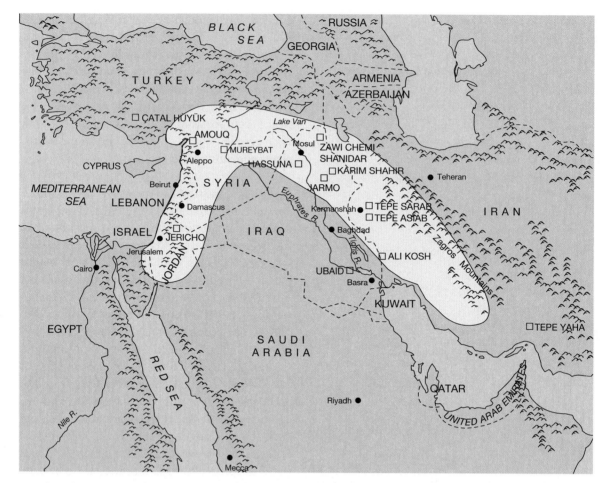

Figure 12–5 Early Agricultural Settlements in the Near East

Modern cities are represented by a dot, early settlements by a square. The yellow colour indicates the area of early agricultural settlement.

and herded rather than hunted. Moreover, it would seem from the horn cores found in the site that mostly young male goats were eaten, suggesting that the females were kept for breeding and milking. Despite all these signs of deliberate food production, there is an enormous amount of evidence—literally tens of thousands of seeds and bone fragments—that the people at the beginning of Ali Kosh depended mostly on wild plants (legumes and grasses) and wild animals (including gazelles, wild oxen, and wild pigs). They also collected fish, such as carp and catfish, and shellfish, such as mussels, as well as waterfowl that visited the area during part of the year.

The flint tools used during this earliest phase at Ali Kosh were varied and abundant. Finds from this period include tens of thousands of tiny flint blades, some only a few millimetres wide. About 1 percent of the chipped stone found by archaeologists was obsidian, or volcanic glass, which came from what is now eastern Turkey, several hundred kilometres away. Thus, the people at Ali Kosh during its earliest phase definitely had some kind of contact with people elsewhere. This contact is also suggested by the fact that the emmer wheat they cultivated did not have a wild relative in the area.

From 6750 to 6000 B.C., the people increased their consumption of cultivated food plants;

40 percent of the seed remains in the hearths and refuse areas were now from emmer wheat and barley. The proportion of the diet coming from wild plants was much reduced, probably because the cultivated plants have the same growing season and grow in the same kind of soil as the wild plants. Grazing by the goats and sheep that were kept may also have contributed to the reduction of wild plant foods in the area and in the diet. The village may or may not have become larger, but the multiroom houses definitely had. The rooms were now larger than 3 metres by 3 metres; the walls were much thicker; and the clay-slab bricks were now held together by a mud mortar. Also, the walls now often had a coat of smooth mud plaster on both sides. The stamped-mud house floors were apparently covered with rush or reed mats (you can see the imprints of them). There were courtyards with domed brick ovens and brick-lined roasting pits. Understandably, considering the summer heat in the area, none of the ovens found were inside a house.

Even though the village probably contained no more than 100 individuals, it participated in an extensive trading network. Seashells were probably obtained from the Persian Gulf, which is some distance to the south; copper may have come from what is now central Iran; obsidian came from eastern Turkey; and turquoise somehow made its way from what is now the border between Iran and Afghanistan. Some of these materials were used as ornaments worn by both sexes—or so it seems from the remains of bodies found buried under the floors of houses.

After about 5500 B.C., the area around Ali Kosh began to show signs of a much larger population, apparently made possible by a more complex agriculture employing irrigation and plows drawn by domesticated cattle. Over the next thousand years, by 4500 B.C., the population of the area probably tripled. This population growth was apparently part of the cultural developments that culminated in the rise of urban civilizations in the Near East (Hole et al., 1969), as we will see in the next chapter.

Population growth may have occurred in and around Ali Kosh but did not continue in all areas of the Near East after domestication. For example, one of the largest early villages in the Near East, 'Ain Ghazal (on the outskirts of what is now Amman, Jordan), suffered a decline in population and standard of living over time, perhaps because the environment around 'Ain Ghazal could not permanently support a large village (Simmons et al., 1988).

Çatal Hüyük. On a windswept plateau in the rugged, mountainous region of southern Turkey stand the remains of a mud-brick town known as Çatal Hüyük (see Figure 12–5). Hüyük is the Turkish word for a mound formed by a succession of settlements, one built on top of another.

About 5600 B.C., Çatal Hüyük was an adobe town. Some 200 houses have been excavated, and they are interconnected in *pueblo fashion* (each flat-roofed structure housed a number of families). The inhabitants decorated the walls of the houses with imaginative murals, and their shrines with symbolic statuary. The murals depict what seem to be religious scenes and everyday events. Archaeologists peeling away frescoes found layer upon layer of murals, indicating that old murals were plastered over to make way for fresh paintings. Several rooms are believed to have been shrine rooms. They contain many large bull murals and clay bull figurines and have full-sized clay heads of cattle on the walls. Other "shrine-room" murals depict scenes of life and death, painted in red and black, respectively. Clay statuettes of a pregnant woman and of a bearded man seated on a bull have also been found in these rooms.

Farming was well advanced at Çatal Hüyük. Lentils, wheat, barley, and peas were grown in quantities that produced a surplus. Archaeologists were astonished at the richly varied handicrafts, including beautifully carved wooden bowls and boxes that the people of the town produced. These people also had obsidian and flint daggers, spearheads, lance heads, scrapers, awls, and sickle blades. Bowls, spatulas, knives, ladles, and spoons were made from bone. The houses contained belt hooks, toggles, and pins carved from bone. Evidence also suggests that men and women wore jewellery fashioned from bone, shell, and copper and that they

RESEARCH FRONTIERS

Did Dogs (and Cats) Domesticate Themselves?

Early evidence of a close relationship between dogs and people comes from an archaeological site in northern Israel dating to nearly 12 000 years ago. At that site, archaeologists found the grave of an elderly woman, lying on her right side with her legs folded up, with a dog under her left hand. Do any of the attributes we associate with this common household pet explain why humans all over the world have had domesticated descendants of wolves around the house for the last 10 000 to 15 000 years?

Dogs were probably the first animals domesticated by humans, some thousands of years before plants, sheep, and goats were domesticated in the Near East. Humans were starting to settle down in semi-permanent camps and villages as they began to depend less on big game (which they had to follow over big distances) and more on relatively stationary food resources, such as fish, shellfish, small game, and wild plants rich in carbohydrates, proteins, and oils.

Why would humans have been interested in taming wolves at that time? One theory is that humans were shifting their prey from large animals to small, and they needed dogs for tracking wounded game or for retrieving killed game from bodies of water or underbrush. Dogs might also have been useful as alarm-givers in case predators came close. Finally, dogs might have helped to keep a camp clean, by scavenging garbage.

It is possible that this last use of dogs suggests an alternative theory of dog domestication. Perhaps it wasn't so much that humans domesticated dogs, but that some wolves domesticated themselves by hanging around human camps. Why would wolves be interested in those humans who were first settling down? It couldn't have been the possibility of a human dinner, because that would have been a possibility for millions of years before. So perhaps something else lured wolves to those early settled camps and villages. What was different about those early settlements? For the first time in human history, people were staying in one place for considerable periods—months at a time, *year after year*—because they could count on being able to "harvest" and live on the wild resources of the area for long periods of time. If they lived there for years, even if only seasonally, they would eventually have had a problem with garbage.

The residues of meals, in particular, would have been a problem. They might not only come to stink; they might also attract rodents and bigger threats to health and children. What could the people do about this problem? Well, as any camper nowadays realizes, they could have buried the garbage so that its scent would not attract unwelcome visitors. Eventually they would have run out of room for garbage pits in or close to the settlement. Of course, they could have moved the settlement,

---

used obsidian mirrors (Mellaart, 1964). (See Figure 12–6 on page 278 for similar tools and ornaments in Neolithic Switzerland.)

Since Çatal Hüyük is located in a region with few raw materials, the town evidently depended on exchange with other areas to secure the rich variety of materials it used. Shells were procured from the Mediterranean, timber from the hills, obsidian from 80 kilometres away, and marble from western Turkey.

Domestication Elsewhere in the Old World

The archaeological record for the domestication of seed crops is better known than for soft-flesh crops because the latter do not preserve well. The earliest clear evidence of cereal cultivation outside the Near East is from China. Late in the sixth millennium B.C. in north China there were sites where foxtail millet was cultivated. Storage pits, storage pots, and large numbers of grinding stones suggest that millet was an enormously important item in the diet. The wild-animal bones and the hunting and fishing tools that have been found suggest that people still depended on hunting and fishing somewhat, even though domesticated pigs (as well as dogs) were present. In south China, from about the same time, archaeologists have found a village by the edge of a small lake where people cultivated rice, bottle gourds, water chestnuts, and the date-like fruit called jujube. The people in south China also raised water buffalo, pigs, and dogs. And, as in the north China sites,

but maybe they didn't want to. After all, they had spent a lot of time and effort building permanent houses that were warm in the winter and dry in the rains. And they had a lot of things stored there. So what *could* they do?

Maybe people didn't have to do anything. Maybe those wolves hanging around the neighbourhood solved the problem for our ancestors. How? By scavenging, which is something most dogs (particularly larger ones, like the first domesticated dogs) do quite naturally and efficiently. So even a few tame wolves or domesticated dogs could have kept a garbage pit or pile from stinking and growing. And the people "feeding" that pit or pile could stay in one place for a long time, safe from smells, vermin, and disease. Dogs may have mostly domesticated themselves because it was good for some of them as well as for those Mesolithic humans.

A similar theory may explain the domestication of cats. Cats are especially good at catching and killing mice. Masses of mice skeletons (of the house mouse) begin to appear in basements of Near East dwellings after the emergence of agriculture. It is possible that humans purposely tried to domesticate cats to catch mice, but it is more likely that cats would have domesticated themselves by adapting to life near or in a granary or storage cellar. Of course, humans might have helped the process of domestication a little, by killing the more ferocious wild cats that were attracted to the settlement. The same was probably true for the wolves attracted to garbage. Even if you didn't at first want to "pet" the canids or felids that were hanging around, you wouldn't want them to attack humans. Wolves in the wild have a dominance-submission hierarchy, so they would be pre-adapted to heeding a "dominant" human; those that were not sufficiently submissive could be killed.

How could these theories of dog and cat domestication be tested? If dogs domesticated themselves as scavengers, archaeologists should find evidence of dog domestication (for example, changes in anatomy) only in sites that were occupied for a good part of the year over a period of years. Only under those circumstances would garbage be a problem and dogs a solution. Similarly, evidence of cat domestication should be found only in sites that show signs of year-to-year storage of grain. Only then would rodents be a problem and cats a solution. Perhaps archaeologists will make these tests in the future.

Sources: Budiansky S. 1992. The Covenant of the Wild: Why Animals Chose Domestication. New York: William Morrow.

Clutton-Brock J. 1984. Dog. In: Mason IL. Evolution of Domesticated Animals. New York: Longman. p 198–210.

Clutton-Brock J. 1992. Domestication of Animals. In: Jones S, Martin R, Pilbeam D, editors. The Cambridge Encyclopedia of Human Evolution. New York: Cambridge University Press. p 380–385.

Hole F. 1992. Origins of Agriculture. In: Jones S, Martin R, Pilbeam D, editors. The Cambridge Encyclopedia of Human Evolution. New York: Cambridge University Press. p 373–379.

Robinson R. Cat. In: Mason IL. Evolution of Domesticated Animals. New York: Longman. p 217–225.

some of their food came from hunting and fishing (Chang, 1981; MacNeish, 1991).

Mainland Southeast Asia may have been a place of domestication as early as the Near East was. The dating of domestication in Southeast Asia is not yet clear; the dates of the oldest site with probable domesticates—Spirit Cave in northwest Thailand—range from about 9500 B.C. to 5500 B.C. Some of the plants found at Spirit Cave are not clearly distinguishable from wild varieties, but others, such as gourds, betel nut, betel leaf, and water chestnut, were probably domesticates (MacNeish, 1991).

Most of the early cultivation in mainland Southeast Asia seems to have occurred in the plains and low terraces around rivers, although the main subsistence foods of early cultivators were probably the fish and shellfish in nearby waters.

The first plants to be domesticated probably were not cereal grains, as they were in the Near East. Indeed, some early cultivated crops may not have been used for food at all. In particular, bamboo may have been used to make cutting tools and for a variety of building purposes, and gourds were probably used as containers or bowls. We do not know yet exactly when rice was first domesticated, but there is definite evidence of cultivated rice in the Yangzi Valley in China around 8500–8000 B.P. (Higham and Lu, 1998). Other major food plants were domesticated first in Southeast Asia, including root crops, such as taro and yams, and tree crops, such as breadfruit, coconuts, and bananas (MacNeish, 1991; Hole, 1992).

Some plants and animals were domesticated first in Africa. Most of the early domestications probably

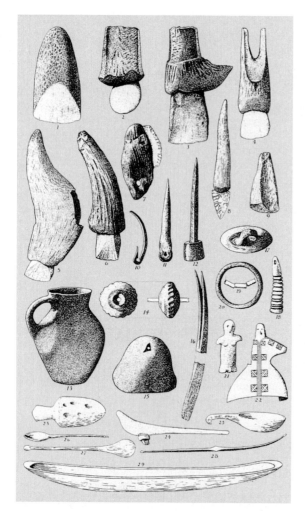

Figure 12–6

Neolithic implements from Switzerland, including axes (1–5, 24), chisels made of stone and bone (6, 9), awls made of bone (11, 12), fling knives (7, 8), weaving implements made of clay and bone (14–16), and ornaments (18–22).

occurred in the wide, broad belt of woodland-savannah country south of the Sahara and north of the equator. Among the cereal grains, sorghum was probably first domesticated in the central or eastern part of this belt, bulrush millet and a kind of rice (different from Asian rice) in the western part, and finger millet in the east. Groundnuts and yams were first domesticated in West Africa (Phillipson, 1993). We do know that farming became widespread in the northern half of Africa after 6000 B.C.; investigators

continue to debate whether the earliest crops grown there were indigenous or borrowed from the Near East. There is little doubt, however, that some of the plant foods were first domesticated in sub-Saharan Africa because the wild varieties occur there (MacNeish, 1991; Phillipson, 1993). Many of the important domestic animals in Africa today—cattle, sheep, and goats—probably were domesticated first in the Near East; most likely the donkey and guinea fowl were first domesticated in Africa (Clutton-Brock, 1988).

Domestication in the New World

In the New World, evidence of independent domestication of plants comes from at least three areas: South America, what is now Mexico, and the eastern United States. Possibly the first plants to be domesticated in the New World were members of the cucurbit family; they included a variety of the bottle gourd, summer squash, and pumpkins. Although probably not an important source of food anywhere, the woody bottle gourd could have been used as a water jug or cut into bowls. People may also have made musical instruments and art objects out of the bottle gourd. It is difficult to establish exactly when and where the New World variety of bottle gourd was first domesticated. Some suspect it is native to Africa and floated to the New World like a runaway buoy (Heiser Jr., 1985). Fragments and seeds of bottle gourd do date from as far back as 7400 B.C. in Oaxaca, Mexico. Summer squash was probably domesticated in Mexico between 7400 and 6700 B.C. (Flannery, 1986).

Although the origins of maize (corn) are controversial, an early domesticated form dating from about 5000 B.C. has been found in Tehuacán, Mexico. Until 1970, the most widely accepted view was that maize was cultivated from a now-extinct "wild maize" that had tiny cobs topped by small tassels. Now other views are considered: that maize was domesticated from teosinte, a tall, wild grass that still grows widely in Mexico, or that it resulted from a cross between a perennial variety of teosinte and a wild corn (Flannery, 1986) (see Figure 12–7).

People who lived in Mesoamerica, Mexico, and Central America are often credited with the

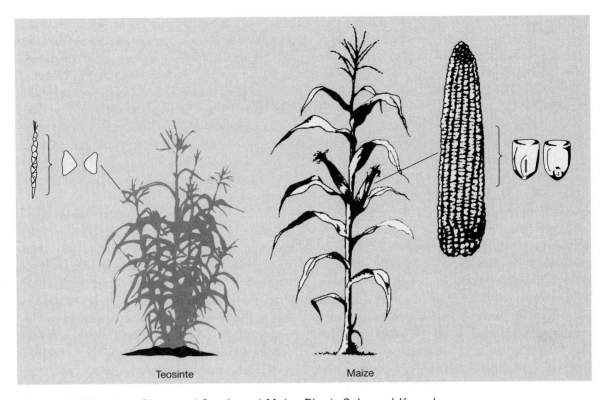

Teosinte   Maize

Figure 12–7 Teosinte Plant and Seeds and Maize Plant, Cob, and Kernels
Note how much larger the domesticated maize cob and kernels are compared with the teosinte spike and seeds.

Source: Feder K. 2000. Past in Perspective. Second edition. Mountain View, CA: Mayfield. Copyright © 2000 by Mayfield Publishing Company. Reprinted by permission of the publisher.

invention of planting maize, beans, and squash together in the same field. This planting strategy provides some important advantages. Maize takes nitrogen from the soil; beans, like all legumes, put nitrogen back into the soil. The maize stalk provides a natural pole for the bean plant to twine around, and the low-growing squash can grow around the base of the tall maize plant. Beans supply people with the amino acid lysine, which is missing in maize. Thus, maize and beans together provide all the essential amino acids that humans need to obtain from food. Whether teosinte was or was not the ancestor of maize, it may have provided the model for this unique combination since wild runner beans and wild squash occur naturally where teosinte grows (Flannery, 1986).

We can trace more than 200 domesticated plants to the Andes in South America, including potatoes, lima beans, peanuts, amaranth, and quinoa. The first clear domesticate was the chili pepper, dating back to about 7300 B.C., which makes domestication in the Andes about as old as in Mexico. The origins of the root crops manioc and sweet potato are less certain, but those crops probably originated in lowland tropical forest regions of South America (MacNeish, 1991; Hole, 1992).

Many of the plants grown in North America, such as corn, beans, and squash, were apparently introduced from Mesoamerica. However, at least three seed plants were probably domesticated independently in North America at an earlier time—sunflowers, sumpweed, and goosefoot. Sunflowers and sumpweed contain seeds that are highly nutritious in terms of protein and fat; goosefoot is high in starch and similar to corn in food value (Smith, 1992b). Sumpweed is an unusually good source of calcium, rivalled only by greens, mussels, and bones. It is also a very good source of iron (better than beef liver) and thiamine (Asch and Asch, 1978). These plants may have been cultivated in the area of the plains around the lower Ohio, Tennessee, and mid-Mississippi River valley beginning around 2000 B.C. (corn was introduced about A.D. 200).

All of the pre-corn domesticates are nutritionally superior to corn, so why did North American agriculturalists switch to a reliance on corn in the last 1000 years (Smith, 1992a; Smith, 1992b)? In the archaeologist Bruce Smith's words, "With the exception of the sunflower, North American seed crops are not exactly household words" (Smith, 1992b). Crop yields of corn would have had to be quite high to surpass the yields of those other crops, so perhaps the crucial factors were the time of harvest and the amount of effort required. Goosefoot, for example, was comparable to corn nutritionally. Harvesting and preparing it for storage though, took a lot of work and had to be done during the fall, the time of year when deer could be hunted intensively. So perhaps the incompatibility of goosefoot production and deer hunting, and the ease of harvesting corn and preparing it for storage, explain the switch to corn (Smith, 1992b).

On the whole, domestic animals were less important economically in the New World than they were in many parts of the Old World. In North America, dogs and turkeys were the main domesticated animals before the arrival of the Spaniards. Dogs in North and South America probably descended from the North American wolf and were domesticated relatively early. Domesticated turkeys from about A.D. 500 have been found in pueblos in the American Southwest (Clutton-Brock, 1988). Their feathers were used for arrows, ornaments, and weaving, and their bones for tools; but they do not seem to have been used frequently for food. However, turkeys were an important food in Mexico, where they may have been independently domesticated, and in Central America. When Cortés came to Mexico in 1519, he found domesticated turkeys in great quantities (Crawford, 1984).

The central Andes was the only part of the New World where domesticated animals were a signif-

icant part of the economy. Used for meat, transportation, and wool, llamas and alpacas (members of the camel family) were domesticated as early as 5000 B.C. in the Andes (Clutton-Brock, 1988). Guinea pigs, misnamed because they are neither pigs nor from Guinea, are rodents that were domesticated in the Andes sometime later. They were an important source of food even before domestication (Müller-Haye, 1984). Since they were domesticated, they have been raised in people's dwellings.

Animal domestication in the New World differed from that in the Old World because different wild species were found in the two hemispheres. The Old World plains and forests were the homes for the wild ancestors of the cattle, sheep, goats, pigs, and horses we know today. In the New World, the Pleistocene herds of horses, mastodons, mammoths, and other large animals were long extinct, allowing few opportunities for domestication of large animals (Wenke, 1984).

Although there is evidence from Mexico and other parts of the Americas that cultivation was under way between the fifth and third millennia B.C., permanent villages probably were not established in Peru until about 2500 B.C. and in areas of Mesoamerica until about 1500 B.C. (Flannery, 1973b; Niederberger, 1979). Archaeologists once thought that people settled into village life as a matter of course as soon as they had learned to domesticate plants. However, evidence from the arid highlands of Mesoamerica contradicts that assumption. In highland Mesoamerica, resources were widely distributed and relatively scarce in the dry season. Richard MacNeish has suggested that the early cultivators depended mostly on hunting during the winter and on seed collecting and pod picking in the spring. In addition to their food-collecting activities, in the summer they planted and harvested crops such as squash, and in the fall they collected fruit and harvested the avocados they had planted. These varied activities seem to have required people to spend most of the year in small groups, gathering into larger groups only in the summer and only in moister areas (MacNeish, 1973).

Why Did Food Production Develop?

We know that an economic transformation occurred in widely separate areas of the world beginning after about 10 000 years ago, as people began to domesticate plants and animals. The question is, why did domestication occur? And why did it occur independently in many different places within a period of a few thousand years? Considering that people depended only on wild plants and animals for millions of years, the differences in exactly when domestication first occurred in different parts of the world seem small. The spread of domesticated plants seems to have been more rapid in the Old World than in the New World, perhaps because the Old World spread was more along an east–west axis (except for the spread to sub-Saharan Africa), whereas the New World

A man harvesting sorghum in Burkina Faso. Sorghum is one of several plant species domesticated in Africa.

spread was more north–south. Spreading north and south may have required more time to adapt to variation in day lengths, climates, and diseases (Diamond, 1997). (Figure 12–1 on page 260 shows a timeline for domestication of plants and animals in the Old and New Worlds.)

There are many theories of why food production developed; most have tried to explain the origin of domestication in the area of early agriculture. Gordon Childe's theory, popular in the 1950s, was that a drastic change in climate caused domestication in the Near East (MacNeish, 1991). According to Childe, the postglacial period was marked by a decline in summer rainfall in the Near East and northern Africa. As the rains decreased, people were forced to retreat into shrinking pockets, or oases, of food resources, which were surrounded by desert. The lessened availability of wild resources provided an incentive for people to cultivate grains and to domesticate animals, according to Childe.

Robert Braidwood criticized Childe's theory for two reasons. First, Braidwood believed that the climate changes may not have been as dramatic as Childe had assumed, and therefore the "oasis incentive" may not have existed. Second, the climatic changes that occurred in the Near East after the retreat of the last glaciers had probably occurred at earlier interglacial periods too, but there had never been a similar food-producing revolution before. Hence, according to Braidwood, there must be more to the explanation of why people began to produce food than simply changes in climate (Braidwood, 1960).

Braidwood and Gordon Willey claimed that people did not undertake domestication until they had learned a great deal about their environment and until their culture had evolved enough for them to handle such an undertaking: "Why did incipient food production not come earlier? Our only answer at the moment is that culture was not ready to achieve it" (Braidwood and Willey, 1962).

Most archaeologists now think we should try to explain why people were not "ready" earlier to achieve domestication. Both Lewis Binford and Kent Flannery suggested that some change in external circumstances must have induced or favoured the changeover to food production (Binford, 1971; Flannery, 1971). As Flannery pointed out, there is no evidence of a great economic incentive for hunter-gatherers to become food producers. In fact, some contemporary hunter-gatherers may actually obtain adequate nutrition with far less work than many agriculturalists. So what might push food collectors to become food producers?

Binford and Flannery thought that the incentive to domesticate animals and plants might have been a desire to reproduce what was wildly abundant in the most bountiful or optimum hunting and gathering areas. Because of population growth in the optimum areas, people might have moved to surrounding areas containing fewer wild resources. It would have been in those marginal areas that people might have first turned to food production in order to reproduce what they used to have.

The Binford-Flannery model seems to fit the archaeological record in the Levant, the southwestern part of the earliest agriculture, where population increase did precede the first signs of domestication (Wright, 1971). However, as Flannery admitted, in some regions, such as southwestern Iran, the optimum hunting-gathering areas do not show population increase before the emergence of domestication (Flannery, 1986).

The Binford-Flannery model focuses on population pressure in a small area as the incentive to turn to food production. Mark Cohen theorizes it was population pressure on a global scale that explains why so many of the world's peoples adopted agriculture within the span of a few thousand years (Cohen, 1977a; Cohen, 1977b). He argues that hunter-gatherers all over the world gradually increased in population so that by about 10 000 years ago the world was more or less filled with food collectors. Thus, people could no longer relieve population pressure by moving to uninhabited areas. To support their increasing populations, they would have had to exploit a broader range of less desirable wild foods; that is, they would have had to switch to broad-spectrum collecting, or they would have had to increase the yields of the most desirable wild plants by weeding, protecting them from animal pests, and perhaps deliberately planting only the most productive among them. Cohen thinks that people might have tried a variety of these strategies but would generally have ended up depending on cultivation because that would have been the most efficient way to allow more people to live in one place.

Recently, some archaeologists have returned to the idea that climatic change (not the extreme variety that Childe envisaged) might have played a role in the emergence of agriculture. It seems clear from the evidence now available that the climate of the Near East about 13 000 to 12 000 years ago became more seasonal: the summers got hotter and drier than before and the winters became colder. These climatic changes may have favoured the emergence of annual species of wild grain, which archaeologically we see proliferating in many areas of the Near East (Byrne, 1987; Henry, 1989; Blumler and Byrne, 1991; McCorriston and Hole, 1991). People such as the Natufians intensively exploited the seasonal grains, developing an elaborate technology for storing and processing the grains and giving up their previous nomadic existence to do so. The transition to agriculture may have occurred when sedentary foraging no longer provided sufficient resources for the population. This could have happened because sedentism led to population increase and therefore resource scarcity (Henry, 1989), or because local wild resources became depleted after people settled down in permanent villages (McCorriston and Hole, 1991). In the area of Israel and Jordan where the Natufians lived, some of the people apparently turned to agriculture, probably to increase the supply of grain, whereas other people returned to nomadic food collection because of the decreasing availability of wild grain (Henry, 1989).

Change to a more seasonal climate might also have led to a shortage of certain nutrients for food collectors. In the dry seasons certain nutrients would have been less available. For example, grazing animals get lean when grasses are not plentiful, so meat from hunting would have been in short supply in the dry seasons. Although it may seem surprising, some recent hunter-gatherers have starved when they had to rely on lean meat. If they could have somehow increased their carbohydrate or fat intake, they might have been more likely to get through the periods of lean game (Speth and Spielmann, 1983). So it is possible that some wild-food collectors in the past thought of planting crops to get them through the dry seasons when hunting, fishing, and gathering did not provide enough carbohydrates and fat for them to avoid starvation.

Consequences of the Rise of Food Production

We know that intensive agriculture (permanent rather than shifting cultivation) probably developed in response to population pressure, but we do not know for sure that population pressure was even partly responsible for plant and animal domestication in the first place. Still, population growth certainly accelerated after the rise of food production (see Figure 12–8). There were other consequences too. Paradoxically, perhaps, health seems to have declined. Material possessions, though, became more elaborate.

Environmental Restraints

How much does the physical environment affect food-getting? Anthropologists have concluded that the physical environment by itself has a restraining, rather than a determining, effect on the major types of subsistence. Since they have very short growing seasons, cold regions of the earth are not particularly conducive to the growing of plants. No society we know of has practised agriculture in the Arctic; instead, people who live there rely primarily on animals for food. Nevertheless, both food collection (as among the Inuit) and food production (as among the Lapps) can be practised in cold areas. Indeed, cross-cultural evidence indicates that neither food collection nor food production is significantly associated with any particular type of habitat (Anonymous, 1967).

We know that food collection has been practised at one time or another in almost all areas of the earth. The physical environment does seem to have some effect on what kind of food collection

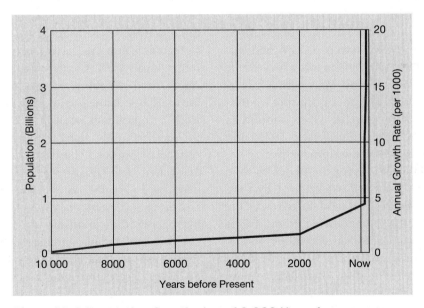

Figure 12–8 Population Growth since 10 000 Years Ago
The rate of population growth accelerated after the emergence of farming and herding 10 000 years ago. The rate of growth has accelerated even more dramatically in recent times.

is practised, that is, on the extent to which food collectors will depend on plants, animals, or fish. Farther away from the equator, food collectors depend much less on plants for food and much more on animals and fish (Binford, 1990; Low, 1990). Lewis Binford argues that fishing becomes increasingly important in cold climates because food collectors need non-portable housing in severe winters to protect themselves from the cold. Therefore, they cannot rely on large animals, which usually have to feed themselves by moving over considerable distances in the winter. Fishing is more localized than hunting, and therefore food collectors who rely on fishing can stay in their non-portable houses in winter (Binford, 1990).

When we contrast horticulture and intensive agriculture, the physical environment appears to explain some of the variation. Approximately 80 percent of all societies that practise horticulture or simple agriculture are in the tropics, whereas 75 percent of all societies that practise intensive agriculture are not in tropical forest environments (Anonymous, 1967). Tropical forests have abundant rainfall. Despite the attractiveness of lush vegetation and brilliant colouring, tropical forest lands do not usually offer favourable environments for intensive agriculture. Perhaps this is because the heavy rainfall quickly washes away certain minerals from cleared land. Also, the difficulty of controlling insect pests and weeds, which abound in tropical forests (Carneiro, 1968; Janzen, 1973), may make intensive agriculture less productive.

Whatever the reasons for the switch to food production, we still need to explain why food production has supplanted food collection as the primary mode of subsistence. We cannot assume that collectors would automatically adopt production as a superior way of life once they understood the process of domestication. After all, as we have noted, domestication may entail more work and provide less security than the food-collecting way of life.

The spread of agriculture may be linked to the need for territorial expansion. As a sedentary, food-producing population grew, it may have been forced to expand into new territory. Some of this

territory may have been vacant, but much of it was probably already occupied by food collectors. Although food production is not necessarily easier than collection, it is generally more productive per unit of land. Greater productivity enables more people to be supported in a given territory. In the competition for land between the faster-expanding food producers and the food collectors, the food producers may have had a significant advantage: they had more people in a given area. Thus, the foraging groups may have been more likely to lose out in the competition for land. Some groups may have adopted cultivation, abandoning the foraging way of life in order to survive. Other groups, continuing as food collectors, may have been forced to retreat into areas not desired by the cultivators. Today, as we have seen, the small number of remaining food collectors inhabit areas not particularly suitable for cultivation—dry lands, dense tropical forests, and polar regions.

Just as prior population growth might account for the origins of domestication, so would further population growth and ensuing pressure on resources at least partly explain the transformation of horticultural systems into intensive agricultural systems at later periods. However, just as the environment can affect the mode of subsistence, so too can the mode of subsistence affect the environment. We are all too familiar with the destruction of the world's tropical rain forests. It is estimated that 31 million hectares of global rain forest is destroyed each year. However, all human behavioural patterns associated with subsistence affect the environment (see Current Issues, *The Effect of Food-Getting on the Environment*). Some environments may make it difficult to adopt certain subsistence practices. For example, intensive agriculture cannot supplant horticulture in some tropical environments and horticulture continues to be practised in these regions.

Accelerated Population Growth

As we have seen, sedentism (even before the rise of food production) may have increased the rate of human population growth. But population growth definitely accelerated after the emergence of farming and herding, possibly because the spacing between births was reduced and therefore fertility increased. Increased fertility may have been an advantage, because of the greater value of children in farming and herding economies; there is evidence from recent population studies that fertility rates are higher where children contribute more to the economy (Kasarda, 1971; White, 1973). Not only may parents desire more children to help with chores; the increased workload of mothers may also (but inadvertently) decrease birth spacing. The busier a mother is, the less frequently she may nurse and the

CURRENT ISSUES

The Effect of Food-Getting on the Environment

Many people are now aware of industrial pollution—the dumping of industrial wastes in the ground or into rivers, the spewing of chemicals into the air through smokestacks—but we don't often realize how much humans have altered the environment by the ways they collect and produce food. Consider irrigation. There are various ways to capture water for irrigation. Water can be channelled from rivers; rainwater can be caught in terraces carved out of hillsides; ancient water can be pumped up from vast underground reservoirs called aquifers. But not all of the water drawn for irrigation seeps into the ground. Much of it evaporates, leaving behind minerals and salts. And the more a piece of land has been irrigated, the saltier the ground becomes. Eventually, the soil becomes too salty to grow crops effectively.

Some archaeologists have suggested that the accumulation of toxic salts in the soil at least partly explains the doom or decline of various groups in the past. For example, salinization may have contributed to the decline of the earliest city-states in Mesopotamia, present-day southern Iraq, and southwestern Iran. The Hohokam farmers who lived in what is now Arizona had about 240 kilometres of canals for irrigation; some of their ditches were 4.5 metres deep and 7.6 metres wide. In fact, their irrigation networks were comparable to those that served the Aztecs in pre-Columbian Mexico City. The

Hohokam seem to have vanished around A.D. 1400, perhaps because the salty soil poisoned their crops. Today much of the soil is still too salty for cultivation.

The lessons of history may not have been learned yet. The San Joaquin Valley of California, perhaps the most productive agricultural area in the world, now has a serious salinization problem. One solution in many of the areas of the Great American Desert is to pump water up from underground. Indeed, in many places there is a great deal of water underground. For example, the Ogallala aquifer, which underlies parts of Nebraska, Kansas, Texas, Oklahoma, Colorado, and New Mexico, contains water left from the Ice Ages. The pumping solution, if it is a solution, is only a short-term fix though, for the huge Ogallala aquifer is also the fastest-disappearing aquifer. The only question is how long it will take to disappear totally.

Too many people raising too many animals can also have serious effects on the environment. We can easily imagine how the possibility of profit might inspire people to try to raise more animals than the land will support. For example, 300 years ago the Great American Desert looked like a vast grassland. It supported large herds of buffalo, which in the next 200 years were all but exterminated by overhunting. The white settlers soon discovered they could raise cattle and sheep on this

grassland, but many parts of it were overgrazed. It took the swirling dust storms of the 1930s to make people realize that overgrazing as well as poor farming practices could be disastrous. These problems are not new. The Norse colonized Greenland and Iceland around A.D. 800; but overgrazing of pasture undoubtedly contributed to soil erosion and the disappearance or decline of the colonies by A.D. 1500.

Are environmental problems associated only with food production? Although food producers may be the worst offenders, there is reason to think that foragers may also have sometimes overfished, overgathered, or overhunted. For example, some scholars suspect that the movement of humans into the New World was mainly responsible for the disappearance of the mammoth. Unfortunately, there is little evidence that humans have been good conservers in the past. That does not mean that humans cannot do better in the future—but they have to want to.

Sources: Dirks R. 1998. Hunger and Famine. In: Ember CR, Ember M, Peregrine PN, editors. Research Frontiers in Anthropology. Upper Saddle River, NJ: Prentice Hall. Prentice Hall/Simon & Schuster Custom Publishing.

Plundering Earth Is Nothing New. 12 June 1994. Los Angeles Times News Service as reported in the New Haven Register. p A18–19.

Reisner M. 1993. Cadillac Desert: The American West and Its Disappearing Water. Revised edition. New York: Penguin.

more likely her baby will be given supplementary food by other caretakers such as older siblings (Ember, 1983). Less frequent nursing (Konner and Worthman, 1980) and greater reliance on other food may result in the earlier resumption of ovulation after the birth of a baby. (Farmers and herders are likely to have animal milk to feed to babies, and also cereals that have been transformed by cooking into soft, mushy porridges.) Therefore, the spacing between births may have decreased (and the number of births per mother, in turn, increased) when mothers got busier after the rise of food production.

Declining Health

Although the rise of food production may have led to increased fertility, this does not mean that health generally improved. In fact, it appears that health declined at least sometimes with the transition to food production. The two trends may seem paradoxical, but rapid population growth can occur if each mother gives birth to a large number of babies, even if many of them die early because of disease or poor nutrition.

The evidence that health may have declined sometime after the rise of food production comes from studies of the bones and teeth of some prehistoric populations, before and after the emergence of food production. Nutritional and disease problems are indicated by such features as incomplete formation of tooth enamel, non-accidental bone lesions (incompletely filled-in bone), reduction in stature, and decreased mean age at death.

In a recent review of the impact of agriculture, Clark Larsen refers to a variety of studies that have observed lower mean ages at death for agricultural populations as compared with earlier hunter-gatherer samples (Larsen, 1995). This, he notes, has been interpreted as a reflection of increased mortality and decreased life expectancy associated with the shift to agriculture. This hypothesis was the central focus of the 1984 volume of papers *Palaeopathology at the Origins of Agriculture* (Cohen and Armelagos, 1984a), in which osteological evidence for demographic patterns and indicators of health are presented for several regions of the world. Many of the prehistoric populations that were studied relied

heavily on agriculture and seemed to show less adequate nutrition and higher infection rates than populations living in the same areas before agriculture. Some of the agricultural populations were of shorter stature and had lower life expectancies (Cohen and Armelagos, 1984b; Roosevelt, 1984; Cohen, 1987; Wood et al., 1992; Cohen, 1998). The general conclusions drawn from studies throughout the 1970s and 1980s was that the shift to an agricultural subsistence and economy was associated with increases in mortality and the prevalence of infectious diseases. However, for populations that were undergoing moderate growth or decline, the effects of changes in mortality are negligible, while the effects of birth rate and therefore fertility are significant (Larsen, 1995). As discussed in Chapter 3, this is critical since life expectancy derived from skeletal samples depends on the simple assumption of mean age at death being approximately equivalent to life expectancy at birth.

Given these arguments, the observed decline in mean age at death among agricultural populations in the archaeological record is more likely a reflection of their rapid population growth (Howell, 1986). The extent to which fertility and mortality increased or decreased with a shift to agriculture is a key question, which as yet remains unsolved (Johansson and Horowitz, 1986). However, given the wide range of ecological conditions in which various populations adopted agricultural practices, there may have been a similarly broad spectrum of demographic responses to this shift with respect to mortality and fertility (Jackes et al., 1997a; Jackes et al., 1997b).

Understanding the biological impact of the Mesolithic–Neolithic transition is in fact not an easy task. Most of the evidence for apparent health declines associated with agriculture comes from Nubia in the Nile Valley and the American Southwest. However, examining this question is difficult since regions with reasonably large samples of Mesolithic skeletons followed immediately by large, well-preserved Neolithic samples are fairly rare (Jackes et al., 1997a; Jackes et al., 1997b). Mary Jackes, David Lubell, and Chris Meiklejohn have studied large samples of Mesolithic and Neolithic skeletal material from central and southern Portugal (Jackes et al., 1997a; Jackes et al., 1997b). In their study of three Mesolithic and eight Neolithic sites, these researchers observed little increase in rates of skeletal infection over this period. They don't find it surprising, however, since the Mesolithic populations show evidence of being relatively sedentary, and the Neolithic populations continued to show some evidence of seasonal foraging (Jackes et al., 1997a; Jackes et al., 1997b). Despite this continuity, there was some apparent increase in fertility and population growth in the Neolithic period. In contrast to the evidence from the Near East, they concluded from their study that there was "no evidence that the comfortable way of life of the Portuguese Mesolithic was replaced by a wretched and unhealthy Neolithic existence" (Jackes et al., 1997a).

The question of a decline in health associated with earlier agricultural populations remains a topic of debate. Greater malnutrition can result from an over-dependence on a few dietary staples that lack some necessary nutrients. Over-dependence on a few sources of food may also increase the risk of famine because the fewer the staple crops, the greater the danger to the food supply posed by a weather-caused crop failure. However, some or most nutritional problems may be the result of social and political factors, particularly the rise of different socio-economic classes of people and unequal access, between and within communities, to food and other resources (Roosevelt, 1984). Social stratification or considerable socio-economic inequality seems likely to have developed after the rise of food production. The effects of stratification and political dominance from afar on the general level of health may be reflected in the skeletal remains of prehistoric Native Americans who died in what is now Illinois between A.D. 950 and 1300, the period spanning the changeover in that region from hunting and gathering to agriculture. The agricultural people living in the area of Dickson's

As this reconstruction shows, transforming grain into flour was a "daily grind," putting a great deal of stress on the lower back and knees of women. Studies of Neolithic skeletons of women show marks of stress on bone and arthritis, probably reflecting their long hours of work at the grinding stone.

Mounds—burial sites named after the doctor who first excavated them—were apparently in much worse health than their hunter-gatherer ancestors. Curiously, archaeological evidence suggests that they were still also hunting and fishing. A balanced diet was apparently available, but who was getting it? Possibly it was the elite at Cahokia, 177 kilometres away, where perhaps 15 000 to 30 000 people lived, who were getting most of the meat and fish. The individuals near Dickson's Mounds who collected the meat and fish may have acquired luxury items such as shell necklaces from the Cahokia elite, but many of the people buried at Dickson's Mounds clearly did not benefit nutritionally from the relationship with Cahokia (Goodman et al., 1984a; Goodman and Armelagos, 1985; Cohen, 1998).

The Elaboration of Material Possessions

Every society makes use of a *technology* to convert raw materials to food and other goods. **Technology** includes tools, constructions (such as fish traps), the required skills (such as how and where to set up a fish trap), and also the political organization required to extract, process, and redistribute resources. Societies vary considerably in their technologies and in the way access to technology is allocated. For example, food collectors and pastoralists typically have fairly small tool kits. They must limit their tools, and their material possessions in general, to what they can comfortably carry with them, or to those that can be expediently manufactured at the place where they are needed.

The tools most needed by food collectors are weapons for the hunt, digging sticks, and receptacles for gathering and carrying. Andaman Islanders used bows and arrows for hunting game and large fish. Australian aborigines developed two types of boomerangs: a heavy one for a straight throw in killing game and a light, returning one for playing games or for scaring birds into nets strung between trees. The Semang of Malaya used poisoned darts and blowguns. The Mbuti Pygmies of the Congo River basin still trap elephants and buffalo in deadfalls and nets. Of all food collectors, the Inuit probably had the most sophisticated weapons, including harpoons, compound bows, and ivory fish hooks. Yet the Inuit also had relatively fixed settlements with available storage space and dog teams and sleds for transportation (Service, 1979).

Societies with intensive agriculture and industrialized societies are likely to have tools made by specialists, which means that tools must be acquired by trade or purchase. Probably because complex tools have greater value, they are less likely than simple tools to be shared except by those who contributed to their production.

In the more permanent villages that were established after the rise of food production about 10 000 years ago, houses became more elaborate and comfortable, and construction methods improved. The materials used in construction depended on whether timber or stone was locally available or whether a strong sun could dry mud bricks. Modern architects might find to their surprise that bubble-shaped houses were known long ago in Neolithic Cyprus. Families in the island's town of Khirokitia made their homes in large, domed, circular dwellings shaped like beehives and featuring stone foundations and mud-brick walls. Often, more space was created by dividing the interior horizontally and firmly propping a second floor on limestone pillars.

Sizable villages of solidly constructed, gabled wood houses were built in Europe on the banks of the Danube and along the rims of Alpine lakes (Clark and Piggott, 1965). Many of the gabled wooden houses in the Danube region were long, rectangular structures that apparently sheltered several family units. In Neolithic times these longhouses had doors, beds, tables, and other furniture that closely resembled those in modern-day societies. We know the people had furniture because miniature clay models have been found at their sites. Several of the chairs and couches seem to be models of padded and upholstered furniture with wooden frames, indicating that Neolithic European artisans were creating fairly sophisticated furnishings (Clark and Piggott, 1965). Such furnishings were the result of an advanced tool technology put to use by a people who, because they were staying in one area, could take time to make and use furniture.

For the first time, apparel made of woven textile appeared. This development was not simply the result of the domestication of flax (for linen), cotton, and wool-growing sheep. These sources of fibre alone could not produce cloth. It was the development by Neolithic society of the spindle and loom for spinning and weaving that made textiles possible. True, textiles can be woven by hand without a loom, but to do so is a slow, laborious process, impractical for producing garments.

The pottery of the early Neolithic was similar to the plain earthenware made by some Mesolithic groups and included large urns for grain storage, mugs, cooking pots, and dishes. To improve the retention of liquid, potters in the Near East may have been the first to glaze the earthenware's porous surface. Later, Neolithic ceramics became more artistic. Designers shaped the clay into graceful forms and painted colourful patterns on the vessels.

It is probable that virtually none of these architectural and technological innovations could have occurred until humans became fully sedentary. Nomadic hunting and gathering peoples would have found it difficult to carry many material goods, especially fragile items such as pottery. It was only when humans became fully sedentary that these goods would have provided advantages, enabling villagers to cook and store food more effectively and to house themselves more comfortably.

There is also evidence of long-distance trade in the Neolithic, as we have noted. Obsidian from southern Turkey was exported to sites in the Zagros Mountains of Iran and to what are now Israel, Jordan, and Syria in the Levant. Great amounts of obsidian were exported to sites about 300 kilometres from the source of supply; more than 80 percent of the tools used by residents of those areas were made of this material (Renfrew, 1969). Marble was sent from western to eastern Turkey, and seashells from the coast were traded to distant inland regions. Such trade suggests a considerable amount of contact among various Neolithic communities.

About 3500 B.C., cities first appeared in the Near East. These cities had political assemblies, kings, scribes, and specialized workshops. The specialized production of goods and services was supported by surrounding farming villages, which sent their produce to the urban centres. A dazzling transformation had taken place in a relatively short time. People had not only settled down but also become "civilized," or urbanized. (The word *civilized* literally means to make "citified" [Anonymous, 1988].) Urban societies seem to have developed first in the Near East and somewhat later around the eastern Mediterranean, in the Indus Valley of northwestern India, in northern China, and in Mexico and Peru. In the next chapter we turn to the rise of these earliest civilizations.

Summary

1. Food collection or foraging—hunting, gathering, and fishing—depends on wild plants and animals and is the oldest human food-getting technology. Food collectors can be found in various physical habitats and most are nomadic and with low population density.

2. In the period before plants and animals were domesticated (called the Mesolithic period in regard to Europe and the Near East), there seems to have been a shift in many areas of the world to less dependence on big-game hunting and greater dependence on what is called broad-spectrum collecting. The broad spectrum of available resources frequently included aquatic resources such as fish and shellfish and a variety of wild plants and deer and other game. Climatic changes may have been partly responsible for the change to broad-spectrum collecting.

3. In some sites in Europe, the Near East, Africa, and Peru, the switch to broad-spectrum collecting seems to be associated with the

development of more permanent communities. In other areas, such as the semi-arid highlands of Mesoamerica, permanent settlements may have emerged only after the domestication of plants and animals.

4. The shift to the cultivation and domestication of plants and animals has been referred to as the Neolithic revolution, and it occurred, probably independently, in a number of areas. To date, the earliest evidence of domestication comes from the Near East about 8000 B.C. Dating for the earliest domestication in other areas of the Old World is not so clear, but the presence of different domesticated crops in different regions suggests that there were independent centres of domestication in China, Southeast Asia (what is now Malaysia, Thailand, Cambodia, and Vietnam), and Africa sometime around or after 6000 B.C. In the New World, there appear to have been several early areas of cultivation and domestication: the highlands of Mesoamerica (about 7000 B.C.), the central Andes around Peru (about the same time), and the Eastern Woodlands of North America (about 2000 B.C.).

5. Theories about why food production originated remain controversial, but most archaeologists think that certain conditions must have pushed people to switch from collecting to producing food. Some possible factors include (1) population growth in regions of bountiful wild resources (which may have pushed people to move to marginal areas where they tried to reproduce their former abundance); (2) global population growth (which filled most of the world's habitable regions and may have forced people to turn to a broader spectrum of wild resources and to domesticate plants and animals); and (3) the emergence of hotter and drier summers and colder winters (which may have favoured sedentism near seasonal stands of wild grain; population growth in such areas may have forced people to plant crops and raise animals to support themselves).

6. Regardless of why food production originated, it seems to have had important consequences for human life. Populations generally increased substantially after plant and animal domestication. Even though not all early cultivators were sedentary, sedentism did increase with greater reliance on agriculture. Somewhat surprisingly, some prehistoric populations that relied heavily on agriculture seem to have been less healthy than prior populations that relied on food collection. In the more permanent villages that were established after the rise of food production, houses and furnishings became more elaborate, and people began to make textiles and to paint pottery. These villages have also yielded evidence of increased long-distance trade.

Glossary Terms

domestication   (p. 272)

food collection   (p. 262)

food production   (p. 262)

foragers   (p. 262)

horticulture   (p. 262)

intensive agriculture   (p. 264)

Neolithic   (p. 272)

rachis   (p. 272)

sedentism   (p. 261)

shifting cultivation   (p. 263)

slash-and-burn techniques   (p. 263)

subsistence technology   (p. 262)

technology   (p. 288)

Critical Questions

1. What might cause people to work harder to get food?

2. How might people have domesticated sheep, goats, and cattle?

3. Why might foragers be less likely then intensive agriculturalists to suffer from food shortages?

Internet Exercises

1. Visit the Çatal Hüyük website **http://catal .arch.cam.ac.uk/catal/catal.html** and learn about the ongoing excavations. Write a brief summary of the most current discoveries.

2. Domestication of wild plants is not without its difficulties. Look at the description of attempts to cultivate wild rice at **www.hort.purdue.edu/ newcrop/proceedings1993/v2-235.html**. Explore the problems of shattering seed casings and increased disease with cultivation.

3. Explore animal domestication at **http:// interactive.usask.ca/ski/agriculture/animals/ breeds.html**. Pick a domestic animal you are interested in and find out when and where it was domesticated.

Suggested Reading

Cohen MN. 1998. Were Early Agriculturalists Less Healthy Than Food Collectors? In: Ember CR, Ember M, Peregrine PN, editors. Research Frontiers in Cultural Anthropology. Upper Saddle River, NJ: Prentice Hall. Prentice Hall/Simon & Schuster Custom Publishing. This article is a specially written chapter for an undergraduate audience, reviewing the evidence for a decline in health with the advent of agriculture.

Cowan CW, Watson PJ, editors. 1992. The Origins of Agriculture: An International Perspective. Washington, DC: Smithsonian Institution Press. Summarizes the geography, climate, botany, and archaeology of the events associated with the emergence of plant cultivation in different parts of the Old and New Worlds.

Henry DO. 1989. From Foraging to Agriculture: The Levant at the End of the Ice Age. Philadelphia: University of Pennsylvania Press. An examination and discussion of theories about the origins of agriculture, with particular reference to the areas bordering the eastern Mediterranean.

MacNeish RS. 1991. The Origins of Agriculture and Settled Life. Norman: University of Oklahoma Press. After reviewing previous theories about the origins of agriculture, the author puts forward his own model and reviews the archaeological sequences in each of the early regions of domestication in order to evaluate his theory.

Price TD, Brown JA, editors. 1985. Prehistoric Hunter-Gatherers: The Emergence of Cultural Complexity. Orlando, FL: Academic Press. A volume of papers by archaeologists on the beginnings of social complexity among hunter-gatherers. The scope is global; most of the papers deal comparatively or cross-archaeologically with the various adaptations of hunter-gatherers in the past.

Thorp IJ. 1999. The Origins of Agriculture in Europe. Routledge. The author presents a comparative analysis from recent literature and archaeological evidence of the late Mesolithic and early Neolithic periods.

13 ORIGINS OF CITIES AND STATES

From the time agriculture first developed until about 6000 B.C., people in the Near East lived in fairly small villages. There were few differences in wealth and status from household to household, and apparently there was no governmental authority beyond the village. There is no evidence that these villages had any public buildings or craft specialists or that one community was very different in size from its neighbours. In short, these settlements had none of the characteristics we commonly associate with "civilization."

Sometime around 6000 B.C., in parts of the Near East—and at later times in other places—a great transformation in the quality and scale of human life seems to have begun. For the first time we can see evidence of differences in status among households. For example, some are much bigger than others. Communities began to differ in size and to specialize in certain crafts, and there are signs that some political officials had acquired authority over several communities, that what anthropologists call "chiefdoms" had emerged.

Somewhat later, by about 3500 B.C., we can see many, if not all, of the conventional characteristics of **civilization**: the first inscriptions, or writing; cities; many kinds of full-time craft specialists; monumental architecture; great differences in wealth and status; and the kind of strong, hierarchical, centralized political system we call the **state**.

This type of transformation has occurred many times and in many places in human history. The most ancient civilizations arose in the Near East around 3500 B.C., in northwestern India after 2500 B.C., in northern China around 1750 B.C., in the New World (Mexico and Peru) just over 2000 years ago, and in tropical Africa somewhat later (Anonymous, 1978; Connah, 1987; Wenke, 1990). At least some of these civilizations evolved independently of the others—for example, those in the New World and those in the Old World. Why did they do so? What conditions favoured the emergence of centralized, state-like political systems? What conditions favoured the establishment of cities? We ask this last question separately, because archaeologists are not yet certain that all the ancient state societies had cities when they first developed centralized government. In this chapter we discuss some of the things archaeologists have learned or suspect about the growth of ancient civilizations. Our discussion focuses primarily on the Near East and Mexico because archaeologists know the most about the sequences of cultural development in those two areas (see Figure 13–1).

Archaeological Inferences about Civilization

The most ancient civilizations have been studied by archaeologists rather than historians because those civilizations evolved before the advent of writing. How do archaeologists infer that a particular people in the preliterate past had social classes, cities, or a centralized government?

As we have noted, it appears that the earliest Neolithic societies were **egalitarian**; that is, people did not differ much in wealth, prestige, or power. Differences in prestige and social power that existed in the Neolithic were conferred upon individuals as a function of respect (status) that was earned through a lifetime of demonstrated skills and accomplishments. This status was not transferable to descendants. Some later societies show signs of social inequality, indicated by burial finds. Archaeologists generally assume that inequality in death reflects inequality in life, at least in status and perhaps also in wealth and power. Thus, we can be fairly sure that a society had differences in status if only some people were buried with special objects, such as jewellery or pots filled with food. Further, we can be fairly sure that high status was assigned at birth rather than achieved in later life if we find noticeable differences in children's tombs. For example, some (but not all) child burials from as early as 5500 to 5000 B.C. at Telles-Sawwan in Iraq, and from about 800 B.C. at La Venta in Mexico, are filled with statues and ornaments, suggesting that some children had high status from birth (Flannery, 1972). However, burials indicating differences in status do not necessarily mean a society had significant differences in wealth. It is only when archaeologists find other substantial differences, as in house size and

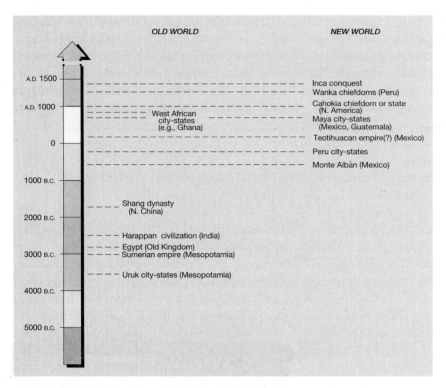

Figure 13–1 The Emergence of Civilization

furnishings, that we can be sure the society had different socio-economic classes of people.

Some archaeologists think that states first evolved around 3500 B.C. in Greater Mesopotamia, the area now shared by southern Iraq and southwestern Iran. Archaeologists do not always agree on how a state should be defined, but most think that hierarchical and centralized decision making affecting a substantial population is the key criterion. Other characteristics are usually, but not always, found in these first states. They usually have cities with a substantial part of the population not involved directly in the collection or production of food (which means that people in cities are heavily dependent on people elsewhere); full-time religious and craft specialists; public buildings; and often an official art style. There is a hierarchical social structure topped by an elite class from which the leaders are drawn (Flannery, 1972; Redman, 1978).

How can archaeologists tell, from the information provided by material remains, whether a society was a state or not? This depends in part on the individual criteria for a state. For example, Henry Wright and Gregory Johnson defined a state as a centralized political hierarchy with at least three levels of administration (Wright and Johnson, 1975). How might archaeologists infer that such a hierarchy existed in some area? Wright and Johnson suggested that the way settlement sites differ in size is one indication of how many levels of administration there were in an area.

During the early Uruk period (just before 3500 B.C.) in what is now southwestern Iran, there were some 50 settlements that seem to fall into three groups in terms of size (Wright and Johnson, 1975; Johnson, 1987). There were about 45 small villages, three or four "towns," and one large centre, Susa. These three types of settlements seem to have been part of a three-level administration hierarchy, since many small villages could not trade with Susa without passing through a settlement intermediate in size. Because a three-level hierarchy is Wright and Johnson's criterion of a state, they think a state had emerged in the area by early Uruk times.

Evidence from the next period, middle Uruk, suggests more definitely that a state had emerged. This evidence takes the form of clay seals that were apparently used in trading (Wright and Johnson, 1975). *Commodity sealings* were used to keep a shipment of goods tightly closed until it reached its destination, and *message sealings* were used to keep track of goods sent and received. The clay seals found in Susa include many message seals and *bullae*, clay containers that served as bills of lading for goods received. The villages, in contrast, had few message seals and *bullae*. Again, this finding suggests that Susa administered the regional movement of goods and that Susa was the "capital" of the state.

Let us turn now to the major features of the cultural sequences leading to the first states in southern Iraq.

Cities and States in Southern Iraq

Farming communities older than the first states have not been found in the arid lowland plains of southern Iraq—the area known as Sumer, where some of the earliest cities and states developed. Perhaps silt from the Tigris and Euphrates rivers has covered them. Or, as has been suggested, Sumer may not have been settled by agriculturalists until people learned how to drain and irrigate river-valley soils otherwise too wet or too dry for cultivation. At any rate, small communities depending partly on agriculture had emerged in the hilly areas north and east of Sumer early in the Neolithic. Later, by about 6000 B.C., a mixed herding-farming economy developed in those areas.

The Formative Era

Elman Service called the period from about 5000 to 3500 B.C. the *formative era*, for it saw the coming together of many changes that seem to have played a part in the development of cities and states. Service suggested that with the development of small-scale irrigation, lowland river areas began to attract settlers. The rivers provided not only water for irrigation but also molluscs, fish, and water birds for food, and they provided routes by which to import needed raw materials, such as hardwood and stone that were lacking in Sumer.

Changes during this period suggest an increasingly complex social and political life. Differences in status are reflected in the burial of statues and ornaments with children. Different villages specialized in the production of different goods—pottery in some, copper and stone tools in others (Flannery, 1972). Temples were built in certain places that may have been centres of political as well as religious authority for several communities (Service, 1975). Furthermore, some anthropologists think that **chiefdoms**, each having authority over several villages, had developed by this time (Flannery, 1972; Service, 1975).

Sumerian Civilization

By about 3500 B.C., there were quite a few cities in the area of Sumer. Most were enclosed in a fortress wall and surrounded by an agricultural area. About 3000 B.C. all of Sumer was unified under a single government. After that time, Sumer became an empire, with great urban centres. Imposing temples, commonly set on artificial mounds, dominated the cities. In the city of Warka the temple mound was about 45 metres high. The empire was very complex and included an elaborate system for the administration of justice, codified laws, specialized government officials, a professional standing army, and even sewer systems in the cities. Among the many specialized crafts were brick making, pottery, carpentry, jewellery making, leatherworking, metallurgy, basket making, stonecutting, and sculpture. Sumerians learned to construct and use wheeled wagons, sailboats, horse-drawn chariots, and spears, swords, and armour of bronze (Kramer, 1963).

As economic specialization developed, social stratification became more elaborate. Sumerian documents describe a system of social classes: nobles, priests, merchants, craft workers, metallurgists, bureaucrats, soldiers, farmers, free citizens, and slaves. Slaves were common in Sumer; they often were captives, brought back as the spoils of war.

A partially restored ziggurat, or temple tower, in what was the Sumerian city of Ur in 2100 B.C.

the form of ledgers containing inventories of items stored in the temples and records of livestock or other items owned or managed by the temples. Sumerian writing had wedge-shaped characters, or **cuneiform**, formed by pressing a stylus against a damp clay tablet. For contracts and other important documents, the tablet was fired to create a virtually permanent record. Egyptian writing, or **hieroglyphics**, appeared about the same time. Hieroglyphics were written on rolls woven from papyrus reeds, from which our word *paper* derives.

Cities and States in Mesoamerica

We see the first evidence of writing around 3000 B.C. The earliest Sumerian writings were in

Cities and states emerged in Mesoamerica—now Mexico and Central America—later than they did

RESEARCH FRONTIERS

Imperialism, Colonialism, and the State

The first city-states in the world seem to have emerged during the Uruk period, roughly the fourth millennium B.C., in the river valleys of southern Mesopotamia, now southern Iraq. From their very beginnings, these first city-states had "foreign trade." This trade may have been indispensable; the riverine environment, though fertile when drained and irrigated, lacked necessary raw materials such as hardwood and stone. The trade with other areas could have been peaceful and balanced, as between equals. After all, it is possible that when one area has something that another wants, and vice versa, the people on both sides could voluntarily arrange to satisfy each other's needs by bargaining and negotiating. However, the archaeological evidence available from the preliterate Uruk period, as well as the documentary evidence available for shortly afterward, suggests that the first city-states in Mesopotamia were engaged in imperialism and colonialism from their very beginnings.

Just like the British and French,

who first came to North America to explore and trade and often used force to protect their settlements and access to trade items, the Uruk city-states seem also to have dominated their peripheral, less-developed trading "partners." For example, before 3000 B.C. there were fortified towns with Uruk-style pottery and administrative artifacts at river junctions in the north of Mesopotamia. Why did the Uruk people go there? One possibility is that they deliberately built outposts to secure their access to needed trade goods, including hides and dried meat.

There was no single state involved in this imperialism and colonialism. Not until after 3000 B.C. was southern Mesopotamia (Sumer) politically unified. Rather, the various Uruk-period polities of the Tigris and Euphrates river valleys seem to have been intensely competitive. The walls around the cities indicate that they were probably subject to attack by their rivals at any time. This imagined scenario is reminiscent of the Greek city-states described by Thucydides.

It is also like the impression we get from the hieroglyphic writings of the Mayan city-states in and around southern Mexico (A.D. 300–800), which, in a mixture of history and propaganda, extol the triumphs of the various rivalrous rulers. And, of course, we all are familiar with how Britain and Spain and Holland and France were rivalrous before and after the New World was discovered.

We know that the Greek city-states were imperialistic colonizers because we have historical evidence of the fact. Greek-speakers, from Athens and other polities, established colonies all over the Mediterranean—Syracuse in Sicily and Marseilles in France, for example. But what about the Uruk city-states? Why should we think they too were imperialistic colonizers? The archaeologist Guillermo Algaze recently reviewed the evidence. First there was the colonization of the plains of southwestern Iran, which people could get to from southern Mesopotamia in seven to ten days by foot or donkey caravan. Then, and maybe overlapping with the

in the Near East. The later appearance of civilization in Mesoamerica may be linked to the later emergence of agriculture in the New World, as we saw in the last chapter, and possibly to the near-absence of large animals such as cattle and horses that could be domesticated (Diamond, 1989). We focus primarily on the developments that led to the rise of the city-state of Teotihuacán, which reached its height almost 2000 years ago. Teotihuacán is located in a valley of the same name, which is the northeastern part of the larger Valley of Mexico.

The Formative Period

The formative period in the area around Teotihuacán (1000–300 B.C.) was characterized initially by small, scattered farming villages on the hilly slopes just south of the Teotihuacán Valley. There were probably a few hundred people in each hamlet, and each of these scattered groups was probably politically autonomous. After about 500 B.C., there seems to have been a population shift to settlements on the valley floor, probably in association with the use of irrigation. Between about 300 and 200 B.C. small "elite" centres emerged in the valley; each had an earthen or stone raised platform. Residences or small temples of poles and thatch originally stood on these platforms. That some individuals, particularly those in the elite centres, were buried in special tombs supplied with ornaments, headdresses, carved bowls, and a good deal of food indicates some social inequality (Helms, 1975; Sanders et al., 1979). The various elite centres may indicate the presence of chiefdoms.

expansion into southwestern Iran, the Uruk polities established outposts or took over already-existing settlements to the north and northwest, on the plains of what are now northern Iraq and Syria; these latter settlements were apparently all located at intersections of the important waterways and overland routes.

According to Algaze, the Uruk enclaves and outposts outside southern Mesopotamia fit what the comparative historian Philip Curtin calls "trade diaspora." Curtin thinks that such movements developed after the emergence of cities, with their vulnerable populations. (An urban population is vulnerable because a city, by definition, is inhabited mostly by people who are dependent for their food on people who live outside the city.) Diasporas have taken various forms, but they all represent ways to organize exchange between areas with different but complementary resources. At one end of the range of possibilities—involving little or no political organization—commercial specialists remove themselves from their own society and settle as aliens somewhere else. At the other end of the range of variation—the most politically organized end—the expanding polity is involved from the beginning in the founding of outposts that secure the required trade.

Algaze thinks that the Uruk expansion was motivated by a lack of resources in southern Mesopotamia, but is that a complete explanation? Other areas of the world, at the time and since, have lacked resources, but they did not all become imperialistic colonizers. So what else, in addition to the need for external resources, might explain the Uruk expansion? And how can we explain why it eventually stopped? Algaze notes that when the Uruk settlers moved into southwestern Iran, they were entering an area that was not so densely settled, so they may have encountered only minimal resistance. Indeed, the various Uruk-period enclaves and outposts outside southern Mesopotamia were apparently larger and more complex than any previous communities in the peripheral areas. Perhaps, then, imperialism and colonialism are possible only in a world of unequals.

Years ago, the anthropologist Stanley Diamond argued that "imperialism and colonialism are as old as the State." Does this mean that states are likely to practice imperialism and colonialism if they can get away with it? Or are only some conditions likely to predispose states to imperialism and colonialism? How strongly are imperialism and colonialism linked to state organization anyway? What makes a humane state possible? Perhaps future research, particularly cross-cultural and cross-historical research, will tell us.

Sources: Algaze G. 1993. The Uruk World System: The Dynamics of Expansion of Early Mesopotamian Civilization. Chicago: University of Chicago Press.

Curtin PD. 1984. Cross-Cultural Trade in World History. Cambridge: Cambridge University Press.

Diamond S. 1974. In Search of the Primitive: A Critique of Civilization. New Brunswick, NJ: Transaction Books.

Marcus J. 1998. Maya Hieroglyphs: History or Propaganda? In: Ember CR, Ember M, Peregrine PN, editors. Research Frontiers in Anthropology. Upper Saddle River, NJ: Prentice Hall. Prentice Hall/Simon & Schuster Custom Publishing.

Zeder MA. 1994. After the Revolution: Post-Neolithic Subsistence in Northern Mesopotamia. American Anthropologist 96:97–126.

The City and State of Teotihuacán

About 150 B.C. no more than a few thousand people lived in scattered villages in the Teotihuacán Valley. In A.D. 100 there was a city of 80 000. By A.D. 500, well over 100 000 people, or approximately 90 percent of the entire valley population, seem to have been drawn or coerced into Teotihuacán (Millon, 1967; Wenke, 1990).

The layout of the city of Teotihuacán, which shows a tremendous amount of planning, suggests that from its beginning the valley was politically unified under a centralized state. Mapping has revealed that the streets and most of the buildings are laid out in a grid pattern, where each grid square measures 57 square metres. Residential structures are often squares of this size, and many streets are spaced apart according to multiples of the basic unit. Even the river that ran through the centre of the city was channelled to conform to the grid pattern. Perhaps the most outstanding feature of the city is the colossal scale of its architecture. Two pyramids dominate the metropolis, the so-called "Pyramid of the Moon" and the "Pyramid of the Sun." At its base the latter is as big as the great Pyramid of Cheops in Egypt.

The thousands of residential structures built after A.D. 300 follow a standard pattern. Narrow streets separate the one-storey buildings, each of which has high, windowless walls. Patios and shafts provide interior light. The layout of rooms suggests that each building consisted of several apartments; more than 100 people may have lived in one of these apartment compounds. There is variation from compound to compound in the size of rooms and the elaborateness of interior decoration, suggesting considerable variation in wealth (Millon, 1976).

Like any major city, Teotihuacán attracted migrants from the surrounding areas. Researchers at the University of Western Ontario are currently examining the question of how migrant populations maintained their ethnic identity within Teotihuacán. Around A.D. 200, a small population of about 1000 Zapotecs emigrated from the Valley of Oaxaca, 400 kilometres southeast of Teotihuacán (Spence, 1992). These people settled in an enclave (Tlailotlacan) at the edge of the city, maintaining their identity for over 500 years (Spence, 1992).

When the Temple of Quetzalcoatl in Teotihuacán was built in A.D. 200, more than 200 individuals were sacrificed. A collaborative effort

The city of Teotihuacán, which had its peak in A.D. 500, was a planned city built on a grid pattern. At the centre was the Pyramid of the Sun shown here.

between Mike Spence at the University of Western Ontario and Mexican physical anthropologists is being undertaken to conduct an osteological analysis of 160 skeletons associated with this event. Using a variety of methods including analysis of ancient DNA, stable isotopes, and skeletal traits, anthropologists hope to be able to paint a clear picture of the health and nutrition, and origin and relationships of those who died.

At the height of its power (A.D. 200–500), the metropolis of Teotihuacán encompassed an area larger than imperial Rome (Millon, 1967). Much of Mesoamerica seems to have been influenced by Teotihuacán. Archaeologically, its influence is suggested by the extensive spread of Teotihuacán-style pottery and architectural elements. Undoubtedly, large numbers of people in Teotihuacán were engaged in production for, and the conduct of, long-distance trade. Perhaps 25 percent of the city's population worked at various specialized crafts, including the manufacture of projectile points and cutting and scraping tools from volcanic obsidian. Teotihuacán was close to major deposits of obsidian, which was apparently in some demand over much of Mesoamerica. This fine-grained volcanic stone was used to produce a variety of items in Teotihuacán (projectile points, knives, scrapers, drills, figurines, etc.) that were distributed at times over distances of more than 1000 kilometres (Spence, 1996). Materials found in graves indicate that there was an enormous flow of foreign goods into the city, including precious stones, feathers from colourful birds in the tropical lowlands, and cotton (Helms, 1975; Weaver, 1993).

The City of Monte Albán

Teotihuacán probably was not the earliest city-state in Mesoamerica: there is evidence of political unification somewhat earlier, about 500 B.C., in the Valley of Oaxaca, in southern Mexico, with the city of Monte Albán at its centre. Monte Albán presents an interesting contrast to Teotihuacán. Whereas Teotihuacán seems to have completely dominated its valley, containing almost all its inhabitants and craftspeople, Monte Albán did not. The various villages in the Valley of Oaxaca seem to have

specialized in different crafts, but Monte Albán did not monopolize craft production. After the political unification of the valley, cities and towns other than Monte Albán remained important; the population of Monte Albán grew only to 30 000 or so. Unlike Teotihuacán, Monte Albán was not an important commercial or market centre, it was not laid out in a grid pattern, and its architecture was not much different from that of other settlements in the valley in which it was located (Blanton, 1981; Marcus, 1983).

Monte Albán did not have the kinds of resources that Teotihuacán had. It was located on top of a mountain in the centre of the valley, far from either good soil or permanent water supplies that could have been used for irrigation. Even finding drinking water must have been difficult. No natural resources for trade were nearby, nor is there much evidence that Monte Albán was used as a ceremonial centre. Because the city was at the top of a steep mountain, it is unlikely that it could have been a central marketplace for valley-wide trade.

Why, then, did Monte Albán rise to become one of the early centres of Mesoamerican civilization? Richard Blanton suggested it might have originally been founded in the late formative period (500–400 B.C.) as a neutral place where representatives of the different political units in the valley could reside to coordinate activities affecting the whole valley. Thus, Monte Albán may have been like the cities of Brasília, Washington, D.C., and Athens, all of which were originally founded in "neutral," non-productive areas. Such a centre, lacking obvious resources, would not, at least initially, threaten the various political units around it. Later it might become a metropolis dominating a more politically unified region, as Monte Albán came to do in the Valley of Oaxaca (Blanton, 1976; Blanton, 1978).

Other Centres of Mesoamerican Civilization

In addition to Teotihuacán and Oaxaca, there were other Mesoamerican state societies, which developed somewhat later. For example, there are a number of centres with monumental architecture, presumably built by speakers of Mayan languages, in the highlands and lowlands of modern-day Guatemala and the Yucatán Peninsula of modern-day Mexico. On the basis of surface appearances, the Mayan centres do not appear to have been as densely populated as Teotihuacán or Monte Albán. It is now evident though that these other Mayan centres were more densely populated and more dependent on intensive agriculture than was once thought (Turner, 1970; Harrison and Turner, 1978), and recent translations of Mayan picture writing indicate a much more developed form of writing than previously thought (Houston, 1988). It is apparent now that Mayan urbanization and cultural complexity were underestimated by earlier archaeologists because of the dense tropical forest that now covers much of the area of Mayan civilization.

The First Cities and States in Other Areas

So far we have discussed the emergence of cities and states in southern Iraq and Mesoamerica

whose development is best, if only imperfectly, known archaeologically. But other state societies probably arose more or less independently in many other areas of the world as well (see Figure 13–2). We say "independently" because such states seem to have emerged without colonization or conquest by other states.

Almost at the same time as the Sumerian empire, the great dynastic age was beginning in the Nile Valley in Egypt. The Old Kingdom, or early dynastic period, began about 3100 B.C., with a capital at Memphis. The archaeological evidence from the early centuries is limited, but most of the population appears to have lived in largely self-sufficient villages. Many of the great pyramids and palaces were built around 2500 B.C. (Wenke, 1984).

In the Indus Valley of northwestern India, a large state society had developed by 2300 B.C. This Harappan civilization did not have much in the way of monumental architecture, such as pyramids and palaces, and it was also unusual in other respects. The state apparently controlled an enormous territory—over a million square kilometres. There was not just one major city but many, each

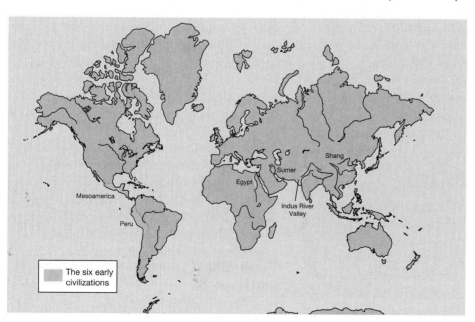

Figure 13–2 Six Early Civilizations

One of the cities of the Harappan civilization in the Indus Valley was Mohenjodaro. Seen here is an excavated large "bath" with surrounding rooms. Columns originally surrounded the pool. (Modern buildings appear in the background.) In contrast to other early civilizations, there was little display of grandeur. All Harappan cities were laid out according to the same plan.

built according to a similar pattern and with a municipal water and sewage system (Wenke, 1984).

The Shang dynasty in northern China (1750 B.C.) has long been cited as the earliest state society in East Asia. Recent research suggests that an even earlier one, the Xia dynasty, may have emerged in the same general area by 2200 B.C. (Chang, 1981). In any case, the Shang dynasty had all the earmarks of statehood: a stratified, specialized society; religious, economic, and administrative unification; and a distinctive art style (Chang, 1986).

In South America, state societies may have emerged after 200 B.C. in the area of modern-day Peru (Wenke, 1984). In sub-Saharan Africa, by A.D. 800, the western Sudan had a succession of city-states. One of them was called Ghana, and it became a major source of gold for the Mediterranean world (Fagan, 1989). In North America, there is also some evidence that a complex chiefdom, and possibly a state-level society, existed in the area around present-day St. Louis by A.D. 1050. Huge mounds of earth 30 metres high mark the site there called Cahokia (Fowler, 1975).

Theories about the Origin of the State

We have seen that states developed in many parts of the world. Why did they evolve when and where they did? A number of theories have been proposed to explain the origins of the state. We consider those that have been discussed frequently by archaeologists (Cohen and Service, 1978; Zeder, 1991).

Irrigation

Irrigation seems to have been important in many of the areas in which early state societies developed. Irrigation made the land habitable or productive in parts of Mesoamerica, southern Iraq, the Nile Valley, and other areas. It has been suggested that the labour and management needed for the upkeep of an irrigation system led to the formation of a political elite, in effect, the overseers of the system, who also eventually became the governors of the society (Wittfogel, 1957). Proponents of this view believe that both the city and civilization were outgrowths of the administrative requirements of an irrigation system.

Critics note that this theory does not seem to apply to all areas where cities and states may have emerged independently. For example, in southern Iraq, the irrigation systems serving the early cities were generally small and probably did not require extensive labour and management. Large-scale irrigation works were not constructed until after cities had been fully established (Adams, 1960; Wright, 1986). Thus, irrigation could not have been the main stimulus for the development of cities and states in Sumer. Even in China, for which the irrigation theory was first formulated, there is no evidence of large-scale irrigation as early as Shang times (Wheatley, 1971).

Although large-scale irrigation may not always have preceded the emergence of the first cities and states, even small-scale irrigation systems could have resulted in unequal access to productive land and so may have contributed to the development of a stratified society (Adams, 1960). In addition, irrigation systems may have given rise to border and other disputes between adjacent groups, thereby prompting people to concentrate in cities for defence and stimulating the development of military and political controls (Adams, 1981). Finally, as Robert Adams and Elman Service both suggested, the main significance of irrigation, either large- or small-scale, may have been its intensification of production, a development that in turn may have indirectly stimulated craft specialization, trade, and administrative bureaucracy (Service, 1975; Adams, 1981).

Population Growth, Circumscription, and War

Robert Carneiro has suggested that states may emerge because of population growth in an area that is physically or socially limited. Competition and warfare in such a situation may lead to the subordination of defeated groups, who are obliged to pay tribute and to submit to the control of a more powerful group (Sanders and Price, 1968; Carneiro, 1970). Carneiro illustrated his theory by describing how states may have emerged on the northern coast of Peru.

After the people of that area first settled into an agricultural village life, population grew at a slow, steady rate. Initially, new villages were formed as population grew. However, in the narrow coastal valleys—blocked by high mountains, fronted by the sea, and surrounded by desert—this splintering-off process could not continue indefinitely. The result, according to Carneiro, was increasing land shortage and warfare between villages as they competed for land. Since the high mountains, the sea, and the desert blocked any escape for losers, the defeated villagers had no choice but to submit to political domination. In this way, chiefdoms may have become kingdoms as the most powerful villages grew to control entire valleys. As chiefs' power expanded over several valleys, states and empires may have been born.

Carneiro noted that physical or environmental circumscription may not be the only kind of barrier that gives rise to a state. Social circumscription may be just as important. People living at the centre of a high-density area may find that their migration is blocked by surrounding settlements just as effectively as it could be by mountains, sea, and desert.

Marvin Harris suggested a somewhat different form of circumscription. He argued that the first states with their coercive authority could emerge only in areas that supported intensive grain agriculture (and the possibility of high food production) and were surrounded by areas that could not support intensive grain agriculture. So people in such areas might tolerate the coercive authority of a state because they would suffer a sharp drop in living standards if they moved away (Harris, 1979; Wenke, 1990).

Carneiro suggested that his theory applies to many areas besides the northern coast of Peru, including southern Iraq and the Indus and Nile valleys. Although there were no geographic barriers in areas such as northern China or the Mayan lowlands on the Yucatán Peninsula, the development of states in those areas may have been the result of social circumscription. Carneiro's theory seems to be supported for southern Iraq, where there is archaeological evidence of population growth, circumscription, and warfare (Young Jr., 1972). And there is evidence of population growth before the emergence of the state in the Teotihuacán Valley (Sanders and Price, 1968).

Population growth does not necessarily mean population pressure though. For example, the populations in the Teotihuacán and Oaxaca valleys apparently did increase prior to state development, but there is no evidence that they had even begun to approach the limits of their resources. More people could have lived in both places (Brumfiel, 1976; Blanton et al., 1981; Feinman et al., 1985). Nor is population growth definitely associated with state formation in all areas where early states arose. For example, according to Wright and Johnson, there was population growth long before states emerged in southwestern Iran, but the population apparently declined just before the states emerged (Wright and Johnson, 1975; Carneiro, 1988; Hole, 1994).

In addition, Carneiro's circumscription theory leaves an important logical question unanswered: Why would the victors in war let the defeated populations remain and pay tribute? If the victors wanted the land so much in the first place, why wouldn't they try to exterminate the defeated and occupy the land themselves, which has happened many times in history?

Local and Long-Distance Trade

It has been suggested that trade was a factor in the emergence of the earliest states (Polanyi, 1957; Sanders, 1968). Wright and Johnson theorized that the organizational requirements of producing items for export, redistributing the items imported, and defending trading parties would foster state formation (Wright and Johnson, 1975). Does the archaeological evidence support such a theory?

In southern Iraq and the Mayan lowlands, long-distance trade routes may indeed have stimulated bureaucratic growth. In the lowlands of southern Iraq, as we have seen, people needed wood and stone for building, and they traded with highland people for those items. In the Mayan lowlands, the development of civilization seems to have been preceded by long-distance trade. Farmers in the lowland regions traded with people in faraway places in order to obtain salt, obsidian for cutting blades, and hard stone for grinding tools (Rathje, 1971). In southwestern Iran, long-distance trade did not become very important until after Susa became the centre of a state society, but short-distance trade may have played the same kind of role in the formation of states.

Kwang-chih Chang put forward a similar theory for the origin of states in China. He suggested that Neolithic societies in the Yellow River valley developed a long-distance trade network, which he called an *interaction sphere,* by about 4000 B.C. Trade spread cultural elements among the societies in the interaction sphere, so that they came to share some common elements. Over time, these societies came to depend on each other both as trade partners and as cultural partners, and around 2000 B.C. they unified into a single political unit under the Shang dynasty (Chang, 1986). Thus, Chang sees political unification in China as an outgrowth of a pre-existing system of trade and cultural interaction.

The Various Theories: An Evaluation

Why do states form? As of now, no one theory seems to fit all the known situations. The reason may be that different conditions in different places may have favoured the emergence of centralized government. After all, the state, by definition, implies an ability to organize large populations for a collective purpose. In some areas, this purpose may have been the need to organize trade with local or far-off regions. In other cases, the state may have emerged as a way to control defeated populations in circumscribed areas. In still other instances, a combination of factors may have fostered the development of the state type of political system (Brumfiel, 1983).

The Consequences of State Formation

We have considered several areas where states arose, as well as a number of theories to explain the origin of states. But what were the consequences for the people living in those societies? The consequences seem to have been dramatic.

One of the ways states change the lifestyles of people is by allowing for larger and denser populations (Johnson and Earle, 2000). As we have already seen, agriculture itself gives populations the potential to grow, and the development of a state only furthers that potential. Why? Because a state is able to build infrastructure—irrigation systems, roadways, markets—that allows both the production and distribution of agricultural products to become more efficient. States are able to coordinate information as well, and can use that information to manage agricultural production cycles and to anticipate or manage droughts, blights, or other natural disasters. States are also able to control access to land (through laws and a military) and thus can both maintain farmers on the land and prevent others (from either within or outside of the state) from removing the farmers or interfering with their ability to produce food.

With increased efficiency of agricultural production and distribution, states also allow many (if not most) people in the society to be relieved of food production. These people are freed to become craftspeople, merchants, and artists, as well as bureaucrats, soldiers, and political leaders. People may also live apart from agricultural fields, and thus cities with dense populations can arise. Cities can also arise in locations that are not suited to agriculture but that perhaps are suited to trade (such as the cities on rivers in southern Mesopotamia) or defence (such as on top of a mountain, as in the case of

NEW PERSPECTIVES ON GENDER

Effects of Imperialism on Women's Status

Archaeologists, particularly those who are women, have begun to pay attention to the gender implications of archaeological materials. Do the findings from excavated houses imply anything about what women and men did where they lived? What do the findings in houses and other places suggest about the division of labour by gender? Can archaeology tell us about women's status in the culture and how it may have changed over time? Research suggests that if you look for gender-related results, you often can find some. For example, the archaeologist Cathy Costin has studied the effects of Inca imperialism on women's status in a conquered area.

Costin participated in a research project that studied culture change in the Yanamarca Valley of highland Peru. The project focused on the development of chiefdoms among the indigenous Wanka ethnic group between A.D. 1300 and 1470 and on the effects of the Inca conquest at the end of that period. According to

the archaeology, most people before the Inca conquest were farmers, but some households specialized part-time in the production of pottery, stone tools, and perhaps textiles. Documents written after the arrival of the Spaniards suggest that the Wanka had developed chiefdoms at about A.D. 1300, possibly as a result of intensified warfare among the various communities. A high level of conflict is inferred from the locations and configurations of the settlements: most people lived in fortified (walled) communities located on hills above the valley floor. According to the documentary sources, the Wanka chiefs had achieved their positions because of success as war leaders.

We know from documents that the Inca conquered the Wanka during the reign of the emperor Pachakuti (about A.D. 1470). The Wanka region became a province within the Inca empire, and bureaucrats from the capital at Cuzco came to govern the Wanka. The Inca conquerors, includ-

ing military personnel, formed the highest class in the valley. The Wanka chiefs became vassals of the Inca state and imitators of Inca ways, using Inca-like pottery and building Inca-style additions to their homes. The economy of the valley became more specialized, apparently to meet the needs of the Inca. People in some villages still mostly farmed, but in other villages most households specialized in the production of pottery, stone tools, and other crafts. Skeletal remains indicate that the commoners became healthier and lived longer after the Inca conquest.

How did the Inca conquest affect the status of women? One key to an answer was suggested by the presence in the excavations of several thousand perforated round ceramic objects. They were spindle whorls, weights used in spinning to keep the thread tight and even. The thread (from llama and alpaca wool) was made into cloth, which became the major form of tax payment after the

Monte Albán). Art, music, and literature often flourish in such contexts, and these too are often consequences of the rise of states. Organized religion also often develops after states appear. Thus, all the hallmarks we associate with civilization can be seen as resulting from the evolution of states (Childe, 1950).

The development of states can have many negative impacts as well. When states develop, people become governed by force and are no longer able to say no to their leaders. Police and military forces can become instruments of oppression and terror (Service, 1975). On a less obvious level, the class stratification of states creates differences in access to resources and an underclass of poor, uneducated, and frequently unhealthy people. Health issues are exacerbated by the concentration of people in cities, an environment in which epidemic diseases can flourish (Diamond, 2003). Without direct access to food supplies, people in cities also face the threat of malnutrition or outright starvation if food production and distribution systems fail (Dirks, 1993).

All states appear to be expansionistic, and the emergence of state warfare and conquest seems one of the most striking negative impacts of the evolution of states. In fact, more human suffering can probably be linked to state expansion than to any other single factor. Why do states expand? One basic reason may be that they are simply able to. States have standing armies ready to fight or be sent to conquer enemies. Another reason for state expansion might be related to the threat of famine and disease, which is more likely with intensive agriculture (Johnson and Earle, 2000).

Inca took over. Each village had to produce a certain amount of cloth for the state tax collectors. The cloth collected was used to clothe men serving in the army and to "pay" other government personnel. The burden of producing the cloth fell on the traditional spinners and weavers, who we know from the post-Spanish documents were females of all ages.

All excavated households, dated to just before the Inca conquest, had spindle whorls, indicating that the female occupants in all households spun and made cloth. More whorls were found the farther up the mountain the house was located, indicating that women who lived closer to the high grasslands, where the flocks of llamas and alpacas were kept, spun more thread than did women who lived farther down from the pastures. We might expect that elite women would do less work. But, to the contrary, the women in elite households seem to have produced more cloth than the women in commoner households; the elite households had twice as many whorls on average as the commoner households had.

After the Inca conquest, households appear to have produced twice the amount of thread they did before, because there are twice the number of recovered spindle whorls. There is no indication, archaeological or documentary, that the women were freed from other tasks to make more time for spinning, so it would appear that women had to work harder under Inca domination to produce thread and cloth. However, the producers do not appear to have benefited from the increased cloth production. Much if not most of the cloth produced was removed from the villages and taken to Inca storage facilities in the capital and redistributed from there.

In addition to working harder for the Inca, women seem to have fared worse than the men when it came to nutrition. Christine Hastorf's chemical analysis of bones from Inca-period graves suggests that women ate less maize (corn) than did men. It seems that the men were "eating out" more than women. Maize was often consumed as *chicha* beer, a key component of state-sponsored feasts, which were probably attended more by men than women. Men also worked more in state-organized agricultural and production projects, where they probably were rewarded with meat, maize, and *chicha* for their service to the state.

Sources: Brumfiel EM. 1992. Distinguished Lecture in Archeology: Breaking and Entering the Ecosystem—Gender, Class, and Faction Steal the Show. American Anthropologist 94:551–567.

Costin CL. 1998. Cloth Production and Gender Relations in the Inka Empire. In: Ember CR, Ember M, Peregrine PN, editors. Research Frontiers in Anthropology. Upper Saddle River, NJ: Prentice Hall. Prentice Hall/Simon & Schuster Custom Publishing.

Gero JM, Conkey MW, editors. 1991. Engendering Archaeology: An Introduction to Women and Prehistory. Oxford: Basil Blackwell.

Hastorf C. 1991. Gender, Space, and Food in Prehistory. In: Gero JM, Conkey MW, editors. Engendering Archaeology: An Introduction to Women and Prehistory. Oxford: Basil Blackwell.

A third answer to the question of why states tend to expand might be that belligerence is simply part of the nature of states. States often arise through military means, and it may be vital to the continuation of some states that military power be continually demonstrated (Ferguson and Whitehead, 1992). Regardless of the causes, war and conquest are the consequences of state formation. Often, too, defeat in war is the fate of states.

The Decline and Collapse of States

All of the most ancient states collapsed eventually. None of them maintained their power and influence into historic times. Why? Might the reasons for their fall tell us something about why they rose in the first place? For example, if a particular factor was partly responsible for the rise of an ancient state, its disappearance or deterioration may partly explain the decline of that state. Then again, the reasons for the decline of states may be quite different from the reasons for the growth of states.

One suggested explanation for the decline and collapse of states, that is, environmental degradation, is perhaps relevant to state development. If states originally arose where the environment was conducive to intensive agriculture and harvests big enough to support social stratification, political officials, and a state type of political system, then perhaps environmental degradation—declining soil productivity, persistent drought, and the like—contributed to the collapse of ancient states. The archaeologist Harvey Weiss has suggested that persistent drought helped to bring about the fall of the ancient Akkadian empire, in the Near East. By 2300 B.C., the Akkadians had established an empire stretching 1300 kilometres from the Persian Gulf in what is now Iraq to the headwaters of the Euphrates River in what is now Turkey. A century later the empire collapsed. Weiss thinks that a long-term drought brought the empire down, as well as other civilizations that existed at that time too. Many archaeologists doubted there was such a widespread drought, but evidence recently presented at a meeting of the American Geophysical Union indicates that the worst dry spell of the past 10 000 years began just as the Akkadians' northern stronghold was being abandoned. The evidence of the drought—windblown dust in sediment retrieved from the bottom of the Persian Gulf—indicates that the dry spell lasted 300 years. Other geophysical evidence suggests that the drought was worldwide (Kerr, 1998).

Environmental degradation may occur for other reasons than natural events. The behaviour of humans may sometimes be responsible. Consider the collapse of Cahokia, a city of at least 15 000 people that thrived for a while in the area

Monk's Mound at Cahokia.

The history of Ephesus, a former city lying in ruins in what is now western Turkey, illustrates the waxing and waning of states and empires. From about 1000 B.C. to 100 B.C., it was controlled by the Greeks, Lydians, Persians, Macedonians, and Romans, among others.

where the Missouri and Mississippi rivers converge. In the twelfth century A.D., Cahokia had large public plazas, a city wall constructed from some 20 000 logs, and massive mounds. But within 300 years only the mounds were left. Silt from flooding covered former croplands and settled areas. The geographer Bill Woods thinks that overuse of woodlands for fuel, construction, and defence led to deforestation, flooding, and persistent crop failure. The result was the abandonment of Cahokia. Timber depletion is also indicated by studies of charcoal from excavations in the area. Apparently the quality of wood used in construction declined over time, suggesting that choice trees became scarcer. Cahokia is just one example of degradation that may have been caused by human behaviour. Another example is the increasing saltiness of soils caused by evaporation of water from fields that have been irrigated over long periods of time, as in what is now southern Iraq (Anonymous, 1996).

Civilizations may sometimes decline because human behaviour has increased the incidence of disease (see discussion on page 243). For example, many lowland Mayan cities were abandoned between 800 and 1000 A.D. Explanations of this collapse have ranged from overpopulation to resource depletion. In fact, another factor may have been increasing incidence of yellow fever. The clearing of forests and the consequent increase of breeding sites for mosquitoes may have favoured the spread of the disease from areas farther south in Central America. Or the planting of particular trees by the Mayans in their urban areas may have increased the populations of co-resident monkeys who carried the disease (which mosquitoes transmitted to people). It should be noted that a disease explanation of the collapse of a state does not help us understand why the state arose in the first place (Wilkinson, 1995).

It is still not clear what specific conditions led to the emergence, or collapse, of the state in each of the early centres of civilization. The question remains as to why states form and decline, so more satisfactory answers may come out of ongoing and future investigations.

Summary

1. Archaeologists do not always agree on how a state should be defined, but most seem to agree that hierarchical and centralized decision making affecting a substantial population is the key criterion. Most states have cities with public buildings, full-time craft and religious specialists, an official art style, and a hierarchical social structure topped by an elite class from which the leaders are drawn. Most states maintain power with a monopoly on the use of force. Force or the threat of force is used by the state to tax its population and to draft people for work or war.

2. Early state societies arose within the Near East in what is now southern Iraq and southwestern Iran. Southern Iraq, or Sumer, was unified under a single government just after 3000 B.C. It had writing, large urban centres, imposing temples, codified laws, a standing army, wide trade networks, a complex irrigation system, and a high degree of craft specialization.

3. The earliest city-state in Mesoamerica probably developed around 500 B.C. in the Valley of Oaxaca, with a capital at Monte Albán. Somewhat later, in the northeastern section of the Valley of Mexico, Teotihuacán developed. At the height of its power, A.D. 200–500, the city-state of Teotihuacán appears to have influenced much of Mesoamerica.

4. City-states arose early in other parts of the New World: in Guatemala, the Yucatán Peninsula of Mexico, Peru, and possibly near St. Louis. In the Old World, early states developed in Egypt, the Indus Valley of India, northern China, and West Africa.

5. There are several theories of why states arose. The irrigation theory suggests that the administrative needs of maintaining extensive irrigation systems may have been the impetus for state formation. The circumscription theory suggests that states emerge when competition and warfare in circumscribed areas lead to the subordination of defeated groups, who are obliged to submit to the control of the most powerful group. Theories involving trade suggest that the organizational requirements of producing exportable items, redistributing imported items, and defending trading parties would foster state formation. Which is correct? At this point, no one theory is able to explain the formation of every state. Perhaps different organizational requirements in different areas all favoured centralized government.

Glossary Terms

chiefdoms   (p. 295)
civilization   (p. 293)
cuneiform   (p. 296)
egalitarian   (p. 293)
hieroglyphics   (p. 296)
state   (p. 293)

Critical Questions

1. Cities and states did not appear until after the emergence of food production. Why might food production be necessary, but not sufficient, for cities and states to develop?

2. As with the emergence of food production, the earliest cities and states developed within a few thousand years of each other. What might be the reasons?

3. How has colonialism shaped today's society? Do colonialism and imperialism still shape society today, and if so in what manner?

4. Can you imagine a future world without states? What conditions might lead to that "state" of the world?

Internet Exercises

1. Visit **http://viking.som.yale.edu/will/finciv/chapter1.htm** and read the essay found there. Give a synopsis of the author's theory on the role of finance in civilization.

2. Visit **www.ambergriscaye.com/earlyhistory/ index.html** and **http://shrike.depaul.edu/ ~mnichol1/papers2/Population.doc/Main_1 .htm** for a wealth of information on early Mesoamerican life.

3. The ancient Greek philosopher Aristotle is considered by some to be the father of modern theories of the state. In about 350 B.C. he proposed, "When several villages are united in a single complete community, large enough to be nearly or quite self-sufficing, the state comes into existence. . . ." Visit **www.fordham.edu/ halsall/ancient/Aristotle-politics-polis.html** to read more of what he had to say about the origin of the state, and compare his version with the theories presented in this text. How has our conception of this matter changed in the intervening centuries?

Suggested Reading

Blanton RE, Kowalewski SA, Feinman G, Appel J. 1993. Ancient Mesoamerica: A Comparison of Change in Three Regions. Second edition. Cambridge: Cambridge University Press. A comparison and analysis of cultural development, and particularly the development of states, in three regions of Mesoamerica—the Valley of Oaxaca, the Valley of Mexico, and the eastern (Mayan) lowlands.

Burenhult G, editor. 1994. Old World Civilizations: The Rise of Cities and States. St. Lucia, Queensland, Australia: University of Queensland Press. A gorgeous book of colour photographs, surveying many of the ancient civilizations in Asia, Africa, and Europe.

Cohen R, Service ER, editors. 1978. Origins of the State: The Anthropology of Political Evolution. Philadelphia: Institute for the Study of Human Issues. A collection of theoretical and empirical papers on the possible origins of states.

Feinman GM, Marcus J, editors. 1998. States. Santa Fe, NM: School of American Research Press. This collection of papers discusses the rise and fall of the ancient states in the Near East, India and Pakistan, Egypt, Mesoamerica, and the Andes, and presents some key questions for future research.

Sanders WT, Parsons JR, Santley RS. 1979. Basin of Mexico: Ecological Processes in the Evolution of a Civilization. New York: Academic Press. A description of a long-term archaeological project that investigated the evolution of civilization in the Valley of Mexico from 1500 B.C. to A.D. 1500, particularly as reflected in the history of its settlement.

Tainter JA. 1988. The Collapse of Complex Societies. Cambridge: Cambridge University Press. Comprehensive description of the theory of collapse as a function of declining marginal returns in complex systems.

Wenke RJ. 1999. Patterns in Prehistory: Humankind's First Three Million Years. Fourth edition. New York: Oxford University Press. Chapters 7 to 15 provide an up-to-date review of what is known and what is controversial about the origins of cities and states around the world.

14 APPLIED ANTHROPOLOGY: PHYSICAL ANTHROPOLOGY AND ARCHAEOLOGY

The news on radio and television and in the newspapers makes us aware every day that social problems threaten people around the world. Every day we see how people in many parts of the world are jeopardized by a variety of social conditions from war to crime and family violence, from diseases like AIDS, from famine, poverty to political corruption.

Worldwide communication has increased our awareness of problems elsewhere, and we seem to be increasingly bothered by problems in our own society. For these two reasons, and perhaps also because we know more than we used to about human behaviour, we may be more motivated to try to solve those problems. We call them "social" problems not only because a lot of people worry about them but also because they have social causes or consequences, and their possible treatments or solutions require at least some changes in social behaviour. For example, a family of viruses may cause AIDS, but it is also a social problem because it is mostly transmitted by sexual contact with another person. Thus, the only ways to avoid it now—abstinence and "safe" sex—require changes in social behaviour. The lives of millions are at risk because of this global social problem.

Anthropology and most of the other social sciences have long been concerned with social problems. One way in which this concern is expressed is through "basic research" that tests theories about the possible causes of social problems. The results of such tests could suggest solutions to the problems if the causes, once discovered, can be reduced or eliminated. Another way to be concerned with social problems is to participate in or evaluate programs intended to improve people's lives. **Applied** or **practising anthropology** as a profession is explicitly concerned with making anthropological knowledge useful. Applied or practising anthropologists may be involved in one or more phases of a program: assembling relevant knowledge, developing plans, assessing the likely social and environmental impact of particular plans, implementing the program, and monitoring the program and its effects (Kushner, 1991).

Clearly, theory testing and applied research may both be motivated by a desire to improve the quality of human life. However, it is often difficult to decide if a particular project is basic or applied. For example, consider a study of the possible causes of war; its results may suggest how the risk of war might be reduced. Is such a study basic or applied research?

This chapter has two major parts. The first deals with applied or practising anthropology including types of application, the ethical issues involved in trying to improve people's lives, the difficulties in evaluating whether a program is beneficial, and the problems in instituting planned change. In the second part of the chapter, we present a variety of examples of applied research in physical anthropology and archaeology.

Applied and Practising Anthropology

Anthropologists care and worry about the people they study, just as they care and worry about family and friends back home. It is upsetting if most of the families in your place of fieldwork have lost many of their babies to diseases that could be eliminated by medical care. It is upsetting when outside political and economic interests threaten to deprive your fieldwork friends of their resources and pride. Anthropologists have usually studied people who are disadvantaged—by imperialism, colonialism, and other forms of exploitation—so it is no wonder that we feel protective about these people, whom we have lived among and shared with in the field.

Nevertheless, caring is not enough to improve others' lives. We may need basic research that allows us to understand how a condition might be successfully treated. A particular proposed "improvement" might actually not be an improvement; well-meaning efforts have sometimes produced harmful consequences. Even if we know that a change would be an improvement, there is still the problem of how to make it happen. The people to be affected may not want to change. Is it ethical to try to persuade them? On the other hand, is it ethical not to try? Applied anthropologists must take all of these matters into consideration in determining whether and how to act in response to a perceived need.

History of Applied Anthropology

In 1934, John Collier, the head of the United States Bureau of Indian Affairs, got legislation passed that provided protections for Native Americans: land could no longer be taken away, lost land was supposed to be restored, tribal governments would be formed, and loans would be made available to reservations. This opened the way toward recognition of the useful roles that anthropologists could play outside academic settings. Events in the 1940s encouraged more applied anthropology. In 1941, anthropologists founded the Society for Applied Anthropology and a new journal devoted to applied anthropology, now called *Human Organization* (Partridge and Eddy, 1987). Following World War II, there was a lull of interest in the field, and it was not until the late 1970s that interest in applied anthropology began to flourish once more.

Applied anthropology in Canada developed much later than in the United States. Early applied work in Canada included a conference organized in 1939 by anthropologists and historians at the University of Toronto on the state of then contemporary Native Canadian populations (Hedican, 1995; Ervin, 2000). Following this in 1947, Harry Hawthorne at the University of British Columbia arranged a meeting of British Columbia Aboriginal chiefs to discuss native life and the role of anthropologists in Aboriginal welfare (Hedican, 1995; Ervin, 2000). In the early 1960s, 50 researchers across Canada conducted a nationwide survey of Aboriginal quality of life, and made a series of recommendations to the federal government. At the same time, anthropological investigations on aspects of development in the Canadian Arctic and subarctic were being undertaken (Hedican, 1995; Ervin, 2000). In particular, researchers at McGill University examined in detail the impact of large development projects like the James Bay hydroelectric project in northern Quebec and the proposed Mackenzie Valley pipeline project in the Northwest Territories on the life of northern Aboriginal peoples (Hedican, 1995; Ervin, 2000). Following this period, applied anthropology in Canada flourished in a variety of areas from Aboriginal self-government and land claims to multiculturalism, mining, fishing, and medical anthropology (Hedican, 1995; Ervin, 2000).

Today anthropologists are interested in studying and solving problems in non-Aboriginal society as well. Anthropologists who call themselves applied or practising anthropologists are usually employed in non-academic settings, working for government agencies, international development agencies, private consulting firms, public health organizations, medical schools, public interest law firms, community development agencies, charitable foundations, and even profit-seeking corporations. Indeed, there are more anthropologists working in non-academic than in academic settings (Frankel and Trend, 1991). These practising anthropologists often work on specific projects that aim to improve people's lives, usually by trying to change behaviour or the environment; or the anthropologists monitor or evaluate efforts by others to bring about change (Hackenberg, 1988). Usually the problems and projects are defined by the employers or clients (the client is sometimes the "target" population), not by the anthropologists (Kushner, 1991). However, anthropologists are increasingly called upon to participate in deciding exactly what improvements might be possible, as well as how to achieve them.

Anthropologists who work in applied fields come out of all sub-fields of anthropology, although most are from ethnology. They may work on public and private programs at home and abroad to provide improvements in agriculture, nutrition, mental and physical health, housing, job opportunities, transportation, education, and the lives of women or minorities. A frequent type of applied work is the "social impact" study required in connection with many programs funded by government or private agencies. For example, archaeologists are hired to study, record, and preserve "cultural resources" that will be disturbed or destroyed by construction projects. Applied anthropologists who were trained in physical anthropology may work in the area of medicine, public health, and forensic investigations.

Ethics of Applied Anthropology

Ethical issues always arise in the course of field-work, and anthropology as a profession has adopted certain principles of responsibility. Above all, an anthropologist's first responsibility is to those who are being studied; everything should be done to ensure that their welfare and dignity will be protected. Anthropologists also have a responsibility to those who will read about their research; research findings should be reported openly and truthfully (Anonymous, 1990b). Since applied anthropology often deals with planning and implementing changes in some target population, ethical responsibilities can become complicated. Perhaps the most important ethical question is: Will the change truly benefit the target population?

In May 1946, the Society for Applied Anthropology established a committee to draw up a specific code of ethics for professional applied anthropologists. After many meetings and revisions, a statement on ethical responsibilities was finally adopted in 1948, and in 1983, the statement was revised (Anonymous, 1990a). According to the code, the target community should be included as much as possible in the formulation of policy, so that people in the community may know in advance how the program will affect them. Perhaps the most important aspect of the code is the pledge not to recommend or take any action that is harmful to the interests of the community.

For archaeology and physical anthropology, a number of professional organizations have implemented specific statements on ethics. The Canadian Archaeological Association has a statement of principles concerning ethical conduct in archaeological excavation and research. Both the Canadian Association for Physical Anthropology and the American Association of Physical Anthropologists have statements on ethical conduct in research; and the Canadian federal government, including the major grant-funding agencies, has statements on human rights, human subjects in research, and Aboriginal rights with respect to research. A variety of museums including the Canadian Museum of Civilization also have policy statements on ethics. While no documents can cover all conceivable circumstances, the spirit of these policies is meant to guide individuals conducting and participating in applied research in archaeology or physical anthropology.

A medical worker in rural Ethiopia vaccinates children. Medical care without a subsequent reduction in births can have harmful consequences because of the increase in population.

Evaluating the Effects of Planned Change

The decision as to whether a proposed change would benefit the target population is not always easy to make. In certain cases, as when improved medical care is involved, the benefits offered to the target group would seem to be unquestionable—we all feel sure that health is better than illness. However, this may not always be true. Consider a public health innovation such as inoculation against disease. Although it would undoubtedly have a beneficial effect on the survival rate of a population, a reduction in the mortality rate might have unforeseen consequences that would in turn produce new problems. For example, once the inoculation program is begun, the number of children surviving would probably increase. However, it might not be possible to increase the rate of food production, given the level of technology, capital, and land resources of the target population. Thus, the death rate, because of starvation, might rise to its previous level and perhaps even exceed it. The inoculation program would not affect the death rate; it might merely change the causes of death. This example shows that even if a program of planned change has beneficial consequences in the short run, a great deal of thought and investigation have to be given to its long-term effects.

In another example, Debra Picchi raised questions about the long-term effects on the Bakairi Indians of a program by the National Brazilian Indian Foundation (FUNAI) to produce rice with machine technology (Picchi, 1991; Picchi, 1998). The Bakairi of the Mato Grosso region largely practise slash-and-burn horticulture in gallery forests along rivers, with supplementary cattle raising, fishing, and hunting. In the early part of the twentieth century their population had declined to 150 people and they were given a relatively small reserve. Some of it was gallery forest, but a larger part was parched and infertile (*cerrado*). When the Bakairi population began to increase, FUNAI introduced a scheme to plant rice on formerly unused *cerrado* land, using machinery, insecticides, and fertilizer. FUNAI paid the costs for the first year and expected that by the third year the scheme would be self-supporting. The project did not go so well because FUNAI did not deliver all the equipment needed and did not provide adequate advice. So only half the expected rice was produced. Still, it was more food than the Bakairi had previously, so the program should have been beneficial to them.

There were, however, negative side effects, not anticipated. Nutritionally, to be sure, the Bakairi were growing an additional starchy food. The use of the *cerrado* for agriculture reduced the area on which cattle can be grazed; cattle are an important source of high-quality protein. So the now-mechanized agriculture has reduced the availability of animal protein. The mechanization also makes the Bakairi more dependent on cash for fuel, insecticides, fertilizer, and repairs. Since cash is hard to come by, only some individuals can be hired—usually men with outside experience who have the required knowledge of machinery. So the cash earned in the now-mechanized agriculture goes mainly to a relatively small number of people. It is debatable whether the new inequalities of income provide long-term effects that are beneficial to the Bakairi.

These failures were not the fault of anthropologists—indeed, most instances of planned change by governments and other agencies usually have begun without the input of anthropologists at all; however, applied anthropologists have played an important role in pointing out the problems with programs like these that fail to evaluate long-term consequences. Such evaluations are an important part of convincing governments and other agencies to ask for anthropological help in the first place. Ironically, failure experiences are learning experiences—applied anthropologists who study previous examples of planned change can often learn a great deal about what is likely or not likely to be beneficial in the long run.

Difficulties in Instituting Planned Change

Whether a program of planned change can be successfully implemented depends largely on whether the targeted population wants the proposed change and likes the proposed program.

Before an attempt can be made at cultural innovation, the innovators must determine whether the target population is aware of the benefits of the proposed change. Lack of awareness can be a temporary barrier to solving the problem at hand. For example, health workers have often had difficulty convincing people that they were becoming ill because something was wrong with their water supply because many people do not believe that disease can be transmitted by water. At other times, the target population is perfectly aware of the problem. A case in point involved Taiwanese women who were introduced to family-planning methods beginning in the 1960s. The women knew they were having more children than they wanted or could easily afford, and they wanted to control their birth rate. They offered no resistance—they merely had to be given the proper devices and instructions and the birth rate quickly fell to a more desirable, and more manageable, level (Niehoff, 1966).

Resistance by Target Population. Not all proposed change programs are beneficial to the target population. Sometimes resistance is rational. Applied anthropologists have pointed to cases where the judgment of the affected population has been better than that of the agents of change. One such example occurred during a Venezuelan government-sponsored program to give infants powdered milk. The mothers rejected the milk, even though it was free, on the grounds that it implied that the mothers' milk was no good (Foster, 1962). But who is to say that the resisting mothers were not in fact intuitively smart, reflecting an awareness that such a milk program would not benefit the children? Medical research now indicates quite clearly that mother's milk is far superior to powdered milk or formula. First, human milk best supplies the nutrients needed for human development. Second, it is now known that the mother, through her milk, is able to transmit antibodies (disease resistances) to the baby. Third, nursing delays ovulation and usually increases the spacing between births (Jelliffe and Jelliffe, 1975).

The switchover to powdered milk and formula in many underdeveloped areas has been nothing short of a disaster, resulting in increased malnutrition and misery. For one thing, powdered milk must be mixed with water, but if the water and the bottles are not sterilized, more sickness is introduced. Then, too, if powdered milk has to be purchased, mothers without cash are forced to dilute the milk to stretch it. If a mother feeds her baby formula or powder for even a short time, the process is tragically irreversible, for her own milk dries up and she cannot return to breastfeeding even if she wants to.

As the Venezuelan example suggests, individuals may be able to resist proposed medical or health projects because acceptance is ultimately a

Breastfeeding is now known to be better for the health of the baby. In many countries, breastfeeding in public is perfectly acceptable, as among the Huastec of Mexico. In North America, the embarrassment of breastfeeding in public may discourage some mothers from breastfeeding.

personal matter. Large development projects planned by powerful governments or agencies are rarely stoppable, but even they can be resisted successfully. In the early 1990s, the Kayapo of the Xingu River region of Brazil were able to cancel a plan by the Brazilian government to build dams along the river for hydroelectric power. The Kayapo gained international attention when some of their leaders appeared on North American and European television and then successfully organized a protest in 1989 by members of several tribal groups. Their success seemed to come in part from their ability to present themselves to the international community as guardians of the rain forest—an image that resonated with international environmental organizations that supported their cause. Although to outsiders it might seem that the Kayapo want their way of life to remain as it was, the Kayapo are not opposed to all change. In fact, they want greater access to medical care, other government services, and manufactured goods from outside (Fisher, 1994).

However, even if a project is beneficial to a population, it may still meet with resistance. Factors that may hinder acceptance can be divided roughly into three sometimes overlapping categories: *cultural*, *social*, and *psychological* barriers.

Cultural barriers are shared behaviours, attitudes, and beliefs that tend to impede the acceptance of an innovation. For example, members of different societies may view gift giving in different ways. Particularly in commercialized societies, things received for nothing are often believed to be worthless. When the government of Colombia instituted a program of giving seedling orchard trees to farmers in order to increase fruit production, the farmers showed virtually no interest in the seedlings, many of which proceeded to die of neglect. When the government realized that the experiment had apparently failed, it began to charge each farmer a nominal fee for the seedlings. Soon the seedlings became immensely popular and fruit production increased (Foster, 1962). The farmers' demand for the seedlings may have

CURRENT ISSUES

Exploring Why an Applied Project Didn't Work

When applied projects do not succeed, it is important for researchers to try to understand why. Part of the problem may be that the intended recipients' ideas about how things work may be very different from the researchers' ideas. Consider the following example. In Guatemala, village health-care workers were not only testing people for malaria but also offering free antimalarial drugs. Yet, surprisingly, a community survey found that only 20 percent of people with malaria symptoms took advantage of the free treatment. More surprisingly, most people with symptoms spent the equivalent of a day's wages to buy an injection that was not strong enough to be effective! Why? What was going on?

Finding the answer was not easy. First, researchers designed interviews to elicit folk concepts about illness. What kinds of illnesses are there? What are their causes? What are their symptoms, and how are different illnesses to be treated? They conducted interviews with a random sample of households to check on what illnesses people had and what they did about them. Then they asked people to consider different hypothetical scenarios (vignettes), with different types of people and different degrees of severity of illness, to find out what treatment they would choose for these other people. All of these methods were well thought out, but the answers still did not predict what people actually did when they thought they had malaria. Finally, the researchers devised precise comparisons of the kinds of pills passed out by health-care workers and the pills and ampoules for injections sold by the drugstore. They compared them two at a time, varying dosages and brands. People did think that more pills were more effective, as indeed they were, but they thought that the colourfully wrapped store-bought pill was more effective than the equivalent white unwrapped free pill, even though it was not. They also thought that one store-bought ampoule used for injections, for which they would pay a day's wages, was more effective than four pills of any kind! In fact, one ampoule was equivalent to only one pill.

Applied researchers often use such trial-and-error methods to find out how to get the information they need. Methods that work in one field setting don't always work in others. To get the information needed,

increased because they were charged a fee and therefore came to value the trees. The market demand for fruit may also have increased. Other examples of cultural resistance to change, which we discuss more fully later in this chapter, are beliefs about sex that make it difficult for people to follow medical guidelines for safer sex.

It is very important for agents of change to understand the shared beliefs and attitudes of a target population. First, indigenous cultural concepts or knowledge can sometimes be used effectively to enhance educational programs. For instance, in a program in Haiti to prevent child mortality from diarrhea, change agents used the terminology for traditional native herbal tea remedies (*rafrechi*, or cool refreshment) to identify the new oral rehydration therapy, which is a very successful medical treatment. In native belief, diarrhea is a "hot" illness and appropriate remedies must have cooling properties (Coreil, 1989). Second, even if indigenous beliefs are not helpful to the campaign, not paying attention to contrary beliefs can under-

mine the campaign. However, uncovering contrary beliefs is not easy, particularly when they do not emerge in ordinary conversation (see Current Issues, *Exploring Why an Applied Project Didn't Work*).

The acceptance of planned change may also depend on social factors. Research suggests that acceptance is more likely if the change agent and the target (or potential adopter) are similar socially. But change agents may have higher social status and more education than the people they are trying to influence. So change agents may work more with higher-status individuals because they are more likely to accept new ideas. If lower-status individuals also have to be reached, change agents of lower status may have to be employed (Rogers, 1983).

Finally, acceptance may depend on psychological factors—that is, how the individuals perceive both the innovation and the agents of change. In the course of trying to encourage women in the southeastern United States to breastfeed rather than bottle-feed their infants, researchers discovered a number of reasons why women were reluctant to

researchers must sometimes let the subjects structure their own answers. At other times, as in this case, they may have to make very specific comparisons to get predictive answers. The people in the Guatemala study didn't believe that the free pills were strong enough to work, so they didn't use them. More research would be needed to uncover why they did not believe the free pills were effective. Was it because they were free? Was it because the store-bought drugs were more nicely packaged? Or was there a belief that injections work better than pills? That's what the research process is like; it always leads to new questions, particularly more general questions requiring more extensive or more comparative research.

For example, the Guatemala project revealed why a particular program was not successful in a particular

area. But how widespread are the interfering beliefs? Are they found throughout Guatemala? Do they interfere with the introduction of other medicines? Are we dealing with problems that exist in other areas of Central and South America? Although we don't yet have answers to these more extensive questions, anthropologists have developed efficient methods for assessing variation in beliefs within and between cultures.

We now know that if we ask one or two informants, we cannot assume that the answer is cultural, but that doesn't mean that we need to ask hundreds of people. If a belief is cultural and therefore commonly held, asking 10 to 20 individuals the same question is sufficient to provide the researcher with a high probability that an answer is correct. (The agreement among respondents is called *cultural consensus*.) So, for

example, Guatemalan respondents mostly agreed about which illnesses were contagious, but they disagreed a lot about whether a particular disease should be treated with a "hot" or a "cold" remedy. Using cultural-consensus methods, researchers can compare rural and urban residents, and they can also compare informants in different cultures. When we have more of these systematic comparisons, medical anthropologists and health practitioners may have a better understanding of how to implement medical care.

Sources: Kimball Romney A, Weller SC, Batchelder WH. 1986. Culture as Consensus: A Theory of Culture and Informant Accuracy. American Anthropologist 88:313–38.

Weller SC. 1998. The Research Process. In: Ember CR, Ember M, Peregrine PN, editors. Research Frontiers in Anthropology. Upper Saddle River, NJ: Prentice Hall. Prentice Hall/Simon & Schuster Custom Publishing, and the research referred to therein.

breastfeed their infants, even though they heard it was healthier. Many women did not have confidence that they would produce enough milk for their babies; they were embarrassed about breastfeeding in public; and their family and friends had negative attitudes (Bryant and Bailey, 1990:32). In designing an educational program, change agents may have to address such psychological concerns directly.

Discovering and Utilizing Local Channels of Influence.

In planning a project involving cultural change, the administrator of the project should determine the normal channels of influence in the population. In most communities, there are pre-established networks for communication, as well as persons of high prestige or influence who are looked to for guidance and direction. An understanding of such channels of influence is extremely valuable when deciding how to introduce a program of change. In addition, it is useful to know at what times, and in what sorts of situations, one channel is likely to be more effective in spreading information and approval than another.

An example of the effective use of local channels of influence occurred when an epidemic of smallpox broke out in the Kalahandi district of the state of Orissa in India in the 1940s. The efforts of health workers to vaccinate villagers against the disease were consistently resisted. The villagers, naturally suspicious and fearful of these strange men with their equally strange medical equipment, were unwilling to offer themselves, and particularly their babies, to the peculiar experiments the strangers wished to perform. Afraid of the epidemic, the villagers appealed for help to their local priest, whose opinions on such matters they trusted. The priest went into a trance, explaining that the illness was the result of the goddess Thalerani's anger with the people. She could be appeased, he continued, only by massive feasts, offerings, and other demonstrations of the villagers' worship of her. Realizing that the priest was the village's major opinion leader, at least in medical matters, the frustrated health workers tried to get the priest to convince his people to undergo vaccination. At first, the priest refused to co-operate with the strange men, but when his

favourite nephew fell ill, he decided to try any means available to cure the boy. He thereupon went into another trance, telling the villagers that the goddess wished all her worshippers to be vaccinated. Fortunately, the people agreed, and the epidemic was largely controlled (Niehoff, 1966).

If channels of influence are not stable, using influential persons in a campaign can sometimes backfire. In the educational campaign in Haiti to promote the use of oral rehydration therapy, Mme Duvalier, the first lady of Haiti at the time, lent her name to the project. Because there were no serious social or cultural barriers to the treatment and mothers reported that children took to the solutions well, success was expected. However, in the middle of the campaign, Haiti became embroiled in political turmoil and the first lady's husband was overthrown. Some of the public thought that the oral rehydration project was a plot by the Duvaliers to sterilize children, and this suspicion fuelled resistance (Coreil, 1989:155). Even after the Duvalier regime had ended, people in Haiti were suspicious of any government-sponsored program.

Applied anthropologists often advocate integrating indigenous healers into medical change programs. This idea may encounter considerable resistance by the medical profession and by government officials who view such healers negatively, but this strategy may be quite effective in more isolated areas where indigenous healers are the only sources of health care. If they are involved in medical change programs, indigenous healers are likely to refer patients to hospitals when they feel unable to cope with an illness, and the hospitals choose sometimes to refer patients to the healers (Warren, 1989).

Other social groups and their attitudes can play important roles in shaping the outcome of the change program. Most often the people who are being helped have few privileges, little political and economic power, and low prestige (Goodenough, 1963:416). Change or development is often regarded as a threat to those with more privilege. If those who do have power object to the new program, they may effectively sabotage it. The development agent, then, not only has to reckon with the local community but may also have to persuade more powerful groups in the society that the new program should be introduced.

Toward Collaborative Applied Anthropology

Most large-scale programs of planned change originate with governments, international aid organizations, or other agencies. Even if the programs are well intentioned and even if the appropriate evaluations are made to ensure that the population will not be harmed, the population targeted for the change is usually not involved in the decision making. Some anthropologists, like Wayne Warry, think that applied anthropology should be more collaborative. Warry explains that a Native Canadian elder asked him whether he (Warry) would tolerate his own methods and interpretations if he were the native (Warry, 1990). This question prompted him to involve himself in a project with Native Canadian collaborators, directed by the Mamaweswen Tribal Council. The project assessed health-care needs and developed plans to improve local community health care. Funding was provided by the Canadian government as part of a program to transfer health care to the First Nations. Native researchers conducted the surveys and workshops to keep the community informed about the project. The tribal council also reviewed any publications and shares in any profits resulting from those publications.

Applied anthropologists may be increasingly asked to work on behalf of indigenous grass-roots organizations. In some cases these small groups and networks of such groups are starting to hire their own technical assistance (Fisher, 1996:57). When such organizations do the hiring, they control the decision making. There is increasing evidence that grass-roots organizations are the key to effective development.

For example, Kenyan farmers who belong to grass-roots organizations produce higher farm yields than those farmers who do not belong, even though the latter group is exposed to more agricultural extension agents (Oxby, 1983; Fisher, 1996).

Women parade to arouse awareness of AIDS in Eritrea.

Grass-roots organizations can succeed where government or outside projects fail. We have plenty of instances of people effectively resisting projects, but their willingness to change, and their participation in the crucial decision making, may be mostly responsible for the success of a change project.

Medical Anthropology

Illness and death are significant events for people everywhere. No one is spared. So it should not be surprising that how people understand the causes of illness and death, how they behave, and what resources they marshal to cope with these events are extremely important parts of culture. Some argue that we will never completely understand how to treat illness effectively until we understand the cultural behaviours, attitudes, values, and the larger social political milieu in which people live.

Anthropologists, particularly medical anthropologists, actively engaged in studying health and illness increasingly recognize the need to consider both social and biological factors—the biocultural model (see p. 12)—for understanding disease processes in populations. For instance, some populations have an appalling incidence of infant deaths due to diarrhea. The origin of this situation is mostly biological, in the sense that the deaths are caused by bacterial infection, but the question is, why are so many infants exposed to those bacteria? Usually, the main reason is social. The affected infants are likely to be poor, and as a result are likely to live with infected drinking water. Similarly, malnutrition may be the biological result of a diet poor in protein, but such a diet is usually also a cultural phenomenon, reflecting a society with classes of people with very unequal access to the necessities of life.

People with more social, economic, and political power in a society are generally healthier (Hahn, 1995). Inequality in health in socially stratified societies is not surprising. The poor usually have more exposure to disease because they live in more crowded conditions. The poor are also more likely to lack the resources to get quality care. For many diseases, health problems, and death rates, incidence or frequency varies directly with social class. In the United Kingdom, for example, people in the higher social classes are less likely to have headaches, bronchitis, pneumonia, heart disease, arthritis, injuries, and mental disorders, to name just a few of the differences (Mascie-Taylor, 1990).

Inequities because of class and ethnicity are not limited to within-society differences. Power and economic differentials between societies also have profound health consequences. Over the course of European exploration and expansion, indigenous peoples died in enormous numbers from introduced diseases, wars, and conquests; they had their lands expropriated and diminished in size and quality. When incorporated into colonial territories or into countries, indigenous peoples usually become minorities and they are almost always very poor. These conditions of life not only affect the incidence of disease, they also tend to lead to greater substance abuse, violence, depression, and other mental pathologies (Cohen, 1999).

The medical profession's ways of treating illness may be able to treat some conditions well, but the medical profession cannot tell us why some groups are more affected than others, or why the effectiveness of treatment varies from group to group. Recognizing the interaction of culture and biology, medical anthropology and anthropology in general utilize the biocultural model for better understanding how illness is manifest and spread within a population.

Cultural Understandings of Health and Illness

Medical researchers and medical practitioners in Canada, the United States and other Western societies do not exist in a social vacuum. Many of their ideas and practices are influenced by the culture in which they live. We may think of medicine as purely based on "fact" but on reflection it is clear that many ideas stem from the culture in which the researchers reside. Discovering the health-related beliefs, knowledge, and practices of a cultural group—its **ethnomedicine**—is one of the goals of medical anthropology. How do cultures view health and illness? What are their theories about the causes of illness? Do those theories affect how illnesses are treated? What is the therapeutic process? Are there specialized medical practitioners, and how do they heal? Are there special medicines, and how are they administered? These are some of the questions asked by the anthropological study of ethnomedicine.

In their extensive research on Mayan ethnomedicine, Elois Ann Berlin and Brent Berlin make a strong case that although studies of the Maya have emphasized beliefs about illness that are based on supernatural causes, a good deal of Mayan ethnomedicine is about natural conditions, their signs and symptoms, and the remedies used to deal with those conditions. In regard to gastrointestinal diseases, the Berlins found that the Maya have a wide-ranging and accurate understanding of anatomy, physiology, and symptoms. Furthermore,

In China and elsewhere, Tai Chi exercises are believed to bring harmony and balance.

the remedies they use, including recommendations for food, drink and herbal medicines, have properties that are not that different from those of the Western medical profession (Berlin, 1996).

Western medicine has increasingly become aware of the value of studying the "traditional" medicinal remedies discovered or invented by people around the world. In studying the indigenous medicines of the Hausa of Nigeria, Nina Etkin and Paul Ross asked individuals to describe the physical attributes of more than 600 plants and their possible medicinal uses, more than 800 diseases and symptoms, and more than 5000 prepared medicines. While many medicines were used for treating sorcery, spirit aggression, or witchcraft, most medicines were used for treating illnesses regarded by the Hausa as having natural causes. Malaria is a serious endemic medical problem in the Hausa region, as in many areas of Africa. The Hausa use approximately 72 plant remedies for conditions connected with malaria—among them anemia, intermittent fever, and jaundice. Experimental treatment of malaria in laboratory animals supports the efficacy of many of the Hausa remedies. Perhaps the most important part of the Etkin and Ross findings is the role of diet. While most medical research does

not consider the possible medical efficacy of foods that people eat in combating illness, food is, of course, consumed in much larger quantities and more often than medicine. It is noteworthy therefore, that the Hausa eat many plants with anti-malarial properties; in fact dietary consumption of these plants appears to be the greatest during the time of year when the risk of malarial infection is at its highest (Etkin and Ross, 1997).

Anthropology contributes to the understanding of health and illness through the development of culturally appropriate interventions. Among North American Aboriginal peoples, there are strong cultural aspects of traditional medicine that can often be a vital part of both the individual and community response to illness. Further, some Aboriginal people, particularly those in remote or small communities, may feel disenfranchised from the Western medical system and the biomedical paradigm. As a result, it is important that public health responses, at both the individual and population levels, recognize and respect the cultural perceptions of health within different groups.

Many diseases, including infectious diseases like AIDS or chronic diseases like diabetes, may be viewed as "Western" diseases. Without acknowledging the perceived risks or responses of community members, it is difficult to develop meaningful and effective tools for educating people or combatting a specific illness. To this end, research on AIDS in Aboriginal groups has promoted understanding community response to HIV/AIDS through traditional mechanisms that recognize the traditional relationships between individuals, families, entire communities, and finally Mother Earth (Lambert, 1993). For example, in Alberta, the Feather of Hope Aboriginal AIDS Prevention Society provides culturally sensitive HIV prevention programs to Aboriginal communities (Mill and DesJardins, 1996). In particular, the society focuses on self-empowerment with respect to health and illness, which reflects broader socio-political aspects of self-determinism within Canadian Aboriginal peoples. Similarly, the Manitoba First Nations Centre for Aboriginal Health Research, a joint project of the University of Manitoba and the Assembly of Manitoba Chiefs, develops and supports research that assists the promotion of healing, wellness, and improved health services in Canadian Aboriginal communities. In this joint project, medical anthropologist John O'Neil and colleagues are engaged in research sponsored by the Canadian Institutes of Health Research (CIHR) to identify factors that enhance or constrain the development of a First Nations–controlled health-care system (O'Neil, 1995; O'Neil and Commanda, 1998; O'Neil et al., 1998; O'Neil et al., 2001). Of particular interest is the assessment of cultural perceptions of health risk, and how to develop a strategy that allows the resources and the appropriate political environment to realize community healing. In northern Saskatchewan, medical anthropologist Sylvia Abonyi and her colleagues at the Saskatchewan Population Health and Evaluation Research Unit (SPHERU) are also working together with Aboriginal groups to deal with health issues. Also working with the Prince Albert Grand Council (PAGC) and the Athabasca Health Authority (AHA), SPHERU researchers are developing tools for use in Aboriginal health organizations. The goal of this research is to develop culturally appropriate indicators to gauge changes in health within the community, and to assess the impact of health-related services, because the ability to understand cross-cultural perceptions of health and illness is critical for any health system to effectively treat and prevent illnesses.

Health Conditions and Diseases

Epidemics of disease have killed millions of people within short periods of time throughout recorded history. The Black Death, a bubonic plague, killed between 25 and 50 percent of the population of Europe, perhaps 75 million people, during the fourteenth century; an epidemic in the sixth century killed an estimated 100 million people in the Middle East, Asia, and Europe. Less noted in our history books, but also devastating, was the enormous depopulation that accompanied the expansion of Europeans into the New World and the Pacific from the 1500s on. Not only were people killed directly by European conquerors; millions also died from introduced diseases to which the natives had little or no resistance, diseases such as smallpox and measles that the Europeans brought with them but were no longer dying from.

The current state of medical science and technology may lull us into thinking that epidemics are a thing of the past. Despite this, the establishment of diseases like **AIDS (acquired immune deficiency syndrome)** over the past few decades or the recent and sudden emergence of diseases like West Nile and SARS (severe acute respiratory syndrome) remind us that new diseases, or new varieties of old diseases, can appear at any time. SARS is a newly emerged disease caused by a coronavirus that spread globally through 30 countries in 2003. Its origins have been traced to Hong Kong, but genetic evidence suggests that several strains of the virus had occurred, but only one was associated with the subsequent outbreak in Hong Kong, which later spread to other areas of the world (Ruan et al., 2003; Guan et al., 2004). A sample of the virus from one of the first victims of SARS in Toronto was taken by the National Microbiology Laboratory in Winnipeg. From that, the genome of the SARS virus was cracked by scientists at the Michael Smith Genome Sciences Centre in Vancouver. Its origins remain debated, though it is possible that the human form is a mutation of an animal coronavirus. Currently, health authorities in China and Canada are working to develop several potential vaccines against the virus, in preparation for future outbreaks. Like all other organisms, disease-causing organisms also evolve—and as discussed in Chapter 11, human behaviour is a major factor in the evolution of diseases.

AIDS

The human immunodeficiency viruses (HIV) that presumably cause AIDS emerged only recently. Viruses and bacteria are always mutating, and new strains emerge that are initially a plague on our genetic resistance and on medical efforts to contain them.

Millions of people around the world already have the symptoms of AIDS and millions more are infected with HIV but do not know they are infected. According to World Health Organization estimates, some 40 million people including 2.5 million children have been infected with HIV. In 2003, more than 3 million people died of AIDS. AIDS is a frightening epidemic not only because of its likely toll but also because it takes a long time (on average, four years) after exposure for symptoms to appear. This means that many people who have been infected by HIV but do not know they are infected may continue unknowingly to transmit the viruses to others (Bolton, 1989).

Transmission occurs mostly via sexual encounters, through semen and blood. Drug users may also transmit HIV by way of contaminated needles. Mothers may transmit the virus to their babies in the womb. Transmission by blood transfusion has been virtually eliminated in this and other societies by medical screening of blood supplies, but in many countries there is still no routine screening of blood prior to transfusions.

Many people think of AIDS as only a medical problem that requires only a medical solution, without realizing that there are behavioural and cultural issues that need to be addressed as well. It is true that developing a vaccine or a drug to prevent people from getting AIDS and finding a permanent cure for those who have it will finally solve the problem of AIDS. However, for a variety of reasons, we can expect that the medical solution alone will not be sufficient, at least not for a while. First, to be effective worldwide, or even within a country, a vaccine has to be inexpensive and relatively easy to produce in large quantities; the same is true of any medical treatment for victims. Second, governments around the world have to be willing and able to spend the money and hire the personnel necessary to manage an effective program (Bolton, 1989). Third, future vaccination and treatment will require the people at risk to be willing to get vaccinated and treated, which is not always easy to arrange. Witness the fact that the incidence of measles is on the rise in the United States because many people are not having their children vaccinated.

There are now expensive drug treatments that significantly reduce the HIV load, but we do not know if an effective and inexpensive vaccine or treatment will be developed soon. In the meantime, the risk of HIV infection can be reduced only by changes in social, particularly sexual, behaviour. But to persuade people to change their sexual behaviour, it is necessary to find out exactly what they do sexually, and why they prefer what they do. The reasons for preferring some activity may make it difficult to change behaviour.

Research so far suggests that different sexual patterns are responsible for HIV transmission in different parts of the world. In the United States, England, northern Europe, Australia, and Latin America, the recipients of anal intercourse, particularly men, are the most likely individuals to acquire HIV infection; vaginal intercourse can also transmit the infection, usually from the man to the woman. In Africa, the most common mode of transmission is vaginal intercourse, and so women get infected more commonly in Africa than elsewhere (Schoepf, 1988; Carrier and Bolton, 1991). Is it reasonable to expect that people can generally be persuaded to stop doing what they prefer to do?

As of now, there are only two known ways to reduce the likelihood of sexual HIV transmission. One way is to abstain from sexual intercourse; the other is to use condoms. Educational programs that teach how AIDS spreads and what the individual can do about it may reduce the spread somewhat. Such programs may fail though, where people have incompatible beliefs and attitudes about sexuality. For example, people in some central African societies believe that deposits of semen after conception are necessary for a successful pregnancy and generally enhance a woman's health and ability to reproduce. It might be expected then that people who have these beliefs about semen would choose not to use condoms; after all, condoms in their view are a threat to public health (Schoepf, 1988). Educational programs may also emphasize the wrong message. Promiscuity may increase the risk of HIV transmission, so hardly anyone would question the wisdom of advertising to reduce the number of sexual partners. What was not anticipated, however, was that individuals in monogamous relationships, who may feel safe, are less likely to use condoms or to avoid the riskiest sexual practices. Needless to say, sex with a regular partner who is infected is not safe (Bolton, 1992)!

The stigma associated with AIDS also hinders efforts to reduce its spread. Possible victims may be unwilling to find out if they have been infected. The stigma, in this and some other societies, is the widespread belief that homosexual men are particularly likely to get infected (Feldman and Johnson, 1986). Of course, not everyone who gets infected has engaged in homosexual behaviour. Indeed, the majority of people now infected with AIDS in the world are heterosexual (Barnett and Blaikie, 1992). Nevertheless, the disease's association with homosexuality, and a general prejudice against homosexuals, may contribute to the spread of AIDS. Some of those infected will continue to transmit the infection because they are afraid to find out that they might be infected. Much of the stigma associated with AIDS derives also from people's misinformation about exactly how AIDS is transmitted; indeed, many people fear contact with AIDS victims, as if any kind of contact could result in infection. Fear that they will be shunned if they are known to have AIDS may also contribute to some persons' unwillingness to be tested.

To solve the problem of AIDS, we may hope that medical science will develop an effective and inexpensive vaccination or treatment that can be afforded by all. In the meantime, we can try to understand why people engage in certain risky sexual practices. Such understanding may allow us to design educational and other programs that would more successfully inhibit the spread of AIDS.

Mental and Emotional Disorders

When Western anthropologists started describing mental illness in non-Western societies, there seemed to be unique illnesses in different cultures. These are referred to as **culture-bound syndromes**. For example, a medical disorder called *pibloktoq* occurred among some Inuit adults of Greenland, usually women, who became oblivious to their surroundings and acted in agitated, eccentric ways. They might strip themselves naked and wander across the ice and over hills until they collapsed of exhaustion. Another disorder, *amok*, occurred in Malaya, Indonesia, and New Guinea, usually among males. It was characterized by John Honigmann as a "destructive maddened excitement ... beginning with depression and followed by a period of brooding and withdrawal [culminating in] the final mobilization of tremendous energy during which the 'wild man' runs destructively berserk" (Honigmann, 1967). *Anorexia nervosa*, a disorder involving aversion to food, may be unique to the relatively few societies that idealize slimness (Kleinman, 1988) (See Current Issues, *Eating Disorders, Biology, and the Cultural Construction of Beauty*.)

Some scholars think that each society's views of the personality and concepts of mental illness have to be understood in its own terms. Western understandings and concepts cannot be applied to other cultures. For example, Catherine Lutz suggested that the Western concept of depression cannot be applied to the Pacific island of Ifaluk. The people there have many words for thinking or feeling about "loss and helplessness," but all their words are related to a specific need for someone, such as when someone dies or leaves the island.

CURRENT ISSUES

Eating Disorders, Biology, and the Cultural Construction of Beauty

Cultures differ about what they consider beautiful, including people. In many cultures, fat people are considered more beautiful than thin people. The second author of this book did fieldwork years ago on the islands of American Samoa. When he returned to the main island after three months on a distant island, he ran into a Samoan acquaintance, a prominent chief. The chief said: "You look good. You gained weight." In reality, the anthropologist had lost 30 pounds [about 14 kilograms]! The chief may not have remembered how heavy the anthropologist had been, but he clearly thought that fat was better than thin.

Why did he think so? One possible idea is that fat is considered beautiful in societies where hurricanes or other disasters frequently cause food shortages. The cultural preference for fat may reflect biological adaptability—people who are fat can better survive starvation.

Being fat may show that you have superior access to resources, mainly food. In such societies the wealthier may be those who are fatter. In other words, fat is beautiful where only the better-off are fat. Compare that situation with the situation in our culture. Clearly, we value thin more than fat. Thinness, for those who can afford it, may symbolize that you don't have to worry about your next meal, that you don't have to store up fat for a rainy day. In fact, in societies where food is bought and sold in the marketplace, those people with more wealth can always buy food. So it is not surprising that in such societies wealthier adults strive to be thin and thinness is considered beautiful. Only richer people look for personal trainers or the newest diet, and of course only they can afford to do so. For the poor, or the insecurely employed, fat may be the best protection against future deprivation.

Our cultural beliefs about what is considered a beautiful body impose enormous pressures on females to be thin. The effort to be thin can be carried to an extreme, resulting in anorexia and bulimia. If you suffer from these often fatal illnesses, you may regularly eat little and you may regularly force yourself to throw up, thus depriving your body of nutrients in the quest to be thinner and thinner. These conditions do not occur commonly among the very poor or in cultures that have frequent food scarcity. Anorexia is a malady found only in affluent cultures.

Sources: Brown PJ. 1997. Cultures and the Evolution of Obesity. In: Podolefsky A, Brown PJ, editors. Applying Cultural Anthropology: An Introductory Reader. Fourth edition. Mountain View, CA: Mayfield.

Loustaunau MO, Sobo EJ. 1997. The Cultural Context of Health, Illness and Medicine. Westport, CT: Bergin and Garvey. p 85.

Wolf N. 1991. The Beauty Myth: How Images of Beauty Are Used against Women. New York: Morrow.

Such thoughts and feelings of loss are considered perfectly normal, and there is no word in their language for general hopelessness or "depression" (Lutz, 1985). Therefore, Lutz questioned the applicability of the Western concept of depression as well as other Western psychiatric disorders.

Other researchers are not so quick to dismiss the possible universality of psychiatric categories. Some think they have found a considerable degree of cross-cultural uniformity in conceptions of mental illness. Jane Murphy studied descriptions by the Inuit and the Yoruba, in Nigeria, of severely disturbed persons. She found that their descriptions not only were similar to each other, but also corresponded to North American descriptions of schizophrenia. The Inuit word for "crazy" is *nuthkavihak*. They use this word when something inside a person

seems to be out of order. *Nuthkavihak* people are described talking to themselves, believing themselves to be animals, making strange faces, becoming violent, and so on. The Yoruba have a word, *were*, for people who are "insane." People described as *were* sometimes hear voices, laugh when there is nothing to laugh at, and take up weapons and suddenly hit people (Murphy, 1981).

Robert Edgerton found similarities in conceptions of mental illness in four East African societies. He noted not only that the four groups essentially agreed on the symptoms of psychosis but also that the symptoms they described were the same ones that are considered psychotic here (Edgerton, 1966). Edgerton believed that the lack of exact translation in different cultures, such as the one pointed out by Lutz regarding Ifaluk, does not make comparison impossible. If researchers can come to understand another culture's views of personality and if the researchers can manage to communicate these views to people of other cultures, we can compare the described cases and try to discover what may be universal and what may be found only in some cultures (Edgerton, 1992).

Some mental illnesses, such as schizophrenia and depression, seem so widespread that many researchers think they are probably universal. Consistent with this idea is the fact that schizophrenic individuals in different cultures seem to share the same patterns of distinctive eye movements (Allen et al., 1996). Still, cultural factors may influence the risk of developing such diseases, the specific symptoms that are expressed, and the effectiveness of different kinds of treatment (Kleinman, 1988; Berry et al., 1992). There may be some truly culture-bound (nearly unique) syndromes, but others thought at one time to be unique may be culturally varying expressions of conditions that occur widely. *Pibloktoq*, for example, may be a kind of hysteria (Honigmann, 1967).

Biological but not necessarily genetic factors may be very important in the etiology of some widespread disorders such as schizophrenia (Kleinman, 1988). With regard to hysteria, Anthony Wallace theorized that nutritional factors such as calcium deficiency may cause hysteria and that dietary improvement may account for the decline of this illness in the Western world since the nineteenth century (Wallace, 1972). By the early twentieth century, the discovery of the value of good nutrition, coupled with changes in social conditions, had led many people to drink milk, eat vitamin-rich foods, and spend time in the sun (although spending a lot of time in the sun is no longer recommended because of the risk of skin cancers). These changes in diet and activity increased the intake of vitamin D and helped people to maintain a proper calcium level. Consequently, the number of cases of hysteria declined.

Regarding *pibloktoq*, Wallace suggested that a complex set of related variables may cause the disease. The Inuit live in an environment that supplies only a minumum amount of calcium. A diet low in calcium could result in two different conditions. One condition, rickets, would produce physical deformities potentially fatal in the Inuit hunting economy. Persons whose genetic makeup made them prone to rickets would be eliminated from the population through natural selection. A low level of calcium in the blood could also cause muscular spasms known as tetany. Tetany, in turn, may cause emotional and mental disorientation similar to the symptoms of *pibloktoq*. Such attacks last for only a relatively short time and are not fatal, so people who developed *pibloktoq* would have a far greater chance of surviving in the Arctic environment with a calcium-deficient diet than would people who had rickets.

Although researchers disagree about the comparability of mental illnesses among cultures, most agree that effective treatment requires understanding a culture's ideas about mental illness. Why people think it occurs, what treatments are believed to be effective, and how families and others respond to those afflicted must all be considered (Kleinman, 1988; Kirmayer et al., 2000).

Environmental Anthropology
Environmental Contaminants

A variety of substances that can be found in the environment can have serious effects on health. As a result, considerable attention is now being paid to those substances, particularly contaminants that humans are introducing into the environment. A *contaminant* is a substance foreign to the environment in which it is found. Industrial contaminants—the result of large-scale manufacturing processes—may or may not be harmful, depending on the kind of substance and the quantity present. The earliest evidence for the effects of industrial contaminants on the environment occurred over two decades ago when the effects of DDT—a pesticide—were observed in the reproductive failure of birds of prey. Polychlorinated biphenyls (PCBs) were commonly used in electrical transformers for many years. While they are no longer produced in North America, PCBs in the northern regions of

Canada and Alaska are still carried by winds and ocean currents from other areas of the world (Oostdam et al., 1999). Very low levels of PCBs are found in water and soil, while higher levels can be found in animals. These are passed up the food chain when a larger predator eats a small animal. Exposure to PCBs can cause cancer as well as reduced immunity, low birth weights, and learning problems. Exposures are higher in the eastern than in the western region of the North and exposure among Dene–Métis populations is generally below a level of concern, although estimated intake has been found to be elevated for certain groups and is a cause for concern if exposures are elevated on a regular basis (Oostdam et al., 1999).

Mercury and cadmium are naturally occurring heavy metals that can be found in rocks, soil, and water. In high doses, mercury is toxic to living things, causing damage to the brain and nerves. Industrial activity has increased the quantity of mercury in the environment. Samples of human hair from Dene, Cree, and Inuit in the Canadian North have indicated that a significant proportion have mean mercury levels within the 5-percent risk range proposed by the World Health Organization for neonatal neurological damage (Oostdam et al., 1999). Most kinds of food contain some cadmium, but organs like the liver and kidneys contain the highest levels. Smoke from cigarettes contains cadmium, and smokers have more cadmium in their blood than non-smokers. Long-term exposure to high levels of cadmium can cause permanent kidney damage.

Many contaminants in food cannot be detected through the senses and are therefore a serious potential health concern, especially when they are not known. For example, environmental contaminants are a real concern among northern Aboriginal peoples who eat caribou, fish, moose, seal, and whale, many of which are known to have trace levels of contaminants like PCBs, mercury, and cadmium (Kuhnlein and Chan, 2000). Consumers of caribou meat in particular are exposed to radiation doses as much as seven times greater than non-consumers of traditional foods. This is due mostly to the cumulative presence of natural *radionuclides* in the food chain (Oostdam et al., 1999). However, because these traditional foods are a source of nutrition not easily replaced by store-bought foods, the implications of contaminants for health are important. Traditional foods are also an economic necessity in many communities (Oostdam et al., 1999). As a result, there has been considerable effort to monitor the level of contaminants in fish and wildlife collected from different regions in northern Canada over the last ten years (Chan, 1998).

In response to requests from Aboriginal peoples, the Centre for Indigenous Peoples' Nutrition and Environment (CINE) was created in 1993 at McGill University. The purpose of the centre was to engage in participatory research and education regarding issues about the safety of consumption of traditional Aboriginal foods. Anthropologists and other researchers at CINE have been involved in the analysis of environmental contaminants for a variety of northern communities.

For example, at the request of the Deninu Kuè First Nation, in the Northwest Territories, researchers at CINE examined levels of cadmium in traditional foods and Dene–Métis food consumption data. They determined that dietary intake of cadmium from traditional foods posed no health risk to the inhabitants of Fort Resolution, a community on the shores of Great Slave Lake (Kim and Chan, 1998). Similarly, Peter Berti and colleagues at CINE examined dietary data collected from over 1000 Aboriginal adults from 16 communities in the Northwest Territories. Combining these data with data concerning the level of contaminants in a variety of traditional foods that were part of the peoples' diets, they calculated a relatively low dietary exposure to 11 chemical contaminants (Berti et al., 1998a; Berti et al., 1998b).

Natural Disasters and Famine

Natural events such as floods, droughts, earthquakes, and insect infestations are usually but not always beyond human control, but their effects are not (Aptekar, 1994). We call such events accidents or emergencies when only a few people are affected, but we call them disasters when large numbers of people or large areas are affected. The harm caused is not just a function of the magnitude of the natural event. Between 1960 and 1980, 43 natural disasters in Japan killed an average of 63 people per disaster. During the same period, 17 natural disasters in Nicaragua killed an average of 6235 people per disaster. In the United States, between 1960 and 1976, the average flood or other environmental disturbance killed just one person, injured a dozen, and destroyed fewer than five buildings. These comparative figures demonstrate that climatic and other events in the physical environment become *disasters* because of events or conditions in the social environment.

If people live in houses that are designed to withstand earthquakes—if governing bodies require such construction and the economy is developed enough so that people can afford such construction—the effects of an earthquake will be minimized. If poor people are forced to live in deforested flood plains in order to be able to find land to farm (as in coastal Bangladesh), if the poor are forced to live in shanties built on precarious hillsides (like those of Rio de Janeiro), the floods and landslides that follow severe hurricanes and rainstorms can kill thousands and even hundreds of thousands.

Thus, natural disasters can have greater or lesser effects on human life, depending on social conditions. Therefore, disasters are also social problems, problems that have social causes and possible social solutions. Legislating safe construction of a house is a social solution. The 1976 earthquake in Tangsham, China, killed 250 000 people, mostly because they lived in top-heavy adobe houses that could not withstand severe shaking, whereas the 1989 earthquake in Loma Prieta, California, which was of comparable intensity, killed 65 people.

One might think that floods, of all disasters, are the least influenced by social factors. After all, without a huge runoff from heavy rains or snowmelt, there cannot be a flood. However, consider why so many people have died from Huang (Yellow) River floods in China. (One such flood, in 1931, killed nearly 4 million people, making it the deadliest single disaster in history.) The floods in the Huang River basin have occurred mostly because enormous quantities of silt wash into the river, raising the riverbed and increasing the risk of floods that burst the dams that normally would contain them. The risk of disastrous flooding would be greatly reduced if different social conditions prevailed—if people did not have to farm close to the river, or if the dams were higher and more numerous.

Famines, episodes of severe starvation and death, often appear to be triggered by physical events such as a severe drought or a hurricane that kills or knocks down food trees and plants. Famines do not though inevitably follow such an event. Social conditions can prevent a famine or increase the likelihood of one. Consider what is likely to happen in Samoa after a hurricane. Whole villages that have lost their coconut and breadfruit trees, as well as their taro patches, pick up and move for some time to other villages where there are relatives and friends. The visitors stay and are fed until some of their cultivated trees and plants start to bear food again, at which point they return home. This kind of inter-village reciprocity probably could occur only in a society that has relatively little inequality in wealth. Now, the central government or international agencies may also help out by providing food and other supplies.

Researchers point out that famine rarely results from just one low-yield food production season. During such a season, people can usually cope by getting help from relatives, friends, and neighbours, or by switching to less desirable foods. The famine in the African Sahel—the belt of marginal grassland that stretches across the African continent south of the Sahara Desert—in 1974 occurred after 8 years of below-average precipitation weather. A combination of drought, floods, and a civil war in 1983–84 contributed to the subsequent severe famine in Ethiopia and Sudan (Mellor and Gavian, 1987). Famine almost always has some social causes. Who has rights to the available food, and do those who have more food distribute it to those who have less? Cross-cultural research suggests that societies with individual property rights rather than shared rights are more likely to suffer famine

(Dirks, 1993). Nonetheless, government assistance can lessen the risk of famine in societies with individual property.

Relief provided by government may not always get to those who need it the most. In India, for example, the central government provides help in time of drought to minimize the risk of famine. However, food and other supplies provided to a village may end up being unequally distributed, following the rules of social and gender stratification. Members of the local elite arrange to function as distributors and find ways to manipulate the relief efforts to their advantage. Lower-class and lower-caste families still suffer the most. Within the family, biases against females, particularly young girls and elderly women, translate into their getting less food. It is no wonder, then, that in times of food shortage and famine, the poor and other socially disadvantaged persons are especially likely to die (Torry, 1986).

Thus, the people of a society may not all be equally at risk in case of disaster. In socially stratified societies, the poor particularly suffer. It is they who are likely to be forced to over-cultivate, overgraze, and deforest their land, making it more susceptible to degradation. A society most helps those it values the most.

To reduce the impact of disasters, then, we need to reduce the social conditions that magnify the effects of disasters. If humans are responsible for those social conditions, humans can change them. If earthquakes destroy houses that are too flimsy, we can build stronger houses. If floods caused by over-cultivation and overgrazing kill defenceless people directly (or indirectly by stripping their soils), we can grow new forest cover and provide new job opportunities to floodplain farmers. If prolonged natural disasters or wars threaten famine, social distribution systems can lessen the risk. In short, we may not be able to do much about the weather or other physical causes of disasters, but we can do a lot—if we want to—about the social factors that make disasters disastrous.

Conservation

Another area of applied interest for physical anthropology is in primate conservation. As we have already discussed in Chapter 6 (see Current Issues, *Endangered Primates*), many groups of non-human primates face certain extinction, often the result of human behaviour. At the University of Calgary, Linda Fedigan, Canada Research Chair in Primatology and Bioanthropology, is involved in the creation of a state-of-the-art primate centre in collaboration with researchers at the university and the Calgary Zoological Society. This facility will allow the integration of field, laboratory, and captive animal research. It will also allow multidisciplinary approaches to both pure and applied conservation research, including non-invasive DNA and hormonal and plant chemistry analyses. Fedigan's research aims to advance knowledge regarding primates, and facilitate their conservation in the wild.

Dr. Kerry Bowman and his colleagues have established the Canadian Great Ape Alliance fund in an effort to coordinate efforts in raising awareness of the threats to the great apes, and develop conservation strategies. The mission statement of this group is to promote conservation strategies that reflect local cultures, as well as economic and political realities. Similarly, the Jane Goodall Canada Institute, established in 1997, implements a variety of educational programs to promote a better understanding of the relationship of all species on earth.

Forensic Anthropology

Perhaps one of the most obvious applications of physical anthropology is the field of forensic anthropology. *Forensic anthropologists* are physical anthropologists trained in human skeletal biology. They use their expertise in the analysis of the human skeleton to help solve questions for medical and law enforcement personnel in cases where skeletal remains are discovered. Further, their expertise in archaeological excavation of human skeletons often provides them with an advantage when excavating an identified or suspected crime scene. Another role of the forensic anthropologist has been to assist in investigations of human rights violations around the world, particularly in the exhumation and analysis of mass graves.

Forensic anthropology has become extremely popular in last two decades, partly as a result of increased media attention, such as the popularity of the fictional works of forensic anthropologist Kathleen Reichs. However, in Canada the demand for the expertise of forensic anthropologists is relatively low, and most physical anthropologists provide consultation for police, medical examiners, and coroners on a part-time or ad hoc basis. The role of the forensic anthropologist is to help reconstruct personal identity in cases where the victim is not known and is represented by skeletal remains. Their training in skeletal biology from archaeological contexts has provided them with the tools for quickly estimating age at death and determining sex, stature, and perhaps population affinity from the skeleton. Often human remains may be discovered accidentally, and a forensic anthropologist is called in to help establish the antiquity or identity of the remains. Sometimes the nature of a scene, like the result of a mass disaster, requires a forensic anthropologist to assist in the identification of victims and the circumstances surrounding their deaths. For example, forensic anthropologists assisted in the recovery and identification of 256 victims of a military aircraft that crashed in Gander, Newfoundland, in 1985 (Hinkes, 1989; Silversides, 2001).

Other times, remains might be discovered under more clearly suspicious circumstances, and the data provided by a forensic anthropologist may assist in resolving a crime. For example, forensic anthropologists played a major role in the recovery and analysis of the Branch Davidian Compound victims near Waco, Texas, in early 1993 (Owsley et al., 1995; Ubelaker et al., 1995).

Now infamous, Canada's largest crime scene was also the largest forensic anthropological investigation in the country. In 2002, the largest serial-killer investigation in Canada began at the farm of Robert Pickton in Port Coquitlam, British Columbia. As of December 2003, Robert Pickton has been charged with 22 counts of first-degree murder. The Joint Missing Women Task Force of the Royal Canadian Mounted Police (RCMP) and the Vancouver Police Department

Aerial view of the forensic investigation site and surrounding area of Port Coquitlam, British Columbia.

worked with forensic anthropologists Tracy Rogers from the University of Toronto and Richard Lazenby from the University of Northern British Columbia. The 21-month-long search of a 7-hectare farm owned by Pickton involved dozens of senior undergraduate and graduate anthropology students with training in human skeletal biology, sifting through hundreds of thousands of cubic metres of soil, watching for and collecting thousands of specimens for evidence. The goal was to screen all the surface dirt piles and to excavate and screen the subsurface material until undisturbed, sterile ground was encountered. The combined process of excavation and sorting materials involved a team of over 100 forensic anthropology, biological anthropology, and archaeology technicians, working in combination with the RCMP, the Vancouver Police Department, as well as with civilian heavy machinery operators—the first time in Canada that civilians have been used to such a degree in the processing of a crime scene.

Forensic anthropology has also had a heightened role in investigations of violations of human rights over the past decade. Forensic anthropologists from Canada and the United States have participated in assessments of war crimes and human rights violations in the former Yugoslavia, Serbia, and Albania and, more recently, following the conflicts in Afghanistan and Iraq (Skinner, 1987; Primorac et al., 1996; Huffine et al., 2001; Komar, 2003; Skinner et al., 2003; Williams and Crews, 2003). In the wake of the September 11, 2001, terrorist attacks on the World Trade Center, forensic anthropologists and archaeologists assisted in the complex task of recovery and analysis of human remains in an effort to help bring closure to the families of the victims (Budimlija et al., 2003). At the same time forensic anthropologists aided in the recovery and identification of human remains from the associated plane crash in Somerset County, Pennsylvania.

A number of international organizations including Human Rights Watch, Physicians for Human Rights, and the United Nations coordinate or participate in forensic investigations of human rights violations around the world. These organizations often rely on the expertise of forensic anthropologists on a case-by-case basis, although some individuals are full-time consultants. Clyde Snow is perhaps the most famous practising forensic anthropologist today. He has worked on such prominent cases as identifying the remains of Dr. Josef Mengele, the Nazi war criminal who fled to Brazil, victims of serial killer John Wayne Gacy, Tutankhamun, and the victims of the Oklahoma City bombing (Anonymous, 1997a). In Argentina in the 1980s he exhumed bodies from the mass graves of civilians killed by government death squads during the war, and he has since worked in Guatemala, Ethiopia, Philippines, Croatia, and other areas.

In some areas of the world, full-time investigative teams have developed in response to local needs for justice and criminal investigations. Two examples are the Argentine Forensic Anthropology Team and the Guatemalan Forensic Anthropology Team.

Since it was founded in 1984, the Argentine Forensic Anthropology Team (EAAF) has investigated cases of persons who disappeared during the

This mass grave is part of the archaeological work developed by the Argentine Forensic Anthropology Team in the cemetery of Avellaneda, outside of Buenos Aires, Argentina. The investigation involved the excavation of 19 mass graves and 11 individual graves, from which the remains of 324 individuals were retrieved—most of them the people who "disappeared" for political reasons in the 1970s in Argentina.

last military dictatorship (1976–83). In 1995 activities relating to the recovery of "disappeared" persons in Argentina increased significantly, and the EAAF continues to be active in Argentina and abroad. In 1997 the EAAF developed a data bank of blood samples from relatives of disappeared citizens. When a skeleton suspected to belong to a "disappeared" person is discovered, the DNA extracted from the remains and from blood samples in the data bank can be compared to help determine the identity of the individual (EAAF, 1997). In 1997 members of the EAAF assisted in planning a forensic investigation in Colombia of the remains of victims killed in a battle between guerrilla troops and the Colombian army. In 1998, four EAAF members took part in the International Criminal Tribunal for the former Yugoslavia's ongoing forensic investigations in Bosnia.

In 1991 the Guatemalan Forensic Anthropology Team (Equipo de Antropología Forense de Guatemala or EAFG) was formed through the initiative of Clyde Snow with the aid of the American Association for the Advancement of Science, which provided formal training by forensic anthropologists and pathologists from the United States. In the summer of 1992, EAFG began the first forensic investigation in Guatemala of several mass graves. It has continued to excavate and analyze remains from the graves of victims of massacres associated with the Guatemalan military during the early 1980s. Currently EAFG consults on an international level with members of international organizations like the United Nations International Criminal Tribunals for Rwanda and for the former Yugoslavia, the Honduran government, the Haitian Truth Commission, and human rights organizations like Physicians for Human Rights.

Nutritional Anthropology

Anthropology has a long tradition of studying variation in human form. Since human variation is partly a result of growth differences among different people, many anthropologists become interested in the study of growth and development as indicators of general health within a population. For the applied anthropologists, **nutritional anthropology** may employ *longitudinal studies*—following the same children at repeated age intervals, or *cross-sectional studies*—looking at many different children at different age intervals. Applied anthropologists may collect data about growth in height and weight, skeletal or dental development, or physiological (sexual) maturity. The end product of such analyses is usually a better understanding of the impact or potential impact of various biocultural factors on the health and nutrition of the population. In this way, nutritional anthropology can help to establish evidence on which public health policy changes or recommendations can be made. In addition, monitoring people's growth in developing nations provides a basis for developing strategies for improving the health and quality of life for all people.

Growth

We can learn about the health of a population by taking body measurements, as these show levels of nutrition (Martorell and Ho, 1984; Haas and Habicht, 1990; Rona, 1991). Studies of infant and childhood health often look at several of these **anthropometric measures** as indicators of health status. This is because body measurements are sensitive over the full range of malnutrition.

Anthropometric studies employ a variety of measurements, including height-for-age, weight-for-height, weight-for-age, arm circumference, and arm-circumference-for-height. Deficits in either of the first two are classified as *stunting* and *wasting* respectively. The most common expression of these deficits is comparison to a healthy population reference standard. The level of reduced growth for a given age is assessed against a reference mean or median. Values between 95 and 90 reflect mild growth deficit, between 90 and 85 moderate growth deficit, and less than 85 percent of the reference standard reflects severe stunting or growth reduction (WHO [World Health Organization], 1986).

Reference standards—growth-for-age standards—for assessing growth are not universal and are often based on growth rates for well-nourished children from Western or developed nations. Some have proposed that a single, universal standard be utilized so that all studies of growth are comparable. This argument rests on the assumption that all populations have the same genetic growth potential. Interpreting differences in growth from standards and saying what that means in terms of the health of the population require additional information about variation and differential nutrition within the populations (Johnston and Ouyang, 1991:338).

Growth retardation is widely recognized as a response to the lack of an adequate diet. During periods of nutritional deficiency, bone continues to grow but at a reduced rate; the "undernourished child slows down and waits for better times" (Tanner, 1990:130). The amount of "slowing" is related to the severity and duration of the malnutrition. Reduced growth is also associated with prolonged periods of infection. More frequent infections will lead to weight loss (wasting) and may prevent or impair normal growth.

Perhaps more than any other factor, socioeconomic status promotes or reduces overall health within a community. Contemporary comparisons of subgroups or populations can provide information about the association between growth and social conditions.

Reduced survival of newborns in any environment is a result of biological, environmental, social, and economic factors; the latter two determinants operate "through more basic proximate determinants that in turn influence the risk of disease and the outcome of disease processes" (Mosley and Chen, 1984). At the individual level, factors related to parental education and cultural behaviours, like gender roles, are stressed. At the household level, simple considerations such as the availability of food, safe water, appropriate clothing and housing, and the interaction with preventive care are important. The community level includes such variables as political economy and public health systems that control availability and distribution of resources and directly shape the components at the household and individual levels (Mosley and Chen, 1984).

In communities where population growth is extremely rapid, economic stress often results, and the resources available cannot always accommodate the constant demand. Such restraints in turn threaten or reduce the quality of health-care services, which in turn can adversely affect the mortality risks of all age groups, particularly infants. Within-family social structure associated with cultural traditions and beliefs can also serve to promote or prevent adequate infant growth. While women in traditional societies are usually responsible for care of the children, they may not have direct control over the resources on which health is dependent (Mosley and Chen, 1984).

Body Composition

Body composition, in particular the distribution of fat, has increasingly been used to answer broader questions of human evolutionary development. Factors affecting how body fat is distributed include age, sex, maturation, ethnicity, and socio-economic status. The question of whether specific patterns of fat distribution in various populations represent an adaptive response to environmental stress continues to be evaluated. The implications of changes in environment associated with migration and modernization for such populations have been examined. Recent studies of body fat patterning in childhood as an indicator of health and risk to certain diseases in adulthood have produced some very interesting results from both academic and applied perspectives.

Body fat composition and distribution can be measured in a variety of ways. Estrogen seems to promote the accumulation of body fat, and thus females with earlier **menarche**—the beginning of reproductive maturity— have more fat during pre-adolescence, adolescence, and later life (Marshall and Tanner, 1986). A variety of studies have observed a correlation between the patterns of fat distribution and rates of sexual maturity (Frisancho and Flegal, 1982). The observed correlation between fat patterning and age at menarche is particularly interesting considering the well-known secular trend toward earlier age at menarche in many populations over the last century or so. Most noticeably, the age of onset of menarche has become two to four years earlier over the past century in Europe, North America, and other parts of the world (Marshall, 1978; Marshall and Tanner, 1986; Eveleth and Tanner, 1990). Coincidentally, biological studies of modernization have consistently observed increased mean adult weight and the prevalence of obesity (Reed et al., 1970; Bindon and Baker, 1985; McGarvey et al., 1989). While this has been associated with excess caloric intake and reduced physical activity, the correspondence with decreased age of sexual maturity should also be considered.

Despite the intrinsic factors that are associated with changes in growth, such as diet, many studies have observed that differences related to the environment in which an individual lives are also associated with total body fat (Johnston et al., 1974; Johnston et al., 1984; Bogin and Sullivan, 1986; Shepard, 1991). Most environmental factors that affect growth can be linked either directly or indirectly to nutrition (Eveleth, 1986). When under nutritional stress, individual fat distribution changes, with a reduction in the extremities and a relative increase around the torso (Bogin and MacVean, 1981; Johnston et al., 1984; Cameron et al., 1992). Inadequate nutrition can slow or halt the production of fat cells, but will have little permanent affect on fat distribution if it occurs while cells are increasing in size only (Tanner, 1990). The fact that infants in developing countries often deviate from the expected pattern of fat deposition has been attributed to poor nutrition associated with breast-feeding and weaning (Eveleth, 1986).

At York University in Toronto, researchers are currently involved in the study of physical activity, fitness, and health, including genetic and environmental determinants of obesity and associated risks of disease. In particular, the group is interested in the relationship between activity and health in youth. Current research includes the analysis of population health data collected in 1981 (Payne et al., 2000) and the 7-year follow-up survey in 1988 (Katzmarzyk et al., 2000). In addition, the group is involved in a collaborative effort with researchers at Laval University on the Quebec Family Study, which is investigating the childhood determinants of obesity and risk factors for coronary heart disease (Katzmarzyk et al., 1999).

A question of major interest to researchers in this field is whether obesity in childhood predisposes obesity in adulthood. Over-nutrition in childhood can lead to increased risks of chronic diseases in adulthood such as diabetes (NIDDM), cardiovascular disease, and site-specific cancers. In many Westernized populations, obesity is the primary factor associated with high risks of hypertension and diabetes (Bruce, 2000) (see the Research Frontiers box on page 249). Presently childhood obesity is a major problem in childhood health in North America (Andersen, 2000). Most studies suggest that while some obese infants and children do become obese adults, most return to near-normal weight for height in early or late childhood (Shapiro et al., 1984; Johnston, 1985).

Archaeology as Culture History

Archaeology and the study of past societies provide an important historical framework for current issues in modern society. Bringing this information to the general public is important for establishing an awareness of cultural variability that is a part of the multicultural society in which Canadians live today, as well as the wider global community. In Canada, anthropological research into past societies offers an opportunity to explore the history and prehistory of Canadian Aboriginal peoples. A primary concern with skeletal remains from North America in general is that these remains are often discovered accidentally and require reburial. Excavation is often undertaken relatively quickly and analysis (when desired by the community) is also limited by time. However, when proper analysis is undertaken, information that can be inferred from human skeletal remains and material culture becomes an important resource for understanding the past. Archaeology can help reconstruct cultural history, including that of Canada's indigenous peoples.

Cultural Resource Management

Cultural resource management (CRM) is about the long-term stewardship of a region's cultural heritage sites—locations of historical, cultural, or spiritual significance to the populations. Because so many of these sites are of interest to the general public, CRM is designed not only to safeguard cultural heritage sites from potential damage, but to provide access to the rich historical and cultural information that can be gained from such sites to the general public. A variety of national and international agencies have the responsibility for large-scale CRM activities. These include UNESCO's World Heritage convention, English Heritage in the United Kingdom, and the Quebec Archaeological Association (AAQ) and Parks Canada in Canada.

As one of the principal cultural resource management organizations in Canada, Parks Canada has a Cultural Resource Management

Students from a First Nations community in Manitoba work with a local archaeological consulting company to survey for sites in the community's traditional land use area.

policy guide. Managing cultural resources for public benefit can be difficult. Some of Canada's most significant cultural resources are, by their very nature, those for which protection and public presentation are most needed. In its commitment to responsible stewardship, Parks Canada balances public awareness and access to cultural resources, while preserving the irreplaceable resources being visited.

These challenges require a holistic framework for policy that deals with cultural resources as symbolic as well as physical entities. Canadian efforts to protect and present cultural resources for public benefit are part of a worldwide endeavour to protect, understand, and appreciate our human heritage. In the past decade, Parks Canada has been involved with Aboriginal communities on a variety of initiatives related to establishing and planning historic sites and new parks and to lands claims settlements (Fox, 1999). At the same time, others have begun to develop Aboriginal tourism from a resource-based industry in the form of big-game hunting, to ecotourism and cultural or ethnic tourism, balancing elements of Aboriginal land-based economy (Notzke, 1999).

As a result of the increasing awareness of cultural heritage issues in Canada, courses in Cultural Resource Management are now offered at various institutions in Canada. The University of Victoria offers a CRM program aimed at people involved with museums, galleries, heritage agencies, and other cultural organizations throughout Canada. The University of Manitoba has developed an innovative new program in Aboriginal Cultural Resource Management that will provide a critical venue for dealing with the often conflicting economic and heritage conservation needs, including the discovery of burials.

With respect to human remains, there has been an increasing involvement of Aboriginal populations in the repatriation and reburial of human remains from museums and institutions throughout the world. Many communities feel that human remains are not at rest until reburied. Perhaps the most infamous example of this is the discovery of the Kennewick skull and the subsequent legal battle between American anthropologists and Aboriginal groups for its reburial (Chatters, 2002; Holden, 2004a; Holden, 2004b; Watkins, 2004).

Canada has seen a variety of repatriations, few as sensational as the Kennewick case. In British Columbia, the Skidegate Repatriation & Cultural Committee have reburied over 390 human remains from various institutions. In 1998, the Canadian Museum of Civilization repatriated a large skeletal sample from a fifteenth-century St. Lawrence Iroquois village to the Mohawk First Nation Council of Chiefs at Akwesasne for reburial.

Others are keen to see how anthropology can help reveal the life history of their ancestors. While these may seem like two extremes, in fact there have been many successful partnerships between Aboriginal communities and anthropologists recently in Canada. There have also been some internationally notable cases of co-operative, multidisciplinary research by Canadian physical anthropologists and archaeologists with great sensitivity to concerns of Aboriginal communities—including repatriation—while still accomplishing significant research. These include the discovery and study of Kwaday Dän Sinchi (discussed in Chapter 1), the archaeological discovery of an extensive Aboriginal settlement, including human remains, on the Canadian side of the river during the "twinning" of the Bluewater Bridge between Sarnia, Ontario, and Port Huron, Michigan, and the 1997 discovery of an Iroquois ossuary in suburban Toronto that resulted in a brief, but intensive, study of the human remains that were recovered, before their repatriation to the Six Nations Reserve near Brantford in early 1998 (Williamson and Pfeiffer, 2003). These cases all stand in sharp contrast to the often contentious nature of similar cases in the United States, like the Kennewick Man. The key to these successes has been mutual respect by all parties involved and an increasing role of Aboriginal communities in controlling and directing research on their cultural heritage. As these partnerships continue to build, we will no doubt see tremendous benefits gained through the ongoing research in cultural heritage.

Landscape Archaeology

Archaeology and historical ecology can also contribute to our understanding of present-day environments. For example, archaeologists from the United States and Bolivia have presented new archaeological evidence on landscape transformation by prehistoric populations in Amazonia that has implications for applied studies of sustainable development, conservation of biodiversity, and indigenous knowledge systems (Erickson, 2000). Archaeological research at the Lake Titicaca region of Peru and Bolivia has documented large agricultural earthworks, long thought to be unproductive agriculturally and referred to as simply "raised fields." Based on an archaeological investigation of land use in prehistoric Bolivia, Clark Erickson and colleagues have argued that Native Americans in late prehistory transformed a marginal environment into a productive landscape capable of supporting large and dense populations. The raised fields were first used around 3000 years ago and subsequently abandoned sometime before the arrival of the Spaniards (Erickson, 2000).

In the early 1980s, Erickson, along with Peruvian agronomist Ignacio Garaycochea, anthropologist Kay Candler, and agricultural journalist Dan Brinkmeier, persuaded some local farmers in the Huatta, a Quechua-speaking community near Lake Titicaca, to rebuild a few of the raised fields, plant indigenous crops, and farm them using traditional methods. Attempts to impose inappropriate Western crops and techniques in the Andes had failed miserably, but the archaeological evidence suggested that raised fields might be appropriate for the region. This small-scale experiment was considered successful and today some farmers in the region are using the technology of their ancestors once again to produce food (Erickson, 2000).

Making the World Better

Many social problems afflict our world, not just the ones discussed in this chapter. We don't have the space to discuss the international trade in drugs and how it plays out in violence, death, and corruption.

We haven't discussed the negative effects of environmental degradation—water and air pollution, global warming, ozone depletion, destruction of forests and wetlands. We haven't said anything about overpopulation, the energy crisis, and a host of other problems we should care and do something about, if we hope to make this a better world.

Anthropology is now an applied as well as a basic science. What anthropology has discovered, and what it can discover, about humans can help solve problems in the real world. No longer is what we do purely academic. Most of the problems anthropology can help solve are of human making; therefore, they are susceptible to human unmaking.

Summary

1. Applied anthropologists may be involved in one or more phases of a program that is designed to change people's lives: assembling relevant knowledge, constructing alternative plans, assessing the likely social and environmental impact of particular plans, implementing the program, and monitoring the program and its effects.

2. Today many anthropologists are finding employment outside of anthropology departments—in medical schools, health centres, development agencies, urban-planning agencies, and other public and private organizations.

3. The code of ethics for those who work professionally as applied anthropologists specifies that the target population should be included as much as possible in the formulation of policy, so that people in the community may know in advance how the program may affect them. But perhaps the most important aspect of the code is the pledge not to be involved in any plan whose effect will not be beneficial. It is often difficult to evaluate the effects of planned changes. Long-term consequences may be detrimental even if the changes are beneficial in the short run.

4. Even if a planned change will prove beneficial to its target population, the people may not accept it. If the intended target does not utilize the proposed innovation, the project cannot be considered a success. Target populations may reject or resist a proposed innovation for various reasons: because they are unaware of the need for the change; because they misinterpret the symbols used to explain the change or fail to understand its real purpose; because their customs and institutions conflict with the change; or because they are afraid of it. The target population may also resist the proposed change because they unconsciously or consciously know it is not good for them.

5. To solve biomedical problems like AIDS, we may hope that medical science will develop an effective and inexpensive vaccination or treatment that can be afforded by all. In the meantime, we can try to understand why people engage in certain risky sexual practices. Medical anthropologists can help in this capacity by exploring culturally appropriate ways in which to design educational and other programs that would more successfully inhibit the spread of AIDS.

6. A variety of substances that can be found in the environment can have serious effects on health. As a result, considerable attention is paid to those substances that humans are leaving behind in their environment. Some biological anthropologists apply their expertise to help identify health concerns from environmental contaminants and make recommendations to communities and government for how to deal with these issues.

7. Forensic anthropologists use their expertise in the analysis of the human skeleton to help solve questions for medical and law enforcement personnel in cases where skeletal remains are discovered. Many forensic anthropologists today are involved in examining human rights violations around the world.

8. Nutritional anthropologists are interested in growth, development, and nutrition in modern children. In particular, they are interested in examining the biocultural factors that influence childhood nutrition and growth in order to make recommendations on how to improve the lives of children around the world.

9. A growing field of applied archaeology is cultural resource management (CRM). CRM is a field that attempts to balance education about, access to, and preservation of the many heritage resources around the world.

10. Landscape archaeology integrates archaeology and historical ecology to examine the use of land by past populations and the environmental impact of changing human populations on the landscape.

Glossary Terms

AIDS (acquired immune deficiency syndrome) (p. 322)

anthropometric measures   (p. 332)

applied (practising) anthropology   (p. 311)

cultural resource management   (p. 335)

culture-bound syndromes   (p. 324)

ethnomedicine   (p. 320)

menarche   (p. 333)

nutritional anthropology   (p. 332)

Critical Questions

1. What particular advantages do anthropologists have in trying to solve practical problems?

2. Is it ethical to try to influence people's lives when they have not asked for help?

3. Do global problems require solutions by global agencies? If so, which?

Internet Exercises

1. Find at least three webpages that are related to AIDS and discrimination. Summarize your findings. While doing the search, focus on the relations between AIDS and anthropology as demonstrated in this chapter.

2. Check out **www.sfaa.net**, which is the home page for the Society for Applied Anthropology. Read the Statement of Ethics at that site.

3. The United Nations has a website with information about natural and other disasters at **www.reliefweb.int/w/rwb.nsf**. Read about one current famine. What can you find out about its causes, and what, if anything, is the rest of the world doing to help?

4. Visit the Parks Canada website at **www .parkscanada.pch.gc.ca** and explore the many cultural heritage sites available throughout Canada. Which interests you the most?

Suggested Reading

Aptekar L. 1994. Environmental Disasters in Global Perspective. New York: G. K. Hall/Macmillan. This volume discusses various kinds of environmental disaster. It is one of a series of monographs, sponsored by the Human Relations Area Files, on the current state of cross-cultural and cross-national research on social problems around the world. Others in the series include Albert SM, Cattell MG. 1994. Old Age in Global Perspective: Cross-Cultural and Cross-National Views.

Bodley JH. 1995. Anthropology and Contemporary Human Problems. Third edition. Mountain View, CA: Mayfield. This book discusses the problems of over-consumption, adaptation to environment, resource depletion, hunger and starvation, overpopulation, violence, and war.

Ervin AM. 2000. Applied Anthropology. Boston: Allyn & Bacon. This book shows how a graduate can use a degree in anthropology. It is the most up-to-date book on the subject, providing an outline of the skills, perspectives, and methodologies needed for working in modern communities and organizations.

Fairgrieve SI. 1999. Forensic Osteological Analysis: A Book of Case Studies. Springfield, IL: Charles C. Thomas Publishers. A series of case studies in forensic osteology with background information on how the analysis of human skeletal material is applied to remains from medico-legal contexts.

Goodman AH, Dufour DL, Pelto GH, editors. 2000. Nutritional Anthropology: Biocultural Perspectives on Food and Nutrition. Mountain View, CA: Mayfield Publishing. This volume of papers provides students with an overview of the variety of issues being explored in the field of nutritional anthropology.

Hedican EJ. 1995. Applied Anthropology in Canada: Understanding Aboriginal Issues. Toronto: University of Toronto Press. An overview of applied anthropology, particularly in the context of Canadian Aboriginal peoples.

Mascie-Taylor CGN, Lasker, GW. 1991. Applications of Biological Anthropology to Human Affairs. New York: Cambridge University Press. Topics covered include reproductive ecology and fertility, nutritional status in relation to health, and the effects of pollution on growth.

McElroy A, Townsend PK. 2002. Medical Anthropology in Ecological Perspective. Boulder, CO: Westview Press. The third edition of this text has been revised to reflect new developments in theory and research including new ways of thinking about political ecology. Topics addressed include AIDS, disability, medical pluralism, and health-care-seeking behaviour.

McManamon F, Hatton A, editors. 1999. Cultural Resource Management in Contemporary Society: Perspectives on Managing and Presenting the Past. Routledge. The papers in this book discuss perspectives on managing and preserving the past.

Nafte M. 2000. Flesh and Bone: An Introduction to Forensic Anthropology. Durham, NC: North Carolina Press. A comprehensive overview of the methods and techniques used in forensic anthropology designed for a broad audience.

Van Willigen J. 1993. Applied Anthropology: An Introduction. Revised edition. Westport, CT: Bergin & Garvey Paperback. With numerous examples of applied projects, this survey of applied anthropology deals with ethics in the subdiscipline, applied research methods, social impact assessment, evaluation research, action anthropology, community development, and the role of cultural broker.

Glossary

Absolute Dating a method of dating fossils in which the actual age of a deposit or specimen is measured. Also known as *chronometric dating*.

Acculturation the process of extensive borrowing of aspects of culture.

Acheulian a stone toolmaking tradition dating from 1.5 million years ago. Compared with the Oldowan tradition, Acheulian assemblages have more large tools created according to standardized designs or shapes. One of the most characteristic and prevalent tools in the Acheulian tool kit is the so-called hand axe, which is a teardrop-shaped bifacially flaked tool with a thinned sharp tip. Other large tools may have been cleavers and picks.

Acquired Inheritance a theory proposed in the late eighteenth century that acquired characteristics could be inherited and therefore species could evolve. Individuals who in their lifetime developed characteristics helpful to survival would pass those characteristics on to future generations, thereby changing the physical makeup of the species.

Adapid a type of prosimian with many lemur-like features; appeared in the early Eocene.

Adaptation changes to biology or behaviour that increase the chances of surviving and leaving viable offspring in a new environment.

Adaptive the concept that a trait or behaviour increases chances of survival under certain environmental conditions (see also *Adaptive Trait*).

Adaptive Trait a trait that enhances survival and reproductive success in a particular environment. Usually applied to biological evolution, the term is also often used by cultural anthropologists to refer to cultural traits that enhance reproductive success.

AIDS (Acquired Immune Deficiency Syndrome) a disease that emerged in the twentieth century, almost always lethal, presumably caused by the HIV virus or viruses.

Allele one member of a pair of genes.

Allen's Rule the rule that protruding body parts (particularly arms and legs) are relatively shorter in the cooler areas of a species's range than in the warmer areas.

Altruism the concept of caring for and sustaining members of the group who may no longer contribute to the group's survival.

Ancient DNA (aDNA) DNA extracted from archaeologically recovered materials.

Anthropoids one of the two suborders of primates; includes monkeys, apes, and humans.

Anthropological Linguistics the anthropological study of languages.

Anthropology the study of differences and similarities, both biological and cultural, in human populations. Anthropology is concerned with typical biological and cultural characteristics of human populations in all periods and in all parts of the world.

Anthropometric Measures measurements of the human body for the purpose of understanding growth and variation.

Applied Anthropology the branch of anthropology that concerns itself with applying anthropological knowledge to achieve practical goals, usually in the service of an agency outside the traditional academic setting. Also called *practising anthropology*.

^{40}Ar-^{39}Ar Dating Method used in conjunction with potassium-argon dating, this method gets around the problem of needing different rock samples to estimate potassium and argon. A nuclear reactor is used to convert the ^{39}Ar to ^{39}K, on the basis of which the amount of ^{40}K can be estimated. In this way, both argon and potassium can be estimated from the same rock sample.

Arboreal adapted to living in trees.

Archaeological Site areas of past human habitation or where fossil remains are found.

Archaeology the branch of anthropology that seeks to reconstruct the daily life and customs of peoples who lived in the past and to trace and explain cultural changes. Often lacking written records for study, archaeologists must try to reconstruct history from the material remains of human cultures. See also *Historical Archaeology*.

Archaic *Homo sapiens* specimens of early *Homo sapiens* that are not exactly like anatomically modern humans are distinguished as Archaic *Homo sapiens*. Neandertals are a specific group of Archaic *Homo sapiens*.

Arctic Small Tool Tradition culture that follows the Palaeo-Arctic tradition, representing the first humans to move into the eastern Canadian Arctic and Greenland. In Alaska the Arctic Small Tool tradition evolved into the Norton tradition, while in the eastern Arctic it became the Dorset culture.

Ardipithecus ramidus an intermittently bipedal species dated to 4 million years ago. It is a possible candidate for the hominid common ancestor.

Artifact item manufactured by people and found in archaeological contexts.

Association the relationship between artifacts and features within archaeological sites.

Atlatl Aztec word for "spear-thrower."

Aurignacian Tools a stone tool technology associated with modern humans that began in Europe around

35 000 years ago. It includes the production of long, narrow blade tools.

Australopithecus genus of Pliocene and Pleistocene hominids.

Australopithecus aethiopicus an early robust australopithecine.

Australopithecus afarensis a species of *Australopithecus* that lived 4 million to 3 million years ago in East Africa and was definitely bipedal.

Australopithecus africanus a species of *Australopithecus* that lived between about 3 million and 2 million years ago.

Australopithecus anamensis a species of *Australopithecus* that lived perhaps 4.2 million years ago.

Australopithecus bahrelghazalia a species of *Australopithecus* discovered by French researchers in Chad in north central Africa and reported in 1995. *A. bahrelghazalia* is dated between 3.5 million and 3 million years ago and is thought to be a second hominid species contemporary with *A. afarensis*.

Australopithecus boisei an East African robust australopithecine species dating from 2.2 million to 1.3 million years ago with somewhat larger cranial capacity than *A. africanus*. No longer thought to be larger than other australopithecines, it is robust primarily in the skull and jaw, most strikingly in the teeth. Compared with *A. robustus*, *A. boisei* has even more features that reflect a huge chewing apparatus.

Australopithecus garhi a species discovered in 1999 in the Afar region of Ethiopia, dating to about 2.5 million years ago. *A. garhi* had a projecting apelike face and small braincase, similar to *A. afarensis* but with much larger teeth.

Australopithecus robustus a robust australopithecine species found in South African caves dating from about 1.8 million to 1 million years ago. Not as large in the teeth and jaws as *A. boisei*.

Balancing Selection a type of selection that occurs when a heterozygous combination of alleles is positively favoured even though a homozygous combination is disfavoured.

Basicranium the base of the skull.

Behavioural Ecology the study of how all kinds of behaviour may be related to the environment. The theoretical orientation involves the application of biological evolutionary principles to the behaviour (including social behaviour) of animals, including humans. Also called *sociobiology*, particularly when applied to social organization and social behaviour.

Bergmann's Rule the rule that smaller-sized subpopulations of a species inhabit the warmer parts of its geographical range and larger-sized subpopulations the cooler areas.

Beringia the land mass that is now under water (the Bering Strait) between Siberia and Alaska.

Bifacial Tool a tool worked or flaked on two sides.

Bilophodont having four cusps on the molars that form two parallel ridges. This is the common molar pattern of Old World monkeys.

Biocultural Model a holistic approach that recognizes the interaction between biology and culture in human populations.

Biological (Physical) Anthropology the study of humans as biological organisms, dealing with the emergence and evolution of humans and with contemporary biological variations among human populations. Also called *physical anthropology*.

Bipedalism locomotion in which an animal walks on its two hind legs.

Blade a thin flake whose length is usually more than twice its width. In the blade technique of toolmaking, a core is prepared by shaping a piece of flint with hammer stones into a pyramidal or cylindrical form. Blades are then struck off until the core is used up.

Brachiators animals that move through the trees by swinging hand over hand from branch to branch. They usually have long arms and fingers.

Broca's Area the area of the brain related to language acquisition. It is important for understanding the origins of language in early hominids.

Burin a chisel-like stone tool used for carving and for making such artifacts as bone and antler needles, awls, and projectile points.

Canines the cone-shaped teeth immediately behind the incisors; used by most primates to seize food and in fighting and display.

Carrying Capacity the estimated population number and density that a given area of land can support, given the technology used by the people at the time.

Catarrhines the group of anthropoids with narrow noses and nostrils that face downward. Catarrhines include monkeys of the Old World (Africa, Asia, and Europe) as well as apes and humans.

Catastrophism the theory that the earth was shaped by a serious of catastrophic events including volcanic eruptions, floods, hurricanes, etc. It preceded later theories to explain evolutionary changes.

Ceramics objects shaped from clay and baked at high temperature (fired) to make them hard. Containers such as pots and jars are typical ceramics though they can take on many forms and uses.

Cercopithecoids Old World monkeys.

Cerebral Cortex the "grey matter" of the brain; the centre of speech and other higher mental activities.

Chiefdom a political unit, with a chief at its head, integrating more than one community but not necessarily the whole society or language group.

Chromosomes paired rod-shaped structures within a cell nucleus containing the genes that transmit traits from one generation to the next.

Chronometric Dating See *Absolute Dating*.

Civilization urban society, from the Latin word for "city-state."

Cline the gradually increasing (or decreasing) frequency of a gene from one end of a region to another.

Conservation techniques used on archaeological materials to stop or reverse the process of decay.

Continental Drift the movement of the continents over the past 135 million years. In the early Cretaceous (about 135 million years ago) there were two "super-continents": *Laurasia*, which included North America and Eurasia, and *Gondwanaland*, which included Africa, South America, India, Australia, and Antarctica. By the beginning of the Paleocene (about 65 million years ago), Gondwanaland had broken apart, with South America drifting west away from Africa, India drifting east, and Australia and Antarctica drifting south.

Coprolites the fossilized remains of feces.

Cretaceous geological epoch 135 million to 65 million years ago, during which dinosaurs and other reptiles ceased to be the dominant land vertebrates and mammals and birds began to become important.

Cross-cultural Researcher an ethnologist who uses ethnographic data about many societies to test possible explanations of cultural variation.

Crossing-over exchanges of sections of chromosomes from one chromosome to another.

Cultural Anthropology the study of cultural variation and universals.

Cultural Ecologist a person concerned with the relationship between culture and the physical and social environments.

Cultural Relativism the attitude that a society's customs and ideas should be viewed within the context of that society's problems and opportunities.

Cultural Resource Management (CRM) the long-term stewardship of a region's cultural heritage sites.

Culture the set of learned behaviours, beliefs, attitudes, values, and ideals that are characteristic of a particular society or population.

Culture-bound syndrome Illnesses unique to a specific culture.

Cuneiform wedge-shaped writing invented by the Sumerians around 3000 B.C.

Darwin, Charles (1809–82) a British naturalist who proposed the theory of evolution by natural selection. Most people equate the theory of evolution with Darwin because of the historical controversy his theory created at the time.

Datum a fixed, permanent reference point within or near an archaeological site used to define the location of all information and specimens collected from the site. As the datum is a permanent fixture, future investigations can be spatially related to all previous work at the site.

Dendrochronology an absolute dating technique based on counting annual tree rings in wood.

Dentition the type, number, and arrangement of teeth.

Diagenesis chemical changes that occur in materials after deposition in the ground.

Diastema a gap between the canine and first premolar found in apes.

Differential Reproductive Success differences in the chances of an organism surviving to leaving offspring that will also survive.

Diffusion the borrowing by one society of a cultural trait belonging to another society as the result of contact between the two societies.

Directional Selection a type of natural selection that increases the frequency of a trait (the trait is said to be positively favoured, or *adaptive*).

Diurnal active during the day.

DNA (Deoxyribonucleic Acid) a long, two-stranded molecule in the genes; directs the making of an organism according to the instructions in its genetic code.

Domestication modification or adaptation of plants and animals for use by humans. When people plant crops, we refer to the process as cultivation. It is only when the crops cultivated and the animals raised have been modified—are different from wild varieties—that we speak of plant and animal domestication.

Dominant the allele of a gene pair that is always phenotypically expressed in the heterozygous form.

Dryopithecus genus of ape from the later Miocene found primarily in Europe. It had thin tooth enamel and pointed molar cusps quite similar to those of the fruit-eating chimpanzees of today.

Ecofacts natural objects that have been used or affected by humans.

Egalitarian Society a society in which all persons of a given age-sex category have equal access to economic resources, power, and prestige.

Electron Spin Resonance Dating like thermoluminescence dating, this technique measures trapped electrons from surrounding radioactive material. The material to be dated is exposed to varying magnetic fields in order to obtain a spectrum of the microwaves absorbed by the tested material. Because no heating is required for this technique, electron spin resonance is especially useful for dating organic materials, such as bone and shell, that decompose if heated.

Endocast a preserved, fossilized relief of a hominid brain, created by the skull filling with minerals and taking on the morphology and structure of the brain. Endocasts are an important source of evidence for understanding the evolution of the brain and questions related to the origins of language, etc.

Environmental Archaeology a field of study that is interested specifically in ecological and climatic conditions of the past as a means for better understanding how various peoples lived—what conditions they lived in and how those conditions affected their lives.

Eocene a geological epoch 55 million to 34 million years ago during which the first definite primates appeared.

Ethnocentric refers to judgment of other cultures solely in terms of one's own culture.

Ethnographer a person who spends some time living with, interviewing, and observing a group of people so that he or she can describe their customs.

Ethnographic Analogy method of comparative cultural study that extrapolates to the past from recent or current societies.

Ethnohistorian an ethnologist who uses historical documents to study how a particular culture has changed over time.

Ethnology the study of how and why recent cultures differ and are similar.

Ethnomedicine the health-related beliefs, knowledge, and practices of a cultural group.

Experimental Archaeology a specialty within archaeology used to explore a variety of historical questions, especially those related to diet and subsistence by reproducing or replicating technological traits and patterns observed in the archaeological record.

Feature the non-portable portions of an archaeological site, some of which can include artifacts.

Fission-Track Dating a chronometric dating method used to date crystal, glass, and many uranium-rich materials contemporaneous with fossils or deposits that are from 20 years to 5 billion years old. This dating method entails counting the tracks or paths of decaying uranium-isotope atoms in the sample and then comparing the number of tracks with the uranium content of the sample.

Food Collection all forms of subsistence technology in which food-getting is dependent on naturally occurring resources—wild plants and animals.

Food Production the form of subsistence technology in which food-getting is dependent on the cultivation and domestication of plants and animals.

Foragers people who subsist on the collection of naturally occurring plants and animals. Also referred to as hunter-gatherers.

Foramen Magnum the hole in the base of the skull through which the spinal cord passes en route to the brain.

Fossil Locales places where fossilized remains of once living organisms are found.

Fossilization the process of becoming a fossil by the replacement of organic materials with an inorganic mineral matrix.

Fossils the hardened remains or impressions of plants and animals that lived in the past.

F-U-N Trio fluorine (F), uranium (U), and nitrogen (N) tests for relative dating. All three minerals are present in groundwater. The older a fossil is, the higher its fluorine or uranium content will be, and the lower its nitrogen content.

Funerary Archaeology the study of burial customs from archaeological evidence.

Gene chemical unit of heredity.

Gene Flow the process by which genes pass from the gene pool of one population to that of another through mating and reproduction.

Genetic Drift the various random processes that affect gene frequencies in small, relatively isolated populations.

Genetic Recombination a random shuffling of the parents' genes.

Genotype the total complement of inherited traits or genes of an organism.

Genus a group of related species; pl., *genera*.

Geographic Information Systems (GIS) integrated software package for the input, analysis, and display of spatial information.

Gloger's Rule the rule that populations of birds and mammals living in warm, humid climates have more melanin (and therefore darker skin, fur, or feathers) than populations of the same species living in cooler, drier areas.

Group Selection natural selection of group characteristics.

Half-life the time it takes for half of the atoms of a radioactive substance to decay into atoms of a different substance.

Haplorhines tarsiers and anthropoids.

Heritability the concept that traits are inherited from parent to offspring.

Heterozygous possessing differing genes or alleles in corresponding locations on a pair of chromosomes.

Hieroglyphics "picture writing," as in ancient Egypt and in Mayan sites in Mesoamerica (Mexico and Central America).

Historical Archaeology a specialty within archaeology that studies the material remains of recent peoples who left written records.

Historical Linguistics the study of how languages change over time.

Holistic refers to an approach that studies many aspects of a multifaceted system.

Hominids the group of hominoids consisting of humans and their direct ancestors. It contains at least two genera: *Homo* and *Australopithecus*.

Hominoids the group of catarrhines that includes both apes and humans.

Homo genus to which modern humans and their ancestors belong.

Homo erectus the first hominid species to be widely distributed in the Old World. The earliest finds are possibly 1.8 million years old. The brain (averaging 895–1040 cc) was larger than that found in any of the australopithecines or *H. habilis* but smaller than the average brain of a modern human.

Homo ergaster classification given by some for *Homo erectus* remains from Africa.

Homo habilis early species belonging to our genus, *Homo*, with cranial capacities averaging about 630–640 cc, about 50 percent of the brain capacity of modern humans. Dating from about 2 million years ago.

Homo heidelbergensis classification given by some for *Homo erectus* remains from Europe.

Homo rudolfensis early species belonging to our genus, *Homo*. Similar enough to *Homo habilis* that some paleoanthropologists make no distinction between the two.

Homo sapiens all living people belong to one biological species, *Homo sapiens*, which means that all human populations on earth can successfully interbreed. The first *Homo sapiens* may have emerged by 200 000 years ago.

Homo sapiens neandertalensis a variety of early *Homo sapiens*.

Homo sapiens sapiens modern-looking humans, undisputed examples of which appeared about 50 000 years ago; may have appeared earlier.

Homozygous possessing two identical genes or alleles in corresponding locations on a pair of chromosomes.

Horticulture plant cultivation carried out with relatively simple tools and methods; nature replaces nutrients in the soil, in the absence of permanently cultivated fields.

Human Palaeontology the study of the emergence of humans and their later physical evolution. Also called *palaeoanthropology*.

Human Variation the study of how and why contemporary human populations vary biologically.

Hylobates the family of hominoids that includes gibbons and siamangs; often referred to as the lesser apes (as compared with the great apes such as gorillas and chimpanzees).

Hypoxia a condition of oxygen deficiency that often occurs at high altitudes. The percentage of oxygen in the air is the same as at lower altitudes, but because the barometric pressure is lower, less oxygen is taken in with each breath. Often, breathing becomes more rapid, the heart beats faster, and activity is more difficult.

Incisors the front teeth; used for holding or seizing food and preparing it for chewing by the other teeth.

Indirect Percussion a toolmaking technique common in the Upper Paleolithic. After shaping a core into a pyramidal or cylindrical form, the toolmaker could put a punch of antler or wood or another hard material into position and strike it with a hammer. Using a hammer-struck punch enabled the toolmaker to strike off consistently shaped blades.

Individual Selection natural selection of individual characteristics.

Insectivore the order or major grouping of mammals, including modern shrews and moles, that is adapted to feeding on insects.

Intensive Agriculture food production characterized by the permanent cultivation of fields and made possible by the use of the plow, draft animals or machines, fertilizers, irrigation, water-storage techniques, and other complex agricultural techniques.

^{40}**K (Potassium-40)** a radioactive form of potassium that decays at an established rate and forms argon-40 used in K-Ar dating.

Kenyapithecus an apelike primate from the Middle Miocene found in East Africa. It had very thickly enamelled teeth and robust jaws, suggesting a diet of hard, tough foods. Probably somewhat terrestrial.

Knuckle Walking a locomotor pattern of primates such as the chimpanzee and gorilla in which the weight of the upper part of the body is supported on the thickly padded knuckles of the hands.

Lamarck, Jean Baptiste (1744–1829) a French naturalist who proposed a theory of evolution through the inheritance of acquired characteristics.

Law of Superposition a law that states that older layers at an archaeological site are generally deeper or lower than more recent layers. The law of superposition provides a framework with which to make inferences regarding the relationship and relative date of cumulative layers of different strata.

Levalloisian Method a method that allowed flake tools of a predetermined size to be produced from a shaped core. The toolmaker first shaped the core and prepared a "striking platform" at one end. Flakes of predetermined and standard sizes could then be knocked off. Although some Levallois flakes date from as far back as 400 000 years ago, they are found more frequently in Mousterian tool kits.

Life Table a tool used by demographers to place individuals into age groups.

Linguistics the study of language.

Linnaeus, Carolus (1707–78) a Swedish naturalist who looked at the similarities and differences among organisms and created a system for naming, ranking, and classifying organisms that is still in use today. This system defined the fundamentals of biology in terms of nomenclature and classification.

Lithics the technical name for the tools made from stone.

Lumbar Curve found only in hominids; the bottom part of the vertebral column forms a curve, causing the spinal column to be S-shaped (as seen from the side).

Material Culture objects that people have and make.

Meiosis the process by which reproductive cells are formed. In this process of division, the number of chromosomes in the newly formed cells is reduced by half, so that when fertilization occurs the resulting organism has the normal number of chromosomes appropriate to its species, rather than double that number.

Mesolithic the archaeological period in the Old World beginning about 12 000 B.C. Humans were starting to settle down in semipermanent camps and villages as people began to depend less on big game (which they used to have to follow over long distances) and more on relatively stationary food resources such as fish, shellfish, small game, and wild plants rich in carbohydrates, proteins, and oils.

Messenger RNA (rDNA) a type of ribonucleic acid that is used in the cell to copy the DNA code for use in protein synthesis.

Microlith a small, razor-like blade fragment that was probably attached in a series to a wooden or bone handle to form a cutting edge.

Midden a pile of refuse, often shells, in an archaeological site.

Miocene the geological epoch from 24 million to 5.2 million years ago.

Mitochondrial DNA (mtDNA) found in the mitochondrion, mtDNA is a part of the cell that converts food into energy for the cell.

Mitosis cellular reproduction or growth involving the duplication of chromosome pairs.

Molars the large teeth behind the premolars at the back of the jaw; used for chewing and grinding food.

Molecular Anthropology the study of anthropological questions using genetic evidence.

Mousterian Tool Assemblage named after the tool assemblage found in a rock shelter at Le Moustier in the Dordogne region of southwestern France. Compared with an Acheulian assemblage, the Middle Palaeolithic (40 000–300 000 years ago) Mousterian has a smaller proportion of large core tools such as hand axes and cleavers and a bigger proportion of small flake tools such as scrapers. Flakes were often altered or "retouched" by striking small flakes or chips from one or more edges.

Multiregional Hypothesis the theory that anatomically modern humans evolved in situ in a variety of different regions around the world.

Mutation a change in the DNA sequence, producing an altered gene.

Natural Selection the outcome of processes that affect the frequencies of traits in a particular environment. Traits that enhance survival and reproductive success increase in frequency over time.

Neandertal the common name for the species *Homo neandertalensis*.

Neolithic originally meaning "the new Stone Age," now meaning the presence of domesticated plants and animals. The earliest evidence of domestication comes from the Near East about 8000 B.C.

Nocturnal active during the night.

Normalizing Selection the type of natural selection that removes harmful genes that arose by mutation.

Nutritional Anthropology seeks to understand the impact of various biocultural factors on the health and nutrition of a population. Nutritional anthropology can help to establish evidence on which public health policy changes or recommendations can be made.

Obsidian Hydration the absorption of water by a piece of obsidian when it is newly exposed to the atmosphere through natural forces or human activity. The layer that is being weathered is invisible, but its thickness can be measured and will depend on the time it has been exposed.

Occipital Torus a ridge of bone running horizontally across the back of the skull in apes and some hominids.

Oldowan the earliest stone toolmaking tradition, named after the tools found in Bed I at Olduvai Gorge, Tanzania; from about 2.5 million years ago. The stone artifacts include core tools and sharp-edged flakes made by striking one stone against another. Flake tools predominate. Among the core tools, so-called choppers are common.

Oligocene the geological epoch 34 million to 24 million years ago during which definite anthropoids emerged.

Omnivorous eating both meat and vegetation.

Omomyid a type of prosimian with many tarsierlike features that appeared in the early Eocene.

Opposable Thumb a thumb that can touch the tips of all the other fingers.

Orrorin tugenensis an apparently bipedal primate dating to between 5.8 million and 6 million years, making it possibly the earliest known hominid.

Osteology the study of the form and function of the skeleton.

Palaeoanthropology the study of the emergence of humans and their later physical evolution. Also called *human palaeontology*.

Palaeo-Arctic Tradition the first undisputed cultural development in the Arctic, after the more tentative early occupation sites associated with the peopling of the New World. The earliest well-documented Palaeo-Arctic sites occur from 8000 B.C. to 5000 B.C.

Palaeodemography the study of demographic structure and processes in past populations from archaeological evidence.

Palaeoethnobotany the study of plant remains from archaeological contexts.

Palaeomagnetic Dating a method used to identify the geomagnetic patterns in rocks, and to date the fossils within those rocks.

Palaeopathology the study of health and disease in the past from skeletal evidence.

Palaeolithic period of the early Stone Age, when flint, stone, and bone tools were developed and hunting and gathering were the means of acquiring food.

Paleocene the geological epoch 65 million to 55 million years ago.

Palynology the study of pollen from archaeological contexts.

Paranthropus some researchers class the robust australopithecines as *Paranthropus* (e.g., *Paranthropus robustus, Paranthropus boisei*).

Parapithecids small monkeylike Oligocene primates found in the Fayum area of Egypt.

Percussion Flaking a toolmaking technique in which one stone is struck with another to remove a flake.

Phenotype the observable physical appearance of an organism, which may or may not reflect its genotype or total genetic constitution.

Physical Anthropology See *Biological Anthropology*.

Phytolith microscopic granules of silicon dioxide that enter a plant's cells and take their shape.

Platyrrhines the group of anthropoids that have broad, flat-bridged noses, with nostrils facing outward; these monkeys are currently found only in the New World (Central and South America).

Polymerase Chain Reaction (PCR) technique for accurate recovery of ancient DNA. PCR requires only a few molecules for the amplification of DNA sequences from trace amounts of the original genetic material.

Pongids hominoids whose members include both the living and extinct apes.

Potassium-Argon (K-Ar) Dating a chronometric dating method that uses the rate of decay of a radioactive form of potassium (^{40}K) into argon (^{40}Ar) to date samples from 5000 to 3 billion years old. The K-Ar method dates the minerals and rocks in a deposit, not the fossils themselves.

Practising Anthropology See *Applied Anthropology*.

Prehensile adapted for grasping objects.

Prehistoric in the time before written records.

Premolars the teeth immediately behind the canines; used in chewing, grinding, and shearing food.

Pressure Flaking toolmaking technique whereby small flakes are struck off by pressing against the core with a bone, antler, or wood tool.

Primate a member of the mammalian order, Primates, divided into the two suborders of prosimians and anthropoids.

Primatologists people who study primates.

Proconsul the best-known genus of proto-apes from the Early Miocene; found mostly in Africa.

Prognathic a physical feature that is sticking out or pushed forward, such as the faces in apes and some hominid species.

Propliopithecids apelike anthropoids dating from the early Oligocene, found in the Fayum area of Egypt.

Prosimians literally "premonkeys," one of the two suborders of primates; includes lemurs, lorises, and tarsiers.

Provenience the location of an artifact or feature within a site. Also called provenance.

Quadrupeds animals that walk on all fours.

Rachis the seed-bearing part of a plant. In the wild variety the rachis shatters easily, releasing the seeds. Domesticated grains have a tough rachis, which does not shatter easily.

Radiocarbon Dating a dating method that uses the decay of carbon-14 to date organic remains. It is reliable for dating once-living matter up to 50 000 years old.

Recessive an allele phenotypically suppressed in the heterozygous form and expressed only in the homozygous form.

Relative Dating a method of dating fossils that determines the age of a specimen or deposit relative to a known specimen or deposit.

Ribosome a structure in the cell used in making proteins.

Sagittal Crest a ridge of bone along the midline of the top of the skull for muscle attachment.

Sagittal Keel an inverted V-shaped ridge running along the top of the skull in *Homo erectus*.

Sahelanthropus tchadensis a hominoid found in Chad dating to about 7 million years ago.

Scientific Method a process that involves the formulation of a problem, the collection of data through observation and experiment, and the formulation and testing of hypotheses.

Secular Trend a change in growth and developmental measures over time.

Sedentism settling in a single, permanent location.

Segregation the random sorting of chromosomes in meiosis.

Settlement Archaeology the study of settlement patterns within the archaeological record.

Sexually Dimorphic refers to a species in which males differ markedly from females in size and appearance.

Shifting Cultivation a type of horticulture in which the land is worked for short periods and then left to regenerate for some years before being used again.

Sickle-Cell Anemia (Sicklemia) a condition in which red blood cells assume a crescent (sickle) shape when deprived of oxygen, instead of the normal (disk) shape. The sickle-shaped red blood cells do not move through the body as readily as normal cells, and thus cause damage to the heart, lungs, brain, and other vital organs.

Single-Origin (or Replacement) Hypothesis the theory that anatomically modern humans evolved in a single region, Africa, and then replaced all existing Archaic populations in other regions of the world.

Site Catchment Analysis an analysis based on the assumption that the more dispersed resources are from habitation sites, the less likely they are to be exploited by a population.

Site Formation Process environmental and cultural factors that affect how and where materials are deposited at an archaeological site or fossil locale.

Sivapithecus a genus of ape from the later Miocene known for its thickly enamelled teeth, suggesting a diet of hard, tough, or gritty items. Found primarily in western and southern Asia and now thought to be ancestral to orangutans.

Skeletal Age-Indicator Techniques osteological techniques that are used to estimate the age at death of an individual from skeletal remains.

Slash-and-Burn a form of shifting cultivation in which the natural vegetation is cut down and burned off. The cleared ground is used for a short time and then left to regenerate.

Socialization a term used by anthropologists and psychologists to describe the development, through the direct and indirect influence of parents and others, of children's patterns of behaviour (and attitudes and values) that conform to cultural expectations.

Sociobiology See *Behavioural Ecology*.

Socio-Cultural Anthropology See *Cultural Anthropology*.

Sociolinguistics the study of cultural and subcultural patterns of speaking in different social contexts.

Speciation the development of a new species.

Species a population that consists of organisms able to interbreed and produce fertile and viable offspring.

Stable Isotopes isotopes of the same elements with different atomic masses.

State a political unit with centralized decision making affecting a large population. Most states have cities with public buildings; full-time craft and religious specialists; an "official" art style; a hierarchical social structure topped by an elite class; and a governmental monopoly on the legitimate use of force to implement policies.

Stationary in demography, a population is considered to be stationary when there is no in-migration or out-migration and the number of deaths equal the number of births per year.

Stratigraphy the study of how different rock formations and fossils are laid down in successive layers or strata. Older layers are generally deeper or lower than more recent layers. See also *Law of Superposition*.

Strepsirhines lemurs and lorises.

Structural Linguistics the study of how languages are constructed. Also called descriptive linguistics.

Subsistence Technology the methods humans use to procure food.

Subsurface Techniques archaeological survey techniques that map features beneath the surface.

Surface Techniques archaeological survey techniques for finding and assessing archaeological sites from surface finds.

Taphonomy the study of changes that occur to organisms or objects after being buried or deposited.

Taurodontism having teeth with an enlarged pulp cavity.

Technology Tools constructions such as traps, skills required to use these constructions, and the organizations needed to extract, process, and redistribute resources.

Terrestrial adapted to living on the ground.

Thermoluminescence Dating a dating technique that is well suited to samples of ancient pottery, brick, tile, or terracotta, which (when they were made) were heated to a high temperature that released trapped electrons from radioactive elements around it; the electrons trapped after manufacture emit light when heated, so the age of the object can be estimated by measuring how much light is emitted when the object is heated.

Trace Elements elements found in extremely small amounts within the body.

Type II Diabetes non-insulin-dependent diabetes mellitus (NIDDM), unlike insulin-dependent diabetes, that tends to manifest itself in adult patients as a result of a sedentary lifestyle, chronic obesity, and excess sugar intake.

Typology a way of organizing artifacts in categories based on their particular characteristics.

Unifacial Tool a tool worked or flaked on one side only.

Uniformitarianism the concept that processes in the past must have behaved in the same manner as they are observed to behave today, and will do so in the future. This is an assumption that is often applied to geological processes (e.g., erosion) or biological processes (e.g., interaction of mortality and fertility).

Upper Palaeolithic the period associated with the emergence of modern humans and their spread around the world.

Uranium-Series Dating a technique for dating *Homo sapiens* sites that uses the decay of two kinds of uranium (^{235}U and ^{238}U) into other isotopes (such as ^{230}Th—thorium). Particularly useful in cave sites. Different types of uranium-series dating use different isotope ratios.

Variation differences in the genotype and phenotype of individual members of a species.

Vertical Clinging and Leaping a locomotor pattern characteristic of several primates, including tarsiers and galagos. The animal normally rests by clinging to a branch in a vertical position and uses its hind limbs alone to push off from one vertical position to another.

Virgin Soil Epidemic occurs when a disease enters a population that has not been previously exposed to it, or has not had exposure for a considerably long time. Because there is no previous immunity within a portion of the population, the disease tends to affect all members of the group equally.

"Y-5" Pattern refers to the pattern of cusps on human molars. When looked at from the top, the cusps of the molars form a Y opening toward the cheek.

Zooarchaeology the study of animals' remains from archaeological contexts.

Literature Cited

Adams R. 1981. Heartland of Cities: Surveys of Ancient Settlement and Land Use on the Central Floodplain of the Euphrates. Chicago: University of Chicago Press.

Adams RM. September 1960. The Origin of Cities. Scientific American 153.

Aiello LC. 1992. Body Size and Energy Requirements. In: Jones S, Martin R, Pilbeam D, editors. The Cambridge Encyclopedia of Human Evolution. Cambridge: Cambridge University Press. p 41–44.

Aiello LC. 1993. The Origin of the New World Monkeys. In: Lavocat GW, Lavocat R, editors. The Africa-South America Connection. Oxford: Clarendon Press. p 100–118.

Aiello LC, Collard M. 29 November 2001. Palaeoanthropology — Our Newest Oldest Ancestor? Nature 410:526–527.

Aiello LC, Dean C. 1990. An Introduction to Human Evolutionary Anatomy. London: Academic Press.

Aitken MJ. 1985. Thermoluminescence Dating. London: Academic Press.

Alberts B, Bray D, Lewis J, Raff M, Roberts K, Watson JD. 1983. Molecular Biology of the Cell. New York: Garland.

Alexander JP. August 1992. Alas, Poor Notharctus. Natural History 55–59.

Allen JS, Lambert AJ, Attah Johnson FY, Schmidt K, Nero KL. 1996. Antisaccadic Eye Movements and Attentional Asymmetry in Schizophrenia in Three Pacific Populations. Acta Psychiatrica Scandinavia 94:258–265.

Allen KMS, Green SW, Zubrow EBW. 1990. Interpreting Space: GIS and Archaeology. London: Taylor & Francis.

Andersen RE. 2000. The Spread of the Childhood Obesity Epidemic. Canadian Medical Association Journal 163:1461–1432.

Andrews P. 2000. Propliopithecidae. In: Tattersall I, Delson E, van Couvering J, editors. Encyclopedia of Human Evolution and Prehistory. New York: Garland Publishing. p 485–487.

Anonymous. 1967. Textor, comp. A Cross-Cultural Summary. New Haven, CT: HRAF Press.

Anonymous. 1969. The Domestication and Exploitation of Plants and Animals. Chicago: Aldine.

Anonymous. 1972. Man, Settlement and Urbanism. Cambridge, MA: Schenkman.

Anonymous. 5 March 1973. The First Dentist. Newsweek 73.

Anonymous. 1978. Pre-Historic Maya Agriculture. Albuquerque: University of New Mexico Press.

Anonymous. 1980. Paper. In: Academic American Encyclopedia. Princeton, NJ: Areté.

Anonymous. 1988. Webster's New World Dictionary. Third College Edition. New York: Webster's New World.

Anonymous. 1989. People of the Earth: An Introduction to World Prehistory. Glenview, IL: Scott, Foresman.

Anonymous. 1990a. Appendix A: Report of the Committee on Ethics, Society for Applied Anthropology, and Appendix F: Professional and Ethical Responsibilities, SFAA. In: Fluehr-Lobban C, editor. Ethics and the Profession of Anthropology: Dialogue for a New Era. Philadelphia: University of Pennsylvania Press.

Anonymous. 1990b. Appendix C: Statements on Ethics: Principles of Professional Responsibility, Adopted by the Council of the American Anthropological Association, May 1971 (as amended through May 1976) and Appendix I: Revised Principles of Professional Responsibility. In: Fluehr-Lobban C, editor. Ethics and the Profession of Anthropology: Dialogue for a New Era. Philadelphia: University of Pennsylvania Press.

Anonymous. 19 April 1996. The Last of the Cahokians. Science 351.

Anonymous. 1997a. Clyde Snow. Current Biography 58:52–54.

Anonymous. 1997b. EAAF (Argentine Forensic Anthropological Team), Annual Report.

Anonymous. 1997c. The First Tool Kit. Science [31 January], 623.

Anonymous. February 1998. Printing, Typography, and Photoengraving: History of Prints: Origins in China: Transmission of Paper to Europe (12th century). Britannica Online.

Aptekar L. 1994. Environmental Disasters in Global Perspective. New York: G. K. Hall/Macmillan.

Arensburg B, Schepartz LA, Tillier AM, Vandemeersch B, Rak Y. 1990. A Reappraisal of the Anatomical Basis for Speech in Middle Palaeolithic Hominids. American Journal of Physical Anthropology 83(2):137–146.

Asch NB, Asch DL. 1978. The Economic Potential of *Iva annua* and Its Prehistoric Importance in the Lower Illinois Valley. In: Ford RI, editor. The Nature and Status of Ethnobotany. Anthropological Papers.

Museum of Anthropology No. 67. Ann Arbor: University of Michigan. p 301–342.

Asfaw B, White T, Lovejoy CO, Latimer B, Simpson S, Suwa G. 1999. *Australopithecus garhi*: A New Species of Early Hominid from Ethiopia. Science 284(5414):629–635.

Ayala FJ. 22 December 1995. The Myth of Eve: Molecular Biology and Human Origins. Science 270(5244):1930–1936.

Bahn PG. 1998. Neanderthals Emancipated. Nature 394:719–720.

Bahn PG. 1999. The Cambridge Illustrated History of Archaeology. Cambridge: Cambridge University Press.

Bailey GN, editor. 1981. Hunter-Gatherer Economy in Prehistory. Cambridge: Cambridge University Press.

Bailey RC, Head G, Jenike M, Owen B, Rechtman R, Zechenter E. 1989. Hunting and Gathering in Tropical Rain Forest: Is it Possible? American Anthropologist 91:59–82.

Barash DP. 1977. Sociobiology and Behavior. New York: Elsevier.

Barnett T, Blaikie P. 1992. AIDS in Africa; Its Present and Future Impact. London: Belhaven.

Barrett DE. 1984. Malnutrition and Child Behavior: Conceptualization, Assessment and an Empirical Study of Social-Emotional Functioning. In: Brozek J, Schürch B, editors. Malnutrition and Behavior: Critical Assessment of Key Issues. Lausanne, Switzerland: Nestlé Foundation. p 280–306.

Bartlett Thompson E. 1966. Africa, Past and Present. Boston: Houghton Mifflin.

Beadle G, Beadle M. 1966. The Language of Life. Garden City, NY: Doubleday.

Bearder SK. 1987. Lorises, Bushbabies, and Tarsiers: Diverse Societies in Solitary Foragers. In: Smuts BB, Cheney DL, Seyfarth RM, Wrangham RW, Struhsaker TT, editors. Primate Societies. Chicago: University of Chicago Press. p 11–24.

Begun D. 1998. Miocene Apes. In: Ember CR, Ember M, Peregrine PN, editors. Research Frontiers in Anthropology. Upper Saddle River, NJ: Prentice Hall/Simon & Schuster Custom Publishing.

Benyshek DC, Martin JF, Johnston CS. 2001. A Reconsideration of the Origins of the Type 2 Diabetes Epidemic among Native Americans and the Implications for Intervention Policy. Medical Anthropology 20:25–64.

Berg P, Singer M. 1992. Dealing with Genes: The Language of Heredity. Mill Valley, CA: University Science Books. p 53, 221–44.

Berlin EA. 1996. General Overview of Maya Ethno-medicine: The Gastrointestinal Diseases. In: Berlin AE, Berlin B, editors. Medical Ethnobiology of the Highland Maya of Chiapas, Mexico. Princeton, NJ: Princeton University Press. p 52–53.

Berry JW, Poortinga YH, Segall MH, Dasen PR. 1992. Cross-Cultural Psychology: Research and Applications. New York: Cambridge University Press.

Berti PR, Chan HM, Receveur O, MacDonald CR, Kuhnlein HV. 1998a. Population Exposure to Radioactivity from Consumption of Caribou among the Dene/Metis of Denendeh (Western Northwest Territories, Canada). Journal of Exposure Analysis and Environmental Epidemiology 8:145–158.

Berti PR, Receveur O, Chan HM, Kuhnlein HV. 1998b. Dietary Exposure to Chemical Contaminants from Traditional Food among Adult Dene/Metis in the Western Northwest Territories, Canada. Environmental Research 76:131–142.

Bilsborough A. 1992. Human Evolution. New York: Blackie Academic & Professional.

Bindon JR, Baker PT. 1985. Modernization, Migration and Obesity among Samoan Adults. Annals of Human Biology 12:67–76.

Binford LR. 1971. Post-Pleistocene Adaptations. In: Struever S, editor. Prehistoric Agriculture. Garden City, NY: Natural History Press. p 27–33.

Binford LR. 1972. Mortuary Practices: Their Study and Potential. In: An Anthropological Perspective. New York: Seminar Press. p 208–243.

Binford LR. 1973. Interassemblage Variability: The Mousterian and the "Functional" Argument. In: Renfew C, editor. The Explanation of Culture Change: Models in Prehistory. Pittsburgh: University of Pittsburgh Press.

Binford LR. 1984. Faunal Remains from Klasies River Mouth. Orlando, FL: Academic Press.

Binford LR. 1987. Were There Elephant Hunters at Torralba? In: Nitecki M, Nitecki DV, editors. The Evolution of Human Hunting. New York: Plenum. p 47–105.

Binford LR. 1990. Mobility, Housing, and Environment: A Comparative Study. Journal of Anthropological Research 46:119–152.

Binford LR, Ho CK. 1985. Taphonomy at a Distance: Zhoukoudian, "The Cave Home of Beijing Man"? Current Anthropology 26:413–442.

Binford SR, Binford LR. April 1969. Stone Tools and Human Behavior. Scientific American 70–84.

Black FL. 11 December 1992. Why Did They Die? Science 1739–1740.

Blaffer Hrdy S. 1977. The Langurs of Abu: Female and Male Strategies of Reproduction. Cambridge, MA: Harvard University Press.

Blanton R. 1976. The Origins of Monte Albán. In: Cleland C, editor. Cultural Continuity and Change. New York: Academic Press. p 223–232.

Blanton R. 1978. Monte Albán: Settlement Patterns at the Ancient Zapotec Capital. New York: Academic Press.

Blanton RE. 1981. The Rise of Cities. In: Sabloff JA, editor. Supplement to the Handbook of Middle American Indians. Volume 1. Austin: University of Texas Press. p 397.

Blanton RE, Kowalewski SA, Feinman G, Appel J. 1981. Ancient Mesoamerica: A Comparison of Change in Three Regions. New York: Cambridge University Press.

Blendon RJ, Benson JM, DesRoches CM, Raleigh E, Taylor-Clark K. 2004. The Public's Response to Severe Acute Respiratory Syndrome in Toronto and the United States. Clinical Infectious Diseases 38:925–931.

Blumler MA, Byrne R. 1991. The Ecological Genetics of Domestication and the Origins of Agriculture. Current Anthropology 32:23–35.

Bodley JH. 1990. Victims of Progress. Third Edition. Mountain View, CA: Mayfield.

Boesch C, Boesch H. 1990. Tool Use and Tool Making in Wild Chimpanzees. Folia Primatology (Basel) 54:86–99.

Bogerhoff Mulder M. 1992. Demography of Pastoralists: Preliminary Data on the Datoga of Tanzania. Human Ecology 20:383–405.

Bogin B. 1988. Patterns of Human Growth. Cambridge: Cambridge University Press.

Bogin B. 1997. Evolutionary Hypotheses for Human Childhood. Yearbook of Physical Anthropology 40:63–89.

Bogin B, MacVean RB. 1981. Nutritional and Biological Determinants of Body Fat Patterning in Urban Guatemalan Children. Human Biology 53:259–268.

Bogin B, Sullivan T. 1986. Socioeconomic Status, Sex, Age, and Ethnicity as Determinants of Body Fat Distribution for Guatemalan Children. American Journal of Physical Anthropology 69:527–535.

Bohannan P, Glazer M, editors. 1988. High Points in Anthropology. New York: Alfred A. Knopf.

Bolton R. 1973. Aggression and Hypoglycemia among the Qolla: A Study in Psychobiological Anthropology. Ethnology 12:227–257.

Bolton R. 1989. Introduction: The AIDS Pandemic, A Global Emergency. Medical Anthropology 10:93–104.

Bolton R. 1992. AIDS and Promiscuity: Muddled in the Models of HIV Prevention. Medical Anthropology 14:145–223.

Bordaz J. 1970. Tools of the Old and New Stone Age. Garden City, NY: Natural History Press.

Bordes F. 22 September 1961. Mousterian Cultures in France. Science 803–810.

Boutton TW, Lynott MJ, Bumstead MP. 1991. Stable Carbon Isotopes and the Study of Prehistoric Human Diet. Critical Reviews in Food Science and Nutrition 30:373–385.

Bowler PJ. 1989. Evolution: The History of an Idea. Berkeley: University of California Press.

Boyd R, Richerson PJ. 1985. Culture and the Evolutionary Process. Chicago: University of Chicago Press.

Boyd R, Richerson PJ. 1990. Group Selection among Alternative Evolutionarily Stable Strategies. Journal of Theoretical Biology 145:331–342.

Boyd R, Silk J. 2000. How Humans Evolved. Second edition. New York: Norton.

Braidwood RJ. September 1960. The Agricultural Revolution. Scientific American 130.

Braidwood RJ, Willey GR. 1962. Conclusions and Afterthoughts. In: Braidwood RJ, Willey GR, editors. Courses toward Urban Life: Archeological Considerations of Some Cultural Alternatives. Viking Fund Publications in Anthropology No. 32. Chicago: Aldine. p 342.

Brain CK, Sillen A. 1 December 1988. Evidence from the Swartkrans Cave for the Earliest Use of Fire. Nature 464–466.

Branda RF, Eaton JW. 18 August 1978. Skin Color and Nutrient Photolysis: An Evolutionary Hypothesis. Science 625–626.

Brandon RN. 1990. Adaptation and Environment. Princeton, NJ: Princeton University Press.

Bräuer G. 1984. A Craniological Approach to the Origin of Anatomically Modern *Homo sapiens* in Africa and Implications for the Appearance of Modern Europeans. In: Smith FH and Spencer F, editors. The Origins of Modern Humans. Chicago: University of Chicago Press.

Bromage TG. 1998. Paleoanthropology and Life History, and Life History of a Paleoanthropologist. In: Ember CR, Ember M, Peregrine PN, editors. Research Frontiers in Anthropology. Upper Saddle River, NJ: Prentice Hall.

Bromage TG, Dean MC. 10 October 1985. Re-evaluation of the Age at Death of Immature Fossil Hominids. Nature 525–527.

Brooks AF, Jackson F, Grinker RR. 1993. Race and Ethnicity in America. Anthro Notes 15[3], 1–15. National Museum of Natural History Bulletin for Teachers.

Brown F, Harris J, Leakey R, Walker A. 29 August–4 September 1985. Early *Homo erectus* Skeleton from West Lake Turkana, Kenya. Nature 316:788–792.

Brown FH. 1988. Geochronometry. In: Tattersall I, Delson E, van Couvering J, editors. Encyclopedia of Human Evolution and Prehistory. New York: Garland. p 225.

Brown FH. 1992. Methods of Dating. In: Jones S, Martin R, Pilbeam D, editors. The Cambridge Encyclopedia of Human Evolution. New York: Cambridge University Press. p 179–186.

Brown JA. 1983. Summary. In: Philips JL, Brown JA, editors. Archaic Hunters and Gatherers in the American Midwest. New York: Academic Press. p 5–10.

Brown JA. 1985. Long-term Trends to Sedentism and the Emergence of Complexity in the American Midwest. In: Price TD, Brown JA, editors. Prehistoric Hunter-Gatherers: The Emergence of Cultural Complexity. Orlando, FL: Academic Press. p 201–231.

Brown JA, Price TD. 1985. Complex Hunter-Gatherers: Retrospect and Prospect. In: Price TD, Brown JA, editors. Prehistoric Hunter-Gatherers: The Emergence of Cultural Complexity. Orlando, FL: Academic Press. p 435–441.

Bruce SG. 2000. The Impact of Diabetes Mellitus among the Metis of Western Canada. Ethnicity & Health 5(1):47–57.

Brumfiel E. 1976. Regional Growth in the Eastern Valley of Mexico: A Test of the "Population Pressure" Hypothesis. In: Flannery KV, editor. The Early Mesoamerican Village. New York: Academic Press. p 234–250.

Brumfiel EM. 1983. Aztec State Making: Ecology, Structure, and the Origin of the State. American Anthropologist 85:261–284.

Brunet M, Beauvilain A, Coppens Y, Heitz E, Moutaye AH, Pilbeam D. 1995. The First Australopithecine 2,500 Kilometers West of the Rift Valley. Nature 378:273–275.

Brunet M, Guy F, Pilbeam D, Mackaye HT, Likius A, Ahounta D, Beauvilain A, Blondel C, Bocherens H, Boisserie JR, De Bonis L, Coppens Y, Dejax J, Denys C, Duringer P, Eisenmann VR, Fanone G, Fronty P, Geraads D, Lehmann T, Lihoreau F, Louchart A, Mahamat A, Merceron G, Mouchelin G, Otero O, Campomanes PP, De Leon MP, Rage JC, Sapanet M, Schuster M, Sudre J, Tassy P, Valentin X, Vignaud P, Viriot L, Zazzo A, Zollikofer C.11 July 2002. A New Hominid from the Upper Miocene of Chad, Central Africa. Nature 418:145–151.

Bryant CA, Bailey DFC. 1990. The Use of Focus Group Research in Program Development. In: van Willigen J, Finan T, editors. Soundings: Rapid and Reliable Research Methods for Practicing Anthropologists, NAPA Bulletin No. 10. Washington, DC: American Anthropological Association. p 24–39.

Buckland PC, Amorosi T, Barlow LK, Dugmore AJ, Mayewski PA, McGovern TH, Sadler AEJ, Skidmore P. 1996. Bioarchaeological and Climatological Evidence for the Fate of Norse Farmers in Medieval Greenland. Antiquity 70:86–88.

Budimlija ZM, Prinz MK, Zelson-Mundorff A, Wiersema J, Bartelink E, MacKinnon G, Nazzaruolo BL, Estacio SM, Hennessey MJ, Shaler RC. 2003. World Trade Center Human Identification Project: Experiences with Individual Body Identification Cases. Croatian Medical Journal 44:259–263.

Burke A, Cinq-mars J. 1998. Paleoethological Reconstruction and Taphonomy of *Equus lambei* from the Bluefish Caves, Yukon Territory, Canada. Arctic 51(2):105–115.

Butzer K. 1982a. Archaeology as Human Ecology. Cambridge: Cambridge University Press.

Butzer KW. 1982b. Geomorphology and sediment Stratigraphy. In: Singer R, Wymer J, editors. The Middle Stone Age at Klasies River Mouth in South Africa. Chicago: University of Chicago Press. p 42.

Byrne R. 1987. Climatic Changes and the Origins of Agriculture. In: Manzanilla L, editor. Studies of Agriculture. British Archaeological Reports International Series 349. Oxford: p 21–34.

Cameron N, Johnston FE, Kgamphe JS, Lunz R. 1992. Body Fat Patterning in Rural South African Black Children. American Journal of Human Biology 4:353–364.

Campbell AM. 1991. Microbes: The Laboratory and the Field. In: Davis BD, editor. The Genetic Revolution: Scientific Prospects and Public Perceptions. Baltimore: Johns Hopkins University Press. p 28–44.

Campbell BG. 2001. Humankind Emerging. Boston: Little, Brown. p 202.

Campbell DT. 1965. Variation and Selective Retention in Socio-Cultural Evolution. In: Barringer H, Blankstein G, Mack R, editors. Social Change in Developing Areas: A Re-interpretation of Evolutionary Theory. Cambridge, MA: Schenkman. p 19–49.

Cann R. 1988. DNA and Human Origins. Annual Review of Anthropology 17:127–143.

Cann RL, Stoneking M, Wilson AC. 1987. Mitochondrial DNA and Human Evolution. Nature 325(6099):31–36.

Cannon A. 1998. Contingency and Agency in the Growth of Northwest Coast Maritime Economies. Arctic Anthropology 35:57–67.

Cannon A. 2000a. Assessing Variability in Northwest Coast Salmon and Herring Fisheries: Bucket-auger

Sampling of Shell Midden Sites on the Central Coast in British Columbia. Journal of Archaeological Science 27:725–737.

Cannon A. January 2000b. Settlement and Sea Level on the Central Coast of British Columbia: Evidence from Shell Midden Cores. American Antiquity 65(1):67–77.

Carneiro RL. 1968. Slash-and-Burn Cultivation among the Kuikuru and Its Implications for Settlement Patterns. In: Cohen Y, editor. Man in Adaptation: The Cultural Present. Chicago: Aldine.

Carneiro RL. 21 August 1970. A Theory of the Origin of the State. Science 733–738.

Carneiro RL. 1988. The Circumscription Theory: Challenge and Response. American Behavioral Scientist 31:506–508.

Carpenter CR. 1940. A Field Study in Siam of the Behavior and Social Relations of the Gibbon (Hylobates lar). Comparative Psychology Monographs 16:1–212.

Carrier J, Bolton R. 1991. Anthropological Perspectives on Sexuality and HIV Prevention. Annual Review of Sex Research 2:49–75.

Carrington Goodrich L. 1959. A Short History of the Chinese People. Third edition. New York: Harper & Row.

Cartmill M. 1974. Rethinking Primate Origins. Science 184:436–443.

Cartmill M. 1992a. New Views on Primate Origins. Evolutionary Anthropology 1:105–111.

Cartmill M. 1992b. Non-Human Primates. In: Jones S, Martin R, Pilbeam D, editors. The Cambridge Encyclopedia of Human Evolution. Cambridge: Cambridge University Press.

Cartmill M. 1998. Explaining Primate Origins. In: Ember CR, Ember ME, Peregrine P, editors. Research Frontiers in Anthropology. Upper Saddle River, NJ: Prentice Hall/Simon & Schuster Custom Publishing.

Chambers E. 1989. Applied Anthropology: A Practical Guide. Prospect Heights, IL: Waveland.

Chan HM. 1998. A Database for Environmental Contaminants in Traditional Foods in Northern and Arctic Canada: Development and Applications. Food Additives and Contaminants 15(2):127–134.

Chang K-C. September 1970. The Beginnings of Agriculture in the Far East. Antiquity 44(175):176.

Chang K-C. 1986. The Archaeology of Ancient China. New Haven, CT: Yale University Press.

Chang KC. 1981. In Search of China's Beginnings: New Light on an Old Civilization. American Scientist 69:148–160.

Chaplin G, Jablonski NG, Cable NT. 1994. Physiology, Thermoregulation and Bipedalism. Journal of Human Evolution 27:497–510.

Chard CS. 1969. Man in Prehistory. New York: McGraw-Hill.

Charles-Dominique P. 1977. Ecology and Behaviour of Nocturnal Primates. Martin, RD, translator. New York: Columbia University Press.

Chase LA. 1937. The Trend of Diabetes in Saskatchewan 1905–1934. Canadian Medical Association Journal 36:366–369.

Chase P, Dibble H. 1987. Middle Paleolithic Symbolism: A Review of Current Evidence and Interpretations. Journal of Anthropological Archaeology 6:263–269.

Chatters J. 2002. Last Word on Kennewick Man? Archaeology 55:17.

Cheney DL, Wrangham RW. 1987. Predation. In: Smuts BB, Cheney DL, Seyfarth RM, Wrangham RW, Struhsaker TT, editors. Primate Societies. Chicago: University of Chicago Press. p 236.

Childe VG. 1950. The Urban Revolution. Town Planning Review 21:3–17.

Chivers DJ. 1974. The Siamang in Malaya. Basel, Switzerland: Karger.

Chivers DJ, editor. 1980. Malayan Forest Primates: Ten Years' Study in Tropical Rain Forest. New York: Plenum.

Chomsky N. 1975. Reflections on Language. New York: Pantheon.

Ciochon R, Olsen J, James J. 1990. Other Origins: The Search for the Giant Ape in Human Prehistory. New York: Bantam.

Ciochon RL, Etler DA. 1994. Reinterpreting Past Primate Diversity. In: Corruccini S, Ciochon RL, editors. Integrative Paths to the Past: Paleoanthropological Advances in Honor of F. Clark Howell. Englewood Cliffs, NJ: Prentice Hall. p 37–68.

Clark G. 1975. The Earlier Stone Age Settlement of Scandinavia. Cambridge: Cambridge University Press.

Clark G, Piggott S. 1965. Prehistoric Societies. New York: Knopf.

Clark JD. 1970. The Prehistory of Africa. New York: Praeger.

Clark JD. 1977. Interpretations of Prehistoric Technology from Ancient Egyptian and Other Sources. Part II: Prehistoric Arrow Forms in Africa as Shown by Surviving Examples of the Traditional Arrows of the San Bushmen. Paleorientology 3:136.

Clark WELG. 1964. The Fossil Evidence for Human Evolution: An Introduction to the Study of Paleoanthropology. Chicago: University of Chicago Press.

Clarke RJ, Tobias PV. 1995. Sterkfontein Member 2 Foot Bones of the Oldest South African Hominid. Science 269:521–524.

Clutton-Brock J. 1988. Domestication of Animals. In: Jones S, Martin R, Pilbeam D, editors. The Cambridge Encyclopedia of Human Evolution. Cambridge: Cambridge University Press. p 380–385.

Clutton-Brock TH, Harvey P. 1977. Primate Ecology and Social Organization. Journal of Zoology 183:8–9.

Clutton-Brock TH, Harvey P. 1980. Primates, Brains and Ecology. Journal of Zoology 190:309–323.

Coe MD. 1966. The Maya. New York: Praeger.

Cohen A. 1999. The Mental Health of Indigenous Peoples: An International Overview. Geneva: Department of Mental Health, World Health Organization.

Cohen MN. 1977a. The Food Crisis in Prehistory: Overpopulation and the Origin of Agriculture. New Haven, CT: Yale University Press.

Cohen MN. 1977b. Population Pressure and the Origins of Agriculture. In: Reed CA, editor. Origins of Agriculture. The Hague: Mouton. p 138–141.

Cohen MN. 1987. The Significance of Long-Term Changes in Human Diet and Food Economy. In: Harris M, Ross EB, editors. Food and Evolution: Toward a Theory of Human Food Habits. Philadelphia: Temple University Press. p 269–273.

Cohen MN. 1989. Health and the Rise of Civilization. New Haven, CT: Yale University Press.

Cohen MN. 1998. Were Early Agriculturalists Less Healthy Than Food Collectors? In: Ember CR, Ember M, Peregrine PN, editors. Research Frontiers in Anthropology. Upper Saddle River, NJ: Prentice Hall/Simon & Schuster Custom Publishing.

Cohen MN, Armelagos GJ. 1984a. Paleopathology at the Origins of Agriculture. Orlando, FL: Academic Press.

Cohen MN, Armelagos GJ. 1984b. Paleopathology at the Origins of Agriculture: Editor's Summation. In: Cohen MN, Armelagos GJ, editors. Paleopathology at the Origins of Agriculture. Orlando, FL: Academic Press. p 585–602.

Cohen RN, Service ER, editors. 1978. Origins of the State: The Anthropology of Political Evolution. Philadelphia: Institute for the Study of Human Issues.

Collier S, White JP. 1976. Get Them Young? Age and Sex Inferences on Animal Domestication in Archaeology. American Antiquity 41:96–102.

Collins D. 1976. Later Hunters in Europe. In: Collins D, editor. The Origins of Europe. New York: Thomas Y. Crowell. p 88–125.

Connah G. 1987. African Civilizations: Precolonial Cities and States in Tropical Africa, an Archaeological Perspective. Cambridge: Cambridge University Press.

Conroy GC. 1990. Primate Evolution. New York: Norton. p 8–15.

Cook DC. 1981. Mortality, Age Structure and Status in the Interpretation of Stress Indicators in Prehistoric Skeletons: A Dental Example from the Lower Illinois Valley. In: Chapman R, Kinnes I, Randsborg K, editors. The Archaeology of Death. Cambridge: Cambridge University Press. p 133–144.

Cook DC. 1984. Subsistence and Health in the Lower Illinois Valley: Osteological Evidence. In: Cohen MN, Armelagos GJ, editors. Palaeopathology at the Origins of Agriculture. Orlando: Academic Press. p 235–269.

Cook DC, Buikstra JE. 1979. Health and Differential Survival in Prehistoric Populations: Prenatal Dental Defects. American Journal of Physical Anthropology 51:649–664.

Corballis MC. March/April 1999. The Gestural Origins of Language. American Scientist 87(2):138–145.

Coreil J. 1989. Lessons from a Community Study of Oral Rehydration Therapy in Haiti. In: van Willigen J, Rylko-Bauer B, McElroy A, editors. Making Our Research Useful: Case Studies in the Utilization of Anthropological Knowledge. Boulder, CO: Westview Press. p 143–157.

Corruccini RS. 1992. Metrical Reconsideration of the Skhul IV and IX and Border Cave 1 Crania in the Context of Modern Human Origins. American Journal of Physical Anthropology 87:433–445.

Crawford GW. 1992. Prehistoric Plant Domestication in East Asia. In: Cowan C, Watson PJ, editors. The Origins of Agriculture. Washington, DC: Smithsonian Institution Press. p 29–30.

Crawford GW, Smith DG. 1996. Migration in Prehistory: Princess Point and the Northern Iroquoian Case. American Antiquity 61(4):782–790.

Crawford GW, Smith DG, Bowyer V. 1997. Dating the Entry of Corn (Zea mays) to the Lower Great Lakes Region. American Antiquity 62(1): 112–119.

Crawford RD. 1984. Turkey. In: Mason IL, editor. Evolution of Domesticated Animals. New York: Longman. p 329–331.

Crockett C, Eisenberg JF. 1987. Howlers: Variations in Group Size and Demography. In: Smuts BB, Cheney DL, Seyfarth RM, Wrangham RW, Struhsaker TT, editors. Primate Societies. Chicago: University of Chicago Press. p 54–68.

Culotta E. 18 August 1995. New Hominid Crowds the Field. Science 918.

Czekala N, Sicotte P. 2000. Reproductive Monitoring of Free-Ranging Female Mountain Gorillas by Urinary Hormone Analysis. American Journal of Primatology 51:209–215.

Daniel IR. 2001. Early Eastern Archaic. In: Peregrine PN, Ember M, editors. Encyclopedia of Prehistory. Volume 6: North America. Kluwer Academic: Plenum.

Daniel M, Green LW, Marion SA, Gamble D, Herbert CP, Hertzman C, Sheps SB. 1999. Effectiveness of Community-Directed Diabetes Prevention and Control in a Rural Aboriginal Population in British Columbia, Canada. Social Science and Medicine 48(6):815–832.

Dart R. 1925. *Australopithecus africanus*: The Man-Ape of South Africa. Nature 115:195.

Dasen PR, Berry JW, Sartorius N, editors. 1988. Health and Cross-Cultural Psychology: Toward Applications. Newbury Park, CA: Sage.

Davis BD. 1991. The Issues: Prospects versus Perceptions; Summary and Comments: The Scientific Chapters. In: Davis BD, editor. The Genetic Revolution: Scientific Prospects and Public Perceptions. Baltimore: Johns Hopkins University Press.

Dawson A. 1992. Ice Age Earth. London: Routledge.

Dean H, Mundy R, Moffatt M. 1992. Non-Insulin-Dependent Diabetes Mellitus in Indian Children in Manitoba. Canadian Medical Association Journal 147(1):1422–1425.

Defleur A, White T, Valensi P, Slimak L, Cregut-Bonnoure E. 1999. Neanderthal Cannibalism at Moula-Guercy, Ardeche, France. Science 286(5437):128–131.

de Lumley H. 1969. A Paleolithic Camp at Nice. Scientific American 220(5):42–50.

Devillers C, Chaline J. 1993. Evolution: An Evolving Theory. New York: Springer-Verlag.

de Waal F, Lanting F. 1997. Bonobo: The Forgotten Ape. Berkeley: University of California Press.

Diamond J. December 1989. The Accidental Conqueror. Discover 71–76.

Diamond J. November 1993. Who Are the Jews? Natural History 16.

Diamond J. 14 November 1997. Location, Location, Location: The First Farmers. Science 1243–1244.

Diamond JM. 2003. Guns, Germs, and Steel. New York: Norton.

Dickson DB. 1990. The Dawn of Belief: Religion in the Upper Paleolithic of Southwestern Europe. Tucson: University of Arizona Press.

Dickson JH, Oeggl K, Handley LL. 2003. The Iceman Reconsidered. Scientific American 288:70–79.

Dincauze DF. 2000. Environmental Archaeology: Principles and Practice. Cambridge, UK: Cambridge University Press.

Dirks R. 1993. Starvation and Famine. Cross-Cultural Research 27:28–69.

Dobzhansky T. 1962. Mankind Evolving: The Evolution of the Human Species. New Haven, CT: Yale University Press.

Dobzhansky T. 1973. Genetic Diversity and Human Equality. New York: Basic Books.

Dohlinow PJ, Bishop N. 1972. The Development of Motor Skills and Social Relationships among Primates through Play. In: Dohlinow PJ, editor. Primate Patterns. New York: Holt, Rinehart & Winston. p 321–325.

Dorit RL, Akashi H, Gilbert W. 1995. Absence of Polymorphism at the ZFY Locus on the Human Y Chromosome. Science 268(5214):1183–1185.

Douglass AE. 1929. The Secret of the Southwest Solved by Talkative Tree Rings. National Geographic Magazine LVI[6].

Doyle GA, Martin RD, editors. 1979. The Study of Prosimian Behavior. New York: Academic Press.

Duarte C, Mauricio J, Pettitt PB, Souto P, Trinkaus E, van der Plicht H, Zilhao J. 1999. The Early Upper Paleolithic Human Skeleton from the Abrigo do Lagar Velho (Portugal) and Modern Human Emergence in Iberia. Proceedings of the National Academy of Sciences 96(13): 7604–7609.

Dukepoo FC. 1998. The Trouble with the Human Genome Diversity Project. Molecular Medicine Today 4(6):242–243.

Dunbar RIN. 1989. Ecological Modelling in an Evolutionary Context. Folia Primatologica 53:235–246.

Dunn FL, Janes CR. 1986. Introduction: Medical Anthropology and Epidemiology. In: Janes CR, Stall R, Gifford SM, editors. Anthropology and Epidemiology. Boston: D. Reidel Publishing Company. p 334.

Durham WH. 1991. Coevolution: Genes, Culture, and Human Diversity. Stanford, CA: Stanford University Press.

Early JD, Peters JF. 1992. The Population Dynamics of the Mucajai Yanomama. San Diego: Academic Press.

Edgerton RB. 1966. Conceptions of Psychosis in Four East African Societies. American Anthropologist 68:408–425.

Edgerton RB. 1992. Sick Societies: Challenging the Myth of Primitive Harmony. New York: Free Press.

Eiseley LC. 1958. The Dawn of Evolutionary Theory. In: Eiseley LC, editor. Darwin's Century: Evolution and the Men Who Discovered It. Garden City, NY: Doubleday. Reprinted in Young, LB, editor. 1970. Evolution of Man. New York: Oxford University Press. p 13–15.

Eiseley LC. 1970. The Dawn of Evolutionary Theory. In: Young LB, editor. Evolution of Man. New York: Oxford University Press. p 13–15.

Eisenberg JF. 1977. Comparative Ecology and Reproduction of New World Monkeys. In: Kleinman D, editor. The Biology and Conservation of the Callitrichidae. Washington, DC: Smithsonian Institution. p 13–22.

Eldredge N, Tattersall I. 1982. The Myths of Human Evolution. New York: Columbia University Press.

Ember CR. 1978. Myths about Hunter-Gatherers. Ethnology 17:439–448.

Ember CR. 1983. The Relative Decline in Women's Contribution to Agriculture with Intensification. American Anthropologist 85:285–304.

Ember CR, Ember M. 1984. The Evolution of Human Female Sexuality: A Cross-Species Perspective. Journal of Anthropological Research 40:202–210.

Ember CR, Levinson D. 1991. The Substantive Contributions of Worldwide Cross-Cultural Studies Using Secondary Data. Behavior Science Research, special issue. Cross-Cultural and Comparative Research: Theory and Model. 25:79–140.

Ember M, Ember CR. 1979. Male–Female Bonding: A Cross-Species Study of Mammals and Birds. Behavior Science Research 14:37–56.

Emery KF, Wright EL, Schwarcz H. 2000. Isotopic Analysis of Ancient Deer Bone: Biotic Stability in Collapse Period Maya Land Use. Journal of Archaeological Science 27(6):537–550.

Erickson C. 2000. An Artificial Landscape-Scale Fishery in the Bolivian Amazon. Nature 408:190–193.

Ervin AM. 2000. Applied Anthropology. Boston: Allyn and Bacon.

Etkin NL, Ross PJ. 1997. Malaria, Medicine and Meals: A Biobehavioral Perspective. In: Romanucci-Ross L, Moermann DE, Tancredi LR, editors. The Anthropology of Medicine: From Culture to Method. Third edition. Westport CT: Bergin and Garvey. p 169–209.

Evans J, O'Connor T. 1999. Environmental Archaeology: Principles and Methods. Sutton Publishing.

Eveleth PB. 1986. Population Differences in Growth: Environmental and Genetic Factors. In: Falkner F, Tanner JM, editors. Human Growth, A Comprehensive Treatise. Volume 3, second edition. New York: Plenum Press. p 221–239.

Eveleth PB, Tanner JM. 1990. Worldwide Variation in Human Growth. Second edition. Cambridge: Cambridge University Press.

Excoffier L, Langaney A. 1989. Origin and Differentiation of Human Mitochondrial DNA. American Journal of Human Genetics 44(1):73–85.

Fagan BM. 1989. People of the Earth: An Introduction to World Prehistory. 6th edition. Glenview, IL: Scott, Foresman.

Fagan BM. 1991. Ancient North America: The Archaeology of a Continent. London: Thames and Hudson.

Fagan BM. 2000. In the Beginning: An Introduction to Archaeology. Upper Saddle River, New Jersey: Prentice Hall.

Falk D. 1988. Enlarged Occipital/Marginal Sinuses and Emissary Foramina: Their Significance in Hominid Evolution. In: Grine FE, editor. Evolutionary History of the "Robust" Australopithecines. New York: Aldine. p 85–96.

Falk D, Byram J. 2000. Primate Diversity. New York: W.W. Norton & Co.

Feder KL, Park MA. 1997. Human Antiquity: An Introduction to Physical Anthropology and Archaeology. Third edition. London: Mayfield Publishing.

Fedigan LM. 1982. Primate Paradigms: Sex Roles and Social Bonds. Montreal: Eden Press..

Feibel CS, Brown FH. 1993. Microstratigraphy and Paleoenvironments. In: Walker A, Leakey R, editors. The Nariokotome *Homo erectus* Skeleton. Cambridge, MA: Harvard University Press. p 21–39.

Feinman GM, Kowalewski SA, Finsten L, Blanton RE, Nicholas L. 1985. Long-Term Demographic Change: A Perspective from the Valley of Oaxaca. Journal of Field Archaeology 12:333–362.

Feldman DA, Johnson TM. 1986. Introduction. In: Feldman DA, Johnson TM, editors. The Social Dimension of AIDS: Methods and Theory. New York: Praeger.

Ferguson RB, Whitehead NL. 1992. The Violent Edge of Empire. In: Ferguson RB, Whitehead N, editors. War in the Tribal Zone. Santa Fe: School of American Research Press. p 1–30.

Fischman J. 1994. Putting Our Oldest Ancestors in Their Proper Place. Science 265:2011–2012.

Fish PR. 1981. Beyond Tools: Middle Paleolithic Debitage Analysis and Cultural Inference. Journal of Anthropological Research 37.

Fisher J. 1996. Grassroots Organizations and Grassroots Support Organizations: Patterns of Interaction. In: Moran EF, editor. Transforming Societies, Transforming Anthropology. Ann Arbor: University of Michigan Press. p 57–101.

Fisher WH. 1994. Megadevelopment, Environmentalism, and Resistance: The Institutional Context of Kayapó Indigenous Politics in Central Brazil. Human Organization 53:220–232.

Fix AG. 1977. The Demography of the Semai Senoi. Ann Arbor, Michigan: Anthropological Papers No. 62. Museum of Anthropology, University of Michigan.

Fladmark KR, Nelson DE, Brown TA, Vogel JS, Southon JR. 1987. AMS Dating of Two Wooden Artifacts from the Northwest Coast. Canadian Journal of Archaeology 11:1–12.

Flannery KV. 12 March 1965. The Ecology of Early Food Production in Mesopotamia. Science1252, 1253.

Flannery KV. 1971. The Origins and Ecological Effects of Early Domestication in Iran and the Near East. In: Struever S, editor. Prehistoric Agriculture. Garden City, NY: Natural History Press. p 50–79.

Flannery KV. 1972. The Cultural Evolution of Civilizations. Annual Review of Ecology and Systematics 3:399–426.

Flannery KV. 1973a. The Origins of Agriculture. Annual Review of Anthropology 2:274.

Flannery KV. 1973b. The Origins of the Village as a Settlement Type in Mesoamerica and the Near East: A Comparative Study. In: Tringham R, editor. Territoriality and Proxemics R1. Andover, MA: Warner Modular. p 1–31.

Flannery KV. 1986. The Research Problem. In: Flannery KV, editor. Guila Naquitz: Archaic Foraging and Early Agriculture in Oaxaca, Mexico. Orlando, FL: Academic Press. p 3–18.

Fleagle JG. 1988. Primate Adaptation and Evolution. San Diego: Academic Press.

Fleagle JG. 1994. Anthropoid Origins. In: Corruccini R, Ciochon RL, editors. Integrative Paths to the Past. Englewood Hills, NJ: Prentice Hall. p 17–35.

Fleagle JG. 1999. Primate Adaptation and Evolution. San Diego, CA: Academic Press.

Fleagle JG, Kay RF. 1983. New Interpretations of the Phyletic Position of Oligocene Hominoids. In: Ciochon RL, Corruccini RS. New Interpretations of Ape and Human Ancestry. New York: Plenum. p 181–210.

Fleagle JG, Kay RF. 1985. The Paleobiology of Catarrhines. In: Delson E, editor. Ancestors: The Hard Evidence. New York: Alan R. Liss. p 23–36.

Fleagle JG, Kay RF. 1987. The Phyletic Position of the Parapithecidae. Journal Human Evolution 16:483–531.

Fleischer RL, Hart Jr HR. 1972. Fission-Track Dating: Techniques and Problems. In: Bishop WA, Miller JA, editors. Calibration of Hominid Evolution. Toronto: University of Toronto Press. p 135–170.

Fleischer RL, Price PB, Walker RM, Leakey LSB. 2 April 1965. Fission-Track Dating of Bed I, Olduvai Gorge. Science 72–74.

Fogel M, Tuross N, Owsley DW. 1989. Nitrogen Isotope Traces of Human Lactation in Modern and Archaeological Populations. Carnegie Institution, Annual Report of the Director. Geophysical Laboratory.

Fortey R. 1999. Life: A Natural History of the First Four Billion Years of Life on Earth. Vintage Books.

Fossey D. 1983. Gorillas in the Mist. Boston: Houghton Mifflin.

Foster GM. 1962. Traditional Cultures and the Impact of Technological Change. New York: Harper & Row.

Fowler ML. August 1975. A Pre-Columbian Urban Center on the Mississippi. Scientific American 92–101.

Fox C, Harris S, Whalen-Brough E. 1994. Diabetes among Native Canadians in Northwestern Ontario: 10 Years Later. Chronic Diseases in Canada 15(3):92–96.

Fox WA. 1999. Aboriginal Peoples, Archaeology and Parks Canada. Plains Anthropologist 44:35–42.

Franciscus RG, Trinkaus E. 1988. Nasal Morphology and the Emergence of *Homo erectus*. American Journal of Physical Anthropology 75:517–527.

Frankel B, Trend MG. 1991. Principles, Pressures and Paychecks: The Anthropologist as Employee. In: Fluehr-Lobban C, editor. Ethics and the Profession of Anthropology: Dialogue for a New Era. Philadelphia: University of Pennsylvania Press. p 175–197.

Frayer DW. 1981. Body Size, Weapon Use, and Natural Selection in the European Upper Paleolithic and Mesolithic. American Anthropologist 83: 57–73.

Frayer DW, Wolpoff MH. 1985. Sexual Dimorphism. Annual Review of Anthropology 14:431–432.

Freeman LG. 1994. Torralba and Ambrona: A Review of Discoveries. In: Corruccini R, Ciochon RL, editors. Integrative Paths to the Past: Paleoanthropological Advances in Honor of F. Clark Howell. Englewood Cliffs, NJ: Prentice Hall. p 597–637.

Fricke HC, O'Neil JR, Lynnerup N. 1995. Oxygen Isotope Composition of Human Tooth Enamel from Medieval Greenland: Linking Climate and Society. Geology 23:869–872.

Friedlaender J. 1993. Update on the Human Genome Diversity Project. Evolutionary Anthropology 2:40.

Friedman SS. 1980. Holocaust. In: Academic American [now Grolier] Encyclopedia. Volume 10. Princeton, NJ: Arete. p 206.

Frisancho AR, Flegal PN. 1982. Advanced Maturation Associated with Centripetal Fat Pattern. Human Biology 54:717–728.

Frisancho AR, Greksa LP. 1989. Development Responses in the Acquisition of Functional Adaptation to High Altitude. In: Little MA, Haas JD, editors. Human Population Biology: A Transdisciplinary Science. New York: Oxford University Press. p 203–221.

Frisch RE. October 1980. Fatness, Puberty, and Fertility. Natural History 16–27.

Fry I. 2000. The Emergence of Life on Earth: A Historical and Scientific Overview. Rutgers University Press.

Gabunia L, Vekua A, Lordkipanidze D, Swisher III CC, Ferring R, Justus A, Nioradze M, Tvalchrelidze T, Anton SC, Bosinski G, Joris O, Lumley MA, Majsuradze G, Mouskhelishvili A. 12 May 2000. Earliest Pleistocene Hominid Cranial Remains from Dmanisi, Republic of Georgia: Taxonomy, Geological Setting, and Age. Science 288(5468):1019–1025.

Galdikas BMF. 1979. Orangutan Adaptation at Tanjung Puting Reserve: Mating and Ecology. In: Hamburg DA, McCown ER, editors. The Great Apes. Menlo Park, CA: Benjamin/Cummings. p 194–233.

Garn SM. 1971. Human Races. Third edition. Springfield, IL: Charles C. Thomas.

Gentner W, Lippolt HJ. 1969. The Potassium-Argon Dating of Upper Tertiary and Pleistocene Deposits. In: Brothwell D, Higgs E, editors. Science in Archaeology. p 72–84.

Gibbons A. 19 April 1995. First Americans: Not Mammoth Hunters, but Forest Dwellers? Science 346–347.

Gibbons A. 2001. The Riddle of Co-Existence. Science 291:1725–1729.

Gibbons A. 29 November 2002. One Scientist's Quest for the Origin of Our Species. Science 298:1708–1711.

Goldizen AW. 1987. Tamarins and Marmosets: Communal Care of Offspring. In: Smuts BB, Cheney DL, Seyfarth RM, Wrangham RW, Struhsaker TT, editors. Primate Societies. Chicago: University of Chicago Press. p 34–43.

Goodall J. August 1963. My Life among Wild Chimpanzees. National Geographic 272–308.

Goodenough WH. 1963. Cooperation in Change. New York: Russell Sage Foundation.

Goodman AH, Armelagos GJ. September 1985. Disease and Death at Dr. Dickson's Mounds. Natural History 12–18.

Goodman AH, Lallo J, Armelagos GJ, Rose JC. 1984a. Health Changes at Dickson Mounds, Illinois (A.D. 905–1300). In: Cohen MN, Armelagos GJ, editors. Paleopathology at the Origins of Agriculture. Orlando, FL: Academic Press. p 300.

Goodman AH, Martin DL, Armelagos GJ, Clark G. 1984b. Indications of Stress from the Bone and Teeth. In: Cohen MN, Armelagos GJ, editors. Palaeopathology at the Origins of Agriculture. Orlando, FL: Academic Press. p 13–49.

Goodman M. 1992. Reconstructing Human Evolution from Proteins. In: Jones S, Martin R, Pilbeam D, editors. The Cambridge Encyclopedia of Human Evolution. Cambridge: Cambridge University Press. p 307–312.

Gorman C. 1970. The Hoabinhian and After: Subsistence Patterns in Southeast Asia during the Late Pleistocene and Early Recent Periods. World Archaeology 2:315–316.

Gray JP. 1985. Primate Sociobiology. New Haven, CT: HRAF Press.

Grayson DK. 18 February 1977. Pleistocene Avifaunas and the Overkill Hypothesis. Science 691–692.

Grayson DK. 1989. Explaining Pleistocene Extinctions: Thoughts on the Structure of a Debate. In: Martin PS, Klein RG, editors. Quaternary Extinctions: A Prehistoric Revolution. Tucson: University of Arizona Press. p 807–823.

Greenberg JH, Ruhlen M. November 1992. Linguistic Origins of Native Americans. Scientific American 94–99.

Greenfield H. 2000. Integrating Surface and Subsurface Reconnaissance Data in the Study of Stratigraphically Complex Sites: Blagotin, Serbia. Geoarchaeology 15:167–201.

Greksa LP, Beall CM. 1989. Development of Chest Size and Lung Function at High Altitude. In: Little MA, Haas JD, editors. Human Population Biology: A Transdisciplinary Science. New York: Oxford University Press. p 222–238.

Grine FE. 1998. Evolutionary History of the "Robust" Australopithecines: A Summary and Historical Perspective. In: Grine FE, editor. Evolutionary History of the "Robust" Australopithecines. New York: Aldine. p 515–516.

Grün R, Beaumont PB, Stringer CB. 1990. ESR Dating Evidence for Early Modern Humans at Border Cave in South Africa. Nature 344:537–539.

Guan Y, Peiris JS, Zheng B, Poon LL, Chan KH, Zeng FY, Chan CW, Chan MN, Chen JD, Chow KY, Hon CC, Hui KH, Li J, Li VY, Wang Y, Leung SW, Yuen KY, Leung FC. 2004. Molecular Epidemiology of the Novel Coronavirus That Causes Severe Acute Respiratory Syndrome. Lancet 363:99–104.

Guthrie RD. 1984. Mosaics, Allelochemics and Nutrients: An Ecological Theory of Late Pleistocene Megafaunal Extinctions. In: Martin PS, Klein RG, editors. Quaternary Extinctions: A Prehistoric Revolution. Tucson: University of Arizona Press. p 259–298.

Haas JD, Habicht JP. 1990. Growth and Growth Charts in the Assessment of Pre-school Nutritional Status. In: Harrison GA, Waterlow JC, editors. Diet and Disease in Traditional and Developing Societies. Cambridge: Cambridge University Press. p 160–183.

Hackenberg RA. 1988. Scientists or Survivors? The Future of Applied Anthropology under Maximum

Uncertainty. In: Trotter II RT, editor. Anthropology for Tomorrow: Creating Practitioner-Oriented Applied Anthropology Programs. Washington, DC: American Anthropological Association. p 170–185.

Hahn RA. 1995. Sickness and Healing: An Anthropological Perspective. New Haven CT: Yale University Press.

Haldane JBS. 1963. Human Evolution: Past and Future. In: Jepsen GL, Mayr E, Simpson GG, editors. Genetics, Paleontology, and Evolution. New York: Atheneum. p 405–418.

Hall ET. 1966. The Hidden Dimension. Garden City, NY: Doubleday. p 144–153.

Hanna JM, Little MA, Austin DM. 1989. Climatic Physiology. In: Little MA, Haas JD, editor. Human Population Biology: A Transdisciplinary Science. New York: Oxford University Press. p 133–136.

Hannah AC, McGrew WC. 1987. Chimpanzees Using Stones to Crack Open Oil Palm Nuts in Liberia. Primates 28:31–46.

Harcourt AH. 1979. The Social Relations and Group Structure of Wild Mountain Gorillas. In: Hamburg DA, McCown ER, editors. The Great Apes. Menlo Park, CA: Benjamin/Cummings. p 187–192.

Harington CR, Cinq-mars J. 1995. Radiocarbon Dates on Saiga Antelope (Saiga-tatarica) Fossils from Yukon and the Northern Territories. Arctic 48(1):105–115.

Harlan JR. June 1967. A Wild Wheat Harvest in Turkey. Archaeology 20(3):197–201.

Harpending HC, Batzer MA, Gurven M, Jorde LB, Rogers AR, Sherry ST. 1998. Genetic Traces of Ancient Demography. Proceedings of the National Academy of Sciences 95(4):1961–1967.

Harpending HC, Pennington R. 1991. Age Structure and Sex-Biased Mortality among Herero Pastoralists. Human Biology 63(3):329–353.

Harris DR. 1977. Settling Down: An Evolutionary Model for the Transformation of Mobile Bands into Sedentary Communities. In: Friedman J, Rowlands MJ, editors. The Evolution of Social Systems. London: Duckworth. p 401–417.

Harris M. 1979. Cultural Materialism: The Struggle for a Science of Culture. New York: Random House.

Harris S, Caulfield LE, Sugamori ME, Whalen EA, Henning B. 1997. The Epidemiology of Diabetes in Pregnant Native Canadians. Diabetes Care 20(9):1422–1425.

Harris S, Perkins B, Whalen-Brough E. 1996. Non-Insulin-Dependent Diabetes Mellitus among First Nations Children. Canadian Family Physician 42:869–876.

Harrison GA, Tanner J, Pilbeam DR, Baker PT. 1988. Human Biology: An Introduction to Human Evolution, Variation, Growth, and Adaptability. Third edition. Oxford: Oxford University Press.

Harrison GG. 1975. Primary Adult Lactase Deficiency: A Problem in Anthropological Genetics. American Anthropologist 77:812–835.

Harrison PD, Turner II BL, editors. 1978. Pre-Hispanic Maya Agriculture. Albuquerque: University of New Mexico Press.

Hartwig WC. 1994. Pattern, Puzzles and Perspectives on Platyrrhine Origins. In: Corruccini RS, Ciochon R, editors. Integrative Paths to the Past: Paleoanthropological Advances in Honor of F. Clark Howell. Englewood Cliffs, N.J.: Prentice Hall. p 69–93.

Hassan FA. 1981. Demographic Archaeology. New York: Academic Press.

Hausfater G, Altmann J, Altmann S. 20 August 1982. Long-Term Consistency of Dominance Relations among Female Baboons. Science 752–754.

Hauspie RC, Vercauteren M, Susanne C. 1996. Secular Changes in Growth. Hormone Research 45(Supplement 2):817.

Hayden B. 1997. The Pithouses of Keatley Creek. New York: Harcourt Brace.

Health Canada. 1997. Medical Services Branch. Diabetes among First Nations People: Information from the 1991 Aboriginal Peoples Survey Carried out by Statistics Canada. Ottawa.

Hedican EJ. 1995. Applied Anthropology in Canada: Understanding Aboriginal Issues. Toronto: University of Toronto Press.

Hegele RA. 2001. Genes and Environment in Type 2 Diabetes and Atherosclerosis in Aboriginal Canadians. Current Atherosclerosis Rep 3:216–221.

Heiser Jr. CB. 1985. Of Plants and People. Norman: University of Oklahoma Press.

Helms MW. 1975. Middle America. Englewood Cliffs, NJ: Prentice Hall.

Henry DO. 1989. From Foraging to Agriculture: The Levant at the End of the Ice Age. Philadelphia: University of Pennsylvania Press.

Henry DO. 1991. Foraging, Sedentism, and Adaptive Vigor in the Natufian: Rethinking the Linkages. In: Clark GA, editor. Perspectives on the Past: Theoretical Biases in Mediterranean Hunter-Gatherer Research. Philadelphia: University of Pennsylvania Press. p 365–368.

Herring DA, Hoppa RD. 1999. Endemic Tuberculosis among Nineteenth Century Cree in the Central Canadian Subarctic. Perspectives in Human Biology 4(1):189–199.

Herring DA, Saunders SR, Katzenberg MA. 1998. Investigating the Weaning Process in Past

Populations. American Journal of Physical Anthropology 105:425–439.

Hewes GW. 1961. Food Transport and the Origin of Hominid Bipedalism. American Anthropologist 63:687–710.

Higham C, Lu T. 1998. The Origins and Dispersal of Rice Cultivation. Antiquity 72:867–877.

Hill JH. 1978. Apes and Language. Annual Review of Anthropology 7:89–112.

Hill JH. 1998. Do Apes Have Language? In: Ember CR, Ember, Ember M, Peregrine PN, editors. Research Frontiers in Anthropology. Upper Saddle River, NJ: Prentice Hall, Prentice Hall/Simon & Schuster Custom Publishing.

Hinkes MJ. 1989. The Role of Forensic Anthropology in Mass Disaster Resolution. Environmental Medicine 60:A60–A63.

Hockett CF, Ascher R. 1964. The Human Revolution. Current Anthropology 5:135–168.

Hoffecker JF, Powers WR, Geobel T. 1 January 1993. The Colonization of Beringia and the Peopling of the New World. Science 46–53.

Holden C. 2004a. Kennewick Man — Court Battle Ends, Bones Still Off-limits. Science 305:591.

Holden C. 2004b. Kennewick Man — Scientists Hope Ruling Will Lead Them to Bones. Science 303: 943.

Hole F. 1992. Origins of Agriculture. In: Jones S, Martin R, Pilbeam D, editors. The Cambridge Encyclopedia of Human Evolution. New York: Cambridge University Press. p 373–379.

Hole F. 1994. Environmental Shock and Urban Origins. In: Stein G, Rothman MS, editors. Chiefdoms and Early States in the Near East: The Organizational Dynamics of Complexity. Madison, WI: Prehistoric Press.

Hole F, Flannery KV, Neely JA. 1969. Prehistory and Human Ecology of the Deh Luran Plain. Memoirs of the Museum of Anthropology No. 1. Ann Arbor: University of Michigan.

Hole F, Heizer RH. 1973. An Introduction to Prehistoric Archeology. New York: Holt, Rinehart & Winston.

Holloway R. 1980. Indonesian "Solo" (Ngangdong) Endocranial Reconstructions: Preliminary Observations and Comparisons with Neandertal and *Homo erectus* Groups. American Journal of Physical Anthropology 53:285–295.

Holloway R. 1981. The Indonesian *Homo erectus* Brain Endocasts Revisited. American Journal of Physical Anthropology 55:502–521.

Holloway RT. July 1974. The Casts of Fossil Hominid Brains. Scientific American 106–115.

Honigmann JJ. 1967. Personality in Culture. New York: Harper & Row.

Hoppa RD. 1998. Mortality in a Northern Ontario Fur-Trade Community: Moose Factory, 1851–1964. Canadian Studies in Population 25(2):175–198.

Hoppa RD, Garlie TN. 1998. Secular Changes in the Growth of Toronto Children During the Last Century. Annals of Human Biology 25(6):553–561.

Hoppa RD, Vaupel JW, editors. 2002. Palaeodemography: Age Distributions from Skeletal Samples. Cambridge: Cambridge University Press.

Houston SD. 1988. The Phonetic Decipherment of Maya Glyphs. Antiquity 62:126–135.

Howell FC. April 1966. Observations on the Earlier Phases of the European Lower Paleolithic. In: Recent Studies in Paleoanthropology. American Anthropologist (special publication) 68:88–201.

Howell N. 1979. Demography of the Dobe, !Kung. New York: Academic Press.

Howell N. 1986. Anthropological Demography. Annual Review of Anthropology 15:219–246.

Hudson J, editor. 1993. From Bones to Behavior: Ethnoarchaeological and Experimental Contributions to the Interpretation of Faunal Remains. Carbondale: Center for Archaeological Investigations, Occasional paper No. 21. Southern Illinois University at Carbondale.

Huffine E, Crews J, Kennedy B, Bomberger K, Zinbo A. 2001. Mass Identification of Persons Missing from the Break-up of the Former Yugoslavia: Structure, Function, and Role of the International Commission on Missing Persons. Croatian Medical Journal 42:271–275.

Huss-Ashmore R, Johnston FE. 1985. Bioanthropological Research in Developing Countries. Annual Review of Anthropology 14:475–528.

Inhorn MC, Brown PJ. 1990. The Anthropology of Infectious Disease. Annual Review of Anthropology 19:89–117.

Irons W. 1979. Natural Selection, Adaptation, and Human Social Behavior. In: Chagnon NA, Irons W, editors. Evolutionary Biology and Human Social Behavior: An Anthropological Perspective. North Scituate, MA: Duxbury. p 10–12.

Isaac G. 1971. The Diet of Early Man: Aspects of Archaeological Evidence from Lower and Middle Pleistocene Sites in Africa. World Archaeology 2:289.

Isaac G. 1977. Ologesailie: Archaeological Studies of a Middle Pleistocene Lake Basin in Kenya. Chicago: University of Chicago Press.

Isaac G. 1984. The Archaeology of Human Origins: Studies of the Pleistocene in East Africa, 1971–1981. In: Wendorf F, Close AE, editors. Advances in World Archaeology. Volume 3. Orlando, FL: Academic Press.

Jackes M, Lubell D, Meiklejohn C. 1997a. Healthy but Mortal: Human Biology and the First Farmers in Western Europe. Antiquity 71:639–658.

Jackes M, Lubell D, Meiklejohn C. 1997b. On Physical Anthropological Aspects of the Mesolithic-Neolithic Transition in the Iberian Peninsula. Current Anthropology 38(5):839–846.

Jacobs P, Blanchard JF, James RC, Depew N. 2000. Excess Costs of Diabetes in the Aboriginal Population of Manitoba, Canada. Canadian Journal of Public Health 91(4):298–301.

Janzen DH. 12 December 1973. Tropical Agro-ecosystems. Science 1212–1218.

Jelliffe DB, Jelliffe EFP. 9 May 1975. Human Milk, Nutrition and the World Resource Crisis. Science 557–561.

Jennings JD. 1968. Prehistory of North America. New York: McGraw-Hill.

Johanson DC, Edey M. 1981. Lucy: The Beginnings of Humankind. New York: Simon & Schuster.

Johanson DC, White TD. 26 January 1979. A Systematic Assessment of Early African Hominids. Science 321–330.

Johansson SR, Horowitz S. 1986. Estimating Mortality in Skeletal Populations: Influence of the Growth Rate on the Interpretations of Levels and Trends during the Transition to Agriculture. American Journal of Physical Anthropology 71:233–250.

Johnson AW, Earle TK. 2000. The Evolution of Human Societies: From Foraging Group to Agrarian State. Stanford, CA: Stanford University Press.

Johnson GA. 1977. Aspects of Regional Analysis in Archaeology. Annual Review of Anthropology 6:479–508.

Johnson GA. 1987. The Changing Organization of Uruk Administration on the Susiana Plain. In: Hole F, editor. Archaeology of Western Iran. Washington, DC: Smithsonian Institution Press. p 107–139.

Johnston FE. 1985. Health Implications of Childhood Obesity. Annals of Internal Medicine 103:1068–1072.

Johnston FE, Bogin B, MacVean RB, Newman BC. 1984. A Comparison of International Standards versus Local Reference Data for the Triceps and Subscapular Skinfolds of Guatemalan Children and Youth. Human Biology 56:157–171.

Johnston FE, Hamill PV, Lemeshow S. 1974. Skinfold Thicknesses in a National Probability Sample of US Males and Females 6 through 17 Years. American Journal of Physical Anthropology 40:321–324.

Johnston FE, Ouyang Z. 1991. Choosing Appropriate Reference Data for the Anthropometric Assessment of Nutritional Status. In: Himes JH, editor. Anthropometric Assessment of Nutritional Status. New York: Wiley-Liss Inc. p 337–346.

Jolly A. 1985. The Evolution of Primate Behavior. Second edition. New York: Macmillan.

Jones S, Martin R, Pilbeam D. 1992. The Cambridge Encyclopedia of Human Evolution. New York: Cambridge University Press.

Jordanova LJ. 1984. Lamarck. Oxford: Oxford University Press.

Judge WJ, Dawson J. 16 June 1972. Paleo-Indian Settlement Technology in New Mexico. Science 1210–1216.

Jungers WL. 1988. Relative Joint Size and Hominoid Locomotor Adaptations with Implications for the Evolution of Hominid Bipedalism. Journal of Human Evolution 17:247–265.

Jungers WL. 1998. New Estimates of Body Size in Australopithecines. In: Grine FE, editor. Evolutionary History of the "Robust" Australopithecines. New York: Aldine. p 115–125.

Kappelman J. 1993. The Attraction of Paleomagnetism. Evolutionary Anthropology 2:89–99.

Kasarda JD. August 1971. Economic Structure and Fertility: A Comparative Analysis. Demography 8(3):307–318.

Katzenberg MA. 1984. Chemical Analysis of Prehistoric Human Bone from Five Temporally Distinct Populations in Southern Ontario. Ottawa: National Museums of Canada.

Katzenberg MA. 1991. Stable Isotope Analysis of Remains from the Harvie Family. In: Saunders SR, Lazenby R, editors. The Links That Bind: The Harvie Family Nineteenth Century Burying Ground. Occasional Papers in Northeastern Archaeology, No. 5. Dundas, ON: Copetown Press. p 65–69.

Katzenberg MA. 1992. Advances in Stable Isotope Analysis of Prehistoric Bones. In: Saunders SR, Katzenberg MA, editors. Skeletal Biology of Past Peoples: Research Methods. New York: Wiley-Liss. p 105–119.

Katzenberg MA. 1993. Applications of Elemental and Isotopic Analysis to Populations in Ontario Prehistory. In: Sandford MK, editor. Investigations of Ancient Human Tissues: Chemical Analyses in Anthropology. Langhorne: Gordon and Breach Science Publishers. p 335–360.

Katzenberg MA. 2000. Stable Isotope Analysis: A Tool for Studying Past Diet, Demography and Life History. In: Katzenberg MA, Saunders SR. Biological Anthropology of the Skeleton. New York: Wiley-Liss. p 305–328.

Katzenberg MA, Herring DA, Saunders SR. 1996. Weaning and Infant Mortality: Evaluating the Skeletal Evidence. Yearbook of Physical Anthropology 39:177–199.

Katzenberg MA, Pfeiffer S. 1995. Nitrogen Isotope Evidence for Weaning Age in a Nineteenth Century Canadian Skeletal Sample. In: Grauer AL, editor. Bodies of Evidence: Reconstructing History through Skeletal Analysis. New York: John Wiley & Sons. p 139–160.

Katzenberg MA, Saunders SR, Fitzgerald W. 1993. Age Differences in Stable Carbon and Nitrogen Isotope Ratios in a Population of Prehistoric Maize Horticulturists. American Journal of Physical Anthropology 90:267–281.

Katzenberg MA, Schwarcz HP, Knyf M, Melbye FJ. 1995. Stable Isotope Analysis for Maize Horticulture and Paleodiet in Southern Ontario, Canada. American Antiquity 60:335–350.

Katzmarzyk PT, Malina RM, Bouchard C. 1999. Physical Activity, Physical Fitness, and Coronary Heart Disease Risk Factors in Youth: The Quebec Family Study. Preventive Medicine 29:555–562.

Katzmarzyk PT, Rankinen T, Perusse L, Malina RM, Bouchard C. 2000. 7-year Stability of Blood Pressure in the Canadian Population. Preventive Medicine 31:403–409.

Kay RF. 1988a. Parapithecidae. In: Tattersall I, Delson E, van Couvering J, editors. Encyclopedia of Human Evolution and Prehistory. New York: Garland. p 441–442.

Kay RF. 1988b. Teeth. In: Tattersall I, Delson E, van Couvering J, editors. Encyclopedia of Human Evolution and Prehistory. New York: Garland. p 571–578.

Kelley J. 1992. The Evolution of Apes. In: Jones S, Martin R, Pilbeam D, editors. The Cambridge Encyclopedia of Human Evolution. New York: Cambridge University Press. p 223–230.

Kent S. 1996. Cultural Diversity among Twentieth-Century Foragers: An African Perspective. Cambridge: Cambridge University Press.

Kerr RA. 16 January 1998. Sea-Floor Dust Shows Drought Felled Akkadian Empire. Science 325–326.

Keuhn S. 1998. New Evidence for Late Paleoindian-Early Archaic Subsistence Behavior in the Western Great Lakes. American Antiquity 63:457–476.

Kim C, Chan HM. 1998. Risk Assessment of Cadmium Exposure in Fort Resolution, Northwest Territories, Canada. Food Additives and Contaminants 15:307–317.

Kingston JD, Marino BD, Hill A. 13 May 1994. Isotopic Evidence for Neogene Hominid Paleoenvironments in the Kenya Rift Valley. Science 955–959.

Kirmayer LJ, Brass GM, Tait CL. 2000. The Mental Health of Aboriginal Peoples: Transformations of Identity and Community. Canadian Journal of Psychiatry 45:607–616.

Klein RG. June 1974. Ice-Age Hunters of the Ukraine. Scientific American 96–105.

Klein RG. 8 July 1977. The Ecology of Early Man in Southern Africa. Science 120.

Klein RG. 1983. The Stone Age Prehistory of Southern Africa. Annual Review of Anthropology 12:38–39.

Klein RG. 1987. Reconstructing How Early People Exploited Animals: Problems and Prospects. In: Nitecki M, Nitecki DV, editors. The Evolution of Human Hunting. New York: Plenum. p 11–45.

Klein RG. 1989. The Human Career: Human Biological and Cultural Origins. Chicago: University of Chicago Press.

Klein RG. 1994. Southern Africa before the Ice Age. In: Corruccini R, Ciochon RL, editors. Integrative Paths to the Past: Paleoanthropological Advances in Honor of F. Clark Howell. Englewood Cliffs, NJ: Prentice Hall.

Klein RG. 2003. Paleoanthropology. Whither the Neanderthals? Science 299:1525–1527.

Kleinman A. 1988. Rethinking Psychiatry: From Cultural Category to Personal Experience. New York: Macmillan.

Klepinger LL. 1984. Nutritional Assessment from Bone. Annual Review of Anthropology 13:75–96.

Klima B. 1962. The First Ground-Plan of an Upper Paleolithic Loess Settlement in Middle Europe and Its Meaning. In: Braidwood RJ, Willey GR, editors. Courses toward Urban Life: Archaeological Consideration of Some Cultural Alternatives. Viking Fund Publications in Anthropology No. 32. Chicago: Aldine. p 193–210.

Komar D. 2003. Lessons from Srebrenica: The Contributions and Limitations of Physical Anthropology in Identifying Victims of War Crimes. Journal of Forensic Sciences 48:713–716.

Konigsberg LW, Frankenberg SR. 1994. Palaeodemography: Not Quite Dead. Evolutionary Anthropology 3(3):92–105.

Konner M, Wortman C. 15 February 1980. Nursing Frequency, Gonadal Function, and Birth Spacing among !Kung Hunter-Gatherers. Science 788–791.

Kottak CP. 1996. The Media, Development, and Social Change. In: Moran EF, editor. Transforming Societies, Transforming Anthropology. Ann Arbor: University of Michigan Press.

Kramer SN. 1963. The Sumerians: Their History, Culture, and Character. Chicago: University of Chicago Press.

Krebs JR, Davies NB, editors. 1984. Behavioural Ecology: An Evolutionary Approach. Second edition. Sunderland, MA: Sinauer.

Krebs JR, Davies NB. 1987. An Introduction to Behavioural Ecology. Second edition. Sunderland, MA: Sinauer.

Krings M, Geisert H, Schmitz RW, Krainitzki H, Paabo S. 1999. DNA Sequence of the Mitochondrial Hypervariable Region II from the Neandertal Type Specimen. Proceedings of the National Academy of Sciences of the United States of America 96:5581–5585.

Krings M, Stone A, Schmitz RW, Krainitzki H, Stoneking M, Paabo S. 1997. Neandertal DNA Sequences and the Origin of Modern Humans. Cell 90:19–30.

Kuehn S. 1998. New Evidence for Late Paleoindian–Early Archaic Subsistence Behavior in the Western Great Lakes. American Antiquity 63:475–476.

Kuhnlein HV, Chan HM. 2000. Environment and Contaminants in Traditional Food Systems of Northern Indigenous Peoples. Annual Review of Nutrition 20:595–626.

Kushner G. 1991. Applied Anthropology. In: Emener WG, Darrow M, editors. Career Explorations in Human Services. Springfield, IL: Charles C. Thomas. p 46–61.

Laitman J, Heimbuch R. 1982. The Basicranium of Plio-Pleistocene Hominids as an Indicator of their Upper Respiratory Systems. American Journal of Physical Anthropology 59:323–343.

Laitman J, Heimbuch RC. 1984. The Basicranium and Upper Respiratory System of African Homo erectus and Early Homo sapiens. American Journal of Physical Anthropology 63:180.

Laitman JT, Heimbuch RC, Crelin ES. 1978. Developmental Change in a Basicranial Line and Its Relationship to the Upper Respiratory System in Living Primates. American Journal of Anatomy 152:467–482.

Lambert DT. 1993. AIDS and the Aboriginal Community. Canadian Journal of Public Health 84 Suppl 1:S46–S47.

Larsen CS. 1995. Biological Changes in Human Populations with Agriculture. Annual Review of Anthropology 24:185–213.

Larsen CS. 1998. Bare Bones Anthropology: The Bioarchaeology of Human Remains. In: Ember CR, Ember M, Peregrine PN, editors. Research Frontiers in Anthropology. Upper Saddle River, NJ: Prentice Hall/Simon & Schuster Custom Publishing.

Leakey LSB. [September] 1960. Finding the World's Earliest Man. National Geographic 420–435.

Leakey MG, Feibel CS, McDougall I, Walker A. 17 August 1995. New Four-Million-Year-Old Hominid Species from Kanapoi and Allia Bay, Kenya. Nature 376:565–571.

Leakey MG, Feibel CS, McDougall I, Ward C, Walker A. 1998. New Specimens and Confirmation of an Early Age for Australopithecus anamensis. Nature 393:62–66.

Lee PC. 1983. Home Range, Territory and Intergroup Encounters. In: Hinde RA, editor. Primate Social Relationships: An Integrated Approach. Sunderland, MA: Sinauer.

Lee RB. 1972. Population Growth and the Beginnings of Sedentary Life among the !Kung Bushmen. In: Spooner B, editor. Population Growth: Anthropological Implications. Cambridge, MA: MIT Press. p 329–342.

Lee RB. 1979. The !Kung San: Men, Women, and Work in a Foraging Society. Cambridge: Cambridge University Press.

Lee RB, DeVore I, editors. 1968. Man the Hunter. Chicago: Aldine.

LeGros Clark WE. 1964. The Fossil Evidence for Human Evolution. Chicago: University of Chicago Press.

Lewin R. 7 January 1983a. Fossil Lucy Grows Younger, Again. Science 43–44.

Lewin R. 1983b. Is the Orangutan a Living Fossil? Science 1222–1223.

Lieberman L. 1999. Scientific Insignificance. Anthropology Newsletter 40:11–12.

Lieberman P. 1992. Human Speech and Language. In: Jones S, Martin R, Pilbeam D, editors. Cambridge Encyclopedia of Human Evolution. Cambridge: Cambridge University Press. p 134–137.

Lieberman P, Laitman J, Reidenberg J, Gannon P. 1982. The Anatomy, Physiology, Acoustics and Perception of Speech: Essential Elements in Analysis of the Evolution of Human Speech. Journal of Human Evolution 22:447–467.

Linton R. 1936. The Study of Man. New York: Appleton-Century-Crofts. p 310–311.

Loomis WF. 4 August 1967. Skin-Pigment Regulation of Vitamin-D Biosynthesis in Man. Science 501–506.

Lopuchin AS. January/April 1975. Structures of Biogenic Origin from Early Precambrian Rocks of Euro-Asia. Origins of Life 6(12):45–57.

Lovejoy AO. 1964. The Great Chain of Being: A Study of the History of an Idea. Cambridge, MA: Harvard University Press.

Lovejoy CO. 23 January 1981. The Origin of Man. Science 341–350.

Lovejoy CO. 1988. Evolution of Human Walking. Scientific American 259(5):118–125.

Lovejoy CO, Heiple K, Bernstein A. 1973. The Gait of Australopithecus. American Journal of Physical Anthropology 38:757–779.

Low B. 1990. Human Responses to Environmental Extremeness and Uncertainty. In: Cashdan E, editor. Risk and Uncertainty in Tribal and Peasant Economies. Boulder, CO: Westview Press. p 242–243.

Low BS. 1998. Behavioral Ecology, "Sociobiology" and Human Social Behavior. In: Ember CR, Ember M,

Peregrine PN, editors. Research Frontiers in Anthropology. Upper Saddle River, NJ: Prentice Hall/Simon & Schuster Custom Publishing.

Lowie RH. 1917, 1988. The Determinants of Culture. In: Bohannan P, Glazer M, editors. High Points in Anthropology. New York: Alfred A. Knopf.

Loy TH. 1998. Blood on the Axe. New Scientist 159(2151):40.

Loy TH, Dixon EJ. 1998. Blood Residues on Fluted Points from Eastern Beringia. American Antiquity 63(1):21–46.

Loy TH, Hardy BL. 1992. Blood Residue Analysis of 90,000-Year-Old Stone Tools from Tabun Cave, Israel. Antiquity 66(250):24–35.

Loy TH, Rhys Jones DE, Nelson BM, Vogel J, Southon J, Cosgrove R. 1990. Accelerator Radiocarbon Dating of Human Blood Proteins in Pigments from Late Pleistocene Art Sites in Australia. Antiquity 64(242):110–116.

Loy TH, Spriggs MJT, Wickler S. 1992. Direct Evidence for Human Use of Plants 28,000 Years Ago: Starch Residues on Stone Artefacts from the Northern Solomon Islands. Antiquity 66(253):898–912.

Lubell D, Jackes M, Schwarcz HP, Knyf M, Meiklejohn C. 1994. The Mesolithic-Neolithic Transition in Portugal: Isotopic and Dental Evidence of Diet. Journal of Archaeological Science 21:201–215.

Lutz C. 1985. Depression and the Translations of Emotional Worlds. In: Kleinman A, Good B, editors. Culture and Depression: Studies in the Anthropology and Cross-Cultural Psychiatry of Affect and Disorder. Berkeley: University of California Press. p 63–100.

Lyell C. 1863. The Geological Evidences of the Antiquity of Man. London: Murray.

MacKinnon J, MacKinnon K. 1980. The Behavior of Wild Spectral Tarsiers. International Journal of Primatology 1:361–379.

MacMillan H, MacMillan AB, Offord DR, Dingle JL. 1996. Aboriginal Health. Canadian Medical Association Journal 155(11):1569–1578.

MacNeish RS. 1973. The Evaluation of Community Patterns in the Tehuacán Valley of Mexico and Speculations about the Cultural Processes. In: Tringham R, editor. Ecology and Agricultural Settlement R2. Andover, MA: Warner Modular. p 1–27.

MacNeish RS. 1991. The Origins of Agriculture and Settled Life. Norman: University of Oklahoma Press.

Madigral L. 1989. Hemoglobin Genotype, Fertility, and the Malaria Hypothesis. Human Biology 61:311–325.

Makristathis A, Schwarzmeier J, Mader RM, Varmuza K, Simonitsch I, Chavez JC, Platzer W, Unterdorfer H, Scheithauer R, Derevianko A, Seidler H. 2002. Fatty Acid Composition and Preservation of the Tyrolean Iceman and Other Mummies. Journal of Lipid Research 43:2056–2061.

Manchester K. 1987. Skeletal Evidence for Health and Disease. In: Boddington A, Garland AN, Janaway RC, editors. Death, Decay and Reconstruction: Approaches to Archaeology and Forensic Science. Manchester: Manchester University Press. p 163–179.

Marcus J. 1983. On the Nature of the Mesoamerican City. In: Vogt EZ, Leventhal RM, editors. Prehistoric Settlement Patterns: Essays in Honor of Gordon R. Willey. Albuquerque: University of New Mexico Press. p 195–242.

Marcus J, Flannery KV. 1996. Zapotec Civilization: How Urban Society Evolved in Mexico's Oaxaca Valley. New York, NY: Thames and Hudson.

Marks J. December 1994. Black, White, Other: Racial Categories Are Cultural Constructs Masquerading as Biology. Natural History 32–35.

Marshack A. 1972. The Roots of Civilization. New York: McGraw-Hill.

Marshall LG. 1984. Who Killed Cock Robin? An Investigation of the Extinction Controversy. In: Martin PS, Klein RG, editors. Quaternary Extinctions: A Prehistoric Revolution. Tucson: University of Arizona Press. p 785–806.

Marshall WA. 1978. The Relationship of Puberty to Other Maturity Indicators and Body Composition in Man. Journal of Reproductive Fertility 52:437–443.

Marshall WA, Tanner JM. 1986. Puberty. In: Falkner F, Tanner JM, editors. Human Growth 2: Postnatal Growth. Second edition. London: Plenum Press. p 171–210.

Martin PS. 9 March 1973. The Discovery of America. Science 969–974.

Martin PS, Wright HE, editors, and National Research Council (U.S.). 1967. Pleistocene Extinctions: The Search for a Cause. New Haven, CT: Yale University Press.

Martin R. 1992. Classification and Evolutionary Relationships. In: Jones S, Martin R, Pilbeam D, editors. The Cambridge Encyclopedia of Human Evolution. Cambridge: Cambridge University Press. p 17–19.

Martin RD. November 1975. Strategies of Reproduction. Natural History 48–57.

Martin RD, Bearder SK. 1979. Radio Bush Baby. Natural History 77–81.

Martin RD, Martin AE. 1990. Primate Origins and Evolution: A Phylogenetic Reconstruction. Princeton, NJ: Princeton University Press.

Martorell R. 1980. Interrelationships between Diet, Infectious Disease and Nutritional Status. In: Greene L, Johnston FE, editors. Social and

Biological Predictors of Nutritional Status, Physical Growth and Neurological Development. New York: Academic Press. p 81–106.

Martorell R, Ho TJ. 1984. Malnutrition, Morbidity and Mortality. In Child Survival: Strategies for Research. In: Mosley WH, Chen LC, editors. Population Development Review, Supplement to Volume 10. Population Council. p 49–68.

Martorell R, Rivera J, Kaplowitz H, Pollit E. 15 September 1991. Long-Term Consequences of Growth Retardation during Early Childhood. Paper presented at the Sixth International Congress of Auxology. Madrid.

Mascie-Taylor CGN. 1990. The Biology of Social Class. In: Mascie-Taylor CGN, editor. Biosocial Aspects of Social Class. Oxford: Oxford University Press. p 118–121.

Maxwell MS. 1985. Prehistory of the Eastern Arctic. Orlando, FL: Academic Press.

Mayr E. 2 June 1972. The Nature of the Darwinian Revolution. Science 981–989.

Mayr E. 1982. The Growth of Biological Thought: Diversity, Evolution, and Inheritance. Cambridge, MA: Belknap Press of Harvard University Press.

Mazess RB. 1975. Human Adaptation to High Altitude. In: Damon A, editor. Physiological Anthropology. New York: Oxford University Press.

McCorriston J, Hole F. 1991. The Ecology of Seasonal Stress and the Origins of Agriculture in the Near East. American Anthropologist 93:46–69.

McDonald KA. 13 March 1998. New Evidence Challenges Traditional Model of How the New World Was Settled. Chronicle of Higher Education A22.

McGarvey ST, Bindon JR, Crews DE, Schendel DE. 1989. Modernization and Adiposity: Causes and Consequences. In: Little MA, Haas JD, editors. Human Population Biology. A Transdisciplinary Science. Oxford: Oxford University Press. p 263–279.

McGhee R. 1996. Ancient People of the Arctic. Vancouver: University of British Columbia Press.

McHenry HM. 1982. The Pattern of Human Evolution: Studies on Bipedalism, Mastication, and Encephalization. Annual Review of Anthropology 11:151–173.

McHenry HM. 1998a. New Estimates of Body Weight in Early Hominids and Their Significance to Encephalization and Megadontia in "Robust" Australopithecines. In: Grine FE, editor. Evolutionary History of the "Robust" Australopithecines. New York: Aldine. p 133–148.

McHenry HM. 1998b. "Robust" Australopithecines, Our Family Tree, and Homoplasy. In: Ember CR, Ember M, Peregrine PN, editors. Research Frontiers in Anthropology. Upper Saddle River, NJ:

Prentice Hall/Simon & Schuster Custom Publishing.

McNeill WH. 1967. A World History. New York: Oxford University Press.

McNeill WH. 1976. Plagues and Peoples. Garden City, NY: Doubleday/Anchor.

Mellaart J. 1961. Roots in the Soil. In: Piggott S, editor. The Dawn of Civilization. London: Thames & Hudson. p 41–64.

Mellaart J. April 1964. A Neolithic City in Turkey. Scientific American 94–104.

Mellars P. 1996. The Neanderthal Legacy: An Archaeological Perspective from Western Europe. Princeton, NJ: Princeton University Press.

Mellars P. 1998. The Fate of the Neanderthals. Nature 395:539–540.

Mellor JW, Gavian S. 30 January 1987. Famine: Causes, Prevention, and Relief. Science 539–544.

Mercader J, Panger M, Boesch C. 2002. Excavation of a Chimpanzee Stone Tool Site in the African Rainforest. Science 296:1452–1455.

Meredith HV. 1976. Findings from Asia, Australia, Europe, and North America on Secular Change in Mean Height of Children, Youths, and Young Adults. American Journal of Physical Anthropology 44(2):315–325.

Mill JE, DesJardins DA. 1996. The Feather of Hope Aboriginal AIDS Prevention Society: A Community Approach to HIV/AIDS Prevention. Canadian Journal of Public Health 87:268–271.

Miller HI. 1991. Regulation. In: Davis BD, editor. The Genetic Revolution: Scientific Prospects and Public Perceptions. Baltimore: Johns Hopkins University Press. p 196–211.

Miller NF. 1992. The Origins of Plant Cultivation in the Near East. In: Cowan CW, Watson PJ, editors. The Origins of Agriculture. Washington, DC: Smithsonian Institution Press. p 41–42.

Millon R. 1967. Teotihuacán. Scientific American 216:38–48.

Millon R. 1976. Social Relations in Ancient Teotihuacán. In: Wolf ER, editor. The Valley of Mexico: Studies in Pre-Hispanic Ecology and Society. Albuquerque: University of New Mexico Press. p 215–220.

Milner GR, Humpf DA, Harpending HC. 1989. Pattern Matching of Age-at-Death Distributions in Palaeodemographic Analysis. American Journal of Physical Anthropology 80:49–58.

Milton K. 1981. Distribution Patterns of Tropical Plant Foods as an Evolutionary Stimulus to Primate Mental Development. American Anthropologist 83:534–548.

Milton K. 1988. Foraging Behaviour and the Evolution of Primate Intelligence. In: Bryne RW, Whiten A, editors. Machiavellian Intelligence: Social Expertise and the Evolution of Intellect in Monkeys, Apes, and Humans. Oxford: Clarendon Press. p 285–305.

Miracle AW. 1998. A Shaman to Organizations. In: Ember CR, Ember M, Peregrine PN, editors. Research Frontiers in Anthropology. Upper Saddle River, NJ: Prentice Hall/Simon & Schuster Custom Publishing.

Mojzsis SJ, Arrhenius G, McKeegan KD, Harrison TM, Nutman AP, Friend CR. 7 November 1996. Evidence for Life on Earth before 3,800 Million Years Ago. Nature 384(6604):55–59.

Molnar S. 1998. Human Variation: Races, Types and Ethnic Groups. Fourth edition. Upper Saddle River, NJ: Prentice Hall.

Moore JA, Swedlund AC, Armelagos GJ. 1975. The Use of Life Tables in Palaeodemography. American Antiquity 40 Part 2(2), Memoir 30:57–70.

Morell V. 31 March 1995. The Earliest Art Becomes Older—and More Common. Science 1908–1909.

Morlan RE, Nelson DE, Brown TA, Vogel JS, Southon JR. 1990. Accelerator Mass Spectrometry Dates on Bones from Old Crow Basin, Northern Yukon Territory. Canadian Journal of Archaeology 14:75.

Mosley WH, Chen LC. 1984. An Analytical Framework for the Study of Child Survival in Developing Countries. In: Mosley WH, Chen LC, editors. Child Survival: Strategies for Research. Population Development Supplement to Volume 10. New York: Population Council. p 25–45.

Motulsky A. 1971. Metabolic Polymorphisms and the Role of Infectious Diseases in Human Evolution. In: Morris LN, editor. Human Populations, Genetic Variation, and Evolution. San Francisco: Chandler Pub. Co.

Müller-Haye B. 1984. Guinea Pig or Cuy. In: Mason IL, editor. Evolution of Domesticated Animals. New York: Longman. p 329–331.

Murphy J. 1981. Abnormal Behavior in Traditional Societies: Labels, Explanations, and Social Reactions. In: Munroe RH, Munroe RL, Whiting BB, editors. Handbook of Cross-Cultural Human Development. New York: Garland.

Murphy WA, Jr., Nedden DD, Gostner P, Knapp R, Recheis W, Seidler H. 2003. The Iceman: Discovery and Imaging. Radiology 226:614–629.

Myers FR. 1988. Critical Trends in the Study of Hunter-Gatherers. Annual Review of Anthropology 17:261–282.

Napier JR. 1970. Paleoecology and Catarrhine Evolution. In: Napier JR, Napier PH, editors. Old World Monkeys: Evolution, Systematics, and Behavior. New York: Academic Press. p 53–95.

Napier JR, Napier PH. 1967. A Handbook of Living Primates. New York: Academic Press.

Nash JM. 2001. The Iceman. Time 158:42–43.

Naylor CD, Chantler C, Griffiths S. 2004. Learning from SARS in Hong Kong and Toronto. Journal of the American Medical Association 291:2483–2487.

Neel JV. 1962. Diabetes Mellitus: A "Thrifty" Genotype Rendered Detrimental by "Progress"? American Journal of Human Genetics 14:353–362.

Nelson AJ, Thompson JL. 1999. Growth and Development in Neandertals and Other Fossil Hominids: Implications for the Evolution of Hominid Ontogeny. In: Hoppa RD, FitzGerald CM, editors. Human Growth in the Past: Studies from Bones and Teeth. Cambridge: Cambridge University Press. p 88–110.

Nicolson NA. 1966. Infants, Mothers, and Other Females. In: Smuts BB, Cheney DL, Seyfarth RM, Wrangham RW, Struhsaker TT, editors. Primate Societies. Chicago: University of Chicago Press. p 330–342.

Niederberger C. 12 January 1979. Early Sedentary Economy in the Basin of Mexico. Science 131–142.

Niehoff AH. 1966. A Casebook of Social Change. Chicago: Aldine.

Nissen HW. 1958. Axes of Behavioral Comparison. In: Roe A, Simpson GG, editors. Behavior and Evolution. New Haven, CT: Yale University Press. p 183–205.

Noble WC. 1968. Iroquois Archaeology and the Development of Iroquois Social Organization (1000–1650 A.D.): A Study in Culture Change Based on Archaeology, Ethnohistory and Ethnology. Ph.D. dissertation. Department of Archaeology, University of Calgary, Calgary, Alberta.

Normile D. 6 March 1998. Habitat Seen Playing Larger Role in Shaping Behavior. Science 1454–1455.

Notzke C. 1999. Indigenous Tourism Development in the Arctic. Annals of Tourism Research 26:55–76.

O'Neil J. 2001. Assembly of Manitoba Chiefs, University of Manitoba, and Centre for Aboriginal Health Research. Building Capacity in Applied Aboriginal Population Health Research. Winnipeg, MB: Centre for Aboriginal Health Research.

O'Neil J, Commanda L. 1998. Determining the Feasibility of the Canadian First Nations and Inuit Regional (Longitudinal) Health Surveys. International Journal of Circumpolar Health 57 Supplement 1:611–616.

O'Neil J, Yassi A, Elias B. 1998. Cultural Environmental Health Risk Perception in the Canadian North. International Journal of Circumpolar Health 57 Supplement 1:543–549.

O'Neil JD. 1995. Issues in Health Policy for Indigenous Peoples in Canada. Australian Journal of Public Health 19:559–566.

Oakley K. 1964. On Man's Use of Fire, with Comments on Tool-Making and Hunting. In: Washburn SL, editor. Social Life of Early Man. Chicago: Aldine. p 186.

Oakley KP. 1963. Analytical Methods of Dating Bones. In: Brothwell D, Higgs E, editors. Science in Archaeology. New York: Basic Books. p 24–34.

Olszewski DI. 1991. Social Complexity in the Natufian? Assessing the Relationship of Ideas and Data. In: Clark GA, editor. Perspectives on the Past: Theoretical Biases in Mediterranean Hunter-Gatherer Research. Philadelphia: University of Pennsylvania Press. p 322–340.

Omoto K, Tobias PV, editors. 1998. The Origins and Past of Modern Humans—Towards Reconciliation. Singapore: World Scientific.

Oostdam JV, Gilman A, Dewailly E, Usher P, Wheatley B, Kuhnlein H, Neve S, Walker J, Tracy B, Feeley M, Jerome V, Kwavnick B. 1999. Human Health Implications of Environmental Contaminants in Arctic Canada: A Review. The Science of the Total Environment 230:182.

Ortner DJ. 1991. Theoretical and Methodological Issues in Palaeopathology. In: Ortner DJ, Aufderheide AC, editors. Human Palaeopathology: Current Synthesis and Future Options. Washington, DC: Smithsonian Institution Press. p 5–11.

Ovchinnikov IV, Gotherstorm A, Romanova GP, Kharitonov VM, Liden K, Goodwin W. 2000. Molecular Analysis of Neanderthal DNA from the Northern Caucasus. Nature 404:490–793.

Owsley DW, Ubelaker DH, Houck MM, Sandness KL, Grant WE, Craig EA, Woltanski TJ, Peerwani N. 1995. The role of forensic anthropology in the recovery and analysis of Branch Davidian Compound victims: techniques of analysis. Journal of Forensic Science 40:341–348.

Oxby C. 1983. Farmer Groups in Rural Areas of the Third World. Community Development Journal 18:50–59.

Park RW. 1993. The Dorset-Thule Succession in Arctic North America: Assessing Claims for Culture Contact. American Antiquity 58(2):203–234.

Park RW. 2000. The Dorset-Thule Succession Revisited. In: Appelt M, Berglund J, Gulløv HC, editors. Identities and Cultural Contacts in the Arctic. The Danish Polar Center Publication No. 8. Copenhagen: The Danish National Museum & Danish Polar Center. p 192–205.

Parker ST. 1990. Why Big Brains Are So Rare. In: Parker ST, Gibson KR, editors. "Language" and Intelligence in Monkeys and Apes: Comparative Developmental Perspectives. Cambridge: Cambridge University Press.

Parker ST, Gibson KR. 1990. "Language" and Intelligence in Monkeys and Apes: Comparative Developmental Perspectives. Cambridge: Cambridge University Press.

Partridge WL, Eddy EM. 1987. The Development of Applied Anthropology in America. In: Eddy EM, Partridge WL, editors. Applied Anthropology in America. New York: Columbia University Press. p 31–40.

Patterson TC. 1971. Central Peru: Its Population and Economy. Archaeology 24:318–319.

Patterson TC. 1973. America's Past: A New World Archaeology. Glenview, IL: Scott, Foresman.

Patterson TC. 1981. The Evolution of Ancient Societies: A World Archaeology. Englewood Cliffs, NJ: Prentice Hall.

Payne N, Gledhill N, Katzmarzyk T, Jamnik VK, Keir PJ. 2000. Canadian Musculoskeletal Fitness Norms. Canadian Journal of Applied Physiology 25:430–442.

Pearsall D. 1992. The Origin of Plant Cultivation in South America. In: Cowan CW, Watson PJ, editors. The Origins of Agriculture. Washington, DC: Smithsonian Institution Press. p 173–205.

Pelto PJ, Miller-Wille L. 1987. Snowmobiles: Technological Revolution in the Arctic. In: Bernard HR, Pelto PJ, editors. Technology and Social Change. Second edition. Prospect Heights, IL: Waveland Press. p 207-243.

Pennington R. 1992. Did Food Increase Fertility? Evaluation of !Kung and Herero History. Human Biology 64(4):497–521.

Pennington R, Harpending HC. 1991. Effect of Infertility on the Population Structure of the Herero and Mbanderu of Southern Africa. Social Biology 38:127–139.

Peregrine PN, Ember CR, Ember M. 2000. Teaching Critical Evaluation of Rushton. Anthropology Newsletter 41:29–30.

Petersen EB. 1973. A Survey of the Late Paleolithic and the Mesolithic of Denmark. In: Kozlowski SK, editor. The Mesolithic in Europe. Warsaw: Warsaw University Press. p 94–96.

Pfeiffer JE. 1978. The Emergence of Man. Third edition. New York: Harper & Row.

Phillipson DW. 1993. African Archaeology. Second edition. Cambridge: Cambridge University Press.

Picchi D. 1991. The Impact of an Industrial Agricultural Project on the Bakairi Indians of Central Brazil. Human Organization 50:26–38.

Picchi D. 1998. Bakairi: The Death of an Indian. In: Ember MC, Ember CR, Levinson D, editors. Portraits of Culture: Ethnographic Originals. Upper Saddle River, NJ: Prentice Hall/Simon & Schuster Custom Publishing.

Pickford M, Senut B, Gommery D, Treil J. 2002. Bipedalism in Orrorin tugenensis Revealed by Its

Femora. Comptes Rendus de l'Académie des Sciences de Paris, Série Palevol 1:191–203.

Pilbeam D. 1972. The Ascent of Man. New York: Macmillan. p 107.

Pilbeam D, Gould SJ. 6 December 1974. Size and Scaling in Human Evolution. Science 899.

Polanyi KC, Arensberg CM, Pearson HW. 1957. Trade and Market in the Early Empires. New York: Free Press.

Polednak AP. 1974. Connective Tissue Responses in Negroes in Relation to Disease. American Journal of Physical Anthropology 41:49–57.

Pope GG. October 1989. Bamboo and Human Evolution. Natural History 48–56.

Post PW, Daniels Jr. F, Binford Jr. RT. 1975. Cold Injury and the Evolution of "White" Skin. Human Biology 47:65–80.

Potts R. 1988. Early Hominid Activities at Olduvai. New York: Aldine de Gruyter.

Preuschoft H, Chivers DJ, Brockelman WY, Creel N, editors. 1984. The Lesser Apes: Evolutionary and Behavioural Biology. Edinburgh: Edinburgh University Press.

Price TD. 1984. The Chemistry of Prehistoric Bone. Cambridge: Cambridge University Press.

Primorac D, Andelinovic S, Definis-Gojanovic M, Drmic I, Rezic B, Baden MM, Kennedy MA, Schanfield MS, Skakel SB, Lee HC. 1996. Identification of War Victims from Mass Graves in Croatia, Bosnia, and Herzegovina by Use of Standard Forensic Methods and DNA Typing. Journal of Forensic Science 41:891–894.

Radinsky L. 1967. The Oldest Primate Endocast. American Journal of Physical Anthropology 27:358–388.

Rathbun TA. 1984. Skeletal Pathology from the Palaeolithic through the Metal Ages in Iran and Iraq. In: Cohen MN, Armelagos JG, editors. Palaeopathology at the Origins of Agriculture. Orlando, FL: Academic Press. p 137–167.

Rathje WL. 1971. The Origin and Development of Lowland Classic Maya Civilization. American Antiquity 36:275–285.

Ray AK, Roth EA. 1984. Demography of the Juang Tribal Population of Orissa. American Journal of Physical Anthropology 65:387–393.

Redman CL. 1978. The Rise of Civilization: From Early Farmers to Urban Society in the Ancient Near East. San Francisco: Freeman.

Reed D, Labarthe D, Stallones R. 1970. Health Effects of Westernization and Migration Among Chamorros. American Journal of Epidemiology 92:96–112.

Reed DM. 1994. Ancient Maya Diet at Copan, Honduras, as Determined through the Analysis of Stable Carbon and Nitrogen Isotopes. In: Sobolik KD, editor. Paleonutrition: The Diet and Health of Prehistoric Americas, Occasional Paper 22. Carbondale: Southern Illinois University Center for Archaeological Investigations. p 210–221.

Reitz EJ, Newsom LF, Scudder SJ, editors. 1996. Case Studies in Environmental Archaeology: Interdisciplinary Contributions to Archaeology. New York: Plenum Press.

Remis M. 1995. Effects of Body Size and Social Context on the Arboreal Activities of Lowland Gorillas in the Central African Republic. American Journal of Physical Anthropology 97:413–433.

Renfrew C. 1969. Trade and Culture Process in European Prehistory. Current Anthropology 10:151–169.

Rice PC, Paterson AL. 1985. Cave Art and Bones: Exploring the Interrelationships. American Anthropologist 87:94-100.

Rice PC, Paterson AL. 1986. Validating the Cave Art–Archeofaunal Relationship in Cantabrian Spain. American Anthropologist 88:658–667.

Richard AF. 1985. Primates in Nature. New York: Freeman.

Richard AF. 1987. Malagasy Prosimians: Female Dominance. In: Smuts BB, Cheney DL, Seyfarth RM, Wrangham RW, Struhsaker TT, editors. Primate Societies. Chicago: University of Chicago Press. p 25–33.

Riesenfeld A. 1973. The Effect of Extreme Temperatures and Starvation on the Body Proportions of the Rat. American Journal of Physical Anthropology 39:427–459.

Rightmire GP. 1984. *Homo sapiens* in Sub-Saharan Africa. In: Smith FH, Spencer F, editors. The Origins of Modern Humans: A World Survey of the Fossil Evidence. New York: Alan R. Liss.

Rightmire GP. 1985. The Tempo of Change in the Evolution of Mid-Pleistocene Homo. In: Delson E. Ancestors: The Hard Evidence. New York: Alan R. Liss. p. 255–264.

Rightmire GP. 1988. *Homo erectus*. In: Tattersall I, Delson E, van Couvering J, editors. Encyclopedia of Human Evolution and Prehistory. New York: Garland. p 259–265.

Rightmire GP. 1990. The Evolution of *Homo erectus*: Comparative Anatomical Studies of an Extinct Human Species. Cambridge: Cambridge University Press.

Rightmire GP. 1998. Human Evolution in the Middle Pleistocene: The Role of *Homo heidelbergensis*. Evolutionary Anthropology 6:218–227.

Rijksen HD. 1978. A Fieldstudy on Sumatran Orang Utans (Pongo Pygmaeus Abelii Lesson 1827): Ecology, Behaviour and Conservation. Wageningen, Netherlands: H. Veenman and Zonen, B.V.

Ritenbaugh C, Goodby C. 1989. Beyond the Thrifty Gene: Metabolic Implications of Prehistoric Migration into the New World. Medical Anthropology 11:227–236.

Roberts DF. 1953. Body Weight, Race, and Climate. American Journal of Physical Anthropology 2:553–558.

Roberts DF. 1978. Climate and Human Variability. Second edition. Menlo Park, CA: Cummings.

Robinson JG, Janson CH. 1987. Capuchins, Squirrel Monkeys, and Atelines: Sociological Convergence with Old World Primates. In: Smuts BB, Cheney DL, Seyfarth RM, Wrangham RW, Struhsaker TT, editors. Primate Societies. Chicago: University of Chicago Press. p 69–82.

Robinson JG, Wright PC, Kinzey WG. 1987. Monogamous Cebids and Their Relatives: Intergroup Calls and Spacing. In: Smuts BB, Cheney DL, Seyfarth RM, Wrangham RW, Struhsaker TT, editors. Primate Societies. Chicago: University of Chicago Press. p 44–53.

Rodrigues S, Robinson E, Gray-Donald K. 1999. Prevalence of Gestational Diabetes Mellitus among James Bay Cree Women in Northern Quebec. Canadian Medical Association Journal 160(9): 1293–1297.

Rogers EM. 1983. Diffusion of Innovations. Third edition. New York: Free Press.

Rona RJ. 1991. Nutritional Surveillance in Developed Countries Using Anthropometry. In: Himes JH, editor. Anthropometric Assessment of Nutritional Status. New York: Wiley-Liss Inc. p 301–318.

Roosevelt AC. 1984. Population, Health, and the Evolution of Subsistence: Conclusions from the Conference. In: Cohen MN, Armelagos GJ, editor. Paleopathology at the Origins of Agriculture. Orlando, FL: Academic Press. p 559–584.

Roosevelt AC, Lima da Costa M, Machado CL, Michab M, Mercier N, Valladas H, Feathers J, Barnett W, Imazio da Silveira M, Henderson A, Silva J, Chernoff B, Reese DS, Holman JA, Toth N, Schick K. 19 April 1996. Paleoindian Cave Dwellers in the Amazon: The Peopling of America. Science 373–384.

Rose MD. 1984. Food Acquisition and the Evolution of Positional Behaviour: The Case of Bipedalism. In: Chivers DJ, Wood BA, Bilsborough A, editors. Food Acquisition and Processing in Primates. New York: Plenum. p 509–524.

Rosenberger AL. 1979. Cranial Anatomy and Implications of *Dolichocebus*, a Late Oligocene Ceboid Primate. Nature 279:416–418.

Ross MH. 1998. Ethnocentrism and Ethnic Conflict. In: Ember CR, Ember M, Peregrine PN, editors. Research Frontiers in Anthropology. Upper Saddle River, NJ: Prentice Hall/Simon & Schuster Custom Publishing.

Ruan YJ, Wei CL, Ee AL, Vega VB, Thoreau H, Su ST, Chia JM, Ng P, Chiu KP, Lim L, Zhang T, Peng CK, Lin EO, Lee NM, Yee SL, Ng LF, Chee RE, Stanton LW, Long PM, Liu ET. 2003. Comparative Full-Length Genome Sequence Analysis of 14 SARS Coronavirus Isolates and Common Mutations Associated with Putative Origins of Infection. Lancet 361:1779–1785.

Ruff CB, Walker A. 1993. Body Size and Body Shape. In: Walker A, Leakey R, editors. The Nariokotome *Homo erectus* Skeleton. Cambridge, MA: Harvard University Press. p 234–265.

Rumbaugh DM. 1970. Learning Skills of Anthropoids. In: Rosenblum LA, editor. Primate Behavior. Volume 1. New York: Academic Press. p 52–58.

Rushton JP. 1995. Race and Crime: International Data for 1989–1990. Psychological Reports 76(1):307–312.

Rushton JP. 1996. Genetics and Race. Science 271(5249):579–580.

Russel DA, Sequin R. 1982. Reconstruction of the Small Cretaceous Theropod *Stenonychosaurus inequalis* and a Hypothetical Dinosauroid. Syllogeous 37:143.

Russon AE. 1990. The Development of Peer Social Interaction in Infant Chimpanzees: Comparative Social, Piagetian, and Brain Perspectives. In: Taylor Parker S, Gibson KR, editors. "Language" and Intelligence in Monkeys and Apes: Comparative Development Perspectives. New York: Cambridge University Press. p 379–419.

Sade DS. 1965. Some Aspects of Parent-Offspring and Sibling Relationships in a Group of Rhesus Monkeys, with a Discussion of Grooming. American Journal of Physical Anthropology 23:1–17.

Sagan C. December 1975. A Cosmic Calendar. Natural History 70–73.

Sanders WT. 1968. Hydraulic Agriculture, Economic Symbiosis, and the Evolution of States in Central Mexico. In: Meggers BJ, editor. Anthropological Archaeology in the Americas. Washington, DC: Anthropological Society of Washington. p 88–107.

Sanders WT, Price BJ. 1968. Mesoamerica. New York: Random House.

Sanders WT, Parsons JR, Santley RS. 1979. The Basin of Mexico: Ecological Processes in the Evolution of a Civilization. New York: Academic Press.

Sandford MK. 1992. A Reconstruction of Trace Element Analysis in Prehistoric Bone. In: Saunders SR, Katzenberg MA, editors. Skeletal Biology of Past Peoples: Research Methods. New York: Wiley-Liss. p 79–103.

Sandford MK. 1993. Investigations of Ancient Human Tissues: Chemical Analysis in Anthropology. Langhorne: Gordon and Breach Science Publishers.

Sandford MK, Weaver DS. 2000. Trace Element Research in Anthropology: New Perspectives and Challenges. In: Katzenberg MA, Saunders SR, editors. Biological Anthropology of the Human Skeleton. New York: Wiley-Liss. p 329–350.

Sarich V, Wilson AC. 23 December 1966. Quantitative Immunochemistry and the Evolution of the Primate Albumins: Micro-Component Fixations. Science 1563–1566.

Sarich VM. 1968. The Origin of Hominids: An Immunological Approach. In: Washburn SL, Phyllis CJ, editors. Perspectives on Human Evolution. Volume 1. New York: Holt, Rinehart, & Winston. p 99–121.

Sassaman K. 1996. Early Archaic Settlement in the South Carolina Coastal Plain. In: Anderson DG, Sassaman K, editors. The Paleoindian and Early Archaic Southeast. Tuscaloosa: University of Alabama Press. p 58–83.

Sattenspiel L. 1990. Modeling the Spread of Infectious Disease in Human Populations. Yearbook of Physical Anthropology 33:245–276.

Sattenspiel L, Herring DA. 1998. Structured Epidemic Models and the Spread of the 1918–1919 Influenza Epidemic in the Central Subarctic. Human Biology 70:91–115.

Saunders SR. 1992. Subadult Skeletons and Growth Related Studies. In: Saunders SR, Katzenberg MA, editors. Skeletal Biology of Past Peoples. New York: Wiley-Liss, Inc. p 1–20.

Saunders SR, Hoppa RD. 1993. Growth Deficit in Survivors and Non-Survivors: Biological Bias in Subadult Skeletal Samples. Yearbook of Physical Anthropology 36:127–151.

Savage-Rumbaugh ES. 1992. Language Training of Apes. In: Jones S, Martin R, Pilbeam D, editors. The Cambridge Encyclopedia of Human Evolution. Cambridge: Cambridge University Press. p 138–141.

Savage-Rumbaugh ES. 1994. Hominid Evolution: Looking to Modern Apes for Clues. In: Quiatt D, Itani J, editors. Hominid Culture in Primate Perspective. Niwot: University Press of Colorado. p 7–49.

Savelle JM. 1997. The Role of Architectural Utility in the Formation of Zooarchaeological Whale Bone Assemblages. Journal of Archaeological Science 24(10):869–885.

Scarr S, McCartney K. 1983. How People Make Their Own Environments: A Theory of Genotype-Environment Effects. Child Development 54:424–435.

Schaller G. 1963. The Mountain Gorilla: Ecology and Behavior. Chicago: University of Chicago Press.

Schaller G. 1964. The Year of the Gorilla. Chicago: University of Chicago Press.

Schaller GB. 1972. The Serengeti Lion: A Study of Predator–Prey Relations. Chicago: University of Chicago Press.

Schick KD, Toth N. 1994. Making Silent Stones Speak: Human Evolution and the Dawn of Technology. New York: Simon & Schuster.

Schoeninger MJ. 1995. Stable Isotopes Studies in Human Evolution. Evolutionary Anthropology 4:83–98.

Schoepf B. 1988. Women, AIDS, and Economic Crisis in Central Africa. Canadian Journal of African Studies 22:625–644.

Scholz M, Bachmann L, Nicholson GJ, Bachman J, Giddings I, Ruschoff-Thale B, Czarnetzki A, Pusch CM. 2000. Genomic Differentiation of Neanderthals and Anatomically Modern Man Allows a Fossil-DNA-Based Classification of Morphologically Indistinguishable Hominid Bones. American Journal of Human Genetics 66:1927–1932.

Schopf JW. 20 June 2000. Solution to Darwin's Dilemma: Discovery of the Missing Precambrian Record of Life. Proceedings of the National Academy of Sciences 97[13], 694–753.

Schrire C. 1984. Past and Present in Hunter-Gatherer Studies. Orlando, FL: Academic Press.

Schurr MR. 1997. Stable Nitrogen Isotopes as Evidence for the Age of Weaning at the Angel Site: A Comparison of Isotopic and Demographic Measures of Weaning Age. Journal of Archaeological Science 24:919–927.

Schwarcz HP. 1993. Uranium-Series Dating and the Origin of Modern Man. In: Schwarcz HP, editor. The Origin of Modern Humans and the Impact of Chronometric Dating. Princeton, NJ: Princeton University Press. p 12–26.

Schwarcz HP, Grun R. 1992. Electron Spin Resonance (ESR) Dating of the Origin of Modern Man. Philosophical Transactions of the Royal Society of London Biological Sciences 337:145–148.

Schwarcz HP, Melbye FJ, Katzenber MA, Knyf M. 1985. Stable Isotopes in Human Skeletons of Southern Ontario: Reconstructing Paleodiet. Journal of Archaeological Science 12:187-206.

Scott GR, Halffman CM, Pedersen PO. 1991. Dental Conditions of Medieval Norsemen in the North Atlantic. Acta Archaeologica 62:183–207.

Scudder T. 1987. Opportunities, Issues, and Achievements in Development Anthropology Since the Mid-1960s: A Personal View. In: Eddy EM, Partridge WL, editors. Applied Anthropology in America. New York: Columbia University Press. p 184–210.

Seidensticker J. 1985. Primates as Prey of Panthera Cats in South Asian Habitats. American Journal of Primatology 8:365–366.

Seielstad M, Bekele E, Ibrahim M, Toure A, Traore M. 1999. A View of Modern Human Origins from Y Chromosome Microsatellite Variation. Genome Research 9(6):558–567.

Semenov SA. 1970. Prehistoric Technology. Thompson MW, translator. Bath, England: Adams & Dart.

Senner WM. 1989. Theories and Myths on the Origins of Writing: A Historical Overview. In: Senner WM, editor. The Origins of Writing. Lincoln: University of Nebraska Press. p 1–26.

Service ER. 1975. Origins of the State and Civilization: The Process of Cultural Evolution. New York: Norton.

Service ER. 1979. The Hunters. Second edition. Englewood Cliffs, NJ: Prentice Hall.

Seyfarth RM, Cheney DL. 1982. How Monkeys See the World: A Review of Recent Research on East African Vervet Monkeys. In: Snowdon CT, Brown CH, Petersen MR, editors. Primate Communication. New York: Cambridge University Press.

Shanklin E. 1994. Anthropology and Race. Belmont, CA: Wadsworth.

Shapiro LR, Crowford PB, Clark MJ, Pearson DL, Raz J, Huenemann RL. 1984. Obesity Prognosis: A Longitudinal Study of Children from the Age of 6 Months to 9 Years. American Journal of Public Health 74:968–972.

Shepard RJ. 1991. Body Composition in Biological Anthropology. Cambridge Studies in Biological Anthropology 6. Cambridge: Cambridge University Press.

Shipman P. 1984. Early Hominid Lifestyle: The Scavenging Hypothesis. Anthroquest 28:910.

Shipman P. 1986. Scavenging or Hunting in Early Hominids: Theoretical Framework and Tests. American Anthropologist 88:27–43.

Shipman P, Rose J. 1983. Early Hominid Hunting, Butchering, and Carcass-Processing Behaviors: Approaches to the Fossil Record. Journal of Anthropological Archaeology 2(1):57–98.

Sicotte P. 1993. Inter-group Encounters and Female Transfer in Mountain Gorillas: Influence of Group Composition on Male Behavior. American Journal of Primatology 30:21–36.

Sicotte P. 1995. Interpositions in Conflicts between Males in Bimale Groups of Mountain Gorillas. Folia Primatology (Basel) 65:14–24.

Sicotte P. 2002. The Function of Male Aggressive Displays towards Females in Mountain Gorillas. Primates 43:277–289.

Silversides A. 2001. Lessons Canada Learned in Swissair Crash Being Applied in New York. Canadian Medical Association Journal 165:1243.

Simmons AH, Köhler-Rollefson I, Rollefson GO, Mandel R, Kafafi Z. 1 April 1988. 'Ain Ghazal: A Major Neolithic Settlement in Central Jordan. Science 35–39.

Simons E. 1992. The Primate Fossil Record. In: Jones S, Martin R, Pilbeam D, editors. The Cambridge Encyclopedia of Human Evolution. New York: Cambridge University Press. p 199–208.

Simpson GG. 1971. The Meaning of Evolution. New York: Bantam.

Simpson SW. 1998. *Australopithecus afarensis* and Human Evolution. In: Ember CR, Ember M, Peregrine PN, editors. Research Frontiers in Anthropology. Upper Saddle River, NJ: Prentice Hall/Simon & Schuster Custom Publishing.

Sinclair AR, Leakey MD, Norton-Griffiths M. 1986. Migration and Hominid Bipedalism. Nature 324(6095):307–308.

Singer R, Wymer J. 1982. The Middle Stone Age at Klasies River Mouth in South Africa. Chicago: University of Chicago Press.

Skinner M. 1987. Planning the Archaeological Recovery of Evidence from Recent Mass Graves. Forensic Science International 34:267–287.

Skinner M, Alempijevic D, Djuric-Srejic M. 2003. Guidelines for International Forensic Bio-archaeology Monitors of Mass Grave Exhumations. Forensic Science International 134:81–92.

Smith BD. 1992a. Prehistoric Plant Husbandry in Eastern North America. In: Cowan CW, Watson PJ, editors. The Origins of Agriculture. Washington, DC: Smithsonian Institution Press. p 101–119.

Smith BD. 1992b. Rivers of Change. Washington, DC: Smithsonian Institution Press.

Smith BH. 25 September 1986. Dental Development in *Australopithecus* and Early *Homo*. Nature 327–330.

Smith FH. 1984. Fossil Hominids from the Upper Pleistocene of Central Europe and the Origin of Modern Humans. In: Smith FH, Spencer F, editors. The Origins of Modern Humans: A World Survey of the Fossil Evidence. New York: Alan R. Liss. p 137–209.

Smith FH, Falsetti AB, Donnelley SM. 1989. Modern Human Origins. Yearbook of Physical Anthropology 32:35–68.

Smith FH, Spencer F. 1984. The Origins of Modern Humans: A World Survey of the Fossil Evidence. New York: A.R. Liss.

Smith FH, Trinkaus E, Pettitt PB, Karavanic I, Paunovic M. 1999. Direct Radiocarbon Dates for Vindija G(1) and Velika Pecina Late Pleistocene Hominid Remains. Proceedings of the National Academy of Sciences 96(22):12281–12286.

Smith JM. 1989. Evolutionary Genetics. New York: Oxford University Press.

Smith MW. 1974. Alfred Binet's Remarkable Questions: A Cross-National and Cross-Temporal

Analysis of the Cultural Biases Built into the Stanford-Binet Intelligence Scale and Other Binet Tests. Genetic Psychological Monographs 89:307–334.

Smuts BB, Cheney DL, Seyfarth RM, Wrangham RW, Struhsaker TT, editors. 1987. Primate Society. Chicago: University of Chicago Press.

Soffer O. 1993. Upper Paleolithic Adaptations in Central and Eastern Europe and Man-Mammoth Interactions. In: Soffer O, Praslov ND, editors. From Kostenski to Clovis: Upper Paleolithic–Paleo-Indian Adaptations. New York: Plenum. p 38–40.

Sohn S, Wolpoff MH. 1993. Zuttiyeh Face: A View from the East. American Journal of Physical Anthropology 91:325–347.

Spence MW. 1992. Tlailotlacan: A Zapotec Enclave in Teotihuacán. In: Berlo J, editor. Art, Ideology, and the City of Teotihuacán. Washington, DC: Dumbarton Oaks Research Library and Collection. p 59–88.

Spence MW. 1996. Commodity or Gift: Teotihuacán Obsidian in the Maya Region. Latin American Antiquity 7(1):21–39.

Spencer F. 1984. The Neandertals and Their Evolutionary Significance: A Brief Historical Survey. In: Smith FH, Spencer F, editors. The Origins of Modern Humans: A World Survey of the Fossil Evidence. New York: Alan R. Liss. p 1–50.

Speth JD. 1998. Were Our Ancestors Hunters or Scavengers? In: Ember CR, Ember M, Peregrine PN, editors. Research Frontiers in Anthropology. Upper Saddle River, NJ: Prentice Hall/Simon & Schuster Custom Publishing.

Speth JD, Davis DD. 1976. Seasonal Variability in Early Hominid Predation. Science 441–445.

Speth JD, Spielmann KA. 1983. Energy Source, Protein Metabolism, and Hunter-Gatherer Subsistence Strategy. Anthropological Archaeology 2:1–31.

Stanford C. 1998. Chimpanzee Hunting Behavior and Human Evolution. In: Ember CR, Ember M, Peregrine PN, editors. Research Frontiers in Anthropology. Upper Saddle River, NJ: Prentice Hall. Prentice Hall/Simon & Schuster Custom Publishing. p 35–41.

Steegman Jr. AT. 1975. Human Adaptation to Cold. In: Damon A, editor. Physiological Anthropology. New York: Oxford University Press. p 130–166.

Steinbock RT. 1976. Palaeopathological Diagnosis and Interpretation. Springfield: Charles C. Thomas.

Stephens JC, Cavanaugh ML, Gradie MI, Mador ML, Kidd KK. 12 October 1990. Mapping the Human Genome: Current Status. Science 237–250.

Stewart A, Friesen TM, Keith D, Henderson L. 2000. Archaeology and Oral History of Inuit Land Use on the Kazan River, Nunavut: A Feature-Based Approach. Arctic 53(3):260–278.

Stini WA. 1971. Evolutionary Implications of Changing Nutritional Patterns in Human Populations. American Anthropologist 73:1019–1030.

Stini WA. 1975. Ecology and Human Adaptation. Dubuque, IA: Wm. C. Brown.

Stinson S. 1992. Nutritional Adaptation. Annual Review of Anthropology 21:143–170.

Stoneking M. 1994. Mitochondrial DNA and Human Evolution. Journal of Bioenergetics and Biomembranes 26(3):251–259.

Strauss LG. 1982. Comment on White. Current Anthropology 23:185–186.

Strauss LG. 1989. On Early Hominid Use of Fire. Current Anthropology 30:488–491.

Stringer C. 1985. Evolution of a Species. Geographical Magazine 57:601–607.

Stringer CB. 1988a. The Dates of Eden. Nature 331:565–566.

Stringer CB. 1988b. Neandertals. In: Tattersall I, Delson E, van Couvering J, editors. Encyclopedia of Human Evolution and Prehistory. New York: Garland.

Stringer CB, Hublin JJ, Vandermeersch B. 1984. The Origin of Anatomically Modern Humans in Western Europe. In: Smith FH, Spencer F, editors. The Origins of Modern Humans: A World Survey of the Fossil Evidence. New York: A.R. Liss.

Susman RL. 9 September 1994. Fossil Evidence for Early Hominid Tool Use. Science 265:1570–1573.

Susman RL, Stern Jr JK, Jungers WL. 1985. Locomotor Adaptations in the Hadar Hominids. In: Delson E, editor. Ancestors: The Hard Evidence. New York: Alan R. Liss. p 184–192.

Sussman RW. 1972. Child Transport, Family Size, and the Increase in Human Population Size during the Neolithic. Current Anthropology 13:258–267.

Sussman RW. 1991. Primate Origins and the Evolution of Angiosperms. American Journal of Primatology 23:209–223.

Sussman RW, Kinzey WG. 1984. The Ecological Role of Callitrichidae: A Review. Journal of Physical Anthropology 64:419–449.

Sussman RW, Raven PH. 19 May 1978. Pollination by Lemurs and Marsupials: An Archaic Coevolutionary System. Science 734–735.

Suwa G, Asfaw B, Beyene Y, White TD, Katoh S, Nagaoka S, Nakaya H, Uzawa K, Renne P, WoldeGabriel G. 1997. The First Skull of Australopithecus boisei. Nature 389:489–492.

Svoboda T, Henry B, Shulman L, Kennedy E, Rea E, Ng W, Wallington T, Yaffe B, Gournis E, Vicencio E, Basrur S, Glazier RH. 2004. Public Health

Measures to Control the Spread of the Severe Acute Respiratory Syndrome During the Outbreak in Toronto. New England Journal of Medicine 350:2352–2361.

Swisher CC, Rink WJ, Anton SC, Schwarcz HP, Curtis GH, Suprijo A, Widasmoro N. 13 December 1996. Latest *Homo erectus* of Java: Potential Contemporaneity with *Homo sapiens* in Southeast Asia. Science 274:1870–1874.

Swisher III CC, Curtis GH, Jacob T, Getty AG, Suprijo A, Widasmoro N. 25 February 1994. Age of the Earliest Known Hominids in Java, Indonesia. Science 1118–1121.

Szalay FS. 1968. The Beginnings of Primates. Evolution 22:32–33.

Szalay FS. 1975. Hunting-Scavenging Protohominids: A Model for Hominid Origins. Man 10:420–429.

Szalay FS, Delson E. 1979. Evolutionary History of the Primates. New York: Academic Press.

Szathmáry EJ. 1990. Diabetes in Amerindian Populations: The Dogrib Studies. In: Armelagos G, Swedlund A, editors. Health and Disease of Populations in Transition. New York: Bergin and Garvey. p 75–103.

Szathmáry EJ. 1994. Non-Insulin-Dependent Diabetes Mellitus among Aboriginal North Americans. Annual Review of Anthropology 23:457–482.

Szathmáry EJE. 1993. Genetics of Aboriginal North Americans. Evolutionary Anthropology 1:202–220.

Tanner JM. 1966. The Secular Trend toward Earlier Physical Maturation. Tijdschrift voor Sociale Geneeskunde 44:524–538.

Tanner JM. 1990. Foetus into Man: Physical Growth from Conception to Mortality. Cambridge: Harvard University Press.

Tanner JM. 1992. Growth as a Measure of the Nutritional and Hygienic Status of Population. Hormone Research 38(Supplement 1):106–115.

Tattersall I. 1982. The Primates of Madagascar. New York: Columbia University Press.

Tattersall I. 1999. The Last Neanderthal: The Rise, Success, and Mysterious Extinction of Our Closest Human Relatives. Boulder, CO: Westview Press.

Tattersall I, Schwartz JH. 1999. Hominids and Hybrids: The Place of Neanderthals in Human Evolution. Proceedings of the National Academy of Science 96:7117–7119.

Tattersall I, Schwartz JH. 2000. Extinct Humans. Boulder, CO: Westview Press.

Teleki G. January 1973. The Omnivorous Chimpanzee. Scientific American 32–42.

Templeton AR. 31 May 1996. Gene Lineages and Human Evolution. Science 1363.

Terborgh J. 1983. Five New World Primates: A Study in Comparative Ecology. Princeton, NJ: Princeton University Press.

Thompson-Handler N, Malenky RK, Badrian N. 1984. Sexual Behavior of *Pan paniscus* under Natural Conditions in the Lomako Forest, Equateur, Zaire. In: Susman RL, editor. The Pygmy Chimpanzee: Evolutionary Biology and Behavior. New York: Plenum. p 347–366.

Thorne AG, Wolpoff MH. 1992. The Multiregional Evolution of Humans. Scientific American 266:76–83.

Tobias PV. 1987. The Brain of *Homo habilis*: A New Level of Organization in Cerebral Evolution. Journal of Human Evolution 16:741–761.

Tobias PV. 1994. The Craniocerebral Interface in Early Hominids: Cerebral Impressions, Cranial Thickening, Paleoneurobiology, and a New Hypothesis on Encephalization. In: Corruccini R, Ciochon RL, editors. Integrative Paths to the Past: Paleoanthropological Advances in Honor of F. Clark Howell. Englewood Cliffs, NJ: Prentice Hall. p 194–197.

Tomasello M. 1990. Cultural Transmission in the Tool Use and Communicatory Signaling of Chimpanzees. In: Taylor Parker ST, Gibson KR, editors. "Language" and Intelligence in Monkeys and Apes: Comparative Developmental Perspectives. New York: Cambridge University Press. p 304–305.

Torry WI. 1986. Mortality and Harm: Hindu Peasant Adjustment to Famines. Social Science Information 25:125–160.

Traore M. 1999. A View of Modern Human Origins from Y Chromosome Microsatellite Variation. Genome Research 9:558–567.

Trinkaus E. 1983. The Shanidar Neanderthals. New York: Academic Press.

Trinkaus E. 1984. Western Asia. In: Smith FH, Spencer F, editors. The Origin of Modern Humans: A World Survey of the Fossil Evidence. New York: Alan R. Liss. p 251–253.

Trinkaus E. 1985. Pathology and the Posture of the La Chapelle-aux-Saints Neandertal. American Journal of Physical Anthropology 67:19–41.

Trinkaus E. 1986. The Neandertals and Modern Human Origins. Annual Review of Anthropology 15:193–218.

Trinkaus E. 1987. Bodies, Brawn, Brains and Noses: Human Ancestors and Human Predation. In: Nitecki M, Nitecki DV, editors. The Evolution of Human Hunting. New York: Plenum. p 107–145.

Trinkaus E, Shipman P. 1993. Neandertals: Images of Ourselves. Evolutionary Anthropology 1:194–201.

Turner BL. 1970. Population Density in the Classic Maya Lowlands: New Evidence for Old Approaches. Geographical Review 66:72–82.

Turner II CG. February 1989. Teeth and Prehistory in Asia. Scientific American 88–96.

Tuross N, Dillehay TD. 1995. The Mechanism of Organic Preservation at Monte Verde, Chile and the Use of Biomolecules in Archaeological Interpretation. Journal of Field Archaeology 97–110.

Tuross N, Fogel ML. 1994. Stable Isotope Analysis and Subsistence Patterns at the Sully Site. In: Owsley DW, Jantz RL, editors. Skeletal Biology in the Great Plains: Migration, Warfare, Health and Subsistence. Washington, DC: Smithsonian Institution Press. p 283–289.

Tuttle RH. 1986. Apes of the World: Their Social Behavior, Communication, Mentality, and Ecology. Park Ridge, NJ: Noyes Publications.

Ubelaker DH, Owsley DW, Houck MM, Craig E, Grant W, Woltanski T, Fram R, Sandness K, Peerwani N. 1995. The Role of Forensic Anthropology in the Recovery and Analysis of Branch Davidian Compound Victims: Recovery Procedures and Characteristics of the Victims. Journal of Forensic Science 40:335–340.

Ucko PJ, Rosenfield A. 1967. Paleolithic Cave Art. New York: McGraw-Hill.

Valladas H, Joron JL, Valladas G, Bar-Yosef O, Vandermeersch B. 18 February 1988. Thermo-luminescence Dating of Mousterian "Proto-Cro-Magnon" Remains from Israel and the Origin of Modern Man. Nature 614–616.

van Lawick-Goodall J. 1971. In the Shadow of Man. Boston: Houghton Mifflin.

Vigilant L, Stoneking M, Harpending H, Hawkes K, Wilson AC. 1991. African Populations and the Evolution of Human Mitochondrial-DNA. Science 253:1503–1507.

Visaberghi E, Munkenbeck Fragaszy D. 1990. Do Monkeys Ape? In: Taylor Parker ST, Gibson KR, editors. "Language" and Intelligence in Monkeys and Apes: Comparative Developmental Perspectives. New York: Cambridge University Press. p 247–273.

Vrba ES. 1995. On the Connection between Paleoclimate and Evolution. In: Vrba ES, Denton GH, Partridge TC, Burckle LH, editors. Paleoclimate and Evolution. New Haven, CT: Yale University Press. p. 24–45.

Waldram JB, Herring DA, Young TK. 1995. Aboriginal Health in Canada: Historical, Cultural and Epidemiological Perspectives. Toronto: University of Toronto Press.

Wallace AFC. 1972. Mental Illness, Biology and Culture. In: Hsu FLK, editor. Psychological Anthropology. Second edition. Cambridge, MA: Schenkman. p 363–402.

Wallace AR. August 1858. On the Tendency of Varieties to Depart Indefinitely from the Original Type. Journal of the Proceedings of the Linnaean Society. Reprinted in Young, LB, editor. 1970. Evolution of Man. New York: Oxford University Press.

Walter RC. 1994. Age of Lucy and the First Family: Single-Crystal 40Ar/39Ar Dating of the Dena Dora and Lower Kada Hadar Members of the Hadar Formation, Ethiopia. Geology 22:6–10.

Warren DM. 1989. Utilizing Indigenous Healers in National Health Delivery Systems: The Ghanaian Experiment. In: van Willigen J, Rylko-Bauer B, McElroy A, editors. Making Our Research Useful: Case Studies in the Utilization of Anthropological Knowledge. Boulder, CO: Westview Press. p 159–178.

Warry W. 1990. Doing unto Others: Applied Anthropology, Collaborative Research and Native Self-Determination. Culture 10:61–62.

Washburn S. 1960. Tools and Human Evolution. Scientific American 203(3):62–75.

Watkins J. 2004. Becoming American or Becoming Indian? NAGPRA, Kennewick and cultural affiliation. Journal of Social Archaeology 4:60–80.

Weaver MP. 1993. The Aztecs, Maya, and Their Predecessors. Third edition. San Diego: Academic Press.

Weiner JS. 1954. Nose Shape and Climate. Journal of Physical Anthropology 4:615–618.

Weiss KM. 1973. Demographic Models for Anthropology. American Antiquity 38(2) Part 2, Memoir 27.

Wenke RJ. 1984. Patterns in Prehistory: Humankind's First Three Million Years. Second edition. New York: Oxford University Press.

Wenke RJ. 1990. Patterns in Prehistory: Humankind's First Three Million Years. Third edition. New York: Oxford University Press.

Werner D. November 1978. Trekking in the Amazon Forest. Natural History 42–54.

Wheat JB. January 1967. A Paleo-Indian Bison Kill. Scientific American 44–47.

Wheatley D, Gillings M. 2002. Spatial Technology and Archaeology: The Archaeological Applications of GIS. New York: Taylor & Francis.

Wheatley P. 1971. The Pivot of the Four Quarters. Chicago: Aldine.

Wheeler PE. 1991. The Thermoregulator Advantages of Hominid Bipedalism in Open Equatorial Environments: The Contribution of Increased Convective Heat Loss and Cutaneous Evaporative Cooling. Journal of Human Evolution 21:107–115.

White B. March 1973. Demand for Labor and Population Growth in Colonial Java. Human Ecology 1(3):217–236.

White CD, Healy PF, Schwarcz HP. 1993. Intensive Agriculture, Social Status, and Maya Diet at Pacbitun, Belize. Journal of Anthropological Research 49:347–375.

White CD, Schwarcz HP. 1989. Ancient Maya Diet at Lamanai, Belize: As Inferred from Isotopic and Chemical Analysis of Human Bone. Journal of Archaeological Science 16:451–474.

White CD, Schwarcz HP. 1994. Temporal Trends in Stable Isotopes for Nubian Mummy Tissues. American Journal of Physical Anthropology 93:165–187.

White FJ. 1996. *Pan paniscus* 1973 to 1996: Twenty-three Years of Field Research. Evolutionary Anthropology 5:11–17.

White LA. 1968. The Expansion of the Scope of Science. In: Fried MH, editor. Readings in Anthropology. Second edition, volume 1. New York: Thomas Y. Crowell. p 15–24.

White R. 1982. Rethinking the Middle/Upper Paleolithic Transition. Current Anthropology 23:169–175.

White TD, Johanson DC, Kimbel WH. 1981. *Australopithecus africanus*: Its Phyletic Position Reconsidered. South African Journal of Science 77:445–471.

White TD, Suwa G, Asfaw B. 1994. *Australopithecus ramidus*, a New Species of Early Hominid from Aramis, Ethiopia. Nature 371:306–312.

White TD, Suwa G, Asfaw B. 1995. *Australopithecus ramidus*, a New Species of Early Hominid from Aramis, Ethiopia. Nature 375:88.

Whiten A, Goodall J, McGrew WC, Nishida T, Reynolds V, Sugiyama Y, Tutin CE, Wrangham RW, Boesch C. 1999. Cultures in chimpanzees. Nature 399:682–685.

Whittaker JC. 1994. Flintknapping: Making and Understanding Stone Tools. Austin: University of Texas Press.

WHO (World Health Organization). 1986. Use and Interpretation of Anthropometric Indicators of Nutritional Status. Bulletin of the World Health Organization 64:929–941.

Wilford JN. 1997. Ancient German Spears Tell of Mighty Hunters of Stone Age. New York Times [March 4], C6.

Wilford N. 1995. The Transforming Leap, from 4 Legs to 2. New York Times [September 5], C1 ff.

Wilkinson RL. 1995. Yellow Fever: Ecology, Epidemiology, and Role in the Collapse of the Classic Lowland Maya Civilization. Medical Anthropology 16:269–294.

Williams ED, Crews JD. 2003. From Dust to Dust: Ethical and Practical Issues Involved in the Location, Exhumation, and Identification of Bodies from Mass Graves. Croatian Medical Journal 44:251–258.

Williams GC. 1992. Natural Selection: Domains, Levels, and Challenges. New York: Oxford University Press.

Williamson RF, Pfeiffer S. 2003. Bones of the Ancestors: The Archaeology and Osteology of the Moatfield Ossuary. Hull, Quebec: Canadian Museum of Civilization.

Wilson EO. 1975. Sociobiology: The New Synthesis. Cambridge, MA: Belknap Press of Harvard University Press. Quoted in Low B. 1998. Behavioral Ecology, "Sociobiology" and Human Behavior. In: Ember CR, Ember M, Peregrine PN, editors. Research Frontiers in Anthropology. Upper Saddle River, NJ: Prentice Hall/Simon & Schuster Custom Publishing.

Wittfogel K. 1957. Oriental Despotism: A Comparative Study of Total Power. New Haven, CT: Yale University Press.

Wolf E. 1984. Culture: Panacea or Problem. American Antiquity 49:393–400.

Wolpoff MH. 1971. Competitive Exclusion among Lower Pleistocene Hominids: The Single Species Hypothesis. Man 6:601–614.

Wolpoff MH. 1983. Ramapithecus and Human Origins: An Anthropologist's Perspective of Changing Interpretations. In: Ciochon RL, Corruccini RS, editors. New Interpretations of Ape and Human Ancestry. New York: Plenum. p 666.

Wolpoff MH, Nkini A. 1985. Early and Early Middle Pleistocene Hominids from Asia and Africa. In: Delson E, editor. Ancestors: The Hard Evidence. New York: Alan R. Liss. p 202–205.

Wolpoff MH, Nkini A. 2001. Early and Early Middle Pleistocene Hominids from Asia and Africa. In Delson E, editor. Ancestors: The Hard Evidence. New York: Alan R. Liss.

Wolpoff MH, Thorne AG, Jelinek J, Yinyun Z. 1994. The Case for Sinking *Homo erectus*: 100 Years of *Pithecanthropus* Is Enough! In: Franzen JL, editor. 100 Years of *Pithecanthropus*: The *Homo erectus* Problem. Frankfurt am Main: Senckenbergische Naturforschende Gesellschaft. p 341–361.

Wong K. January 2003. An Ancestor to Call Our Own. Scientific American 288:54–63.

Wood B. 1994. Hominid Paleobiology: Recent Achievements and Challenges. In: Corruccini R, Ciochon RL, editors. Integrative Paths to the Past. Englewood Cliffs, NJ: Prentice Hall. p 147–165.

Wood BA. 1992. Evolution of Australopithecines. In: Jones S, Martin R, Pilbeam D, editors. The Cambridge Encyclopedia of Human Evolution. New York: Cambridge University Press. p 236.

Wood JW, Milner GR, Harpending HC, Weiss KM. 1992. The Osteological Paradox: Problems of Inferring Prehistoric Health from Skeletal Samples. Current Anthropology 33:343–370.

Wrangham RW. 1980. An Ecological Model of Female-Bonded Primate Groups. Behaviour 75:262–300.

Wright GA. 1971. Origins of Food Production in Southwestern Asia: A Survey of Ideas. Current Anthropology 12:470.

Wright HT. 1986. The Evolution of Civilizations. In: Meltzer DJ, Fowler DD, Sabloff JA, editors. American Archaeology Past and Future. Washington, DC: Smithsonian Institution Press. p 323–365.

Wright HT, Johnson GA. 1975. Population, Exchange, and Early State Formation in Southwestern Iran. American Anthropologist 77:267–289.

Wright L, White C. 1996. Human Biology in the Classic Maya Collapse: Evidence from Palaeopathology and Paleodiet. Journal of World Prehistory 10:147–198.

Xinzhi W, Maolin W. 1985. Early *Homo sapiens* in China. In: Rukang W, Olsen JW, editors. Paleoanthropology and Paleolithic Archaeology in the People's Republic of China. Orlando, FL: Academic Press. p 91–106.

Yamei H, Potts R, Baoyin Y, Zhengtang G, Deino A, Wei W, Clark J, Guangmao X, Weiwen H. 3 March 2000. Mid-Pleistocene Acheulian-like Stone Technology of the Bose Basin, South China. Science 287(5458):1622–1626.

Yellen JE, Brooks AS, Cornelissen E, Mehlman M, Stewart K. 1995. A Middle Stone Age Worked Bone Industry from Katanda, Upper Semliki Valley, Zaire. Science 268:553–556.

Young H. 1995. Integrating HIV/AIDS into First Nations Health Services. AIDS STD Health Promotion Exchange 4:3.

Young TK, Dean HJ, Flett B, Wood-Steiman J. 2000a. Childhood Obesity in a Population at High Risk for Type 2 Diabetes. Journal of Pediatrics 136(3):365–369.

Young TK, McIntyre LL, Dooley J, Rodriguez J. 1985. Epidemiological Features of Diabetes Mellitus among Indians in Northwestern Ontario and Northeastern Manitoba. Canadian Medical Association Journal 132:793–797.

Young TK, Reading J, Elias B, O'Neil JD. 2000b. Type 2 Diabetes Mellitus in Canada's First Nations: Status of an Epidemic in Progress. Canadian Medical Association Journal 163(5):561–566.

Young TK, Szathmáry EJ, Evers S, Wheatley B. 1990. Geographical Distribution of Diabetes among the Native Population of Canada: A National Survey. Social Science and Medicine 31(2):129–139.

Young Jr. TC. 1972. Population Densities and Early Mesopotamian Urbanism. In: Ucko P, Tringham R, Dimbleby GW, editors. Man, Settlement and Urbanism. Cambridge, MA: Schenkman. p 827–842.

Zeder MA. 1991. Feeding Cities: Specialized Animal Economy in the Ancient Near East (Chapter I). Washington, DC: Smithsonian Institution Press.

Zeller A. 1987. Communication by Sight and Smell. In: Smuts BB, Cheney DL, Seyfarth RM, Wrangham RW, Struhsaker TT, editors. Primate Societies. Chicago: University of Chicago Press. p 433–439.

Zeller A. 1992. Communication in the Social Unit. In: Burton FD, editor. Social Processes and Mental Abilities in Non-Human Primates. Queenston: Edwin Mellen Press. p 61–89.

Zeller A. 1994. Evidence of Structure in Macaque Communication. In: Gardner RA, Gardner BT, Chiarelli B, editors. The Ethological Roots of Culture. Netherlands: Kluwer Academic Publishers. p 15–39.

Zihlman A. 1992. The Emergence of Human Locomotion: The Evolutionary Background and Environmental Context. In: Nishida T, editor. Topics in Primatology. Tokyo: University of Tokyo Press.

Name Index

Subject Index

Note: Entries for figures are followed by "*f.*"

Photo Credits

Chapter 1: 1: Robert Frerck/Odyssey Productions. 6: Courtesy Anne Keenleyside. 7: Courtesy Sarah Gaunt, Heritage Planner, Champagne and Aishihik First Nations. 9: Irven DeVore/Anthro-Photo. 13: Courtesy Tina Moffat. 14: Photo Researchers, Inc. 15 (top): William Strode/Woodfin Camp & Associates. 15 (bottom): Arne Hodalic/Corbis Bettmann.

Chapter 2: 19: Haskel Greenfield. 21: Canadian Press/AP Photo/Tsugufumi Matsumoto. 22: Ric Ergenbright/Corbis. 23: James L. Amos/Photo Researchers; Inc. 25: Haskel Greenfield. 26: Ariane Burke. 29: Priscilla Renouf. 30: Corbis Bettmann/© Asian Art & Archaeology, Inc./Corbis.

Chapter 3: 43: Greg Monks. 44: Greenberg, Jeff/Omni-Photo Communications, Inc. 51: Dongya Yang. 55: Haskel Greenfield. 58: Gianni Dagli Orti/Corbis. 63: Haskel Greenfield.

Chapter 4: 71: E. R. Degginger/Animals Animals/Earth Scenes. 72: SETI League. 76: Adam Jones/Photo Researchers, Inc. 78: The Bridgeman Art Library International Limited/National History Museum, London, UK/Bridgeman Art Library. 80 (top): M. W. Tweedie/Photo Researchers, Inc. 80 (bottom): Photo Researchers, Inc. 82: Canadian Press/CP Photo/Clement Allard.

Chapter 5: 86: Nick Koudis/PhotoDisc. 87: Archiv/Photo Researchers, Inc. 89 (left and right): Lester V. Bergman/Corbis Bettmann. 96: Stephen J. Krasemann/Photo Researchers, Inc. 97: Alan Carey/Photo Researchers, Inc. 98 (left): Barbara Campbell/Gamma Liaison. 98 (right): Noboru Komine/Photo Researchers.

Chapter 6: 106: Kennan Ward Photography/Corbis-Bettman. 111 (top): Photo Researchers, Inc. 111 (bottom): Sygma. 115 (left): Wardene Weisser/Bruce Coleman, Inc. 115 (right): Animals Animals/Earth Scenes. 116: Bruce Coleman, Inc. 117: K&K Ammann/Bruce Coleman, Inc. 119: Tom McHugh/Photo Researchers, Inc. 120: Photo Researchers, Inc. 121 (top): Pascale Sicotte. 121 (bottom): Michael K. Nichols/National Geographic Society.

Chapter 7: 134: The Natural History Museum of London. 138: The Natural History Museum of London. 142: Gary W. Carter/Corbis Bettmann. 144: David L. Brill Photography/Brill Atlanta.145: Dororthy Norton/Pearson Education/PH College. 146: Peabody Museum of Natural History. 147: Russell L. Ciochon, University of Iowa. 150: David R. Begun. 151: E.R. Degginger/Photo Researchers, Inc.

Chapter 8: 156: John Reader/Science Photo Library/Photo Researchers, Inc. 160: Art Wolfe, Inc. 167: John Reader/Science Photo Library/Photo Researchers, Inc. 168 (top): © Christian Jegou/Photo Researchers, Inc. 168 (bottom): John Reader/Science Photo Library/Photo Researchers, Inc. 169: David L. Brill Photography/Brill Atlanta. 170 (bottom left): John Reader/Science Photo Library/Photo Researchers, Inc. 170 (top right): David L. Brill Photography/Brill Atlanta. 170 (bottom right): Bossu Regis/Corbis Bettmann.

Chapter 9: 182: Photo Researchers, Inc. 187: Russell L. Ciochon, University of Iowa. 189: Colin Keates/Dorling Kindersley Media Library/DK/Natural History Museum, London. 191: © Christian Jegou/Photo Researchers, Inc. 193: Chris Hellier/Corbis. 195 (left): Corbis Bettmann/© Bettmann/Corbis. 195 (right): Graham Ford/Getty Images Inc.—Stone Allstock. 202: Kenneth Garrett/National Geographic Society. 204: Unidentified/Dorling Kindersley Media Library.

Chapter 10: 208 & 221 (top): Archivo Iconografico, S. A./Corbis. 223: Sygma. 224: Kenneth Garrett/National Geographic Society. 225: Anthro-Photo File. 228: Joe Ben Wheat/University of Colorado Museum. 231: Robert W. Park.

Chapter 11: 234: Lawrence Migdale/PIX. 238: Ettagale Blauer/Laure Communications. 239: David Hiser/Getty Images Inc.—Stone Allstock. 240: Alison Wright/Panos Pictures. 243: The Image Bank. 244: Reuters NewMedia Inc./Corbis Bettmann. 249: Wolfgang Kaehler Photography. 250: *Saturday Review*, January 10, 1970.

Chapter 12: 259: Wolfgang Kaehler Photography. 265: Jonathan Blair/Woodfin Camp & Associates. 270: Irven DeVore/Anthro-Photo. 271: Sher/Anthro-Photo File. 281: Mark Edwards/Still Pictures/Peter Arnold, Inc. 287: Robert Osti/Courtesy of *Scientific American*.

Chapter 13: 292: Photo Researchers, Inc. 296: The Granger Collection. 298: Frerck/Odyssey Productions. 301: Paolo Koch/Photo Researchers, Inc. 306: Cahokia Mounds State Historic Site, painting by Michael Hampshire. 307: Wolfgang Kaehler/Corbis-Bettmann.

Chapter 14: 310: Comstock. 313: John Moss/Photo Researchers, Inc. 315: Photo Researchers, Inc. 319: David Orr/Panos Pictures. 321: Jeffrey Aaronson/Network Aspen. 330: Courtesy of Dr. Tracy Rogers, University of Toronto. 331: Argentine Forensic Anthropology Team (EAAF)/Luis Fondebrider. 335: Courtesy of L. Larcombe Archaeological Consulting.